D1591929

DENSE CHLORINATED SOLVENTS

and other DNAPLs in Groundwater: History, Behavior, and Remediation

James F. Pankow
John A. Cherry

WATERLOO
PRESS

Pankow, James F., Cherry, John A.
    Dense Chlorinated Solvents and other DNAPLs in Groundwater
    Includes index and bibliographical references.

Editorial/production supervision: *James F. Pankow*
Interior design/production: *ETP/Harrison*
Cover design: *Jonathan Pennell*

Printed in the United States of America

10 9 8 7 6 5 4 3 2 1

Library of Congress Catalog Card Number: 95-61690

Dedication

This book is dedicated to the following individuals who helped establish the research path that has led to the present understanding of dense chlorinated solvents in groundwater described here.

The late Richard M. Spann, formerly Manager of Environmental Programs for IBM in Poughkeepsie, New York, who in 1982 focused our research interests on the behavior of chlorinated solvents in groundwater by insisting on a scientific basis for remediation decision making at the industrial sites in his care.

Dr. Friedrich Schwille, formerly Chief Groundwater Hydrologist at the Federal Institute of Hydrology in Koblenz, Germany (now retired), whose laboratory experimentation in the late 1970s and early 1980s provided the scientific foundation for our subsequent research, and who provided advice and encouragement for our research efforts.

Dr. Rolf Bernegger, formerly Corporate Vice-President of the Ciba-Geigy Corporation in Ardsley, New York (now retired), who in 1987, through encouragement and initial funding, fostered the concept of a major research program focused on the behavior of dense chlorinated solvents performed by a consortium of university groups and supported by a consortium of corporations and funding agencies.

For their influences, we are truly grateful.

John A. Cherry
Waterloo, Ontario
June 1995

James F. Pankow
Portland, Oregon
June 1995

Stanley Feenstra
Waterloo, Ontario
June 1995

Contents

Preface

A decade ago, little was known concerning the behavior of dense chlorinated solvents and other dense non-aqueous phase liquids (DNAPLS) in the subsurface. Even less was known about what options and prospects existed for the remediation of sites contaminated with DNAPLs. Research activity in this area grew rapidly in the late 1980s, and has accelerated in the current decade. The first major research program in North America to focus on dense organic solvents was the *University Consortium Solvents-In-Groundwater Research Program*. This program was initiated in 1987, became well-established in 1988, and continues today. The consortium is made up of four principal collaborating universities: two in Canada (University of Waterloo and Queens University), and two in the United States (Colorado State University and the Oregon Graduate Institute). Several other universities and government organizations have been involved as collaborators over the years. These include SUNY/Buffalo, the University of Toronto, the University of Western Ontario, Environment Canada (National Water Research Institute), the U.S. Geological Survey (Water Resources Division), and Mitre Corporation. Most recently, the University of Stuttgart and the Danish Geological Survey have become collaborating organizations.

Financial support for the *Solvents-In-Groundwater Research Program* has come from The Boeing Company, Ciba-Geigy Corporation, Dow Chemical Canada/USA, Eastman Kodak Co., General Electric Co., Laidlaw Environmental Systems Ltd., Mitre Corporation, The Natural Sciences and Engineering Research Council of Canada, the Ontario University Research Incentive Fund, PPG Industries Corporation, and United Technologies Corporation. Infrastructure support has been provided by the Waterloo Centre for Groundwater Research (an Ontario Centre of Excellence) at the University of Waterloo and Canadian Forces Base Borden. The administrative framework for the corporate and government funding for the program is distinctive. Each member company and government agency makes an equal, annual contribution to the research program. The funds are pooled, and then allocated to the researchers based on an annual plan determined by the university consortium members in consultation with the sponsors. The goal has been to provide a maximum of scientific and operational flexibility with a minimum of bureaucracy. The research program has many components. As components are completed, the results are presented in M.S. and Ph.D. theses, and published as peer-reviewed journal articles, conference proceedings, and symposia. Many of these publications are cited in the chapters in this book. Each year, new projects within the program are begun.

The goals of the research program are to acquire and integrate information regarding DNAPLs in the subsurface, and the associated groundwater- and vadose-zone contamination. A range of laboratory experiments, field experiments, and mathematical modeling studies have been used in this work. The research is being conducted by a group of faculty members, research associates, technicians, and graduate students in science and engineering, a group whose size varies from 50 to 70 people. Large, controlled, field experiments in which liquid chlorinated solvents have been introduced into a sandy aquifer on a military base (Canadian Forces Base Borden) and into large tanks packed with layered porous media have been used as reality checks on the mathematical models, and for performance assessments of selected technologies for remediating contaminated groundwater and vadose zone systems.

Much of the information presented in this book has been developed in the context of the above research program. Although our understanding of the behavior of dense chlorinated solvents and other DNAPLs in groundwater systems is continuing to advance, the body of scientific knowledge on many aspects of this subject has reached sufficient maturity to warrant a synthesis at this time. The intention of this book is to provide that synthesis. We thank the corporate sponsors and government agencies that have made this work possible, and we thank the authors whose commitment and attention to detail have made this book a reality.

John A. Cherry
Waterloo, Ontario
June 1995

James F. Pankow
Portland, Oregon
June 1995

Sponsors of the University Consortium *Solvents in Groundwater Research Program*

The Boeing Company, Seattle, WA, 1991-present;
Ciba-Geigy Corporation, Ardsley, NY, 1988-present;
Dow Chemical Company, Midland, MI, 1988-1991;
Eastman Kodak Company, Rochester, NY, 1990-present;
General Electric Company, Hartford, CT, 1988-present;
Laidlaw Environmental Services, Burlington, ON, 1992-1995;
Mitre Corporation, 1993-present;
Natural Sciences and Engineering Research Council of Canada, 1988-1994;
The Ontario University Research Incentive Fund, 1988-1994;
PPG Industries Corporation, Pittsburgh, PA, 1994-present; and
United Technologies Corporation, 1994-present.

1

Dense Chlorinated Solvents in Groundwater: Background and History of the Problem

James F. Pankow[1], **Stan Feenstra**[2,3], **John A. Cherry**[3], **and M. Cathryn Ryan**[3]

[1]Department of Environmental Science and Engineering
Oregon Graduate Institute
P.O. Box 91000
Portland, Oregon
U.S.A. 97291-1000

[2]Applied Groundwater Research, Ltd.
The Pentagon Building, Suite 207
2550 Argentia Road
Mississauga, Ontario
Canada L5N 5R1

[3]Waterloo Centre for Groundwater Research
University of Waterloo
Waterloo, Ontario
Canada N2L 3G1

ABSTRACT

Chlorinated organic solvents like trichloroethylene are common groundwater contaminants. Contamination levels are usually in the μg/L to mg/L range (dissolved). The U.S. production is in the hundreds of millions of kg per year for most of the chlorinated solvents. When found in the subsurface as organic liquids, these compounds are denser than water, and are then commonly referred to as "dense non-aqueous phase liquids" (DNAPLs). If spilled into the subsurface in sufficient quantities, a DNAPL has the capacity to penetrate below the water table where it can provide a long term source of contamination. Other reasons why chlorinated solvents are common groundwater contaminants are that they exhibit: 1) low liquid viscosities (are able to move easily into the subsurface); 2) low interfacial tensions with water (are able to enter into water-wet fractures relatively easily); 3) high volatilities (are able as gases to diffuse rapidly downwards into the unsaturated zone); 4) low absolute solubilities (are difficult to remove from the groundwater zone); 5) high solubilities relative to drinking water limits (are able to cause significant contamination even when small amounts dissolve); 6) low partitioning to soils (are not retarded by aquifer materials); and 7) low degradabilities. At many sites of contamination by chlorinated solvents, the amounts that are present in dissolved form in the groundwater are relatively small, often no more than the equivalent of a few tens of drums liquid solvent. Since spill volumes have in most cases been much larger than this, significant DNAPL solvent still exists in the subsurface at most of these sites.

    The history of the problem of chlorinated solvents in groundwater is examined in this chapter in the hopes that doing so will help scientists and engineers avoid other environmental problems in the future. The physical and chemical properties of the chlorinated solvents should have led scientists and engineers to anticipate that these compounds would be prone to causing groundwater contamination. Unfortunately, their common presence in important aquifers was only discovered by accident during the mid-to-late 1970s as a result of an interest in the trihalomethane compounds (*e.g.*, chloroform) that can be formed when drinking water is chlorinated. Late 1981 can be viewed as the point in time at which the problem of *dissolved* chlorinated solvents in groundwater became widely recognized. However, the fact that chlorinated solvents also exist in the subsurface in *DNAPL* form at many important sites did not become generally recognized until the mid-to-late 1980s. By this point in time, many remediation efforts had already failed because they had not taken into account the large, persistent DNAPL sources present in the subsurface at those sites.

1.1 BACKGROUND

1.1.1 General

Chlorinated solvents were first produced in Germany in the nineteenth century; production in the United States began around 1906. Widespread use of chlorinated solvents in manufacturing industries began during World War II, and increased markedly during the next three decades. Contamination of groundwater by these compounds went largely unrecognized until the late 1970s. The denser-than-water nature of liquid chlorinated solvents has led to their becoming known as "dense non-aqueous phase liquids" (**DNAPLs**, see Tables 1.1 and 1.2).

Like petroleum products (*e.g.*, gasoline and fuel oil), chlorinated solvents are produced and usually used in an organic liquid form (*i.e.*, as "neat", "free product" liquids), but are generally found in water supplies in dissolved form at μg/L (ppb) to mg/L (ppm) concentrations. Unlike petroleum products, however, the chlorinated solvents are generally: 1) not noticed by taste or odor at typical groundwater contamination levels; and 2) not stopped at the water table when released in DNAPL form to the subsurface in significant quantities. Once in an aquifer, DNAPL source material is usually very difficult to find. In contrast, when petroleum products are spilled in significant volumes, being *light* NAPLs (*i.e.*, being **LNAPLs**), they "float" on the water table where they can be detected easily (*e.g.*, see McKee *et al.*, 1972). Historically, since chlorinated solvents in DNAPL form were found only rarely in wells, recognition of the problems posed by these compounds in groundwater had to await the development *and* general availability of analytical methods which allowed the determination of dissolved organic contaminants in water at the μg/L to mg/L level.

It is now apparent that of the many industrial organic chemicals identified to date in groundwater, the common chlorinated organic solvents are the most ubiquitous. In a survey in New Jersey of 1,070 wells, trichloroethylene (TCE) was found in 58% of the wells, carbon tetrachloride in 65%, and tetrachloroethylene (PCE) in 43% (Page, 1981). Because of the DNAPL nature of many of the corresponding contamination source zones, the chlorinated solvents pose great challenges in groundwater remediation (Plumb and Pitchford, 1985; Abelson, 1990).

TABLE 1.1   Organic Compounds That Are DNAPLs.

Compound class	Compound
Chlorinated solvents	Tetrachloroethylene
	Trichloroethylene
	1,1,1-Trichloroethane
	Dichloromethane
	Chloroform
	Carbon tetrachloride
	1,2-Dichloroethane
	Chlorobenzene
	1,2-Dichlorobenzene
	1,3-Dichlorobenzene
	1,1,2-Trichloroethane
	1,2,4-Trichlorobenzene
Other halogenated organics	Benzyl chloride
	Bromobenzene
	Bromochloromethane
	Bromodichloromethane
	Bromoform
	4-Bromophenyl phenyl ether
	bis(2-Chloroethyl)ether
	2-Chloroethyl vinyl ether
	bis(2-Chloroisopropyl)ether
	1-Chloro-1-nitropropane
	4-Chlorophenyl phenyl ether
	Dibromochloromethane
	1,1-Dichloroethane
	1,2-Difluorotetrachloroethane
	1-Iodopropane
	Hexachlorobutadiene
	Pentachloroethane
	1,1,2,2-Tetrabromoethane
	1,1,2,2-Tetrachloroethane
	1,2,3-Trichloropropane
	1,1,2-Trichloro-1,2,2-trifluoroethane

The first significant recognition in the research community of the potential DNAPL character of chlorinated solvents in groundwater is attributable to **Friedrich Schwille**. As a result of two case studies in West Germany during the late 1960s and early 1970s involving chlorinated solvents, Schwille developed conceptual models and conducted physical model studies on the behavior of these compounds at the Federal Institute of Hydrology in Koblenz from 1977 to 1984. Schwille examined how and when chlorinated solvents could penetrate into unsaturated and saturated sands, and into fractured media, and how liquid solvents could be dissolved by flowing groundwater. Unfortunately, this research remained largely unknown in North America and even in Europe until the late 1980s. At that time, an understanding of the behavior of chlorinated solvents in the

TABLE 1.1   (*continued*)

Substituted aromatics, phthalates, and miscellaneous organics	Chloroanilines
	Chlorotoluenes
	Nitrotoluenes
	Nitrobenzene
	Benzyl butyl phthalate
	Di-*n*-butyl phthalate
	Diethyl phthalate
	o-Anisidine
	Phenyl ether
	Tri-*o*-cresol phosphate
PCB mixtures	Aroclor 1221
	Aroclor 1232
	Aroclor 1242
	Aroclor 1248
	Aroclor 1254
Pesticides	Chlordane
	Chloropicrin
	1,2-Dibromo-3-chloropropane
	1,2-Dichloropropane
	1,2-Dichloropropylene
	Dichlorvos
	Disulfoton
	Ethion
	Ethylene dibromide
	Malathion
	Parathion

TABLE 1.2   The Most Common Chlorinated Solvents With Some of Their Chemical Synonyms and Commerical Product Names (Merck Index, 1989).

Chemical name	Synonyms
Perchloroethylene	PCE, tetrachloroethylene, ethylene tetrachloride, Nema, Tetracap, Tetropil, Perclene, Ankilostin, Didakene, PerSec
Trichloroethylene	TCE, ethinyl trichloride, Tri-Clene, Trielene, Trilene, Trichloran, Trichloren, Algylen, Trimar, Trline, Tri, Trethylene, Westrosol, Chlorylen, Gemalgene, Germalgene
1,1,1-Trichloroethane	TCA, methyl chloroform, Chlorothene, Solvent 111, TRI-ETHANE
Dichloromethane	DCM, methylene chloride, methylene dichloride, methylene bichloride

subsurface was being developed independently, largely without knowledge of Schwille's pioneering studies[†].

[†]Schwille was also involved in early research into the behavior of LNAPLs in the subsurface (Schwille, 1967).

Schwille (1981) was the first English language publication to present the concept of heavier-than-water solvents sinking below the water table. Feenstra (1984), Cherry (1984a, 1984b), Villaume (1985), and Feenstra (1986) also provided descriptions of the general concepts governing DNAPL behavior in the subsurface. A summary report on Schwille's impressive accomplishments was published in German (Schwille, 1984a), then in English translation (Schwille, 1988). More recent discussions have been presented by Feenstra and Cherry (1988), Hunt *et al.* (1988a, 1988b), Mercer and Cohen (1990), and Cohen and Mercer (1993).

This chapter provides background information on chlorinated solvent usage, and examines the history of the two-staged discovery of the extent and causes of groundwater contamination by these compounds. The **first stage** of the discovery involved the simple recognition of the prevalence of chlorinated solvents as groundwater contaminants; the **second stage** involved the recognition of the common presence of these compounds as difficult-to-remediate DNAPL source zones in the subsurface at many sites of contamination. This history is presented so as to place the following chapters in context in the field of contaminant hydrogeology, and also to permit an understanding how and when we came to only belatedly appreciate the nature and magnitude of this problem. Indeed, an analysis of how we came to appreciate the chlorinated solvents problem will permit us to critically evaluate the way in which science has progressed in the groundwater community.

1.1.2 DNAPLs and LNAPLs

Historically, the term "**NAPL**" was coined in 1981 during studies of a hazardous waste landfill (the "S-Area Landfill") in Niagara Falls, New York. At this site, a black, denser-than-water, "immiscible" organic liquid was discovered in the soil and bedrock underlying the site. The liquid was found to be a complex mixture of halogenated benzenes, chlorinated solvents, and other halogenated hydrocarbons. Engineers, scientists, and attorneys dealing with the site selected the term "NAPL" to differentiate this liquid from other contaminated materials, and from the groundwater (Kolmer, 1991), though we would now refer to it more specifically as a "DNAPL".

DNAPLs have sometimes also been referred to as "dense immiscible liquids", and LNAPLs have sometimes been referred to as "light immiscible liquids". However, as with the use of "non-aqueous" in the terms DNAPL and LNAPL, the descriptor "immiscible" is misleading. Indeed, an organic liquid can exist as a stable, **separate phase** in equilibrium with water *only* after its dissolved concentration in the water has reached the saturation limit for that liquid. Thus, no organic liquid is ever totally immiscible with water. We also note that there will always be some water dissolved in any "non-aqueous" phase.

Although DNAPL solvents are now recognized as a major groundwater problem, only a few published descriptions of actual field cases are readily available at this time. We have, however, reviewed unpublished data pertaining to a large number of industrial and waste disposal sites across North America where DNAPL solvents are the key cause of groundwater contamination. These include many sites at which data has been collected as a result of *Superfund* (*i.e.*, *CERCLA*) and *RCRA* legislation, though most of this voluminous information lies buried in the files of regulatory agencies.

1.2 CHLORINATED SOLVENT USAGE

In hindsight, it is not surprising that widespread groundwater contamination by chlorinated solvents has occurred. Very large quantities of these chemicals have been, and continue to be produced, transported, used, and disposed of by many sectors of our modern society. Production of chlorinated solvents began in the U.S. in 1906 with carbon tetrachloride, which remained the main solvent used in North America for the first half of the century. Production of TCE and PCE began in 1923. Carbon tetrachloride was commonly used for dry cleaning in the 1930s, having replaced gasoline. TCE and PCE became the most commonly used solvents in the 1960s when the post-World War II manufacturing economy expanded greatly. Increased chlorinated solvent use paralleled economic growth into the 1970s. Human health and environmental concerns, first raised in the 1970s, have since caused a decline in the production of PCE and TCE to fifth and sixth rank in U.S. production (Figure 1.1). Table 1.3 shows the 1986 U.S. production of selected chlorinated organic solvents. Production quantities range from hundreds of millions to billions of kg per year.

A very wide range of industries use chlorinated solvents in large quantities. The principal current uses of the four most common chlorinated solvents are given in Table 1.4, and the principal uses of several less common chlorinated solvents are given in Table 1.5. As a result of their widespread use, the release of chlorinated solvents to the subsurface has by no means been limited to the *"smoke stack"* industries that have traditionally been associated with pollution. Indeed, the electronic, instrument manufacturing, and aerospace industries, all generally regarded as relatively "clean" with respect to pollution, have used very large quantities of chlorinated solvents, and have caused numerous spills. Also, a range of small businesses in virtually every community use chlorinated solvents, and have been responsible for problematic spills. These include dry cleaning, machine, photographic processing, and printing shops. The principal uses of other organic chemicals which are DNAPLs in pure form are given in Tables 1.6 to 1.9. An overview of the industrial and commercial activities which have produced or used DNAPL chemicals is given in Table 1.10.

1.3 SOURCE TYPES FOR SOLVENTS IN GROUNDWATER

Table 1.11 summarizes the different ways in which chlorinated organic solvents have been released to the subsurface environment. Because chlorinated solvents are now recognized as being among the most problematic groundwater contaminants in industrialized countries, some major solvent users are switching to other chemicals where possible, and/or are implementing much more careful solvent-handling procedures. For example, many underground solvent storage tanks are being replaced with above-ground tanks which can be more effectively inspected for leaks. However, usage has been and will continue to be widespread because the common chlorinated solvents have exceptionally good properties

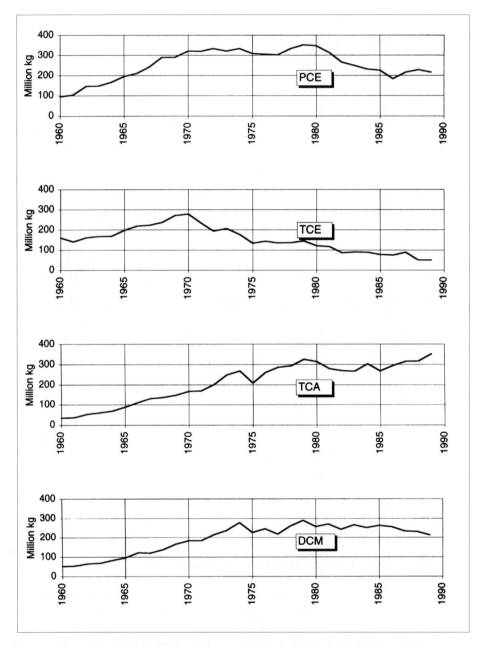

Figure 1.1 U.S. production of common chlorinated solvents during the period 1960-1990. Data are from the Halogenated Solvents Industry Alliance (1987) and the U.S. International Trade Commission (1991).

TABLE 1.3   1986 U.S. Production of Chlorinated Organic Solvents.

Compound	Abbreviation	$(10^6$ lb.)	$(10^6$ kg)	Drums[c]
1,2-Dichloroethane[a]	1,2-DCA	12,940	5,871	22,900,000
1,1,1-Trichloroethane[b]	1,1,1-TCA	648	294	1,100,000
Carbon tetrachloride[a]	CTET	627	284	890,000
Methylene chloride[b]	DCM	561	255	960,000
Chloroform[a]	TCM	422	191	640,000
Tetrachloroethylene[b]	PCE	405	184	560,000
Trichloroethylene[b]	TCE	165	75	260,000

[a]American Chemical Society (1986)

[b]Halogenated Solvents Industry Alliance

[c]Based on 200 L, or approximately 55 US gallons per drum

TABLE 1.4   Principal Current Uses of the Major Chlorinated Solvent Products. (Data from Halogenated Solvents Industry Alliance, 1987.)

Application	Percentage use			
	1,1,1-TCA	DCM	PCE	TCE
Adhesives	9	—	—	1
Aerosols	11	29	—	—
Chemical intermediate	—	—	29	—
Cold cleaning	20	—	—	—
Dry cleaning/textile production	—	—	56	—
Electronics	6	8	—	—
Metal cleaning/degreasing	44	9	11	85
Paint removal/stripping	—	27	—	1
Urethane foam	—	10	—	—
Miscellaneous	3	8	4	6

TCA - 1,1,1-Trichloroethane

DCM - Methylene chloride

PCE - Tetrachloroethylene

TCE - Trichloroethylene

for their intended uses. Thus, it seems likely that releases of chlorinated solvents to the subsurface (and therefore to groundwater zones) will continue to occur at some rate in nearly all urban or suburban areas in the industrialized world.

1.4 THE PHYSICAL, CHEMICAL, AND BIOLOGICAL PROPERTIES OF CHLORINATED SOLVENT COMPOUNDS

In addition to the facts that: 1) large quantities of DNAPL solvents have been produced and used (Table 1.3); and that 2) these solvents have been able to enter the subsurface environment due to a variety of different source types (Table 1.11), it is important to recognize that the **physical**, **chemical**, **and biological properties** of the chlorinated solvents have made these chemicals particularly likely causes of groundwater contamination

TABLE 1.5 Principal Uses of Other Common Chlorinated Organic Compounds Which Are DNAPLs or DNAPL Components.

Chemical	Uses
Chloroform	Solvent for fats, oils, rubber, waxes, resins; manufacture of rubber
Carbon tetrachloride	Solvent in oils, fats, laquers, varnishes, waxes, resins; dry cleaning; seed fumigant; extraction of seed oils
1,2-Dichloroethane	Solvent for fats, oils, waxes, gums, resins, rubber; seed fumigant, manufacture of acetyl cellulose; manufacture of vinyl chloride
Chlorobenzene	Solvent for paints; manufacture of phenol, aniline, DDT, dyes; heat transfer liquid
1,2-Dichlorobenzene	Solvents for waxes, gums, resins, tars, rubber, oils, asphalts; insecticide for termites; degreasing of leather and wool; manufacture of dyes; heat transfer medium
1,3-Dichlorobenzene	Fumigant and insecticide
1,1,2-Trichloroethane	Solvent for fats, waxes, resins
1,2,4-Trichlorobenzene	Dielectric fluids; manufacture of chemicals, dyes; heat transfer medium

(Pankow and Cherry, 1988). These properties and their implications are summarized in Table 1.12.

As pointed out in Tables 1.1 and 1.5-1.9, organic compounds besides the chlorinated solvents are classifiable as DNAPLs. These compounds include the halogenated benzenes, the polychlorinated biphenyls (PCBs), some pesticides, coal tar, and creosote. These chemicals have not been found in groundwater nearly as frequently as have the chlorinated solvents. There are several reasons for this. Firstly, compared to the chlorinated solvents, these other chemicals have not been used in as many industrial applications, or in quantities that are nearly as large. Secondly, they do not possess a combination of physical and chemical properties that impart a high propensity for widespread groundwater contamination. For example, some of these other DNAPL chemicals are much less soluble than the chlorinated solvents, and so they are much less mobile because they partition strongly to soil materials. As another example, important soluble components of creosote and coal tar are more degradable in the groundwater zone than are most chlorinated solvents.

1.5 DRINKING WATER LIMITS

The drinking water limits (or "maximum concentration limits", MCLs) for several of the chlorinated solvents have been set at very low levels, *e.g.*, 5 μg/L for TCE (EPA, 1987a). The justification for these standards has been that compounds like TCE, chloroform, and carbon tetrachloride are suspected carcinogens. There is also evidence that excessive exposure to carbon tetrachloride and PCE may result in kidney and liver damage. Table 1.13 illustrates how the solubilities of the chlorinated solvents are all many orders of magnitude higher than their corresponding drinking water limits.

TABLE 1.6   Principal Uses of Less Common Halogenated Industrial Chemicals Which Are DNAPLs.

Chemical	Uses
Benzyl chloride	Manufacture of benzyl compounds, perfumes, pharmaceuticals, dyes, tannins, resins
Bromobenzene	Organic synthesis; solvent; additive in motor oils
Bromochloromethane	Used in fire extinguishers; organic synthesis
Bromodichloromethane	Solvent for waxes, oils, fats, resins; used in fire extinguishers; flame retardant; organic synthesis
Bromoform	Mineral separations
4-Bromophenyl phenyl ether	Research chemical
bis(2-chloroethyl) ether	Cleaning textiles; soil fumigant; Processing of fats, waxes, greases; solvent in paints, varnishes, lacquers; manufacture of lubricating oils, finish removers, cleaners
2-chloroethyl vinyl ether	Manufacture of anesthetics, sedatives, cellulose ethers
bis(2-chloroisopropyl) ether	Manufacture of dyes, resins, pharmaceuticals; solvent for fats, waxes, greases; used in textile manufacturing; paint and spot removers
1-Chloro-1-nitropropane	Fungicide
4-Chlorophenyl phenyl ether	Research chemical
Dibromochloromethane	Used in fire extinguishers; aerosol propellants; refrigerants; organic synthesis
1,1-Dichloroethane	Used in paint, varnish and finish removers; manufacture of vinyl chloride and 1,1,1-TCA; rubber cement; solvent for plastics, oils and fats; insecticide and fumigant
1,2-Difluorotetrachloroethane	Used in organic synthesis
1-Iodopropane	Used in organic synthesis
Hexachlorobutadiene	Solvent for elastomers, rubbers; manufacture of fluorinated lubricants and rubber compounds; heat transfer medium; transfomer and hydraulic fluid; fumigant for grapes
Pentachloroethane	Solvent for oil and grease in metal cleaning
1,1,2,2-Tetrabromoethane	Mineral separation
1,1,2,2-Tetrachloroethane	Solvent for chlorinated rubber; manufacture of insecticides, bleach, paint/varnish/polish removers; metal cleaning; manufacture of 1,1-DCE; solvent for oils and fats, pesticides
1,2,3-Trichloropropane	Solvent; paint and varnish remover
1,1,2-Trichloro-1,2,2-trifluoroethane	Solvent used in electronics and precision equipment manufacture; used in fire extinguishers; dry cleaning; blowing agent

The chlorinated solvents are thus characterized by **high solubility/MCL ratios** (see also item 6 in Table 1.12). Therefore, although the chlorinated solvents have low absolute solubilities, the contamination coming off of a pool of chlorinated solvent DNAPL will typically be greatly in excess of its MCL: even relatively small quantities of these materials in the subsurface can result in large-scale groundwater contamination problems.

TABLE 1.7   Principal Uses of Substituted Aromatic Compounds and Phthalates Which Are DNAPLs.

Chemical	Uses
Chloroanilines	Manufacture of dyes, pharmaceuticals and agricultural chemicals
Chlorotoluenes	Manufacture of dyes; organic synthesis
Nitrotoluenes	Manufacture of dyes, nitrobenzoic acids, toluidenes; organic synthesis
Nitrobenzene	Solvent for cellulose ethers; used in metal and shoes polishes; manufacture of aniline, benzidine, quinoline, azobenzene, drugs, photographic chemicals
Benzyl butyl phthalate	Plasticizer for polyvinyl chloride (PVC); additive in polyvinyl actetate emulsions, ethylene glycol, ethyl cellulose
Di-n-buytl phthalate	Plasticizer; organic synthesis; insect repellant
Diethyl phthalate	Plasticizer; denaturant for ethanol; ingredient in insecticide sprays, explosives; used in dyes, perfumes; solvent for nitrocellulose and cellulose acetate
o-Anisidine	Manufacture of azo dyes
Phenyl ether	Heat transfer medium; perfuming soaps; resins for laminated electrical insulation; organic synthesis
Tri-*o*-cresol phosphate	Plasticizer in lacquers, varnishes, PVC, polystrene, nitrocellulose; waterproofing; heat transfer medium; hydraulic fluids; fire retardant for plastics; additive to high pressure lubricants

TABLE 1.8   Principal Uses of PCB Aroclors Which Are DNAPLs.

PCB mixture	Uses
Aroclor 1221	Capacitors, gas-transmission turbines, hydraulic fluids, adhesives, plasticizer in rubbers
Aroclor 1232	Hydraulic fluids, adhesives, plasticizer in rubbers
Aroclor 1242	Transformers, hydraulic fluids, adhesives, plasticizer in rubbers, heat transfer medium, wax extender, carbonless reproducing paper
Aroclor 1248	Vacuum pumps, gas-transmission turbines, hydraulic fluids, plasticizer in resins, adhesives, plasticizer in rubbers
Aroclor 1254	Capacitors, transformers, vacuum pumps, hydraulic fluids, plasticizer in resins, adhesives, plasticizer in rubbers, wax extender, dedusting agent, extender in pesticides/inks/lubricants/cutting oils

1.6 TYPICAL CHLORINATED SOLVENT PLUMES IN GROUNDWATER

Mackay and Cherry (1989) have calculated that the dissolved solvents in several problematic plumes measuring up to several kilometers in length represent the equivalent of only 0.5 to 70 drums of liquid solvent. Our unpublished assessments of more than 30 other major chlorinated solvent plumes at *Superfund* sites show that this range for plume mass is typical of large plumes. These amounts represent small fractions of the quantities of solvent that presumably entered the groundwater zone at these sites. Therefore, significant DNAPL source zones presumably: 1) still exist at these sites; 2) will be feeding their respective plumes long into the future.

TABLE 1.9   Principal Uses of Pesticide Products Which Are DNAPLs.

Pesticide product	Uses
Chlordane	Insecticide, acaricide, termite control
Chloropicrin	Seed and grain fumigant
1,2-Dibromo-3-chloropropane	Soil fumigant, nematocide
1,2-Dichloropropane	Soil fumigant, nematocide; manufacture of PCE; solvent
1,3-Dichloropropylene	Soil fumigant, nematocide
Dichlorvos	Insecticide and fumigant
Disulfoton	Insecticide for tobacco and vegetables
Ethion	Insecticide, acaricide
Ethylene dibromide	Grain and fruit fumigant; anti-knock additive in gasoline
Malathion	Insecticide
Parathion	Insecticide, acaricide

TABLE 1.10   Industrial and Commercial Activities Which Produced or Used DNAPL Chemicals.

Chemical production and distribution	Manufacturing uses
Solvents	General metal fabrication
Solvents (recycled)	Tool and die making
Dyes and paints	Aircraft production
Adhesives	Electronics/electrical fabrication
Pharmaceuticals	Automobiles and parts production
Plastics and polymers	Printing
Pesticides	Weapons production
Coal tar distillates	Photographic work
Creosote	Wood preserving
Transformer and capacitor production	
Foundry operations and castings	

Service uses	Waste products
Commercial and retail dry cleaning	Coal and oil gasification by-products
Pesticide application	Blast furnace coking by-products
Food processing (decaffeinated coffee)	

Compared to the number of DNAPL sites, there are many more sites where LNAPLs (*e.g.*, gasoline, fuel oil, and aviation fuel) have been spilled or leaked into groundwater systems. However, large plumes of dissolved chemicals (*e.g.*, benzene, toluene, ethyl benzene, and the xylenes) from LNAPL source zones are rare in comparison

TABLE 1.11   Source Types for Chlorinated Solvent Contamination of
Groundwater.

1. Leaking underground or above-ground storage tanks.
2. Leaking drum storage areas.
3. Leaking, buried chemical distribution pipelines.
4. Spillage at chemical loading and off-loading facilities.
5. Spillage during highway accidents and train derailments.
6. Intentional disposal into the subsurface in various ways, including:
   a. domestic septic tile fields (due to the use of solvent-containing
       septic tank cleaning fluids);
   b. municipal landfills;
   c. chemical waste disposal landfills;
   d. settling ponds and lagoons;
   e. landfarming of contaminated sludges and solids; and
   f. injection well disposal of either used liquid solvent, or contaminated liquids.

TABLE 1.13   Pure Compound Solubilities at $\sim$20 °C for Selected
Chlorinated Organic Solvents and Corresponding Maximum Concentration
Limits (MCLs) for Drinking Water Set By EPA (1987).

	Solubility (mg/L)	MCL (EPA) (mg/L)	Solubility/MCL ratio
1,2-Dichloroethane	8,690	0.005	2×10^6
1,1,1-Trichloroethane	720	0.2	4×10^3
Carbon tetrachloride	785	0.005	2×10^5
Methylene chloride	20,000	0.01[a]	2×10^6
Chloroform	8,200	0.1[a]	8×10^4
Tetrachloroethylene	200	0.005	4×10^4
Trichloroethylene	1,100	0.005	2×10^5

[a]New York State Department of Environmental Conservation Guidelines for
Groundwater

to plumes of dissolved chlorinated solvents. The fact that LNAPLs do not penetrate much
below the water table, and the fact that the most mobile chemicals from LNAPLs are
prone to microbial degradation apparently account for the large difference in groundwater
impacts of chlorinated solvents and petroleum products.

Spills of chlorinated solvents in aquifers are, in general, exceptionally difficult to
clean up. At some sites, the plumes have reached water supply wells at concentrations
that are much above the MCLs for drinking water, thereby threatening public health
and valuable groundwater resources. Although some steps must be taken in such circumstances, given the typically long term nature of chlorinated solvent sites, it may
sometimes be more cost effective to simply prevent further release by isolating and/or
controlling the source zone rather than attempting a complete remediation. At other sites,

TABLE 1.12 Physical, Chemical, and Biological Properties of the Chlorinated Solvent Compounds Which Have Helped Lead to Extensive Groundwater Contamination by this Compound Class.

1. The **high volatilities** of the chlorinated solvents led to a false sense of security regarding how these chemicals must be handled. Historically, it was believed that chlorinated solvent released to the unsaturated zone would easily volatilize to the atmosphere. Thus, when poured on dry ground, although a chlorinated solvent may *appear* to be lost entirely to the atmosphere, some will be transported into the subsurface by gaseous diffusion, by infiltration of contaminated water, and as a moving DNAPL phase. And, once contamination reaches the saturated zone (including direct releases to the saturated zone), high volatility is of little assistance in removing the solvents: transport across the capillary fringe can be exceedingly slow (McCarthy and Johnson, 1992).

2. The **high densities** of the chlorinated solvents (1.2 to 1.7 g/cm^3) relative to that of water (1 g/cm^3) mean that if a sufficient volume of a typical chlorinated solvent is spilled, then liquid solvent may be able to penetrate the water table. In the saturated zone, the unstable nature of the solvent flow causes the solvent to form thin "fingers" which can lead to the collection of large amounts of solvent in one or more "pools" on top of less permeable layers. Since a pool presents a very low cross section to on-coming groundwater flow, absolute removal rates of dissolved solvent from the pool will usually be very low (Johnson and Pankow, 1992).

3. The relatively **low viscosities** of the chlorinated solvents allow relatively rapid downward movement in the subsurface. Chlorinated solvent mobility in the subsurface increases with increasing density/viscosity ratios (Cohen and Mercer, 1993).

4. The **low interfacial tension** between a liquid chlorinated solvent phase and water allows a liquid chlorinated solvent to enter easily into small fractures and pore spaces, facilitating deep penetration into the subsurface. Low interfacial tension also contributes to the low retention capacities of soils for chlorinated solvents.

5. The **low *absolute* solubilities** of the chlorinated solvents (typically on the order of hundreds of mg/L) mean that when a significant quantity of such a compound is spilled on the ground surface, liquid solvent will be able to migrate as a DNAPL phase in the subsurface, potentially accumulating as one or more pools on the tops of low permeability layers. The low solubility will then permit such pools to persist for decades to centuries (Johnson and Pankow, 1992).

6. The **high *relative* solubilities** of the chlorinated solvents mean that a solvent spill can cause groundwater contamination at levels which are high *relative* to concentrations which appear harmful to human health.

7. The **low partitioning to soil materials** exhibited by the chlorinated solvents means that soil and rock materials will bind these compounds only weakly. This applies to both the unsaturated and saturated zones. Thus, sorption to soils will not significantly retard the movement of a chlorinated solvent, and zones of contamination can grow essentially as quickly as the groundwater can move.

8. The **low degradabilities** of the chlorinated solvent compounds, either by biological means, or by abiotic-chemical reactions, mean that subsurface lifetimes of these chemicals can be very long.

the plumes terminate at hydrologic boundaries such as rivers or lakes. In such cases, the mass flux is transferred from the groundwater zone to surface waters where, because of dilution and volatilization, usually little or no degradation of the water quality occurs. Large remediation efforts may not always be warranted at sites where the plumes have reached surface water bodies: unlike many other well-known industrial contaminants such as PCBs and some pesticides, the chlorinated solvents do not accumulate in ecological food chains.

1.7 A HISTORY OF HOW WE BECAME AWARE THAT DENSE CHLORINATED SOLVENTS CAN POSE SERIOUS THREATS TO GROUNDWATER SYSTEMS

1.7.1 General

1.7.1.1 Basis of interest

Widespread understanding in government, industry, and the professional groundwater community of the exceptional propensity for chlorinated solvents to cause severe and persistent contamination of groundwater was not achieved until most of today's problems had already been created. It is now apparent that if the groundwater research community had been quicker to recognize the importance of chlorinated solvents, many crucial studies of solvent behavior in the subsurface could have been carried out decades earlier, even though advanced methods for chemical analyses were not yet available. (All of Schwille's work was conducted without such methods.) And, if awareness of and concern for solvent hazards to groundwater had developed earlier, then practices for storage, handling, transportation, and disposal of solvents could also have been improved more quickly so that much of today's contamination of groundwater by chlorinated solvent compounds could have been averted.

With the benefit of hindsight, it is apparent that the late awareness of the hazards posed by chlorinated solvents to groundwater represents a **failure** of several segments of modern society: governmental regulation, industrial practice, and environmental research in the professional groundwater community. This failure makes it important to analyze the history according to which our society came to realize that chlorinated solvents must be handled with exceptional care. Such an analysis may: 1) provide insight that will reduce the possibility for other environmental problems: and 2) result in research and government regulations that prevent future problems in all compartments of the environment.

We also note that the history according to which the threats posed by chlorinated solvents to groundwater became recognized is a matter of current legal interest to the site owners, insurance companies, local governments, lawyers, and consulting scientists and engineers that are involved in disputes over matters of liability at contaminated sites. For example, at a site where agreement has been reached as to who caused the contamination problem, there is oftentimes considerable disagreement regarding when and if the responsible party should have been aware of the threats posed by chlorinated solvents.

1.7.1.2 The history has two stages

As noted in Section 1.1.1, the discovery of the chlorinated solvents problem occurred in two stages: 1) the simple recognition of their prevalence as groundwater contaminants; and 2) the recognition of the common presence of these compounds as difficult-to-remediate, subsurface DNAPL source zones. Neither of these discoveries was anticipated by the North American groundwater community.

1.7.2 Timelines in the History

The evolution of knowledge regarding the threats posed by chlorinated solvents to groundwater has been reconstructed in Table 1.14 as four parallel timelines detailing events in four different areas: *Analytical Developments, Societal and Anecdotal Events, Literature Reports,* and *Federal (U.S.) Government Actions.*

   Analytical Developments (column **a**) is a crucially important category for the history in Table 1.14 since it may have been unreasonable to have expected industrial or consulting parties to analyze groundwater for chlorinated solvents before routine analytical methods were available. For example, since analytical methods were not readily available in the early 1960s to detect chlorinated solvents at a level like 5 μg/L, then that situation makes it difficult to argue that a site owner should have been analyzing groundwater samples at that time to ensure that contamination at that type of level had not occurred.

   Societal and Anecdotal Events (column **b**) is a significant category for the history because it is important to document the evolution of environmental issues and perceptions during the last 40 or so years.

   Literature Reports (column **c**) is an important component of the history because many reports of important developments regarding chlorinated solvents first appeared in the scientific and engineering literature. Once those publications began to appear, then one can argue that after some reasonable length of time, responsible parties should have begun to take appropriate precautions to prevent further releases of contamination.

   Federal (U.S.) Government Actions (column **d**) is included as a category in the history because there are many examples of how a step taken by the federal government was either an important regulatory climax of other events in the history, and/or an action that initiated additional developments in the other categories. For example, the *Safe Drinking Water Act* of 1974 was the culmination of events in the other three categories, and then itself caused further developments in the other categories. In the next section, a reference to one of the elements in one of the timelines will be followed by a bold letter which will indicate the column in which that element appears. For the sake of brevity, not all of the elements in Table 1.14 will be discussed; the reader can examine the table to fill in some of the details.

1.7.3 The First Stage: Discovering that Chlorinated Solvents are in Groundwater

1.7.3.1 The 1950s to mid-1960s: the early years

Prior to the 1960s, the measurement of organic contamination in water was largely limited to a few indicator parameters such as **biological oxygen demand (BOD)** and **bacterial concentration counts**. It was generally assumed that groundwater quality was largely unaffected by man. The subsurface was believed to be particularly capable of absorbing "organic" contaminants: organic contaminants were thought at that time to include mainly putrescible waste and sewage, which, indeed, are substantially renovated by natural processes in the subsurface. In one of the early textbooks on groundwater, Thomas (1951) stated that organic wastes are *"the easiest to eliminate [through the] natural processes of separation, filtration, dilution, oxidation, and chemical reaction"*, and that if *"powerful influences of protection or purification were not at work in nature, it would be almost impossible to find unpolluted [ground]water anywhere."* Thus, in the nascent field of contaminant hydrogeology, "organic" contaminants (including those which could be detected by taste or smell) were receiving very little attention. The contaminant that received the most attention in the early decades of the field was salt, mostly from seawater intrusion.

Table 1.14 begins in 1953 (**a**) when the prominent journal *Analytical Chemistry* published an article entitled *"Mass Spectrometer Determination of Volatile Contaminants in Water"* by Melpolder *et al.* (1953). This article described a primitive purge and trap method that involved the use of mass spectrometry to measure μg/L levels of petroleum products in water. The authors stated: *"The method may be extended to volatile compounds other than hydrocarbons, such as industrial solvents and cleaning fluids"*. On the basis of this publication and others (*e.g.*, Seto and Schultze, 1956 (**a**); Montgomery and Conlon, 1967 (**a**)), it can be argued that if an analyst had set out with determination and good laboratory resources to measure chlorinated solvents at tens of μg/L and higher in groundwater, then suitable methods could probably have been derived from publications available in the 1950s and 1960s.

As evidence in support of the above argument, we note that during the 1950s to 1960s time frame, chemists had undertaken to measure trace levels of certain organic contaminants in water in which they were especially interested. For example, alkyl benzene sulfonate (ABS) detergents were being measured at this time in surface waters at the $\sim$10 μg/L level (Rosen *et al.*, 1956 (**a**)). (Interest in the ABS detergents was due to their increasingly ubiquitous presence as foaming agents in waste waters and in certain receiving waters.) A concerted effort was also made in the late 1950s to measure μg/L levels of certain organic pesticides like DDT and aldrin (Middleton and Lichtenberg, 1960 (**a**); see also the history provided by Rosen, 1976), and methods for the determination of selected pesticides were published in the water works literature in the 1960s (Goodenkauf and Erdie, 1964 (**a**); Gutenmann and Lisk, 1964 (**a**)).

We can conclude that while anthropogenic organic compounds in general were not of widespread interest during this time period, when there was a will to measure specific organic compounds in water, then analytical methods suitable for use at the μg/L level could be developed. And, although the chlorinated solvents were being produced in quantities that were similar to those of the pesticides and the foaming, ABS detergents, the inability to detect the chlorinated solvents by taste, smell, or sight caused them to be simply overlooked as groundwater contaminants until much later in time.

1.7.3.2 The Mid-1960s to 1972: finding toxic organic compounds in some drinking water supplies

On March 23, 1967 (**b**), Dr. Leslie L. Glasgow, Chairman of the Louisiana Stream Control Commission, wrote to the Commissioner of the U.S. Federal Water Pollution

Control Administration[†] requesting technical assistance in determining the extent to which organic chemicals were affecting the quality of **New Orleans drinking water**. The reason for the request was that there were many complaints of "**chemical**" and "**oily**" flavors in the Mississippi River-derived water. These complaints resulted in a concerted effort to identify and measure trace organics in water using gas chromatography coupled with mass spectrometry (GC/MS). Most of this work was carried out at the Southeast Water Research Laboratory in Athens, Georgia in the late 1960s (**d**) (Keith, 1974)[‡]. EPA, formed in October of 1970 (**d**) by President Nixon, continued the study. Using an analytical method using adsorption on carbon followed by solvent extraction with chloroform, the study was completed in April, 1972 (**d**), confirming the presence of a wide variety of "extractable" organic compounds in New Orleans drinking water. EPA (1972) concluded that the problem was due to **industrial wastes** discharged to the river, and that **chlorination** of the drinking water may also have been playing a role. As a direct result of these findings, Congress enacted the *Clean Water Act* (*CWA*) on October 18 of 1972 (**d**) to regulate waste discharges into all navigable waters of the U.S. The *CWA* did not deal in a significant way with groundwater, and ironically, had an adverse effect on groundwater because it directed waste discharges from surface waters to the land, where they no doubt degraded groundwater quality in some locations.

Since the method that EPA (1972) (**d**) used to analyze the New Orleans samples used recovery with chloroform, no other volatile, chlorinated solvents that might have been present could be easily determined at that time in the face of the overwhelming amount of that chlorinated solvent. Therefore, there was as yet little indication that volatile organic compounds (VOCs) might be a problem in drinking waters obtained from surface water supplies, and certainly no indication to the hydrogeology, industrial, or regulatory communities that chlorinated solvent VOCs might be prevalent groundwater contaminants. Indeed, the Manufacturing Chemists' Association was stating in "Chemical Safety Data Sheets" for TCE, PCE, and 1,1,1-TCA distributed as late as 1968 (**b**) that for disposal, these solvents "*. . . may be poured on dry sand, earth, or ashes . . . and allowed to evaporate into the atmosphere.*" The disposal method suggested in a similar data sheet for TCE dated 1971 (**b**) and distributed by a large manufacturer stated that one should "*Bury [the TCE] away from water supply or allow solvent to evaporate to atmosphere at a safe distance from inhabited buildings*"*. Despite the widespread ignorance of the effects that

---

[†]The Federal Water Pollution Control Administration was one of the federal agencies that formed the basis of, and was superceded by the EPA.

[‡]By 1970, computerized GC/MS equipment had become commercially available, greatly increasing the speed of organic pollutant analysis (Keith, 1974).

*Prior, related comments on this subject were made in the *Handbook of Vapor Degreasing* (American Society for Testing and Materials (ASTM), 1962) This handbook advised that for the disposal of spent solvents, "*If there are no local regulations forbidding it, the sludge may be poured on dry ground at a safe distance from buildings and allowed to evaporate. If the solvent is free-flowing and can soak into the ground before the solvent evaporates, it may be poured into shallow containers to permit the solvent to evaporate before dumping*". We note in this context that in the U.S. in the 1960s, no local regulations of which we are aware forbade ground disposal of solvent sludge.

such chlorinated solvent disposal practices would have on groundwater quality, as seen by various entries in column **b** in Table 1.14, concern regarding the safety of groundwater supplies was nevertheless beginning to grow in the late 1960s and early 1970s.

1.7.3.3 1972 to 1975: finding the first chlorinated VOCs in drinking water; the trihalomethanes (THMs)

With interest increasing during the early 1970s in the matter of organic compounds in drinking water, Rook (1972) (**a**) adapted a method from the field of beverage flavor analysis to determine VOCs in water. In this method, a large (10 L) sample was heated to 60°C, and the "headspace" gas above the liquid was directed over silica gel to concentrate the VOCs. After concentration, the VOCs were determined by gas chromatography (GC). In the same article, Rook (1972) (**c**) went on to discuss the fact that analyses at a Rotterdam drinking water plant indicated that **trihalomethane (THM)** compounds (*e.g.*, chloroform) were somehow being formed during the chlorination of the drinking water. Then, in the summer of 1974, Rook (1974) (**c**) made the connection that it was reactions between aqueous chlorine and natural humic materials that were responsible for the formation of the haloforms.

In December of 1974, using an approach for VOC analysis that was similar to that devised by Mieure and Dietrich (1973) (**a**), Bellar and Lichtenberg (1974) (**a**) developed the current form of the now very-well-known purge and trap method. Purge and trap was used by Bellar *et al.* (1974) (**c**) in conjunction with GC/MS in a study which revealed that haloform compounds were also present in U.S. drinking waters. Consequently, in December of 1974 (**d**), EPA began the *National Organics Reconnaissance Study (NORS)* which examined surface water and groundwater supplies used to provide drinking water for 80 U.S. cities. The water samples were analyzed for several THMs, 1,2-dichloroethylene, and carbon tetrachloride (Symons *et al.*, 1975). In May of 1975 (**d**), results of the *NORS* project revealed the essentially **ubiquitous presence of haloforms in chlorinated drinking water in the U.S.**

During the same time period that the issue of haloforms in drinking water was being investigated in Europe and in the U.S., the matter of organic contaminants in New Orleans drinking water came to a climax when EPA (1974) (**d**) reported to the public in November of 1974 that at least 66 trace organic chemicals (including four chlorinated solvents: carbon tetrachloride, 1,1,1-TCA, TCE, and PCE) had been identified in Mississippi River water. Almost immediately thereafter, the *Safe Drinking Water Act* was signed into law on December 16, 1974 (**d**) by President Ford. This act dealt primarily with the protection of surface waters, though it also brought the first Federal action to protect groundwater resources inasmuch as it required the States to regulate all direct injections of wastes to the subsurface.

We see then that by the end of 1975, concern about organic contaminants in water was focussed primarily on: a) the new issue of contamination of *drinking water* by THMs as produced during chlorination; and b) problems with contamination of *surface water* supplies, primarily by industrial pollutants. Concern about contamination of groundwater by organic chemicals, however, was as yet very limited. Indeed, in a Chemical Safety Data Sheet that was dated 1973 (**b**) and distributed over the next several years, the same large chemical manufacturer of chlorinated solvents discussed in the previous section stated for the disposal of waste methylene chloride that "*In some cases, it can be transported to an area where it can be placed on the ground and allowed to evaporate*".[†] Thus, since direct pouring of solvents on the ground was not ruled out in this recommendation, the likely impact on groundwater of chlorinated solvents had not yet been clearly recognized. And, although some specialists were beginning to fear that groundwater supplies were in danger (*e.g.*, see the opinions of Geraghty and Miller published in June of 1973 (**b**) as well as the discussion in *ES&T* in December of 1973 (**c**) of a national policy on subsurface management), there was as yet no clear evidence that groundwater contamination was actually already a problem.

1.7.3.4 1976 to 1979: widespread testing for THMs in drinking water reveals the presence of other VOCs: coming to the conclusion that many important aquifers are contaminated with chlorinated solvents

As noted above, the *NORS* project demonstrated that chloroform and other THMs were very common in U.S. drinking waters, and that the chlorination process was responsible for that presence. However, *NORS* revealed relatively little about VOCs other than the THMs. Therefore, in order to: 1) investigate the relationships between the nature of a water supply and the resulting degree of THM formation upon chlorination; and to 2) expand the list of VOCs of interest beyond the THMs, in March of 1976 (**d**), EPA initiated the ***National Organics Monitoring Study (NOMS)***. In *NOMS*, 113 different public drinking water supplies representing various types of raw water sources and drinking water treatment processes were selected for examination. Of these supplies, 21 depended primarily on groundwater. Several important chlorinated solvent compounds were included as target analytes. The detection limits by the purge and trap method used (with GC/MS) ranged from 0.01 to 0.3 μg/L.

The first published *NOMS* results appeared in 1977 (**c**) in a book chapter by Brass *et al.* (1977). For the "Phase II" portion of the *NOMS* sampling (May to July of 1976), Brass *et al.* (1977) noted that TCE was found in 28 of the 113 drinking water systems. There was no discussion of the implications of this EPA finding either in Brass *et al.* (1977), or in the final EPA report for *NOMS* (EPA, 1977b) even though some of these systems were supplied by groundwater. This meant that it would be necessary for other studies of THMs in drinking water to *rediscover* the presence of chlorinated solvents in important groundwater supplies. Fortunately, the publicity surrounding the THM problem generated by the study of Bellar *et al.* (1974), by *NORS*, and by *NOMS* led directly to a large number of **local studies of THMs** in drinking water. The fact that the chlorinated

[†]Even in 1976, in their new edition of *Handbook of Vapor Degreasing*, ASTM (1976) used wording regarding spent solvent disposal which was identical to that given in the preceding footnote regarding the 1962 edition.

solvents are VOCs just as are the THMs meant that chlorinated solvent compounds would be found in many of these local studies.

Facilitating the local studies of THMs in drinking water was the important fact that by 1977, purge and trap had become a tested and proven method for determining VOCs at the low ppb level. Also, during this same general time period, rapid improvements were being made in the application of GC/MS in environmental organic analysis (Heller *et al.*, 1975 (**a**)). In addition, micro-solvent extraction with ~5 mL of pentane and ~35 mL of water (Henderson *et al.*, 1976, (**a**)) became available as an alternative to purge and trap with GC/MS for trace levels of chlorinated compounds in water samples. The main advantage of micro-solvent extraction in analyses for aqueous chlorinated compounds is that the extract can be analyzed on a GC fitted with an electron capture detector (ECD): a GC/ECD allows the sensitive and rather specific detection of many chlorinated compounds at very low levels, without requiring the complexity and cost of a GC/MS.

The **ready availability of suitable analytical methods for VOCs** together with the **motivation to look for THMs** in local water supplies quickly led to a series of reports of local groundwater contamination by chlorinated solvents. As examples, consider the following occurrences. In 1976 (**b**), New York State revealed that aquifers on Long Island were severely contaminated with TCE that had been used by many homeowners as a septic tank cleaner. In 1977 (**b**), 16 private wells in Gray, Maine were found to be contaminated with various chlorinated solvents. In 1978 (**b**), New York State officials reported that a search for THMs in drinking water had led to the discovery of a well field that was highly contaminated with TCE: the well field was closed. In 1978 (**b**), officials of the Nassau-Suffolk (Long Island, New York) Regional Planning Board reported widespread contamination by several chlorinated solvents: up to 375 μg/L of PCE, up to 310 μg/L of 1,1,1-TCA, and up to 300 μg/L of TCE were found in 36 wells; the wells were quickly closed (Koppleman, 1978). In May of 1978 (**b**), 80% of the drinking water of Bedford, Massachusetts was found to be contaminated with TCE at levels as high as 500 μg/L. Towards the end of the 1970s, hundreds of water supply wells had been closed in the U.S. due to contamination by chlorinated solvent compounds. The increasing evidence of contamination of groundwater was reviewed during this time frame by Pojasek (1977) (**c**).

As the **evidence mounted that many groundwater supplies were contaminated** with chlorinated solvents, some **local reconnaissance studies** were begun which had the goal of determining the extent of the contamination. For example, in 1978 (**c**), New Jersey began testing 500 public and private wells located near industrial sites for 50 organic compounds; a number of these compounds were chlorinated solvents. This reconnaissance for chlorinated solvents in groundwater was very analogous to EPA's use of *NORS* to determine the extent of the nation's THM problem in chlorinated drinking water supplies.

Drinking water regulations for various VOCs began to be promulgated in the U.S. in the late 1970s. New York State (1978) (**b**) published standards which included limits for three chlorinated solvent compounds; these are the first drinking water limits for chlorinated solvents of which we are aware. On November 20, 1979 (**d**) **EPA's final**

THM regulations stated that total THMs in drinking water should not exceed 100 μg/L, foreshadowing the regulations that would later be put in place for chlorinated solvents like TCE (see 1987 (**d**)). In 1979 (**d**), EPA also promulgated their list of *"priority pollutants"* (see Keith and Telliard, 1979) which were to be determined in waste water discharges. The priority pollutant list includes all of the common chlorinated solvents, and has become a commonly-used list of target analytes in many environmental water analyses. In this same context, we note that EPA's 600 series methods for VOCs were also formally issued in 1979 (**a**). Since these methods were designed to be sensitive at the μg/L level, additional advances in analytical chemistry had virtually no further effect on the history of interest here, and so entries in column **a** in Table 1.14 end at this point in time.

We see then that by the end of 1979, a reasonable amount of hard evidence had accumulated indicating that groundwater contamination by solvent chemicals might be a significant problem, especially in densely populated and/or industrialized areas. However, as has been typical in the discovery of other environmental problems (*e.g.*, stratospheric ozone depletion by chlorofluorocarbons), the **general recognition** of the problem of solvents in groundwater was not to take place until the weight of the evidence became overwhelming. Thus, the same major producer of chlorinated solvents mentioned above for 1973 was still saying in 1979 (**b**) that, for the disposal of methylene chloride, one could: *"Send solvent to a reclaimer. In some cases, small amounts can be transported to an area where it can be placed on the ground and allowed to evaporate safely if local, state, and federal regulations permit".*[†] There is also evidence that throughout the 1970s, chlorinated solvents were being disposed of at U.S. military bases by pouring them on the ground (New York Times, November 2, 1980; Schroeder, 1985; Schaumburg, 1990). Thus, since: 1) disposal on the ground was still viewed by many as a viable disposal option; and 2) groundwater protection was as yet largely not provided at either the state or federal level, it would not be until sometime in the 1980s that the dangers posed by chlorinated solvents to groundwater would receive widespread recognition in government, industry, and in the professional groundwater community.

1.7.3.5 1980 to 1981: The evidence that chlorinated solvents are widespread groundwater contaminants becomes overwhelming

The period 1980 to 1981 was characterized by a **virtual explosion** of reports which indicated that many important groundwater supplies were contaminated by chlorinated solvents. As an important example, the January 1980 (**c**) issue of the widely-read journal *Environmental Science and Technology* gave a **cover-story account** of the facts that: 1) groundwater contamination (including contamination by chlorinated organic compounds) had become a matter of very serious concern; and that 2) tight federal and state rules

---

[†]We note that relative to the 1973 recommendations, the qualifier concerning "local, state, and federal regulations" was now included, and so apparently the company's concern about chemicals such as methylene chloride was increasing.

requiring groundwater monitoring and protection would soon be coming. In the same month (**b**), public health officials for the State of California closed 39 TCE-contaminated public wells that had been providing water to 400,000 people in 13 cities in the **San Gabriel Valley**. 1980 (**b**) was also the year of discovery of the now well-known, large scale contamination of groundwater in California's Santa Clara "**Silicon" Valley**. By May of 1980 (**b**), agencies in **18 states** had measured numerous VOCs, most commonly TCE, in 2894 wells (see CEQ, 1981).

As of early 1980, although reasons to be concerned with groundwater contamination by chlorinated solvents were accumulating at a rapid pace, other than the rules regarding the injections of waste imposed by the *Safe Drinking Water Act* (see above), there were very few regulatory protections in place for groundwater resources. Indeed, in May of 1980 (**b**) in a special, red-paged "Regulatory Alert", *ES&T* (1980) reported that: "*Approximately 50% of the [nation's] population depends on groundwater for its drinking water supply. Yet, unlike surface water or air, there is no specific federal statute to protect it from pollution.*" In the same month, the *Environment Reporter* (1980a) (**b**) stated that **few states had acted** as yet to declare authority to protect groundwater supplies, and that **most did not even recognize** the magnitude of the problem. In August of 1980 (**b**), *Environment Reporter* (1980b) stated that existing **federal regulations** were still being viewed by some as **so weak that new laws would be needed** to provide effective groundwater protection.

In terms of EPA's role in the evolving circumstances, it was in May of 1980 (**d**) that EPA Administrator Costle, speaking on NBC's *Meet the Press* (see Josephson, 1980), identified groundwater protection as a **principle EPA priority**. In the same month (**d**), in an effort to deal with the deficiencies in groundwater legislation that were discussed in the preceding paragraph, EPA promulgated the *RCRA* regulations that required large scale groundwater monitoring at disposal sites. By the mid-1980s, groundwater from tens of thousands of monitoring wells at industrial sites had been analyzed for chlorinated solvent compounds and other VOCs: in an early survey of data from 183 hazardous waste sites in the U.S., four of the top five[†], and 10 of the top 20 most-frequently identified organic chemical contaminants were chlorinated solvents (Plumb and Pitchford, 1985)[‡]. In June of 1980 (**d**), EPA (1980a) conducted a planning workshop on the groundwater contamination problem, and in November of 1980 (**d**), EPA (1980b) announced their resulting **National Ground Water Protection Strategy**, with publication of the strategy to occur in the Federal Register in January 1981. In December of 1980 (**d**), U.S. Congress passed the EPA-administered *Superfund (i.e., CERCLA) Program* to deal with *"uncontrolled"* hazardous waste sites.

Naturally, a great deal of publicity surrounded the events described in the preceding paragraph. It is not surprising therefore that in 1980, just one year after the

---

[†] The four were TCE, PCE, dichloromethane (DCM), and 1,1-dichloroethane.

[‡]More recently, EPA's 1993 *Superfund Chemical Analysis Result Report* indicated that seven of the 20 most frequently detected organic contaminants at *Superfund* sites are chlorinated solvents. The Comprehensive Environmental Response, Compensation and Liability Information System (CERCLIS) lists over 32,000 sites in the U.S., and EPA has estimated that over one third of these are contaminated with solvents (EPA, 1991).

release of its prior version of its Chemical Safety Data Sheet on methylene chloride, the same major chemical company mentioned above for 1973 and 1979 tightened considerably its recommendations for disposal of this chemical. In particular, in 1980 (**b**), the data sheet on methylene chloride was revised to state: *"... Dumping into sewers, on the ground, or into any body of water is strongly discouraged, and may be illegal."*

The arrival of January 1981 (**b**) brought a **landmark report** from the President's Council on Environmental Quality (CEQ). Entitled *Contamination of Groundwater by Organic Chemicals*, this report detailed the avalanche of reports on groundwater contamination in the U.S. Identifying chlorinated solvents as the most common type of contaminants, CEQ (1981) noted that *"These incidents involve discoveries – sometimes completely accidental [e.g., looking for THMs, but finding other compounds as well] – of high concentrations of synthetic organic chemicals in a community or private drinking water well. It is now evident that hundreds of drinking water wells affecting millions of people have been closed because of contamination by toxic organic chemicals. ... No one can say for sure how long the contamination has existed, ...". "... the EPA regions report serious contamination of drinking water wells in 34 states, and there are indications that the true number is at least 40".* The release of this study was immediately reported upon in the February 1981 issue of *ES&T* (1981b) (**c**), and again in the July issue (**c**). With respect to what was beginning to occur at this time on the remediation front, we note that the January 1981 issue of *ES&T* (1981a) (**c**) reported as a news item that Recon Systems, Inc. (Somerville, NJ) had built and was operating an air stripping tower to remove 1,1,1-TCA from groundwater that was being pumped at 100,000 gpd from an aquifer in the Northeast.

ES&T was not the only journal reporting with urgency during early 1981 on the problem of chlorinated solvents in groundwater systems. For example, in April of 1981 in the *Journal of the American Water Works Association,* Petura (1981) (**c**) wrote an article entitled *"Trichloroethylene and methyl chloroform [1,1,1-TCA] in groundwater: A problem assessment".* The article stated that groundwater pollution was a *"problem of immense concern"*, with TCE and 1,1,1-TCA having been found in groundwater in numerous states including Pennsylvania, Delaware, New Hampshire, and California. *"Hundreds of wells, many in totally unrelated aquifers"* were described as being contaminated with these two compounds. At about the same time, in a book entitled *Quality of Groundwater*, Giger and Schaffner (1981) (**c**) and Zoeteman *et al.* (1981) (**c**) documented the presence of chlorinated hydrocarbons (including TCE, chloroform, and carbon tetrachloride) in groundwater at various sites in Switzerland and The Netherlands, respectively. Zoeteman *et al.* (1981) found TCE in 67% of the wells tested, carbon tetrachloride in 43%, and PCE in 19%. 1981 (**c**) also brought Schwille's first mainstream, English language journal article on the behavior of NAPLs in subsurface systems (Schwille, 1981).

Perhaps the clearest indication of the widespread nature of groundwater contamination by chlorinated solvents in the Northeast appeared in December of 1981 (**c**) in a study published in *ES&T* by Page (1981). Using data for **1076 wells in New Jersey**, Page (1981) found that **NJ groundwaters were at least as contaminated as**

NJ surface waters. A total of 17 halogenated solvent compounds were found in the groundwaters. For TCE, of 669 wells sampled, 388 were found to be contaminated, with 635 μg/L being the highest concentration. For 1,1,1-TCA, of 1071 wells sampled, 835 were contaminated, with 608 μg/L being the highest concentration. For PER, of 421 wells sampled, 179 were contaminated, with 91 μg/L being the highest concentration.

By mid-1981, EPA was beginning to recognize the scale of the problem posed by chlorinated solvents. In particular, on June 9, 1981 (**d**), in a presentation at a national meeting of the American Water Works Association, EPA employee Herbert J. Brass discussed results of the nationwide **Community Water Supply Survey (CWSS)** (Brass *et al.*, 1981). Based on samples from 106 surface water sources and 330 groundwater sources, Brass *et al.* (1981) found clear evidence for the presence of compounds like PCE, TCE, and 1,1,1-TCA in many groundwater supplies. These three compounds were found in about 5% of the groundwater sources tested, with maximum concentrations of 30, 650, and 210 μg/L. Of the 330 groundwater systems tested, 50 (15%) were found to be contaminated with some VOCs.

Based on the above evidence, we believe that it is clear that it is **the end of 1981** that provides the milestone for the end of the period of general ignorance of the fact that poor solvent handling practices and careless disposal can cause severe contamination of groundwater. Nevertheless, we know that contamination continued to take place beyond this date. For example, in their January 1981 (**b**) report, CEQ (1981) discussed the fact that septic tank cleaning fluids (most of which contained TCE, benzene, and/or methylene chloride) could still be purchased in most of the U.S. during 1981, with the 1979 usage estimated at 400,000 gallons on Long Island alone. Also, some of the common chlorinated solvents were still being used as "inactive" ingredients in pesticide formulations; these "inactive" ingredients often comprised most of the mass of such products. Regulations forbidding their use in this manner were not promulgated until the late 1980s (**d**) (EPA, 1987b).

What is notable about the discovery of the prevalence of dissolved-phase chlorinated solvents in groundwater is that it occurred almost entirely outside the realm of the groundwater science and engineering community. Nearly all of the surveys that revealed such contamination were conducted by state and federal agencies using samples pumped from water supply wells. We also note that in the late 1970s through 1981, there was essentially no discussion of dissolved chlorinated solvent contamination of groundwater in the major journals dedicated to groundwater science and engineering, *e.g.*, *Ground Water* and *Water Resources Research*; hydrology professionals were learning of the problem from developments taking place outside of their field.

1.7.4 The Second Stage: Discovering the DNAPL Nature of Liquid Chlorinated Solvents

1.7.4.1 1982 to the late 1980s

From 1982 onward, new reports of groundwater contamination by chlorinated solvents continued to appear (see columns **b** and **c** in Table 1.14). The issue of solvents in groundwater had by then evolved from the stage wherein the problem was being discovered and understood, to a stage wherein the goal was to have contamination contained, remediated, and prevented. Thus, in 1982 (**b**), the San Francisco Bay **Regional Water Quality Control Board (*RWQCB*)** launched a program to inventory underground storage systems in the industrialized areas under its jurisdiction. The resulting survey by mail to 2644 companies in the key groundwater basins ultimately lead to the publication of RWQCB's "*205J*" report (Industry Clean Water Task Force, 1985) which indicated that a significant amount of the contamination in the valley was due to high-tech industrial operations. As of September of 1985, the *RWQCB* had listed 75 sites within their jurisdiction at which groundwater contamination was: 1) under investigation; 2) in the process of being defined; 3) being cleaned up; or 4) had been cleaned up. On the Federal scene, in July of 1982, EPA (1982) (**d**) issued new rules governing hazardous wastes in landfills, surface impoundments, and other repositories. In 1986 (**d**), the *Hazardous and Solid Waste Amendments to RCRA* were passed mandating monitoring of the groundwater and vadose zones at many underground storage tank locations. On July 8, 1987 (**d**) a final drinking water standard value for TCE of 5 μg/L was published by EPA (1987a).

Although they had become aware of the general presence of dissolved chlorinated solvents in groundwater by about 1981, for perhaps five to seven years afterward, groundwater scientists and engineers in North America and in Europe remained almost entirely unaware of two facts: 1) that **DNAPL-phase solvent could be present in large amounts in the subsurface** at sites contaminated with chlorinated solvents; and 2) that **such a presence posed many difficult problems in remediating such sites**. In the early 1980s, the pioneering laboratory experiments of Schwille in these topic areas were largely unknown to these scientists and engineers (most of the European groundwater community was also unaware of this work). Although Schwille had published two English-language papers in the early 1980s (Schwille, 1981; Schwille, 1984b) (**c**), neither had been placed in the widely-read literature, and Schwille's (1984a) (**c**) summary report on the behavior of chlorinated solvents as DNAPLs in subsurface systems had been published in German. Thus, although the general presence of chlorinated solvents in groundwater had become recognized, it was not yet realized that long term source zones of DNAPL-phase chlorinated solvent were present below the water table at many contamination sites. Without knowledge of Schwille's work, North American groundwater scientists and engineers began now to rediscover what Schwille had concluded a decade earlier.

An understanding of how DNAPLs behave in the subsurface evolved in North America within a few groups of groundwater scientists and engineers who had each encountered DNAPLs at depth in the subsurface in the late 1970s. As was discussed in Section 1.1.2, the term "NAPL" was first coined in 1981 (**b**) during studies of a hazardous waste landfill in Niagara Falls, New York. At this site, a denser-than-water, organic liquid was discovered when it was bailed from wells installed in the soil and bedrock underlying the site. The liquid was a complex mixture of halogenated benzenes, chlorinated solvents, and other halogenated hydrocarbons. Similar organic liquids were discovered at about the same time at two other sites in the Niagara area, the Hyde Park

Landfill and Love Canal, and at a handful of unrelated sites elsewhere in North America. Thereafter, it soon became clear that NAPLs were an important source of the groundwater contamination at these sites. Unfortunately, nearly all of the information regarding NAPL and DNAPL behavior at those sites was the subject of litigation, usually in the context of *RCRA* and *Superfund* issues, and so that information did not become available until the late 1980s.

The development of conceptual models regarding how DNAPLs behave in the subsurface began in North America with conference proceedings and publications of limited circulation (*e.g.,* Feenstra, 1984; Cherry, 1984a and 1984b; Miller, 1984) (**c**). Although the number of mainstream, English-language publications reporting the presence of dissolved chlorinated solvents in groundwater had exploded in the 1980-1981 time frame, the first widely-read publications to discuss DNAPL behavior were those of Villaume (1985) and Mackay *et al.* (1985) (**c**). Both of these publications contained schematic diagrams of plumes emanating from DNAPL source zones in the subsurface, both as residual zones and as pools. However, neither of these publications emphasized the far-reaching implications of subsurface DNAPLs for groundwater quality.

1.7.4.2 The late 1980s to the present

At the time that the papers discussed in the preceding paragraph were being published, tremendous efforts and finances were being directed towards remediation efforts at countless *Superfund* and *RCRA* sites. Unfortunately, many of these efforts were largely unsuccessful. These efforts failed because in their design, the likely presence and nature of DNAPL source zones had not been considered (Bredehoft, 1992).

Schwille's work finally received wide North American recognition when an English translation of his comprehensive monograph was published in 1988 (**c**) (Schwille, 1988). The first textbook to include the DNAPL conceptual model, at least in a cursory way, was Fetter (1988) (**c**). The first substantive textbook treatment of DNAPLs appeared in Domenico and Schwartz (1990) (**c**). These and other publications brought at least a general understanding of how DNAPL solvents behave in the subsurface into full circulation within the groundwater science and engineering community. However, even into the early 1990s, only a relatively small fraction of the groundwater and environmental science community was aware of how DNAPL solvents could behave in the subsurface.

The first indication that EPA, the agency regulating the *Superfund* investigations, recognized some aspects of the DNAPL issue consists of a cursory reference in their document entitled *Guidance on Remedial Actions for Contaminated Ground Water at Superfund Sites* (**d**) (EPA, 1988). Evidence that EPA recognized the full implications of DNAPL behavior for *Superfund* investigations was not apparent until the publication of a *Ground Water Issue Paper* on DNAPLs (**d**) (Hurling and Weaver, 1991), and their sponsorship of a two day DNAPL workshop at the Kerr Laboratory in Ada, Oklahoma in April, 1991 (**d**). A comprehensive monograph entitled *DNAPL Site Investigation* sponsored by EPA was published in 1993 (**d**) (Cohen and Mercer, 1993). 1993 also brought the EPA report entitled "*Evaluation of Likelihood of DNAPL Presence at NPL Sites - National Results* (EPA, 1993). Thus, although EPA had led the way in identifying and determining trace organic contaminants in groundwater in the 1970s, official recognition by EPA of the important ways in which DNAPLs affect groundwater contamination and remediation came more than a decade after the presence of dissolved chlorinated solvents had been generally recognized around 1981. We conclude from this that a strong science program within EPA is still needed to support its official and regulatory actions.

1.8 CONCLUSIONS

Major production and use of dense chlorinated solvents began in the 1950s and 1960s. Given the properties of these compounds, in hindsight, it is not surprising that these compounds are now problematic groundwater contaminants. Simply put, it was the extensive and widespread industrial usage of these compounds coupled with some naive attitudes about how they could be handled that led to most of today's problems with these compounds.

Recognition of the importance of chlorinated solvents in groundwater arrived very late in the research community. Indeed, after about 30 years of unwise practices, it was in the late 1981 time frame that our industrialized society came to a wide recognition of the environmental hazards posed by this class of chemicals. The special DNAPL nature of chlorinated solvents in the subsurface became recognized in the late 1980s/early 1990s; other than Schwille's studies of the late 1970s and early 1980s, there had been little substantial research directed specifically at the behavior of chlorinated solvents in groundwater.

The ability of chlorinated solvents in DNAPL form to persist in the subsurface for long periods of time, even in the face of aggressive remediation efforts, is the most vexing aspect of groundwater contamination by such compounds. The length of time required to dissolve a typical accumulation of solvent on top of an aquitard can be hundreds of years under natural conditions; significant decreases in the time for complete dissolution for such an accumulation will in general require aggressive treatment efforts (Johnson and Pankow, 1992).

Much of the information presented in the chapters of this book is the result of recent study. Some of the topics included are the subjects of intensive on-going research. Our understanding of the movement and fate of chlorinated solvents in groundwater has now advanced sufficiently that most of the major aspects of how chlorinated solvents move in the subsurface after spills are reasonably well understood. In contrast, much less is known about the behavior of chlorinated solvents in the subsurface when subjected to remediation efforts. The remaining chapters in this book will seek to provide a clear understanding of the pertinent properties of the chlorinated solvents so that contamination assessment, control, and remediation (when possible) can take place at sites of interest throughout the world.

TABLE 1.14 A History of the Problem of Chlorinated Solvents in Groundwater in Four Parallel Timelines.

a. Analytical developments	b. Societal and anecdotal events
1953: The journal *Analytical Chemistry* publishes the article *"Mass Spectrometer Determination of Volatile Contaminants in Water"* by Melpolder *et al.* (1953).	
1956: The journal *Analytical Chemistry* publishes the article *"Determination of Trichloroethylene, Trichloroacetic Acid, and Trichloroethenol in Urine"* by Seto and Schultze (1956).	
1964: Methods for the determination of various pesticides are published in the water works literature by Goodenkauf and Erdie (1964) and Gutenmann and Lisk (1964).	
1967: The journal *Water Pollution Control* publishes the article *"The Detection of Chlorinated Solvents in Sewage Sludge"* by Montgomery and Conlon (1967).	**1967, March 23:** Dr. Leslie L. Glasgow (Chairman, Louisiana Stream Control Commision) asks the Commissioner of the U.S. Federal Water Pollution Control Administration for technical assistance in determining the extent to which organic chemicals are affecting water quality in the Mississippi River. There have been many complaints that the drinking water in New Orleans has *"chemical"* and *"oily"* flavors.
	1967 and 1968: In *Chemical Safety Data Sheets* SD-14, SD-24, SD-90, dated 1956, 1948, and 1965, respectively, but still being distributed, the *Manufacturing Chemists Assoc.* states that *"Residue[s] [of TCE, PCE, and 1,1,1-TCA] may be poured on dry sand, earth, or ashes . . . and allowed to evaporate into the atmosphere."* The *Chemical Hazards Bulletin* of the American Insurance Association (1967) contains similar wording.
	1969: Charles F. Luce, chairman of the *National Water Commission*, tells the 5th Annual Meeting of the *Ground Water Resources Institute* at Gov. Winthrop Rockefeller's Winrock Farm (Morrilton, Ark.) that the quality of ground water is in grave danger. Carl F. Klein, Asst. Secretary of Interior, reports that "Most of the same types of pollution that affect surface water will eventually affect groundwater with greater impact and longer lasting harm."

c. Literature   **d. Federal governmental**
  reports   **actions**

1956: Rosen *et al.* (1956) report the
identification of anionic synthetic
detergents in surface waters.

1960: Middleton and Lichtenberg
(1960) report the presence of
pesticides like DDT and aldrin in
certain of the nation's rivers.

Late 1960s: Most of the work to identify and measure the organic
contaminants in the Mississippi River water is conducted at the
federal Southeast Water Research Laboratory in Athens, Georgia
(see Keith, 1974).

1970, October: EPA is established by President Nixon.

1971: A patent is given to Warner   **1971, February 22:** William Ruckelshaus is sworn in as first
Co. (Philadelphia, Penn.) for an   Administrator of EPA.
impermeable membrane to line the
base of a landfill.

TABLE 1.14   *(continued)*

a. Analytical developments	b. Societal and anecdotal events
	1971: A large manufacturer states in a chemical data handling sheet for TCE that one should *"Bury [the TCE] away from water supply or allow solvent to evaporate to atmosphere at a safe distance from inhabited buildings."*
1972, Fall: Rook (1972) adapts a beverage analysis method for use in determining VOCs in drinking water. The headspace above 10 L of 60 °C water is passed through silica gel. Compounds collected on the silica gel are analyzed by gas chromatography with detection by mass spectrometry (*i.e.*, by GC/MS). This a forerunner of the P&T method later developed by EPA.	**1972, March:** *ES&T* (1972) reports that: *"After many years of apathy and indifference, private citizens, industry, and government are now advocating national policies for groundwater pollution and conservation."* Although groundwater has always been considered insulated against contamination, *ES&T* notes that groundwater contamination is increasing. **1972:** The revised *Chemical Hazards Bulletin* of the American Insurance Association (1972) contains the same wording given above regarding disposal, but does add a qualifier regarding complying with new federal regulations. **1973, June:** *ES&T* (1973) reports that *"Geraghty and Miller, a firm of consulting groundwater specialists, is performing a 14 month study of groundwater contamination problems in 11 northeastern states which account for 26% of the nation's population. Project leader David Miller says, 'No one really knows how severe the groundwater contamination problem is in the Northeast and one of the goals of the study is to put this problem in its proper perspective.'"*
1973, November: Mieure and Dietrich (1973) publish a method for determining VOCs in which the headspace over a sample of water is passed through a trap (Tenax-GC). The contents of the trap are subsequently thermally desorbed to a gas chromatography column for analysis. This is a forerunner of the P&T method developed later by EPA.	**1973:** A major chemical company recommends for disposal that users of methylene chloride can *"Send solvent to a reclaimer. In some cases, it can be transported to an area where it can be placed on the ground and allowed to evaporate."* **1974, July:** State of Louisiana and City of New Orleans ask EPA Region VI to undertake another analytical survey of the organic chemicals present in the finished water of three drinking water treatment plants in New Orleans.

**c. Literature
  reports**

**d. Federal governmental
  actions**

1972, April: EPA (1972) reports that there is a problem with New Orleans drinking water that is drawn from the Mississippi River. Using a solvent extraction based method, 46 specific organic compounds are found in drinking water from three drinking water treatment plants. (44 more compounds are found in wastewaters discharged by 10 industrial plants to the Mississippi just above New Orleans.) EPA (1972) concludes that the problem is due to *wastes* from industries discharging to the river, and the *chlorination* of the drinking water may also be playing a role.

1972, Fall: Rook (1972) reports that haloform compounds are somehow formed during the chlorination of Rotterdam drinking water.

1972, October: The *Clean Water Act* (*CWA*) is enacted over a Nixon veto as a major amendment to the *Federal Water Pollution Control Act* (Public Law 92-500). The *CWA* provides for the regulation of the discharges into all navigable waters of the U.S. There are two goals: 1) "*fishable*" and "*swimmable*" waters by 1983; and 2) eventually, no discharges at all of pollutants into waterways. The Act provides federal funding to states to set up and implement water quality management programs. Although the main focus of the Act is the protection of surface water quality, some funding is provided to protect groundwater resources from contamination due to the land application of municipal wastes.

1972, November: Kleopfer and Fairless (1972) report the presence of numerous, industrially-related organic compounds in the municipal water obtained for Evansville, Indiana from the Ohio River. The compounds that were found include toluene, ethylbenzene, the xylenes, and PCE.

1973, December: *ES&T* (1973) reports that *"Injection wells for industrial and sewage waste waters increase slowly in number as the call goes out for a national policy on underground space and wastes management."*

1974, Summer: Rook (1974) shows that haloform compounds like chloroform can form during chlorination of drinking water due to reactions with natural humic compounds present in raw drinking water. (As a group, trihalomethanes are referred to as "THMs".)

1974, July: EPA Region VI accepts the request of the State of Louisiana and City of New Orleans for more help with their drinking water problem, and begins a study using GC/MS and other methods to determine organic compounds in selected samples.

1974, November: EPA (1974) releases a preliminary report on the New Orleans situation, listing 66 organic chemicals in the finished water from the three New Orleans drinking water treatment plants. Most concentrations range from 0.01 to 5 μg/L. Later, the total number of compounds identified is raised to 94.

1974, November 8: Concurrently with releasing the report on New Orleans drinking water, EPA announces plans for a *National Organics Reconnaissance Survey* (*NORS*) of water supplies for many of the nations' cities (see Symons *et al.*, 1975). Both raw and finished water are to be studied to see how raw water quality and chlorination affect the concentrations of THMs. *NORS* will begin as soon as the *Safe Drinking Water Act* is signed.

TABLE 1.14   *(continued)*

a. Analytical developments	b. Societal and anecdotal events
1974, December: Working for EPA, Bellar and Lichtenberg (1974) publish the basis of EPA's purge and trap (P&T) procedure. Gas is bubbled through a water sample, the VOCs are stripped from the water, adsorbed on a trap containing adsorbents like Tenax-GC and carbon, and the trap is then thermally desorbed to a gas chromatography column for analysis.	
1975, March: EPA scientists Heller *et al.* (1975) advocate GC/MS as an accurate and economical approach for the determination of organic pollutants in all media.	**1975, November:** The *Safe Drinking Water Committee* of the National Research Council holds its first public meeting. The study will evaluate health effects due to contaminants in drinking water. (See *ES&T*, 1976a.)
1976, January: Henderson *et al.* (1976) publish a method for determining trace levels of chlorinated organic compounds using micro solvent extraction (μSE). A portion of the solvent extract is injected onto a gas chromatograph, and detection is with an electron capture detector (ECD).	**1976:** New York State Department of Health (1980) first learns of severe groundwater contamination on Long Island due to TCE and other chemicals. TCE is being used extensively as a septic tank cleaner by homeowners.

**c. Literature
   reports**

1974, December: Bellar *et al.*
(1974) report that haloforms are
formed when drinking waters
are chlorinated in the U.S., just
as Rook (1972) has found in
The Netherlands. (As a group,
trihalomethanes are referred to as
"THMs".)

1975, August: Dowty *et al.*
(1975) report the presence of
numerous industrial-waste and
chlorination-related organic
compounds in New Orleans drinking
water. GC/MS was used to identify
major aromatic and halogenated
aliphatic compounds. Approximately
60-70 compounds were commonly
found in the finished drinking water.

**d. Federal governmental
   actions**

1974, December 16: *Safe Drinking Water Act* is signed into law
by Pres. Ford. Although originally expected to be vetoed, its
passage is due in large part to the storm of controversy that has
erupted over the New Orleans problem (see above). The Act
gives the EPA Administrator the power to take such action as is
needed to protect drinking water supplies. Also, to help protect
groundwater resources, the Act requires that EPA must develop
regulations governing how states control the disposal of wastes
by underground injection.

1974, December 18: The 80 cities selected for *NORS* are
identified. 16 cities depend on groundwater, 64 depend on
surface water. Of the 80 cities, 10 cities have been selected
for comprehensive study. Two of these ten, namely Miami and
Tucson, are selected as representatives of cities depending on
groundwater. The compounds to be quantitated in the samples
will be the THMs (*e.g.*, chloroform), plus 1,2-dichloroethane
and carbon tetrachloride. Other VOCs like TCE and PER are
not included in the study because they cannot be determined
easily using the existing P&T method. The compound-dependent
detection limits ranged from 0.2 (1,2-dichloroethane) to 2 μg/L
(carbon tetrachloride).

1975, January-April: Sampling for *NORS* is carried out.

1975, May: EPA (1975) releases interim report to Congress
on results of the *National Organics Reconnaissance Survey*
(*NORS*) for halogenated organics. *NORS* confirms that THMs are
essentially ubiquitous in chlorinated drinking water, and that their
formation involves the chlorination process (see discussion in
Symons *et al.*, 1975).

1976, March: In part because of the limited nature of the group
of compounds determined in *NORS* (*i.e.*, primarily THMs), EPA
begins the *National Organics Monitoring Study (NOMS)* of 113
public water supplies representing various types of sources
and drinking water treatment processes (21 of these supplies
depend primarily on groundwater). The goal is to provide data
for possible establishment of additional maximum concentration
levels of organic compounds in drinking water. *NOMS* will
include as target analytes several important chlorinated solvent
compounds. Detection limits for various halogenated purgeables
vary from 0.01 to 0.3 μg/L. (See Brass *et al.*, 1977.)

1976, October 11: *Toxic Substances Control Act* is signed. The
Act establishes a regulatory framework for controlling the release
of toxic substances to the environment.

TABLE 1.14   (*continued*)

a. Analytical developments	b. Societal and anecdotal events
	1977: 16 private wells are closed in Gray, Maine due to contamination with various chlorinated solvents, as well as certain other compounds.
	1977: In this year alone, in 58 square miles of densely populated Nassau County (Long Island, New York), homeowners buy 67,500 gallons of septic tank cleaners (NRC, 1984). CEQ (1981) notes that such fluids are typically used in a dose of 1 gallon to dissolve sludge (*i.e.*, grease) in a septic tank. The cleaners contain 80% aromatic and chlorinated solvents (NRC, 1984).
	1978: In anticipation of the Feb. 9, 1978 EPA regulations, New York State undertakes a statewide survey to evaluate the degree to which THMs (and other selected compounds) are present in their drinking waters. As described by Schreiber (1981), New York State discovers definite evidence of groundwater contamination, *e.g.*, a well supply is found to be highly contaminated with TCE. The well field is closed.
	1978: Nassau-Suffolk (Long Island, New York) Regional Planning Board finds that organic chemical contamination is widespread in the upper glacial aquifer (Koppleman, 1978). 36 wells are closed. The closed wells contain up to 375 μg/L of PER, 310 μg/L of 1,1,1-TCA, and 300 μg/L of TCE.

c. Literature reports

d. Federal governmental actions

1976, October: *Resource Conservation and Recovery Act* (*RCRA*) is passed by Congress as an amendment to the *Solid Waste Disposal Act* of 1965. The main purpose of *RCRA* is to address the problem of how to safely dispose of the huge volumes of solid and hazardous waste generated in the U.S. each year. However, it is not until 1980 that regulations authorized under *RCRA* bring about large scale groundwater monitoring at disposal sites, and not until 1986 that amendments to *RCRA* mandate monitoring of the groundwater and vadose zones at many underground storage tank locations.

1977, April: Pojasek (1977) reports that: *"in the past 5-10 years, the number of major incidents of groundwater contamination have increased dramatically. These incidents involved chemical spills, municipal landfills, wastewater lagoon seepage, and industrial waste burial."*

1977, February 9: EPA proposes regulations to limit certain organic contaminants (including THMs) in drinking water because there is a reason to believe that such compounds pose a serious threat to health (Kimm, 1978).

1977: In a book chapter that precedes the final EPA report on *NOMS*, Brass *et al.* (1977) indicate that 1,1,1-TCA, TCE, and carbon tetrachloride, which are not formed in the chlorination process, are present in raw waters used as drinking water. For the May to July, 1976 sampling, TCE was found in 28 out of 113 drinking waters. While this evidence for groundwater contamination by solvent compounds was obtained in *NOMS*, the implications of this finding were not discussed in this chapter, nor in the final report (EPA, 1977b). It is only much later that Westrick (1990) will note that 6 of the 21 groundwater-dependent supplies were found to be contaminated with TCE, and that such *"industrial chemicals can occur frequently in water supplies using either surface water or groundwater."*

1977, June: Interim EPA drinking water regulations go into effect for 10 inorganics and 6 organic pesticides, but no other organic compounds (*ES&T*, 1976b).

1977, December: Amendments to the *Clean Water Act* of 1977 give EPA's Environmental Monitoring and Support Laboratory in Cincinnati (EMSL/Cin) the responsibility for developing adequate and sensitive methods for the determination of trace organic compounds in municipal and industrial wastewater, including the chlorinated solvents (EPA, 1977a).

1978, February 9: Under provisions of the *Safe Drinking Water Act*, EPA (1978) publishes interim primary regulations for certain organics in drinking water, including THMs. Total THMs not to exceed 100 μg/L.

1978, February: Barrett (1978) reports on the *"EPA Consent Decree* that ultimately leads to the promulgation of the "priority pollutant" list. This list contains many of the important chlorinated solvents.

1978: EPA (1978) publishes results of the National Organics Monitoring Survey (*NOMS*) for Halogenated Organics. *NOMS* confirms the widespread occurrence of THMs in chlorinated drinking water.

TABLE 1.14   (*continued*)

a. Analytical
   developments

b. Societal and
   anecdotal events

1978, May: Four wells providing 80% of the drinking water to Bedford, Mass. are found to be contaminated with dioxane at up to 2100 μg/L and with TCE at up to 500 μg/L. The discovery was accidental: a resident engineer was testing the water in preparation for a paper he was writing (Mass. Special Legislative Commission on Water Supply, 1979).

1978: New York State publishes drinking water standards for three chlorinated solvent compounds.

1979: The same major chemical company mentioned in 1973 above qualifies its prior recommendations for disposal of methylene chloride. It now says: *"Send solvent to a reclaimer. In some cases, small amounts can be transported to an area where it can be placed on the ground and allowed to evaporate safely if local, state, and federal regulations permit."*

1979, April-May: GC/MS is proposed in the literature as the best all around method for determination of organic compounds in environmental samples (Keith and Telliard, 1979; and Finnigan *et al.*, 1979).

1980, January: California public health officials close 39 public wells providing water to 400,000 people in 13 cities in the San Gabriel Valley, due to TCE contamination.

1979, December: EPA (1979) publishes a series of organic analytical methods (including purge and trap) that use GC/MS and other forms of gas chromatography. The methods have been developed for use in determining toxic organic pollutants in wastewaters as mandated by the 1977 Amendments to the *Clean Water Act*, and specifically for the list of 114 organic *"priority pollutants"* arising from the *EPA Consent Decree* of 1978.

1980, March: By this point in time, agencies in 18 states have measured VOCs, most commonly TCE, in water from 2894 wells (see CEQ, 1981).

1980, May: In a special, red-paged "Regulatory Alert", *ES&T* (1980) reports that: *"Approximately 50% of the [nation's] population depends on groundwater for its drinking water supply. Yet, unlike surface water or air, there is no specific federal statute to protect it from pollution. . . . Recently, EPA set as one of its 'highest priorities' the development of a National Groundwater Protection Strategy."*

1980, May: Few states have as yet acted to declare authority to protect groundwater supplies, and most do not even recognize the magnitude of the problem (*Environ. Reporter*, 1980a).

1980, August: Mieure (1980) reviews methods that can be used to determine trace levels of chlorinated solvents in water: headspace, purge and trap, and the micro solvent extraction (μSE) method proposed by Henderson *et al.* (1976). μSE needs to be used with a specific detector such as an electron capture detector (ECD). Detection limits for numerous chlorinated solvents are: tens of μg/L by headspace/FID,

1980, August: Existing federal regulations are viewed by some as still so weak that new laws will be needed to provide effective groundwater protection (*Environ. Reporter*, 1980b). In this time frame, the federal government promulgates new regulations affecting: 1) waste disposal sites under *RCRA* in May 1980; and later 2) uncontrolled sites under *CERCLA* in December 1980; and 3) underground storage tank sites under amendments to *RCRA* in 1986.

c. Literature
   reports

1978, May: *ES&T* (1978) reports that: *"The New Jersey Dept. of Env. Protection is testing 500 public and private wells located near industrial sites for 50 selected toxic and cancer causing chemicals, including organic compounds."*

1980, January: In a cover story on groundwater contamination, the journal *ES&T* (1980) discusses how groundwaters can become contaminated, how they can be protected, and how tight federal and state rules requiring monitoring and protection will be coming.

1980, February: Smith *et al.* (1980) discuss a careful study of variations in THM concentrations in a chlorinated drinking water supply.

d. Federal governmental
   actions

1978, June 7: The *"EPA Consent Decree"* is signed by EPA and several environmentally-concerned plaintiffs (Natural Resources Defense Council, Environmental Defense Fund, Businessmen for the Public Interest, National Audubon Society, and Citizens for a Better Environment). The Consent Decree starts the process by which the EPA establishes their list of *129 priority pollutants*; 114 of these pollutants are organic. The list, which includes nearly all of the chlorinated solvent compounds, is to be the basis for regulation of effluent discharges (see Keith and Telliard, 1979).

1979, July 30: EPA (1979) publishes the list of *"priority pollutants"* in the Federal Register as mandated by the *EPA Consent Decree* of 1978.

1979, November 20: Under provisions of the *Safe Drinking Water Act*, EPA releases final regulations to control total trihalomethanes (THMs) in drinking water at 100 μg/L.

1980, May: EPA Administrator Costle identifies groundwater as a principle EPA priority on NBC's *Meet the Press* (see Josephson, 1980).

1980, May: Regulations authorized under *RCRA* are promulgated by EPA, and bring about large scale groundwater monitoring at disposal sites.

1980, June: EPA (1980a) discusses in a planning workshop that a landfill in Jackson Township that was licensed to accept sewage sludge and septic wastes has caused extensive groundwater contamination. Approximately 100 wells around the landfill are closed. Analyses reveal concentrations of up to 3,000 μg/L of methylene chloride, and 1,000 μg/L of TCE.

TABLE 1.14   (*continued*)

a. Analytical developments	b. Societal and anecdotal events

a. Analytical developments

hundredths of μg/L by headspace/ECD, and about 1 μg/L by both P&T/FID and P&T/GC/MS.

b. Societal and anecdotal events

1980: San Francisco Bay Regional Water Quality Control Board (*RWQCB*) begins to receive numerous reports of leaks to the subsurface from local industrial chemical storage systems in "Silicon Valley" (see: Industry Clean Water Task Force, 1985).

1980: In just one year, the same major chemical company mentioned above for 1973 and 1979 completely changes its recommendations for disposal of methylene chloride: "... *Dumping into sewers, on the ground, or into any body of water is strongly discouraged, and may be illegal.*"

1981, January: The Council on Environmental Quality (CEQ, 1981), located in the Executive Office of the U.S.President, releases their landmark, comprehensive report entitled *Contamination of Groundwater by Organic Chemicals*. The document painstakingly compiles the avalanche of reports on groundwater contamination in the U.S. Chlorinated solvents are the most common type of contaminants. CEQ (1981) notes: "*These incidents involve discoveries – sometimes completely accidental – of high concentrations of synthetic organic chemicals in a community or private drinking water well. It is now evident that hundreds of drinking water wells affecting millions of people have been closed because of contamination by toxic organic chemicals. ... No one can say for sure how long the contamination has existed, ... the EPA regions report serious contamination of drinking water wells in 34 states, and there are indications that the true number is at least 40.*"

January, 1981: CEQ (1981) reports that septic tank cleaning fluids, most of which contain TCE, benzene, or methylene chloride, can still be purchased in most areas by homeowners. CEQ (1981) notes that an estimated 400,000 gallons of such septic tank cleaners were used by homeowners in 1979 on Long Island alone. This subsurface release of solvents has been the cause of extensive contamination.

1981: DNAPLs are encountered in the subsurface at several sites in the Niagara Falls area (Kolmer, 1990).

**c. Literature
   reports**

**d. Federal governmental
   actions**

1980, November 24: EPA (1980b) announces a National Ground Water Protection Strategy. The Strategy has three phases. Phase I: data was gathered during the winter and spring of 1980. Phase II: two workshops were conducted in June, 1980 with 80 participants. Phase III: the planning document is now released to the public, with proposed strategy to be published in the Federal Register in January 1981.

1980, December: U.S. Congress passes the *Comprehensive Environmental Response, Compensation, and Liability Act (CERCLA)*, better known as "Superfund" to deal with the threats caused by "*uncontrolled*" hazardous waste sites.

1981, January: *ES&T* (1981a) reports that Recon Systems, Inc. (Somerville, NJ) has built and is operating an air stripping tower to remove 1,1,1-TCA from groundwater that is being pumped at 100,000 gpd from an aquifer in the Northeast.

1981, February: *ES&T* (1981b) reports that studies sponsored by the Council on Environmental Quality (CEQ) have found "*Significant evidence of increased cancer risks from drinking chlorinated drinking water*". The studies indicated increased risk of rectal cancer of 13-93% in groups that drank chlorinated drinking water.

1981, April: Petura (1981) describes groundwater pollution as a "*problem of immense concern*" with TCE and 1,1,1-TCA having been found in groundwater in numerous locations, *e.g.*, Penn., Del., New Hamp., and Calif. "*Hundreds of wells, many in totally unrelated aquifers*" are described as being contaminated with these two compounds.

1981, April: *ES&T* (1981c) reports that: 1) despite the fact that she has no environmental experience, Anne Gorsuch has been named EPA Administrator; and 2) that President Reagan had been considering doing away with the Council on Environmental Quality (CEQ), and is proposing to cut CEQ's budget by 70%. Council members say that the budget cut will not permit them to carry out the tasks that have been assigned to them by the *National Environmental Policy Act* of 1979.

1981, July: *ES&T* (1981d) reports again that CEQ (1981) has found that U.S. groundwater is surprisingly contaminated (see also Jan. 1981, column **b**).

1981, June 9: In a presentation at the national meeting of the American Water Works Association, EPA employee H. J. Brass with co-authors presents results of the *Community Water Supply Survey* (*CWSS*, Brass *et al.*, 1981). The survey compares water quality for surface water samples from 106 sources to ground water samples from 330 sources. Clear evidence is found for the presence PER, TCE, 1,1,1-TCA, and other chlorinated solvent compounds in many groundwater supplies. These three

TABLE 1.14   (*continued*)

a. Analytical developments	b. Societal and anecdotal events
	1982: The San Francisco Bay area "*RWQCB*" launches a program to inventory underground storage systems in industrialized areas. *RWQCB* undertakes a large survey by mail to 2644 companies in the key groundwater basins. Most of the sites are in the Santa Clara ("Silicon") Valley. The survey ultimately leads to the publication of RWQCB's "*205J*" report (see: Industry Clean Water Task Force, 1985). A significant amount of the contamination in the valley is due to high tech industrial operations.

c. Literature reports

1981: Giger and Schaffner (1981) and Zoeteman *et al.* (1981) document the presence of TCE, chloroform, and carbon tetrachloride in groundwater in Europe.

1981: Schwille (1981) discusses behavior of NAPLS in subsurface systems (in English).

1981, December: Page (1981) notes *"contamination of public drinking water supplies by toxic substances poses a serious problem in the U.S."*. Data for 1076 wells in NJ indicate that groundwaters in NJ are at least as contaminated as surface waters. 17 halogenated solvent compounds are found in the groundwater. For TCE, of 669 wells sampled, 388 were found to be contaminated, with 635 μg/L being the highest concentration. For 1,1,1-TCA, of 1071 wells sampled, 835 were contaminated, with 608 μg/L being the highest concentration. For PER, of 421 wells sampled, 179 were contaminated, with 91 μg/L being the highest concentration.

1982, August: Dyksen and Hess (1982) state *"the infiltration of organic compounds into groundwater resources has been occurring for decades.... organic infiltration of groundwater supplies is widespread"*, *e.g.*, 31 municipal wells within 13 different water systems have been closed due to high levels of TCE. Affected groundwater supplies typically contain numerous organic compounds; TCE is the most common.

1983, November: *ES&T* (1983) reports on the solvent injection/tracer test occurring at the Borden Landfill.

d. Federal governmental actions

compounds are each found in about 5% of the groundwater sources tested, with maximum concentrations of 30, 650, and 210 μg/L. The large number of groundwater systems tested (as compared to the 21 groundwater supplies tested in *NOMS*) allowed some very serious groundwater contamination to be found. Of the 330 groundwater systems tested, 50 were found to be contaminated with some VOCs. (See also Westrick, 1990.)

1982, July: EPA (1982) issues new rules (taking effect in January of 1983) governing hazardous wastes in landfills, surface impoundments, and other repositories. The rules state, that liners must be used to prevent leaching of contaminants from such facilities, and that backup leachate collection must be provided.

TABLE 1.14   (*continued*)

a. **Analytical**
   developments

b. **Societal and**
   anecdotal events

1985, September: San Francisco Bay area *RWQCB* lists 75 sites within their jurisdiction at which groundwater contamination is: 1) under investigation; 2) in the process of being defined; 3) being cleaned up; or 4) has been cleaned up (see: Industry Clean Water Task Force, 1985).

c. Literature
   reports

1983: Pye *et al.* (1983) observe:
*"The contamination of groundwater
by synthetic organic chemicals
has come to light recently, mainly
because they are not routinely
monitored."*

1984: Schwille's (1984a)
comprehensive monograph on
chlorinated solvent behavior in
subsurface systems appears, but in
German.

1984: Westrick *et al.* (1984)
report the findings of EPA's
*Ground Water Supply Survey
(GWSS)*. GWSS concludes that
contamination of groundwater by
chlorinated solvent type compounds
is common and widespread. Of
500 randomly-selected community
groundwater supplies, 230 were
found to be contaminated. (See also
Westrick, 1990.)

1984: Several reports in conference
proceedings and publications of
limited circulation describe the
DNAPL nature of liquid chlorinated
solvents, and the dangerous
implications of that nature for
groundwater (Feenstra, 1984; Cherry
1984a and 1984b; Miller, 1984).

1985: The first widely-read
publications describing the DNAPL
nature of liquid chlorinated solvents
appear (Villaume, 1985; and Mackay
et al., 1985).

1988: Schwille's (1984a) monograph
(see above) appears in translation in
English as Schwille (1988).

1988: Fetter (1988) provides a
brief discussion of DNAPLs and
groundwater in his textbook on
applied hydrogeology.

d. Federal governmental
   actions

1986: *Hazardous and Solid Waste Amendments* to *RCRA* are
passed. The amendments mandate monitoring of groundwater and
vadose zone at many underground storage tank locations.

1987, July 8: Final drinking water standard value for TCE is
published by EPA (1987) as 5 μg/L.

1987: EPA (1987b) promulgates regulations prohibiting the used
of certain dense chlorinated solvents as "inactive ingredients" for
pesticide formulations.

1988: EPA provides a cursory reference to the behavior of
DNAPLs in the subsurface in their document *Guidance on Remedial Actions for Contaminated Ground Water at Superfund Sites.*

TABLE 1.14 (*continued*)

a. Analytical developments	b. Societal and anecdotal events

ACKNOWLEDGEMENT

Funding support for this research was provided in part by the University Consortium Solvents-in-Groundwater Research Program. Sponsors of the Program between 1988 and 1994 have included: The Boeing Company, Ciba-Geigy Corporation, Dow Chemical Canada/USA, Eastman Kodak Co., General Electric Co., Laidlaw Environmental Systems Ltd., Mitre Corporation, The Natural Sciences and Engineering Research Council of Canada, and the Ontario University Research Incentive Fund.

1.9 REFERENCES

Abelson, P. H. (1990) "Volatile contaminants of drinking water", *Science*, **247**, 141.

American Insurance Association (1967) *Chemical Hazards Bulletin*, Engineering and Safety Dept., 85 John St., New York, NY, October 1967.

American Insurance Association (1972) *Chemical Hazards Bulletin*, Revised, Engineering and Safety Service, 85 John St., New York, NY, March 1972.

ASTM (1962) Committee D-16 on Halogenated Organic Solvents, *Handbook of Vapor Degreasing*, American Society for Testing and Materials, Special Publication No. 310. Philadelphia, Penn.

ASTM (1976) Committee D-26 on Halogenated Organic Solvents, *Handbook of Vapor Degreasing*, American Society for Testing and Materials, Special Publication No. 310A. Philadelphia, Penn.

Barrett, B. R. (1978) "Controlling the entrance of toxic pollutants into U.S. waters", *Environ. Sci. Technol.* **12,** 154-162.

Bellar, T. A. and J. J. Lichtenberg (1974) "Determining volatile organics at the microgram per litre level by gas chromatography", *J. Am. Water Works Assoc.* **66**, 739-744.

Bellar, T. A., J. J. Lichtenberg, and R. C. Kroner (1974) "The occurrence of organohalides in chlorinated drinking water", *J. Am. Water Works Assoc.* **66**, 703-706

c. Literature
reports

d. Federal governmental
actions

1990: Domenico and Schwartz
(1990) provide the first substantive
textbook treatment of DNAPLs and
groundwater.

1991: EPA publishes their *Ground Water Issue Paper* on DNAPLs
(Hurling and Weaver, 1991).

1993: EPA sponsors publication of a comprehensive monograph
on DNAPLs *DNAPL Site Investigation* (Cohen and Mercer, 1993).

1993: EPA (1993) publishes the final report *Evaluation of
Likelihood of DNAPL Presence at NPL Sites - National Results*

Brass, H. J., M. A. Feige, T. Halloran, J. W. Mello, D. Munch, and R. F. Thomas (1977) "The National Organic Monitoring Survey: Samplings and analyses for purgeable organic compounds", in *Drinking Water Quality Enhancement through Source Protection*, R. B. Pojasek (Ed.) Ann Arbor Science, Ann Arbor, MI, pp. 393-416.

Brass, H. J., M. J. Meisner, and B. A. Kingsley (1981) "Community Water Supply Survey: Sampling and analysis for purgeable organics and total organic carbon". Paper presented at the Annual Meeting of the American Water Works Association, Water Quality Division, June 9, 1981.

Bredehoft, J. (1992) "Much contaminated groundwater can't be cleaned up", *Ground Water*, **30**, 834-835.

CEQ (Council on Environmental Quality) (1981) *Contamination of Ground Water by Toxic Organic Chemicals*, January, 1981, U.S. Government Printing Office, Washington, D.C., 84 pages.

Cherry, J. A. (1984a) "Contaminant migration in groundwater: Processes and problems". In: *Proceedings: Second National Water Conference: The Fate of Toxics in Surface and Ground Water*, Philadelphia Academy of Science, January 24-25, 1984.

Cherry, J. A. (1984b) *Groundwater Contamination*, Mineralogical Association of Canada Short Course in Environmental Geochemistry, Short Course Handbook Vol. 10, M.E. Fleet (Ed.), May, 1984, London, Ontario.

Cohen, R. M. and J. W. Mercer (1993) *DNAPL Site Evaluation*, (EPA Project Officer: J. Matthews), C. K. Smoley/CRC Press, Boca Raton, Florida.

Domenico, P. A. and F. W. Schwartz (1990) *Physical and Chemical Hydrogeology*, John Wiley & Sons, New York.

Dowty, B. J., D. R. Carlisle, and J. L. Laseter (1975) "New Orleans drinking water sources tested by gas chromatography-mass spectrometry", *Environ. Sci. Technol.* **9**, 762-766.

Dyksen, J. E. and A. F. Hess, III (1982) "Alternatives for controlling organics in groundwater supplies", *J. Am. Water Works Assoc.* **74**, 394-403.

Environment Reporter (1980a) May 30, 1980, 142.

Environment Reporter (1980b) August 1, 1980, 477.

EPA (1972) "Industrial pollution of the Lower Mississippi River in Louisiana", Region VI, Dallas, Texas, Surveillance and Analysis Division.

EPA (1974) "Draft analytical report, New Orleans area water supply study", Region VI, Surveillance and Analysis Division, EPA Report 906/10-74-002, November, 1974.

EPA (1975) "Preliminary assessment of suspected carcinogens in drinking water: Interim report to Congress", and "Appendix to the interim report to Congress", June 1975.

EPA (1977a) "The Clean Water Act showing changes made by the 1977 amendments", *Federal Register*, 95-12, December, 1977.

EPA (1977b) "The National Organic Monitoring Survey", Technical Support Division, Office of Water Supply, U.S. Environmental Protection Agency.

EPA (1978) "Control of organic chemical contaminants in drinking water", *Federal Register*, **43**, No. 28, Feb. 9, 1978, pp. 5775 *et seq.*, and "Identification of Conventional Pollutants", *Federal Register*, **44**, pp. 44501-44503.

EPA (1979) "Guidelines establishing test procedures for the analysis of pollutants: proposed regulations", *Federal Register*, **44**, (233) 69464.

EPA (1980a) *Planning Workshops to Develop Recommendations for a Ground Water Protection Strategy, Appendices*, Washington, D.C.

EPA (1980b) *Proposed Ground Water Protection Strategy*. Office of Drinking Water. 61 pp.

EPA (1982) *Federal Register*, **47**, No. 143, 32274.

EPA (1987a) *Federal Register*, **52**, No. 130, 25690-25691, July 8, 1987.

EPA (1987b) *Federal Register*, **52**, No. 77, 13305-13309.

EPA (1988) *Guidance on Remedial Actions for Contaminated Ground Water at Superfund Sites*, EPA/540/G-88/003, Office of Emergency and Remedial Response, U.S. EPA, Washington, D.C., December 1988.

EPA (1991) *CERCLIS Characterization Project - National Results*, EPA 540-8-91/080.

EPA (1993) *Evaluation of Likelihood of DNAPL Presence at NPL Sites - National Results, Final Report*, EPA/540/R-93-073.

ES&T (1972) "Groundwater pollution and conservation", *Environ. Sci. Technol.* **6**, 213-215.

ES&T (1973) "Currents", *Environ. Sci. Technol.* **7**, 485.

ES&T (1976a) "Currents", *Environ. Sci. Technol.* **10**, 11.

ES&T (1976b) "Currents", *Environ. Sci. Technol.* **10**, 115.

ES&T (1978) "Currents", *Environ. Sci. Technol.* **12**, 503.

ES&T (1980) "Safeguards for groundwater", *Environ. Sci. Technol.* **14**, 38-44.

ES&T (1981a) "Currents", *Environ. Sci. Technol.* **15**, 11.

ES&T (1981b) "Currents", *Environ. Sci. Technol.* **15**, 131.

ES&T (1981c) "Currents", *Environ. Sci. Technol.* **15**, 373.

ES&T (1981d) "Currents", *Environ. Sci. Technol.* **15**, 727

ES&T (1983) "Subsurface organic contaminants" *Environ. Sci. Technol.* **17**, 518A-521A.

Feenstra, S. (1984) "Groundwater contamination by dense non-aqueous phase liquid (DNAPL) chemicals", Geological Association of Canada, Annual Meeting, May 14-16, 1984, London, Ontario.

Feenstra, S. (1986) "Subsurface contamination from spills of dense non-aqueous phase liquid (DNAPL) chemicals". In: *Proceedings: Technical Seminar on Chemical Spills*, Environment Canada, February 5-7, 1986, Montreal, Quebec, p. 11-22.

Feenstra, S. and J. A. Cherry (1988) "Subsurface contamination by dense non-aqueous phase liquid (DNAPL) chemicals". In: *Proceedings: International Groundwater Symposium*, International Association of Hydrogeologists, May 1-4, 1988, Halifax, Nova Scotia.

Fetter, C. W. (1988) *Applied Hydrogeology*, 2nd Edition, Merrill Publishing Company, Columbus, Ohio.

Finnigan, R. E., D. W. Hoyt, and D. E. Smith (1979) "Priority pollutants. II. Cost-effective analysis", *Environ. Sci. Technol.* **13**, 534-541.

Giger, W. and C. Schaffner (1981) "Groundwater pollution by volatile organic chemicals". In *Quality of Groundwater*, W. van Duijvenbooden, P. Glasbergen, and H. van Lelyveld (Eds.) Elsevier, Amsterdam, pp. 511-522.

Goodenkauf, A. and J. Erdie (1964) "Identification of chlorinated hydrocarbon pesticides in river water", *J. Am. Water Works Assoc.*, **56**, 600-606.

Gutenmann, W. H. and D. J. Lisk (1964) "Gas chromatographic methods for Silvex", *J. Am. Water Works Assoc.* **56**, 189-190.

Halogenated Solvents Industry Alliance (1987) personal communication.

Heller, S. R., J. M. McGuire, and W. L. Budde (1975) "Trace organics by GC/MS", *Environ. Sci. Technol.* **9**, 210-212.

Henderson, J. E., G. R. Peyton, and W. H. Glaze (1976) "A convenient liquid/liquid extraction method for the determination of halomethanes in water at the parts per billion level". In: *Identification and Analysis of Organic Pollutants in Water*. L. H. Keith (Ed.) Ann Arbor Science, Ann Arbor, Michigan, pp. 105-111.

Hunt, J. R., N. Sitar, and K. S. Udell (1988a) "Nonaqueous phase liquid transport and cleanup. 1. Analysis of mechanism", *Water Resources Research*, **24**, 1247-1258.

Hunt, J. R., N. Sitar and K. S. Udell (1988b) "Nonaqueous phase liquid transport and cleanup. 2. Experimental studies", *Water Resources Research*, **24**, 1259-1269.

Hurling, S. G. and J. W. Weaver (1991) Dense nonaqueous phase liquids. U.S. EPA Ground Water Issue Paper. EPA/540/4-91-002. 40 p.

Industry Clean Water Task Force (1985) *Protecting the Valley's Water: A Factual Summary of Actions Taken by Industry to Remove Solvents from Soil and Groundwater in the "Silicon Valley"*, September, 1985, 8 pages.

Josephson, J. (1980) "Groundwater strategies" *Environ. Sci. Technol.* **14**, 1030-1036.

Johnson, R. L. and J. F. Pankow (1992) "Dissolution of dense chlorinated solvents into groundwater. 2. Source functions for pools of solvents", *Environ. Sci. Technol.* **26**, 896-901.

Keith, L. H. (1974) "Chemical characterization of industrial wastewaters by gas chromatography-mass spectrometry", *The Science of the Total Env.*, **3**, 87-102.

Keith, L. H. and W. A. Telliard (1979) "Special Report: Priority pollutants. I. A perspective view", *Environ. Sci. Technol.* **13**, 416-423.

Kimm, V. J. (1978) "*ES&T* Guest Editorial: Control of organic contaminants in drinking water", *Environ. Sci. Technol.* **12**, 363.

Kleopfer, R. D. and B. J. Fairless (1972) "Characterization of organic components in a municipal water supply" *Environ. Sci. Technol.* **6**, 1036-1037.

Kolmer, J. (1991) "The history of the term "dense non-aqueous phase liquid". In: *DNAPLs in Porous and Fractured Media: A Short Course*. Waterloo Centre for Groundwater Research, October 7-10, 1991. Kitchener, Ontario.

Koppleman, L. E. (1978) "The Long Island Waste Treatment Management Plan", Nassau-Suffolk Regional Planning Board, Hauppague, New York.

Mackay, D. M., P. V. Roberts, and J. A. Cherry (1985) "Transport of organic contaminants in groundwater", *Environ. Sci. Technol.*, **19**, 384-392.

Mackay, D. M. and J. A. Cherry (1989) "Groundwater contamination: Pump and treat remediation", *Environ. Sci. Technol.* **23**, 630-636.

Massachusetts Special Legislative Commission on Water Supply (1979) *Chemical Contamination*, Boston.

McCarthy, K. A. and R. L. Johnson (1992) "Transport of volatile organic compounds across the capillary fringe", *Water Resources Research*, **29**, 1675-1683.

McKee, J. E., F. B. Laverty, and R. M. Hertel (1972) "Gasoline in groundwater", *J. Water Poll. Control Fed.*, **44**, 293-302.

Melpolder, F. W., C. W. Warfield, and C. E. Headington (1953) "Mass spectrometer determination of volatile contaminants in water", *Anal. Chem.*, **25**, 1453-1456.

Merck & Co., Inc. (1989) *The Merck Index: An Encyclopedia of Chemicals, Drugs and Biologicals*, Eleventh Edition, Merck & Co. Inc., Rahway, New Jersey.

Mercer, J. W. and R. M. Cohen (1990) "A review of immiscible fluids in the subsurface: properties, models, characterization and remediation", *J. Contaminant Hydrology*, **6**, 107-163.

Middleton, F. M. and J. J. Lichtenberg (1960) "Measurements of organic contaminants in the nation's rivers", *Ind. Eng. Chem.*, **52**, 99A-102A.

Mieure, J. P. and M. W. Dietrich (1973) "Determination of trace organics in air and water" *J. Chromatographic Science*, **11**, 559-570.

Mieure, J. P. (1980) "Determining volatile organics in water", *Environ. Sci. Technol.* **14**, 930-935.

Miller, D. W. (1984) *Groundwater Contamination: A Special Report*, American Assoc. for Advancement of Science, Washington, D.C., 25 p.

Montgomery, H. A. C. and M. Conlon (1967) "The detection of chlorinated solvents in sewage sludge", *J. Water Poll. Control. Fed.*, **66**, 190-192.

New York State (1978) *Ground Water Classifications, Quality Standards, and Effluent Standards and/or Limitations* (Title 6, Official Compilation of Codes, Rules, and Regulations, Part 703), Department of Environmental Conservation, Effective September 1, 1978.

New York State (1980) *Organic Chemicals and Drinking Water*, Department of Health, Albany.

New York Times (1980, November 2) *Dumped Plane Fuel at Lakehurst Stirs Water-Pollution Fear*, pages 1 and 26.

NRC (National Research Council) (1984) *Groundwater Contamination*, National Academy Press, Washington, D.C., p. 124.

Page, G. W. (1981) "Comparison of groundwater and surface water for patterns and levels of contamination by toxic substances", *Environ. Sci. Technol.* **15**, 1475-1480.

Pankow, J. F. and J. A. Cherry (1988) *Foreward* to Dense Chlorinated Solvents in Porous and Fractured Media: Model Experiments, Schwille, F. (1988), translated from the German by J. F. Pankow, Lewis Publishers, Boca Raton, Florida, 146 pages.

Petura, J. C. (1981) "Trichloroethylene and methyl chloroform in groundwater: A problem assessment", *J. Am. Water Works Assoc.* **73**, 200-205.

Plumb, R. H. Jr. and A. M. Pitchford (1985) "Volatile organic scans: Implications for ground water monitoring. In: *Proceedings: Petroleum Hydrocarbons and Organic Chemicals in Groundwater*, National Water Well Association, Houston, November 13-15, 1985, pp. 207-222.

Pojasek, R. B. (1977) "How to protect drinking water sources", *Environ. Sci. Technol.*, **11**, 343-347.

Pye, V. I., R. Patrick, and J. Quarles (1983) *Groundwater Contamination in the United States*, Univ. Penn. Press, Philadelphia, p. 108.

Rook, J. J. (1972) "Production of potable water from a highly polluted river", *J. Water Treatment Exam.* **21**, 259-274.

Rook, J. J. (1974) "The formation of haloforms during chlorination of natural waters", *J. Water Treatment Exam.* **23**, 234-243.

Rosen, A. A., F. M. Middleton, and N. W. Taylor (1956) "Identification of anionic synthetic detergents in foams and surface waters", *J. Am. Water Works Assoc.*, **48**, 1321-1330.

Rosen, A. A. (1976) "The foundations of organic pollutant analysis", In: *Identification and Analysis of Organic Pollutants in Water*, L. H. Keith (Ed.) Ann Arbor Science, Mich. pp. 3-14.

Schaumburg, F. D. (1990) "Banning trichloroethylene: Responsible reaction or overkill?", *Environ. Sci. Technol.*, **24**, 17-22.

Schreiber, J. (1981) "The occurrence of trihalomethanes in public water supply systems of New York State", *J. Am. Water Works Assoc.*, **73**, 154-159.

Schroeder, E. H. (1985) "Learning from the past, looking to the future. The Air Force and Hughes Aircraft: Working together to protect groundwater", *J. Freshwater*, 1985.

Schwille, F. (1967) "Petroleum contamination of the subsoil - A hydrological problem". In: *The Joint Problems of the Soil and Water Industries*. Proceedings of a symposium held at the Hotel Metropole, Brighton, Jan. 18-20, 1967. Institute of Petroleum. Elsevier, London. pp. 23-54.

Schwille, F. (1981) "Groundwater pollution in porous media by fluids immiscible with water", *The Sci. of the Total Environment*, **21**, 173-185.

Schwille, F. (1984a) *Leichtflüchtige Chlorkohlenwasserstoffe in porösen und klüftigen Medien*, Besondere Mitteilungen zum Deutschen Gewässerkundlichen Jahrbuch, Nr. 46, Bundesanstalt für Gewässerkunde, Koblenz.

Schwille, F. (1984b) "Migration of organic fluids immiscible with water in the unsaturated zone". In: *Pollutants in Porous Media: The unsaturated zone between soil surface and groundwater*, Springer-Verlag, Germany.

Schwille, F. (1988) *Dense Chlorinated Solvents in Porous and Fractured Media: Model Experiments*, translated from the German by J. F. Pankow, Lewis Publishers, Boca Raton, Florida, 146 pages.

Seto, T. A. and M. O. Schultze (1956) "Determination of trichloroethylene, trichloroacetic acid, and trichloroethanol in urine", *Anal. Chem.*, **28**, 1625-1629.

Smith, V. L., I. Cech, J. H. Brown, and G. F. Bogdan (1980) "Temporal variations in trihalomethane content of drinking water", *Environ. Sci. Technol.* **14**, 190-196.

Symons, J. M., T. A. Bellar, J. K. Carswell, J. CeMarco, K. L. Kropp, G. G. Robeck, D. R. Seeger, C. J. Slocum, B. L. Smith, and A. A. Stevens (1975) "National Organics Reconnaissance Survey for halogenated organics", *J. Am. Water Works Assoc.*, **67**, 634-647.

Thomas, H. E. (1951) *The Conservation of Groundwater: A Survey of the Present Groundwater Situation in the United States*, McGraw-Hill, New York.

United States International Trade Commission (1991) *Synthetic Organic Chemicals: United States Production and Sales*, USITC Publication 2470, Washington, D.C.

Villaume, J. F. (1985) "Investigations at sites contaminated with dense non-aqueous phase liquids (NAPLs)", *Ground Water Monitoring Review*, Spring, **IV**, 60-74.

Westrick, J. J., J. W. Mello, and R. F. Thomas (1984) "The groundwater supply survey", *J. Am. Water Works Assoc.* **76**, 52-59.

Westrick, J. J. (1990) "National Surveys of Volatile Organic Compounds in Groundwater and Surface Waters". In: *Significance and Treatment of Volatile Organic Compounds in Water Supplies*. Ram, N. J., R. F. Christman, and K. P. Cantor (Eds.), Lewis Publishers, Boca Raton, Florida.

Zoeteman, B. C., E. de Greef, and F. J. J. Brinkman (1981) "Persistency of organic contaminants in groundwater, lessons from soil pollution incidents in The Netherlands". In: *Quality of Groundwater*, W. van Duijvenbooden, P. Glasbergen, and H. van Lelyveld (Eds.). Elsevier, Amsterdam, pp. 465-476.

2

Conceptual Models for the Behavior of Dense Non-Aqueous Phase Liquids (DNAPLs) in the Subsurface

Stan Feenstra[1,2], John A. Cherry[2], and Beth L. Parker[2]

[1]Applied Groundwater Research, Ltd.
The Pentagon Building, Suite 207
2550 Argentia Road
Mississagua, Ontario
Canada L5N 5R1

[2]Waterloo Centre for Groundwater Research
University of Waterloo
Waterloo, Ontario
Canada N2L 3G1

ABSTRACT

Dense non-aqueous phase liquids (DNAPLs) behave differently in the subsurface than do other contaminants. Their behavior normally results in complex DNAPL distributions which are strongly influenced by geologic heterogeneities. This chapter qualitatively describes the factors that control subsurface DNAPL behavior and the plumes of vadose- and groundwater-zone contamination that can emanate from DNAPL source zones. Also presented are conceptual models for DNAPL behavior in permeable porous media, fractured media with porous low-permeability matrix material, and fractured media with non-porous matrix material. Most of the conceptual models apply to all DNAPLs, though some are specific to halogenated organic solvents. The high densities, low interfacial tensions, and low viscosities of halogenated solvents can lead to deep DNAPL penetration at many sites. DNAPL movement through small fractures in low permeability aquitards is common.

In permeable porous media, much of the DNAPL contaminant mass that enters a groundwater zone can remain as a persistent source zone of "residual" and/or "free-phase" DNAPL for many years and decades after the release. In some types of fractured porous media such as fractured clay, shale, and sandstone, DNAPL dissolution and subsequent diffusive loss from the fractures into the surrounding porous matrix can permit DNAPL disappearance from the fractures so that most of the contaminant ends up in the dissolved and sorbed states in the porous matrix. In either case, without appropriate remedial action, the source zone can contribute contaminants to a groundwater plume for decades to centuries. Plumes originating from such source zones commonly travel large distances and ultimately impact water-supply wells, or enter rivers or lakes. The conceptual models discussed here constitute a paradigm for DNAPL behavior which provides a framework for developing new strategies for site investigations and remediation as discussed in subsequent chapters of this book.

2.1 INTRODUCTION

Conceptual models for the movement, distribution and fate of **"dense non-aqueous phase liquids"** (DNAPLs) in the subsurface have evolved from a primitive state a decade ago, to groups of models that are designed to consider many of the large variety of hydrogeological conditions occurring at field sites. The conceptual models are based on laboratory studies, field experiments, mathematical model results, as well as observations that have been made at many chemical spill and waste disposal sites across North America. The conceptual models and the many implications derived from them constitute a **paradigm** for the behavior of DNAPLs in groundwater. This paradigm provides the scientific basis for the monitoring, diagnosis, and remediation of sites where DNAPLs are the primary cause of subsurface contamination. Prior to the development of the DNAPL paradigm, these sites were being assessed using the same general paradigm applied for many decades to all types of industrial sites where groundwater contamination occurs, with the implicit assumption that DNAPLs were not present and did not cause unique problems. It was believed during that earlier period that groundwater contamination was caused at industrial sites by discharges of aqueous waste, or because of leaching of contaminated soil/waste situated above the water table (*i.e.*, in the vadose zone). In contrast, in the DNAPL paradigm, much of the contaminant mass in the groundwater can come from the dissolution of persistent DNAPL mass(es) situated below the water table. This chapter describes conceptual models for how DNAPLs can behave in common hydrogeologic settings. The physical and chemical processes influencing subsurface DNAPL behavior as well as plume behavior are also described briefly; detailed discussions of these behaviors and of the implications of the conceptual models for site investigations, site diagnosis, and site remediation are presented in subsequent chapters.

The movement and ultimate distribution of a DNAPL in the subsurface depends on many factors, *e.g.*, the type of geologic medium into which the DNAPL enters. Three broad categories of geological media can be identified: 1) **porous media**, also referred to as granular media; 2) **fractured porous media**; and 3) **fractured non-porous media**. In porous media, the water and contaminant movement can occur in the connected pore space between the solid grains or particles. At many sites, the geologic media present fit conveniently into these categories. However, in the most general context, geologic media offer a continuum of properties ranging from ideal porous media such as coarse-grained sand to relatively non-porous fractured rock. Unconsolidated sand or gravel are commonly found in porous-media **aquifers**. Unweathered silty or clayey strata devoid of fractures are examples of porous-media **aquitards**.

In most saturated fractured porous media, the term **"fractures"** is used to refer collectively to the open joints, fissures, and or faults that are present. Water flow through a fractured porous medium occurs exclusively, or nearly so, through the fractures. The flow of a DNAPL phase through this type of medium is also generally limited to the fractures. The low-permeability porous medium between the fractures is known as the **matrix**. Fractured silty or clayey deposits are common examples of fractured porous media, as are many types of fractured sedimentary rocks such as fractured sandstone and shale. The porosity of matrix material is in the range of a few percent for low porosity sedimentary rock to 50 percent or more for some types of unconsolidated clayey deposits. This porosity is sufficient to significantly affect the migration rates and distributions of contaminants in these fractured porous media.

In fractured non-porous media, the matrix has both negligible permeability and negligible porosity. All significant groundwater flow and contaminant migration (including DNAPL flow) takes place in the open space of the fracture network. Fractured crystalline rock such as granite and marble are common examples of fractured non-porous rock. Fractured non-porous media differ from fractured porous media primarily by the influence of the matrix porosity. In fractured porous media, the matrix has sufficient interconnected porosity to allow significant **diffusion** of contaminants into and out of the matrix. In fractured non-porous media, no appreciable contaminant migration occurs within the matrix.

Figure 2.1 is a schematic representation of what can occur when DNAPLs and LNAPLs (light non-aqueous phase liquids) are released from leaky storage tanks into a granular porous medium. The DNAPL penetrates below the water table due to its density.

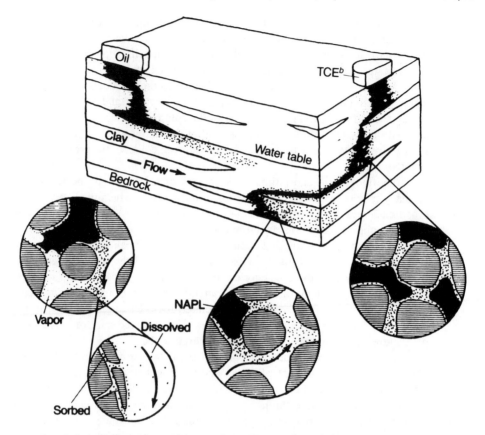

Figure 2.1 Schematic illustration of a DNAPL and a LNAPL in a porous medium, showing geologic and pore scales. A low-permeability clay layer deflects the DNAPL. DNAPL dissolution causes a plume (from Mackay and Cherry, 1989).

Both the DNAPL and LNAPL can dissolve into water. These dissolved components form plumes of contamination that travel in the direction of the groundwater flow. Any partitioning of contaminants onto the aquifer solids will **retard** this movement relative to the velocity of the groundwater flow.

Figure 2.2 represents a release of a DNAPL into a thin layer of permeable overburden overlying fractured porous bedrock. The DNAPL sinks through the overburden into the fracture network. Once in the fractures, the DNAPL dissolves, causing a plume of dissolved contamination in the fracture network as well as entry of dissolved contamination into the matrix. The movement and distribution of DNAPL here are both very different from that presented in Figure 2.1 for a non-fractured porous medium.

The conceptual models presented in this chapter are generally relevant to all of the important types of DNAPLs found in groundwater, including **chlorinated solvents, creosote, coal tar**, and **PCB oils**. While the specific intent of this chapter is to discuss the aspects of these models that are the most relevant to chlorinated solvents, there are

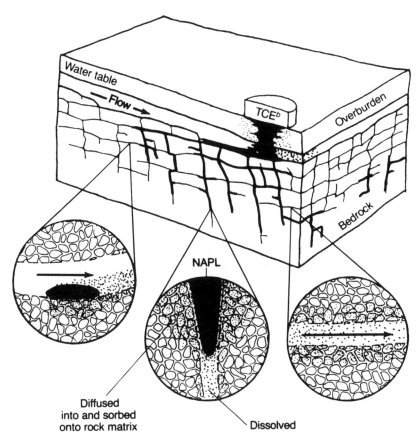

Figure 2.2   Schematic illustration of a DNAPL in a fractured porous medium showing geologic and pore scales. The DNAPL dissolves to create contamination in the fractures and in the low-permeability rock matrix (from Mackay and Cherry, 1989).

important differences between the groundwater impacts of solvent DNAPLs relative to other DNAPLs; some of these differences will be discussed.

2.2 PHYSICAL AND CHEMICAL PRINCIPLES

2.2.1 Immiscible-Phase Physics

Although the subsurface behavior characteristics of DNAPLs differ considerably from those of petroleum hydrocarbon LNAPLs, the basic physics and mathematics describing the multiphase flow of DNAPLs and LNAPLs in the subsurface are the same. In the vadose zone, consideration of DNAPL migration must account for the interactions between the DNAPL, the water, and the air. In the groundwater zone, interaction between the DNAPL and water phases are important. For the purpose of this discussion, it is convenient to consider three different but related aspects of DNAPL migration through geologic media: 1) conditions of DNAPL entry; 2) conditions for DNAPL flow; and 3) the ultimate static distribution of the DNAPL after the flow of DNAPL has ceased. Before proceeding, we emphasize that the term DNAPL refers only to an actual non-aqueous phase so that "liquid DNAPL" would be redundant, and "dissolved DNAPL" would be contradictory.

The entry of DNAPL into porous or fractured media is controlled primarily by **capillary phenomena** arising from the facts that an interfacial tension is present between two mutually immiscible fluids (*e.g.*, air/DNAPL or water/DNAPL), and that the pores or fracture openings are small. In addition, the **wettability** of the water/DNAPL/solid system influences the conditions under which a DNAPL enters a given permeable geologic medium. We note that most DNAPLs of interest will be non-wetting on geologic solids with respect to water, but wetting with respect to air. This typical behavior is observed in both laboratory and field experiments involving pure chlorinated solvents. However, because the wettability of a given system is a function of the surface chemistry of the solid geologic material, the groundwater composition, and the DNAPL composition, each of which may vary greatly at a site or from site to site, complex wettability relationships may need to be taken into consideration at actual field sites.

For a DNAPL which is non-wetting on the geologic solids with respect to water, water will coat the soil grains and occupy the smaller pores and pore throats: the DNAPL is restricted to the larger pore openings (see Figure 2.3). In the less common situation where the DNAPL is the wetting phase with respect to water, the situation is reversed; the DNAPL coats the soil grains and occupies the smaller pores. When the DNAPL is the non-wetting phase, capillary forces oppose the entry of the DNAPL into wet geologic media.

The forces driving subsurface DNAPL movement are a function of the DNAPL density and the pressures resulting from its release into the subsurface. As is discussed in detail in Chapter 3, for DNAPL movement to occur in wet media, these driving forces

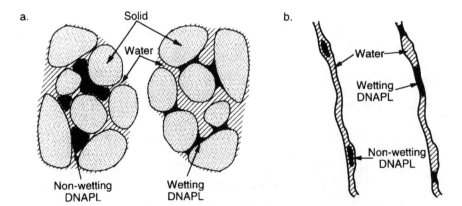

Figure 2.3 Pore-scale representation of non-wetting and wetting DNAPL residual in: a) water-saturated sand; and b) a fracture.

must overcome the capillary resistance. The DNAPL in the larger pore openings must deform to pass through smaller pore throats to reach other pore openings. The pressure required for this deformational movement is the **entry pressure**. The value of the entry pressure is proportional to the **interfacial tension** between the DNAPL and the water, and inversely proportional to the size of the pore throats. Therefore, the entry of a DNAPL into a fine-grained porous medium or into a fractured medium having small apertures requires high driving forces to overcome high entry pressures. Consequently, low permeability strata can be barriers to DNAPL migration. If the water/DNAPL interfacial tension is reduced, for example as a result of surfactant compounds in the groundwater, the DNAPL can enter fine-grained media more easily. If the DNAPL is wetting with respect to water, capillary forces will *enhance* rather than resist DNAPL entry into fine-grained media; the DNAPL in that case moves preferentially into smaller pore openings.

As is discussed in detail in Chapters 3 and 11, the rate of flow of a DNAPL through a geologic medium depends on: 1) the **density** and **viscosity** of the DNAPL; 2) the **pressure** driving the DNAPL migration; 3) the intrinsic **permeability** of the geologic medium; and 4) the degree of DNAPL **saturation** of the pore space in the medium. More permeable media and higher DNAPL saturations will permit higher rates of DNAPL flow. Higher density and lower viscosity fluids also permit higher flow rates. Most pure chlorinated solvents are much denser than water, and have viscosities lower than water, so that in a given geologic medium with conditions of high DNAPL saturation, most liquid chlorinated solvents can migrate at rates comparable to, or faster than, those of water.

Nearly all movement of subsurface DNAPL occurs within zones of continuous (*i.e.*, connected) DNAPL. In such zones, the DNAPL in different pore openings forms an immiscible-phase continuum through the intervening pore throats. Once the release of DNAPL into the subsurface ceases, the forces driving DNAPL movement eventually dissipate and the DNAPL in the pore openings become disconnected to form a zone of **residual** DNAPL. Very high hydraulic gradients are then required in groundwater to induce movement of this residual DNAPL.

2.2.2 Phase Transfer Processes

We have thus far only discussed the presence of contaminants and their movement as immiscible liquids. However, chlorinated solvents and other chemicals of interest have tendencies to partition among all of the phases in the subsurface (DNAPL, air, water, and geologic solids). Therefore, contaminant molecules in the subsurface will tend to partition to all local phases, seeking an **equilibrium distribution** condition. At equilibrium, there is a defined contaminant concentration in each phase of the system. A partition coefficient describes the relative abundance of a chemical between two adjacent phases in equilibrium.

In the context of the subsurface fate and behavior of chlorinated solvent DNAPLs, there are four phase partitioning processes of particular interest: 1) *dissolution* of DNAPL into water (as has already been mentioned); 2) *volatilization* of dissolved chemicals from water into air; 3) *vaporization* of DNAPL into air; and 4) *sorption* of dissolved chemicals from water to solid surfaces. In general, the chlorinated solvents have vapor pressures which are relatively high, and aqueous solubilities which are low in absolute terms. However, even though the aqueous solubilities of these compounds allow them to persist as DNAPLs for very long times in many hydrogeologic situations, their solubilities are still four to seven orders of magnitude greater than their current drinking water quality standard values. These factors combine to provide DNAPL chlorinated solvents with exceptional potential for causing significant groundwater contamination. (See also the related discussion in Chapter 1.)

Under non-equilibrium, dynamic conditions, the relative importances of the various phase transfer mechanisms are determined not only by the corresponding partition coefficients, but also by the kinetic rates at which the various interphase mass transfers can occur. These case-dependent interphase **mass transfer rates** have important implications for DNAPL flow, the ultimate distance of DNAPL penetration, and the overall contaminant mass distribution in the subsurface. Indeed, as DNAPL flows through the unsaturated zone, mass transfer from the DNAPL to both the air and water will reduce the DNAPL phase volume and will tend to reduce the rate of DNAPL flow and as well as the ultimate depth of migration. Overall, this diminishes the bulk volume of the medium containing the immiscible liquid. That is, it increases the overall **retention capacity** of the medium for the DNAPL.

In the vadose zone, mass transfer to the soil air occurs directly from the DNAPL phase as well as from the aqueous phase following dissolution. Due to the high volatilities of the common chlorinated solvents, mass transfer from the DNAPL phase to the soil gas is expected to be the most significant phase transfer mechanism for DNAPLs in the vadose zone. The vaporization and vadose zone transport of chlorinated solvents is facilitated by the very high diffusion coefficients of compounds in the gas phase. In some circumstances, the vaporization of a DNAPL causes rapid depletion of the DNAPL phase and significant vapor plumes can form rather quickly.

In the interface zone and below the water table, partitioning into the gas phase is minimal to non-existent. Dissolution of DNAPL is then the most important phase transfer process. Once in the aqueous phase, dissolved chemicals can partition to the solids. The front of the groundwater plume emanating from a DNAPL zone will travel in the dominant direction of groundwater flow. In situations where the DNAPL source is removed or isolated so that the DNAPL no longer contributes dissolved contaminants to the plume, the back end of the plume will separate from the former source zone and travel downgradient. In all cases, part of the contaminant mass in the plume will be dissolved, and the remainder will be **sorbed** (*i.e.*, adsorbed and/or absorbed). Partitioning in the plume prevents contaminants from being in the dissolved phase all the time, with the result that the front of the plume as well the main body of the plume advances more slowly than the mean groundwater velocity.

The effects of sorption on plume behavior depend strongly on the type of geologic medium and the identities of the dissolved chemical constituents that emanate from the DNAPL. Plumes from solvent DNAPLs are only slightly retarded by sorption because their sorption affinities for nearly all types of geologic media are weak. In contrast, plumes from PCB DNAPLs rarely travel far because of the strong sorption of dissolved PCBs.

However, DNAPLs that contain PCBs commonly also contain other contaminants such as chlorinated benzenes that are less sorbed, and therefore form much more extensive plumes.

The influence of sorption is generally greater in fine-grained porous media and in fractured porous media (*e.g.*, unfractured and fractured clayey or silty deposits) than in granular aquifers. In fractured porous media, sorption in the low-permeability matrix is generally much more important than sorption in the fractures. As a plume in a fractured porous medium advances, sorption in the matrix maintains concentration gradients that are directed from the fractures to the matrix. This helps maintain the transfer of contaminant mass to the matrix. Sorption processes are considered in further detail in Chapter 8.

2.3 DNAPLS IN THE VADOSE ZONE

2.3.1 The Non-Aqueous Phase

Studies at industrial sites show that, with few exceptions, DNAPLs will tend to penetrate through the vadose zone into the groundwater zone where much of the DNAPL mass then accumulates to cause persistent contamination. Nevertheless, at some sites, *e.g.* those where the water table is exceptionally deep or where the volume of DNAPL released to the soil is very small, it is possible that the entire mass of DNAPL will reside in the vadose zone (Figure 2.4).

For a known volume of DNAPL released into a particular granular geologic medium, the depth of penetration is influenced by the **area** over which the release occurs, the **rate** of the release, and the nature of the geological **layering** in the system. The natures of the pore-size distributions in the layers depend largely on the type and scale of geologic heterogeneity in the system. Poulsen and Kueper (1992) performed two experimental field releases of tetrachloroethylene (PCE), six liters each, into the vadose zone of a slightly-stratified beach sand aquifer. One release was an instantaneous spill to 0.1 m^2 on bare ground. This release caused PCE to penetrate to a depth of 2.15 m. In the second release, the six liters of PCE were dripped onto a soil surface area of 1 cm^2 during 100 minutes so as to simulate a very slow, point-source leak. The PCE from the second spill penetrated through the vadose zone to the water table at a depth of 3.3 m, leaving a trail of DNAPL residual all the way from ground surface to the water table. The drip release penetrated deeper because the surface area of the input was much smaller. For both spills, the DNAPL migration was strongly influenced by the small (millimeter) scale of the stratifications in the sand. The DNAPL migrated preferentially along coarser-grained layers, and did not enter fine-grained layers.

Laboratory column experiments using "homogeneous" sand indicate immiscible-phase retention capacities for solvents in dry homogeneous sands in the range of 3 to 30 L/m^3, on average, or 1 to 10% of the pore space (Schwille, 1988). For the moist stratified vadose-zone sands considered in the field experiments of Poulsen and Kueper (1992), retention capacities of the DNAPL-containing layers were in the range of 2 to 18% of the pore space. These values are similar to those measured for petroleum hydrocarbons in unsaturated sands (Wilson and Conrad, 1984). In assessing the movement and fate of

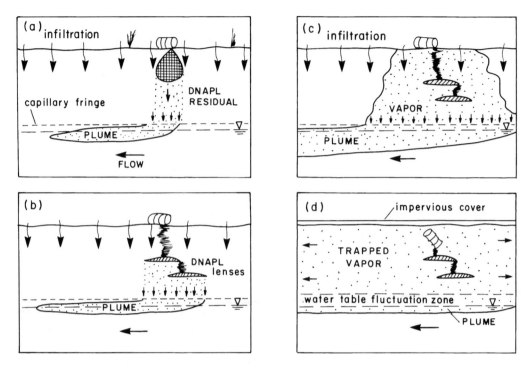

Figure 2.4 Conceptual scenarios for a DNAPL in the vadose zone in granular geologic deposits: a) homogeneous case - no vapor plume; b) heterogeneous case - no vapor plume; c) heterogeneous case - vapor plume; and d) effect of impervious ground cover over vapor-releasing DNAPL source.

a DNAPL at a spill or disposal site, predictions of the depth of penetration based on the DNAPL volume, the area of release, and estimates of the retention capacity of the geologic medium beneath the spill can be useful. However, because of the influence of site-specific geologic heterogeneities on DNAPL migration and thus on the distribution of residual DNAPL, depth predictions are commonly so unreliable that they are misleading or even useless.

In the experiments conducted by Poulsen and Kueper (1992), small stratifications caused the downward-moving DNAPL to be distributed in a complex manner; they did not serve as significant impediments to downward penetration. Impediment can nevertheless occur where lower-permeability layers of sufficient size and permeability contrast exist in the vadose zone. Figures 2.4.b and 2.4.c show that such layers can cause perched zones of free-phase DNAPL in the vadose zone. DNAPL accumulation will not take place in near-surface deposits when erosional or depositional gaps, fractures, root holes, worm holes, and/or animal burrows exist through low permeability layers.

Because the retention capacities of most porous media are relatively small in absolute terms, and because of the channels that exist through many large clay and silt layers, at many sites where only relatively "small" volumes of solvent were released to the soil, we can conclude that DNAPL solvent has penetrated to considerable depths.

There is controversy over what numerical quantities should be associated with a likelihood of penetration. As a general rule, we propose that at sites where the water table exists at depths of a few tens of meters or less, and where there are no geologic strata with exceptional capability for impeding DNAPL penetration, a solvent DNAPL release of a few tens of liters at a single location should be considered capable of permitting DNAPL to enter the groundwater zone. If the water table is much deeper, penetration of the groundwater zone may require a release of a few hundred liters, *i.e.*, a few drums of solvent. However, repeated small releases at precisely the same location can also produce deep penetration. Indeed, we note that significant accumulation of DNAPL below the water table can occur at sites as a result of storage and handling activities where only small amounts of solvent are released at any single location, but the releases are repeated.

2.3.2 The Vapor Phase

In Figures 2.4.a and 2.4.b, the DNAPL in the vadose zone has a very low vapor pressure and therefore causes no vapor plume. In these cases, a groundwater plume results only from leaching of the residual DNAPL when water infiltrates through it; if infiltration is prevented by an impervious surface cover such as parking-lot asphalt or a building, little groundwater contamination can form. In Figure 2.4.c, the DNAPL is volatile, and a **vapor plume** emanates from the source zone. Indeed, as has been noted above, most liquid chlorinated solvents have high vapor pressures, and therefore where solvent DNAPL exists in the vadose zone, a vapor plume will develop in the surrounding soil air. Infiltrating water that contacts the vapor will cause the development of a groundwater plume. Infiltration through the residual zone will also cause groundwater contamination. Within a period of weeks or months, a small mass of solvent DNAPL in the vadose zone can produce a vapor plume in a sandy medium that has grown, by means of **gas phase molecular diffusion**, to sizes extending to a few tens of meters. After many years or decades, vapor can move downward through very thick vadose zones to depths of many tens of meters or more. For high vapor pressure chemicals that also have large vapor densities, density-driven advection in high permeability media can enhance downward movement of vapor to the water table (Mendoza and Frind, 1990a, 1990b).

The conceptual model for a high-vapor pressure DNAPL source zone covered with an impervious barrier is given in Figure 2.4.d. Even though no water infiltrates through the DNAPL residual or through the vapor, a groundwater plume is caused by fluctuations in the water table that trap vapor in the water table zone. Also, the diffusion of solvent vapor to and across the capillary fringe contributes solvent mass to the groundwater zone.

In a field experiment in an unconfined sandy aquifer, Hughes *et al.* (1992) placed a 0.5 cubic meter volume of sand mixed with trichloroethylene (TCE) at residual levels in a one meter deep hole in the 3.5 m thick vadose zone. This DNAPL-laden sand was removed by excavation after a month. Prior to the excavation, a vapor plume emanated rapidly outwards 10 m, and downwards to the water table. The experiment was repeated half a year later. After three years, the vapor plumes caused by the temporarily-emplaced TCE sources ultimately caused a thin (1-2 m), shallow plume, 40 m wide and more than

130 m long. Maximum concentrations in the plume were in the thousands of μg/L range. The front of the groundwater plume was captured by pump-and-treat (Rivett, 1994).

Thin shallow plumes caused by vapor transport are difficult to locate when conventional approaches to aquifer monitoring are used. Conventional monitoring wells generally have screened intervals of two to five meters, and draw most or all of their water from depths below the water table. The behavior of vapor in the vadose zone is discussed further in Chapter 6; implications for monitoring are discussed in Chapter 13.

2.4 DNAPLS IN THE GROUNDWATER ZONE

2.4.1 Granular Aquifers

Much of the groundwater supply in North America and Europe comes from sand or gravel aquifers, and many large plumes of chlorinated solvent contamination occur in such aquifers. Some of these plumes extend for many kilometers from the industrial sites where they originate. Almost without exception, these plumes result from the dissolution of persistent DNAPL sources situated below the water table.

Figure 2.5.a shows the result of a release of DNAPL small enough to cause penetration below the water table, but insufficient for DNAPL to reach the bottom of the aquifer. The distribution of the DNAPL below the water table is affected by the geologic layering present. In granular aquifers, small horizontal zones of residual or free-phase DNAPL need not be caused by particularly low permeability zones such as silt or clay. A minor contrast in grain size distribution and hence permeability, as from a coarse sand layer to a finer sand, causes variation in DNAPL entry pressure (Kueper *et al.* 1989; see also Chapter 3). A DNAPL moving downwards through a coarse-grained material will encounter a higher entry pressure when a finer-grained layer is contacted. This will cause **lateral spreading** of the DNAPL. The DNAPL will accumulate on the finer-grained layer while spreading laterally until it reaches the edge of the layer (Figure 2.5.c), or until the height of free-product accumulation on the layer exceeds the entry pressure for the layer. In the latter case, the DNAPL will pass through the layer and continue its downward movement towards the bottom of the aquifer.

The cases shown in Figures 2.5.b and 2.5.c have much of the DNAPL mass in the aquifer offset horizontally from the DNAPL release point. In these particular cases, the DNAPL mass in the groundwater zone is situated upgradient or downgradient from the DNAPL release point. Given the subtlety of geologic heterogeneity that can cause a deflection of DNAPL in the saturated zone, as well as the complexity of the spatial distribution of such geologic heterogeneity in most systems, DNAPL pathways are generally **unpredictable** in the saturated zone (see Section 2.3.1 for similar comments about the vadose zone), even when considerable information on the stratigraphy of the subsurface environment is available. Indeed, although site investigations normally provide information on the macrostratigraphy, as has been noted above, the microstratigraphy can have an important or even dominant influence on DNAPL pathways.

The plumes of dissolved contamination shown in Figures 2.5.a and 2.5.b occupy only the upper part of the aquifer because the residual and perched DNAPL exists only in

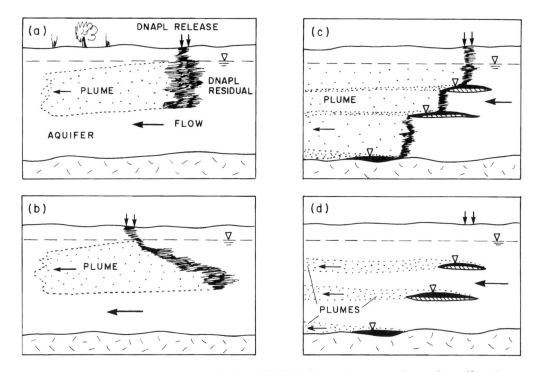

Figure 2.5 Conceptual scenarios for a DNAPL in the groundwater zone in granular aquifers: a) partial penetration; b) partial penetration with offset; c) full penetration with offset; and d) same as part c, but at a later stage after DNAPL residual has disappeared due to dissolution in flowing groundwater.

the upper portion of the aquifer. Vapor in the vadose zone contributes contaminant mass only to the very shallow part of the plume. Locating the interface between the portion of the plume contamination that originated in the vadose-zone with the portion originating in the groundwater zone is difficult to impossible.

The volume of DNAPL released in the case shown in Figure 2.5.c is larger than in Figures 2.5.a and 2.5.b, causing the DNAPL to penetrate to the bottom of the aquifer. Therefore, in Figure 2.5.c the plume of dissolved contamination spans all depths in the aquifer at some locations because DNAPL residual is present at all depths. An accumulation of free-phase DNAPL occurs in a depression on the aquitard surface. This accumulation or **"pool"** is a major feature of Figure 2.5.c. In field investigations of sites where extensive solvent contamination exists, pools of free-product solvent are found only rarely, even when their existence is not in doubt. Such accumulation zones are rarely found because conventional site investigation techniques are not well-suited for their detection, and because drilling and sampling the large number of boreholes necessary to encounter small to medium size pools is usually not practical.

A considerable volume of free-phase DNAPL can occur in a relatively small depression on the aquitard surface. For example, a spill of 800 liters of DNAPL could be

contained in a pool at the bottom of a sand aquifer, with the pool measuring only 3 m
× 3 m in area and 0.3 m thick. A grid of boreholes with exceptionally close spacing,
such as 50 m, would have only a low probability of detecting such a pool. Even a pool
occupying a much larger depression on the aquitard surface would have a low probability
of being detected in most site investigations because of small pool dimensions relative to
borehole spacing, and because of the difficulty in detecting thin DNAPL accumulations
during drilling and sampling.

The few data available on residual contents of chlorinated solvents in saturated
granular materials indicate values that are higher than those for unsaturated materials
(Schwille, 1988). The values for saturated soils range from 5 to 50 L/m^3, or 2 to 15%
of the pore space). Although the presence of residual solvent DNAPL in the pore space
reduces the permeability of the aquifer only slightly, in a pool, the DNAPL can occupy
40 to 70% of the bulk pore space, will preferentially occupy the larger pores, and will
therefore cause the permeability in such zones to be reduced substantially: groundwater
flow through these zones will occur only very slowly.

As is discussed in detail in Chapter 7, even though flowing groundwater causes
dissolution of DNAPL solvents, chlorinated solvents in residual zones and in pools do
not rapidly disappear from a groundwater system. Consider, for example, a 3 m cube
of sandy aquifer materials that contains TCE at residual levels. Within the cube, the
residual level varies from 0 to 15% of the pore space; the average residual content will
be assumed to be 10 L/m^3. This corresponds to about 270 liters, or 1.5 drums of TCE.
The linear groundwater velocity will be assumed to be 53 m/year, *i.e.*, the rate that would
be found for a sandy aquifer with a hydraulic conductivity of 10^{-2} cm/s, a porosity of 0.3,
and under the influence of a hydraulic gradient of 0.005. The groundwater exiting such
a variable residual zone would likely have dissolved concentrations ranging from low
levels up to the solubility limit. Even if the average TCE concentration in groundwater
exiting this residual zone was only 10% of the TCE solubility (110,000 μg/L), and this
is higher than what is typically found at actual field sites, 25 or more years would need
to pass before the residual DNAPL was completely dissolved and thereby removed as a
source zone. Moreover, based on laboratory experiments (Schwille, 1988; Imhoff *et al.*,
1989), the actual time required for complete dissolution of this residual DNAPL can be
expected to be longer than 25 years because the dissolved concentrations resulting from
dissolution and consequently the mass rate of dissolution both tend to decline with time
as a residual DNAPL mass is depleted.

For a pool of DNAPL, one can expect that the time required for the complete dissolution by natural groundwater flushing of a given mass of DNAPL will be much longer
than for the complete dissolution of the same DNAPL mass distributed in residual form.
The low relative permeability to water in a pool zone limits the groundwater flux through
such a zone. Also, the DNAPL content is higher in a pool than in a residual zone. Based
on the results of a laboratory experiment by Schwille (1988) and the analysis by Johnson
and Pankow (1992), for a pool of TCE in a sandy aquifer in which the groundwater is
moving with a linear groundwater velocity of 275 m/year, then a 1.5 m long, 0.5 m wide,
and 0.2 m thick pool containing only 50 L of TCE would require at least **100 years** to
be dissolved completely (see also Chapter 7). (We note here that this hypothetical pool

is much smaller than pool sizes expected at many sites. Also, the assumed velocity of 275 m/year is relatively high.) Such long source lifetimes are consistent with common field observations which indicate that severe groundwater contamination from subsurface DNAPL sources continues to be generated at sites where the chemical release(s) or disposal(s) occurred decades ago, and in some cases more than 50 years ago.

Figure 2.5.d pertains to the same case as Figure 2.5.c, but at a much later time when the zones of residual DNAPL below the water table have disappeared due to groundwater flushing. The zone of DNAPL in the vadose zone has disappeared due to vapor loss and infiltration leaching. Only the perched and bottom pool zones below the water table remain. The plume of dissolved contamination now derives only from these accumulation zones, and therefore the plume at this stage is much different than the one generated at the early stages when the DNAPL residual zones also contributed dissolved contaminants to the plume. At many sites where plumes of solvent contamination are observed, the DNAPL entered the aquifers long ago. At some sites, then, one can expect that long-term dissolution has caused disappearance of many of the residual zones, leaving only the larger residual zones and the accumulation zones to cause continued plume generation.

Many DNAPLs are **mixtures** of several chemical compounds. For example, a solvent DNAPL could be an equal mixture of TCE, PCE, and dichloromethane (DCM). These three compounds have very different solubilities in water (DCM > TCE > PCE). For this mixture, the high solubility of the DCM causes it to be dissolved first, followed by the TCE, then followed by the PCE. The chemical composition of such a DNAPL and the plume would change as this occurs. Related discussions for DNAPLs which are mixtures can be found in Chapters 7 and 13.

2.4.2 Fractured Non-Porous Media

As mentioned above, at many DNAPL sites, where a thin overburden covers fractured bedrock, DNAPL has moved through the overburden and into the fractures (Figure 2.2). At some sites, the DNAPL has moved through thick overburden into fractured bedrock. DNAPLs like the chlorinated solvents that have high densities, low water/DNAPL interfacial tensions, and low viscosities, have exceptional propensity to penetrate into small fractures in bedrock and into fractures in other geologic media such as clayey deposits.

The pattern of DNAPL movement and ultimate distribution in fractured geologic media is controlled primarily by the orientation and interconnection of the fractures. Figure 2.6.a shows fractured non-porous rock that has horizontal fractures along bedding planes, or along stress relief planes. Vertical fractures connect the horizontal fractures. DNAPL moves downward through the vertical fractures and laterally along the horizontal fractures. As it moves along the horizontal fractures, the DNAPL can encounter more vertical fractures that allow downward movement to continue. The horizontal fractures, like all fractures, have irregular surfaces. Hence, fracture apertures vary along the length and across the plane of the fracture. The horizontal fractures therefore provide small but numerous depressions for free-phase DNAPL to exist as small, disconnected free-phase accumulations. This situation is accentuated in cavernous or karstic rock where

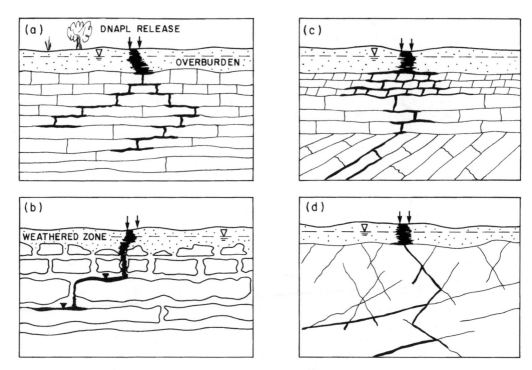

Figure 2.6 Conceptual scenarios for a DNAPL in the groundwater zone in fractured non-porous media: a) regular bedded rock with bedding plane fractures and connecting vertical fractures; b) solution-channelled carbonate rock with free-phase DNAPL accumulations; c) layered rock with contrasting fracture networks; and d) complex fracture network in a single rock type.

large amounts of DNAPL can accumulate in the depressions of major flow channels or cavities (see Figure 2.6.b).

Bedrock typically has permeable zones separated vertically by less permeable zones in which vertical fractures are much less frequent. Such a case is represented in Figure 2.5.c where a DNAPL exists in numerous fractures in the upper fractured zone. From this zone, DNAPL has drained through sparse vertical fractures into the lower fractured zone where it spreads along a different set of fractures. In site investigations, detection of DNAPL in the more permeable zones could be feasible, whereas detection in the intermediate zone where fractures are sparse is unlikely. In the deeper fractured zone, fewer fractures contain DNAPL and therefore the dissolved concentrations observed in monitoring wells downgradient from this DNAPL zone would be expected to be much lower than those in the shallow plume, even though both aquifers have DNAPL in fractures. Interpretation of dissolved concentrations from monitoring wells in fractured rock is typically very difficult.

Figure 2.6.d shows DNAPL penetration into a much less ordered fracture network, *i.e.*, of the type commonly observed in crystalline rock such as granite. DNAPL enters fractures at the bottom of the overburden. As in the cases already considered, these fractures act as conduits to other fractures. Some of these fractures are dead ends for DNAPL, either because they do not intersect other fractures, or because they intersect fractures that are too small for DNAPL entry.

Schwille (1988) conducted laboratory experiments using rough-walled glass plates to represent planar vertical fractures above and below the water table. From experiments with 200 μm apertures, he estimated the retention capacity (residual retention content) of such fractures to be less than 0.05 L/m^2. For a fractured rock of moderate hydraulic conductivity having a three-dimensional fracture network with fracture frequency of one fracture per meter and fracture apertures of 200 μm, this represents a residual content, expressed relative to the bulk rock volume, of approximately 0.15 L/m^3. Although this is large relative to the total fracture porosity, it is much smaller than the retention capacity expected for granular aquifers which have a bulk granular porosity that is two to four orders of magnitude larger than the fracture porosity of most bedrock. Therefore, for a given volume of chlorinated solvent released to fractured rock, the solvent can spread to occupy a volume of the subsurface domain that is much greater than in granular aquifers or other porous geologic media. Indeed, in the previous example for a sand aquifer, an 800 liter pool of DNAPL was calculated to occupy a volume of aquifer measuring 3 m × 3 m in area and 0.3 m in thickness. The same volume of DNAPL in fractured rock with a bulk retention capacity in the fracture network of 0.15 L/m^3 would occupy a zone measuring 130 m by 130 m with the same 0.3 m thickness. This could suggest that DNAPL accumulation zones in fractured rock are much more readily detected because of their size than those in granular aquifers. However, in fractured rock, it can be difficult to detect free product or residual DNAPL even where boreholes penetrate such zones. Often, so little free product drains into wells from fractures or is flushed to the surface during drilling that its presence goes unnoticed.

The **maximum depth** to which a DNAPL penetrates in fracture networks depends on several factors, including the fracture aperture, the number and type of fracture connections, the physical properties of the DNAPL, and the height of the column of continuous DNAPL above the fractures at the front of the DNAPL zone. At some fractured-rock sites, DNAPL is known to have penetrated to depths of several hundred meters and more. At many fractured rock sites, investigations have not yet conclusively established the maximum depth of DNAPL penetration. In some cases, the maximum depth is likely greater than 1000 m. If the nature of the release and fracture network geometry are such that a large column of continuous DNAPL forms, the propensity to travel through to great depths is large, thereby causing deep penetration even where the fracture apertures are very small. It is generally not possible to predict the maximum depth of DNAPL penetration at fractured rock sites even where there is exceptionally-detailed information on the geology, groundwater flow, and fracture network properties because the fracture-specific data for such predictions generally cannot be obtained from our limited investigative methods. Attempts at measuring fracture apertures generally provides inaccurate values, or the measured values reflect apertures altered due to the test methods. The maximum depth of penetration must be inferred from monitoring of the dissolved contaminant distribution. Chapter 11 describes the physics of DNAPL behavior in fractured media in further detail.

2.4.3 Fractured Porous Media

In fractured porous media, the relatively large volume of voids in the matrix between the fractures influences: 1) the migration of DNAPL and of the dissolved-plume; 2) the persistence of the DNAPL phase; and 3) the design of remediation efforts. As in fractured non-porous media, groundwater in the fractures causes DNAPL to gradually dissolve. However, as has been noted above, in fractured porous media the dissolved-phase mass can also enter the water in the porous matrix, and can sorb to the matrix solids. For the most soluble DNAPLs, such as the common chlorinated solvents, mass loss from the fractures to the matrix can eventually cause complete **disappearance** of the DNAPL from some or all fractures, particularly in situations where the thickness of DNAPL in each fracture is small and the fracture spacing and matrix porosity are appreciable (see Figure 2.7). Thus, dissolution combined with diffusion causes a change in the physical state of the solvent mass, from the DNAPL phase to the dissolved and sorbed phases. As has been discussed by Parker *et al.* (1994), this change of state was recognized only recently. The implications of this disappearance and the rates at which it can take place are subjects of current research. In fracture networks in very porous geologic deposits such as unconsolidated silt or clay, the disappearance of solvent DNAPL may occur within days or weeks or, in some types of porous sedimentary rocks such as sandstone or shale, within months to several years. Chapter 12 provides more details regarding this process.

In fractured non-porous media, dissolution of DNAPL solvent feeds contaminant mass to the plume as the plume travels along the fracture network. However, once the DNAPL source mass is totally dissolved, groundwater flushes the remaining dissolved and sorbed contaminant mass out of the fractures in the former source zone relatively rapidly. In contrast, in fractured porous media, because significant contaminant mass has dissolved and diffused into the matrix, contaminant mass can **persist** in the former DNAPL zone long after the DNAPL phase has disappeared. This mass will diffuse back out of the matrix when clean water begins to flush through the fracture network.

As noted above, once DNAPL has entered fractures in rock with a non-porous matrix, the propensity for deep penetration is high because the height of free-phase DNAPL accumulation in the fractures adds to the effective pool height. The DNAPL can then move downward into smaller and smaller fractures as the effective pool height increases. In fractured porous media, however, the transfer of DNAPL contaminant mass from fractures to the matrix diminishes the propensity for downward penetration because loss of mass from the DNAPL diminishes the volume of DNAPL. Given certain fracture conditions, diffusion can also cause a **disconnection** of the DNAPL phase, further reducing the height of the free-phase DNAPL and hence reducing downward DNAPL movement (see Figure 2.8).

In fractured non-porous media, the total pore space in which contaminant mass can reside is measured by the fracture porosity. In contrast, the total volume ultimately available for contaminant mass in fractured porous media is the total of the fracture porosity plus the matrix porosity. In situations where entry of DNAPL to the fracture network continues (*i.e.*, DNAPL release replenishes the DNAPL in the fractures), the

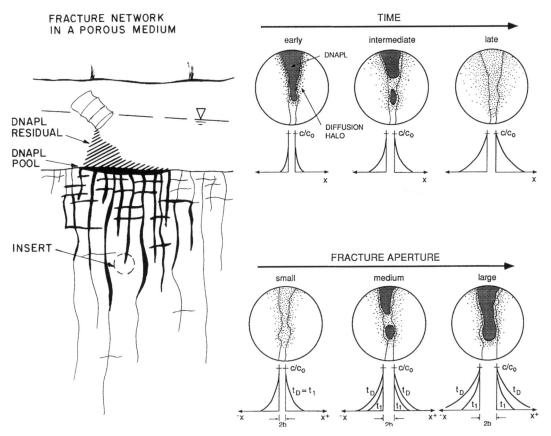

Figure 2.7 Conceptualization of DNAPL persistence and distribution with DNAPL mass loss due to diffusion in water-saturated fractures in a porous medium (such as a fractured clay till or sedimentary rock) as a function of: a) time; and b) fracture size (aperture). Diffusion halos around fractures containing DNAPL become large (more developed) with increases in time, as shown with the concentration *vs.* distance plots for the three relative time periods in part a. At any particular time t_1, the DNAPL mass distribution will vary in different size fractures, with DNAPL disappearance occurring most rapidly in the smallest fractures; residual or disconnected DNAPL will be present in medium-sized fractures, and free DNAPL will be present in the largest fractures that are connected to overlying DNAPL pools. DNAPL disappearance times (t_D) increase with an increase with fracture aperture.

maximum storage capacity is attained when all of the pore water in the matrix is at the solubility limit.

2.4.4 Layered Aquifer-Aquitard Systems

There are several industrialized regions in the U.S., such as the Santa Clara ("Silicon") Valley in California and parts of the Gulf Coast, where solvent production, usage, and/or disposal have been large, and where the geology comprises layered sequences of uncon-

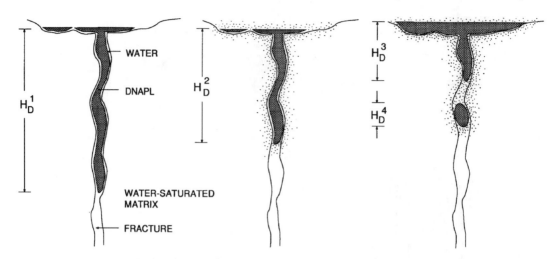

Figure 2.8   The effects of diffusive mass loss on DNAPL invasion distances and resultant height of interconnected DNAPL in a single, water-saturated fracture in a porous medium: a) no diffusive mass transfer and DNAPL pool height H_D^1; b) reduced DNAPL invasion distance due to diffusion into the porous matrix adjacent to the fracture with a subsequent reduction in DNAPL mass and in the interconnected pool height H_D^2; and c) reduced invasion distance due to diffusive mass loss from DNAPL in the fracture *and* disconnection of DNAPL phase during flow causing further reduction in interconnected DNAPL heights H_D^3 and H_D^4.

solidated sandy aquifers separated by clayey or silty aquitards. The thickness of aquifers and aquitards is variable, generally from a few meters to several tens of meters. On a regional scale, many of the strata are not extensive. However, at many sites, the layers are continuous across the "source zone" of DNAPL. Immense financial and technical resources have been invested for the study and remediation of solvent sites in these layered sedimentary environments.

Prior to the mid- to late-1980s, it was commonly thought that clayey or silty aquitards situated beneath aquifers would prevent DNAPLs from penetrating below the uppermost aquifer. However, field data from countless sites now show that many (if not most) silty or clayey aquitards allow DNAPL to move through them, thereby causing contamination of underlying aquifers. At some sites, solvent DNAPL has penetrated through several aquitards to cause contamination much deeper than was believed possible a few years ago.

Penetration of DNAPL through aquitards may occur through one or more of the following types of vertical pathways: 1) **unsealed or improperly-sealed boreholes**; 2) **disposal wells**; 3) **stratigraphic windows**; and 4) **open fractures or faults**. The first three types of pathways have been recognized for many years. The origin and occurrence of open fractures in aquitards is an emerging research topic. Deep, open fractures are now known to be common in many clayey aquitards. The intuitive notion that fractures in unconsolidated or semi-consolidated silty or clayey deposits are closed due to overburden stress is generally not valid, except perhaps at very great depths or in very plastic clayey deposits.

An accumulation of DNAPL on top of a fractured aquitard allows several possible outcomes. Figure 2.9.a shows a static DNAPL pool resting on the top of the fractured aquitard with no entry of DNAPL into fractures because the fracture entry pressure is not

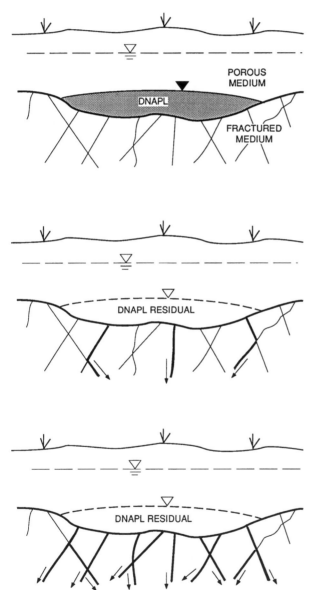

Figure 2.9 Conceptual scenarios for a DNAPL accumulation zone on a fractured aquitard: a) height of free-phase DNAPL insufficient for DNAPL entry into fractures; b) only largest fractures allow DNAPL entry; and c) DNAPL entry into all fractures.

achieved at the bottom of the pool. Figure 2.9.b shows the same situation, except that a few of the fractures are larger, which allow DNAPL entry into them. In Figure 2.9.c, all of the fractures are large enough for DNAPL entry, which is a less likely situation because it is probable that entry into the largest fractures and subsequent DNAPL flow in these fractures would limit build up of the pool heights, thereby preventing sufficient height to develop for entry into the smaller fractures. Given that fracture networks in aquitards are generally difficult to delineate, and that it is expected that not all fractures contain DNAPL, locating those particular fractures that contain DNAPL is very difficult.

Figure 2.10 shows four scenarios in which DNAPL enters into, and in some cases travels through, an aquitard. In Figure 2.10.a, the fractures do not penetrate to the bottom of the aquitard and therefore the aquitard protects the aquifer from actual DNAPL entry. Figures 2.10.b and 2.10.c show aquitards that have a few fractures that extend to the bottom of the aquitard, providing pathways for DNAPL entry to the underlying aquifers. In Figure 2.10.d, the DNAPL pathway through the aquitard is a stratigraphic window rather than fractures. At some sites, it is not possible to discern from the available field

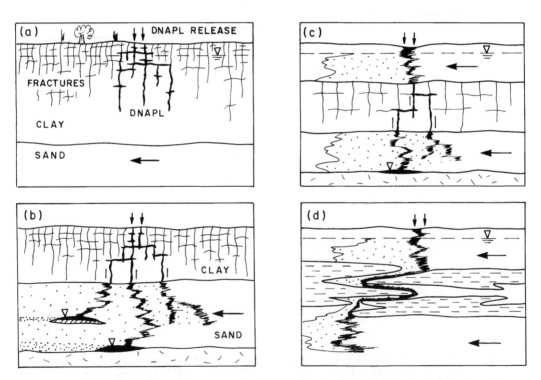

Figure 2.10 Conceptual scenarios for DNAPL movement through clayey aquitards: a) partial penetration because open fractures do not extend to the bottom of the clay deposits; b) penetration through a few deep fractures causes DNAPL accumulation in the underlying aquifer; c) penetration through fractures in an aquitard between two sand aquifers; and d) a stratigraphic window in the aquitard provides a pathway for DNAPL flow.

data whether the cause of DNAPL contamination in an underlying aquifer is fractures or such windows.

The capacity of fractured clayey or silty aquitards to retain DNAPL material is small because the fracture apertures are small, generally less than 100 μm for fractures below the water table. Even if DNAPL dissolution causes the matrix pore water to reach the solubility limit, the mass retention capacity is relatively small, ranging from the *liquid equivalent* of less than 5 to 10 L/m^3 for the most soluble chlorinated solvent (DCM) down to 0.05 to 0.5 L/m^3 for PCE, which is a low-solubility solvent. These calculations take into consideration what would be considered typical sorption properties of aquitard solids. Therefore, this low mass retention capacity and the small thickness of many aquitards reduces the chances that such a fractured aquitard will be depth-limiting with respect to the contamination. In the underlying aquifer, however, geologic heterogeneity will permit horizontal DNAPL accumulations (perched pools) at various depths; this provides much larger retention than in the aquitard.

The actual maximum depth of DNAPL penetration in a given system will be attained when the driving forces for DNAPL flow are balanced by the forces resisting flow. This can take place anywhere within a layered heterogeneous system, depending on the volume of DNAPL released, the nature of the DNAPL, and the various sequences of geologic conditions encountered along the pathway. At sites where multiple aquifers and aquitards exist, there is usually no reliable basis for predicting the maximum depth of DNAPL penetration, even when release volume, geologic, geophysical, and stratigraphic data are available. Direct monitoring of the presence of DNAPL, and/or inferences of such a presence based on dissolved concentrations are necessary for conclusions about the depth of penetration to be made.

As is discussed in detail in Chapter 10, there is debate in the literature about whether DNAPL accumulations on clayey strata can cause vertical pathways through these strata to open up due to chemical **desiccation** of the clay minerals. In particular, the desiccation is believed by some to cause bulk shrinkage and thus formation of open fractures. However, the mineralogical properties of natural clayey strata and the chemical properties of the common chlorinated solvent DNAPLs make this chemical desiccation scenario unlikely, except possibly in rare specific circumstances.

2.5 PLUMES FROM DNAPLS

2.5.1 Dispersion, Diffusion, and Density

Plumes of dissolved contamination at DNAPL sites exhibit various shapes and internal concentration distributions that depend on the aquifer characteristics and the morphology and extent of the subsurface DNAPL source zone. Figure 2.11 shows two hypothetical cases for sand or gravel aquifers. One of these cases assumes that hydrodynamic **dispersion** causes considerable lateral spreading; the other assumes little spreading because of weak dispersion.

The influence of dispersion on plumes from DNAPL source zones is no different from its influence on plumes of other types of dissolved chemicals, whether they be

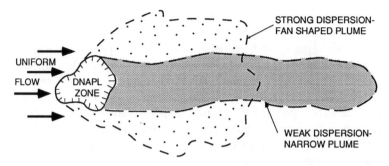

Figure 2.11 Influence of hydrodynamic dispersion on plumes from a DNAPL source zone in a sand or gravel aquifer with uniform steady flow. The plume is long and narrow for the weak dispersion case, and fan-shaped for the strong dispersion case.

organic or inorganic. Studies of dispersion in numerous sand and gravel aquifers in the 1980s showed that, almost without exception, dispersion is weak, particularly in the directions transverse to groundwater flow. In the fan-shaped plume of Figure 2.11, transverse and longitudinal dispersion causes considerable decline in concentration as the plume spreads in the aquifer with groundwater flow. In the narrow plume, on the other hand, rate of concentration decline with distance in the direction of flow is much smaller.

The type of nearly uniform plume width found in Figure 2.11 is expected in aquifers where the groundwater flow is relatively uniform, devoid of diverging or converging flowpaths. Because dispersion is typically weak, many solvent plumes emanating from DNAPL source zones exhibit high concentrations far from the source zone. And, since the maximum contaminant levels (MCLs) specified in drinking water standards are very low, concentrations far from the source can be much above these MCLs. Although plume concentrations for chlorinated solvents and other DNAPLs are large relative to drinking water standards, they are not large enough to cause the plumes to **sink** due to density of the aqueous solution. Density is an important factor at DNAPL sites, but only with respect to movement of the DNAPL and not the migration of plumes.

The shape and size of a source zone has a strong influence on plume dimensions. Thus, although many solvent plumes in granular aquifers are long and narrow, many others are wide because their DNAPL source zones are wide. The details of the distribution of DNAPL residual and accumulation zones below the water table are rarely known. However, at most sites, it is expected that they are complex due to geologic heterogeneity and variable DNAPL releases. Downgradient of such DNAPL source zones, weak dispersion allows the distribution of dissolved concentrations to be highly variable spatially, particularly close to the source zone. Farther downgradient, dispersion causes variability of the concentration profiles to diminish. Figure 2.12 shows a schematic example of this dispersion effect. The actual distance at which the concentration profiles become less irregular depends on site conditions.

Little is known about dispersion in fractured geologic media. Although there are many large contaminant plumes in fractured-rock aquifers, none has been monitored in

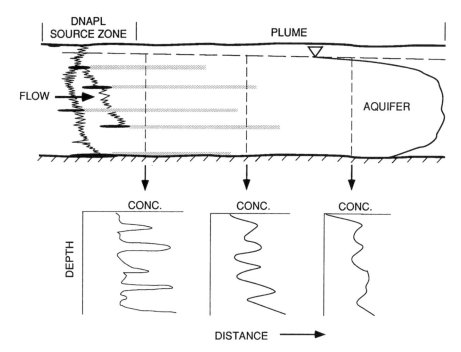

Figure 2.12   Influence of dispersion on saturated-zone concentration distribution in a plume caused by a complex DNAPL source zone.

sufficient detail to provide much information on dispersion. The generalizations presented above for granular media are probably not relevant to fractured media.

In low permeability zones, **molecular diffusion** in the aqueous phase governs the migration of dissolved contaminants. Where DNAPL accumulations rest on unfractured clayey or silty layers, diffusion of dissolved contaminants occurs into these layers (Figure 2.13). The rate of penetration of the front is slow for chlorinated solvents, less than 1 m in the first decade, and decreases with time. Therefore, molecular diffusion is generally not the cause of significant breakthrough of contaminants through aquitards. Unfractured low-permeability aquitards of appreciable thickness can therefore provide long-term protection of aquifers from contamination.

Many granular aquifers have numerous thin interbeds or lenses of silt or clay. In these aquifers, advection (bulk groundwater flow) advances the plume front and governs the flux of contaminant mass in the flow direction. At the same time, diffusion causes loss of mass from the permeable zones to the low-permeability layers in the aquifer. The low permeability of these zones combined with sorption to the layer solids can temporarily immobilize contaminants. When a plume is advancing through the aquifer, the low-permeability layers act as a sink for contaminant mass. However, at later time when the DNAPL source zone (or parts of this zone) is depleted by dissolution or has been isolated by engineered enclosures or hydraulic containment, complete flushing of the plume from the aquifer is delayed because of diffusive release from the layers.

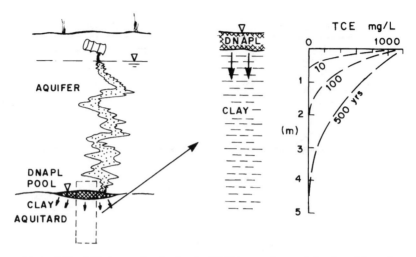

Figure 2.13   Diffusion profiles for dissolved TCE in an unfractured clay deposit beneath a free-phase TCE accumulation. TCE solubility is 1100 mg/L; there is no sorption.

Loss of dissolved contaminants from a plume into low-permeability layers is shown schematically in Figure 2.14. The concentration profiles for TCE in one of these layers assuming a porosity of 0.3 and a retardation factor of 1.4 are represented as a function of a dimensionless time T. The profiles approach equilibrium (*i.e.*, $T > 0.9$) rapidly (months) in thin beds (< 10 cm thickness) and slowly (decades and longer) in thick beds (> 1 m). Once the permeable zones in the aquifer are cleaned by pump-and-treat, or by natural flushing, compared to the time required for contaminants to diffuse in, the time required for diffusion out of the layers is longer.

2.5.2 Transformations

As described in detail in Chapter 9 and also in Vogel *et al.* (1987), chlorinated solvents can be transformed **microbiologically or abiotically** to other organic compounds. Anaerobic conditions, which will favor some of these transformations, are more prevalent in low-permeability zones. Therefore, in addition to providing for the temporary storage of dissolved and sorbed solvents, low-permeability layers may act as sources that slowly release both solvents and their transformation products to plumes. In fractured porous media, the matrix blocks between fractures can act in much the same manner.

Nearly all of the compounds produced by degradation reactions are relatively stable, and some are more hazardous in drinking water than the initial compounds. Figure 2.15 displays the transformation sequences for PCE and TCE. Of particular importance in the transformation series is the production of vinyl chloride (VC). VC is a known carcinogen for which the U.S.EPA has specified the very low MCL in drinking water of

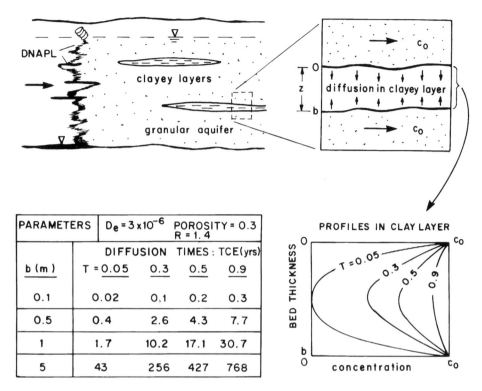

Figure 2.14   Loss of contaminant mass from a plume by diffusion into a low-permeability layer. Lower insert shows calculated concentration profiles for TCE in the layer at four values of the dimensionless time *T*. Actual times for layers of various thickness are listed in the table.

2 μg/L. VC is found in many plumes at DNAPL sites. These plumes are commonly decades old, therefore it is evident that VC can be persistent, presumably due to continued formation.

The formation of hazardous products such as VC complicates and enlarges the contamination problem at chlorinated solvent sites. VC sorbs on aquifer and aquitard solids less than does its parent compounds, and it is therefore more mobile in plumes. Also, the complexity in the spatial and temporal distribution of contaminants at a site caused by such transformations makes the task of site characterization and remedial investigations more difficult. This increases investigation costs and causes confusion in data interpretation. The recognition in the scientific community that the common chlorinated solvents can transform in groundwater to hazardous compounds such as VC did not come until the early 1980s; the conclusion that these transformations are common was not established until the late 1980s. The scientific, engineering, and regulatory communities are still adjusting to the complications and challenges posed by these transformations.

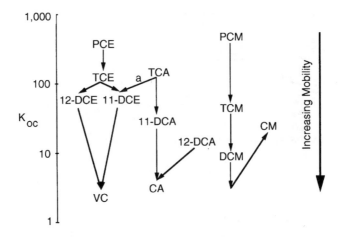

a - Abiotic transformation

Solvent Products:
PCE -   Perchloroethene
TCE -   Trichloroethene
TCA -   1,1,1-Trichloroethane
12-DCA - 1,2-Dichoroethane
PCM -   Carbon Tetrachloride
TCM -   Chloroform
DCM -   Dichloromethane

Transformation Products:
12-DCE - 1,2-Dichloroethene
11-DCE - 1,1-Dichloroethene
VC -   Vinyl choride
11DCA - 1,2-Dichloroethane
CA -   Chloroethane
CM -   Chloromethane

Figure 2.15 Products of biotic and abiotic transformations of chlorinated solvents dissolved in groundwater and their relative mobilities expressed by their organic carbon-water partition coefficient (K_{oc}).

2.5.3 Mass Considerations

At creosote and coal tar sites, the volume or mass of DNAPL situated in the vadose and groundwater zones can be estimated with some degree of reliability using drilling records and core analyses from DNAPL zones. At chlorinated solvent sites, however, residual or free-phase DNAPL is much less frequently encountered in boreholes or wells below the water table because of the effect of geologic variability and generally smaller release volumes compared to creosote and coal tar sites. As a result, for chlorinated solvents, estimates of total DNAPL mass in the groundwater zone and comparisons with the mass in the vadose zone are unreliable; even order-of-magnitude estimates normally are very uncertain. The uncertainty derives from difficulty in delineating the overall dimensions of the source zone and the wide range in possible DNAPL saturations in pools and residual zones due to microscale heterogeneities. Reliable conclusions that a DNAPL actually exists below the water table at at given site must be based on several lines of **indirect evidence** (see Chapter 13); these indirect methods do not provide DNAPL mass estimates.

At solvent DNAPL sites in granular aquifers where plumes are delineated using extensive monitoring well networks, useful estimates of dissolved contaminant masses in the plumes can be made. Table 2.1 provides six examples from Mackay and Cherry (1989). These plumes occur in sand or gravel aquifers at Superfund or similar sites where they have evolved over several decades. The **plume mass** for each plume is expressed in terms of the equivalent number of 55 gallon drums of DNAPL, based on the dissolved mass and the pure-phase DNAPL densities of the dominant solvents in the plumes. Although the dissolved plumes are large, extending between 2 and 5 km downgradient from their respective DNAPL source zones, the dissolved masses are small. These masses range between 0.4 and 190 drums of equivalent DNAPL. When the quantities and periods of DNAPL use and disposal at these sites as well as the persistence of the plumes are

TABLE 2.1 Solvent Plumes in Sand-Gravel Aquifers. (Reprinted with permission from MacKay and Cherry, 1989.)

Site location and plume map	Presumed sources	Predominant DNAPL contaminants	Plume volume (liters)	Estimated chemical mass dissolved in plume (as equivalent DNAPL volume in liters or 55-gal drums)
Ocean City, New Jersey	chemical plant	Trichloroethylene 1,1,1-Trichloroethane Tetrachloroethylene	5,700,000,000	15,000 (72 drums)
Mountain View, California	electronics plant	Trichloroethylene 1,1,1-Trichloroethane	6,000,000,000	9800 (47 drums)
Cape Cod, Massachusetts	sewage infiltration beds	Trichloroethene Tetrachloroethylene	40,000,000,000	1500 (7 drums)
Gloucester, Ontario	special waste landfill	1,4-Dioxane Freon 113	102,000,000	190 (0.9 drum)
San Jose, California	electronics plant	1,1,1-Trichloroethane Freon 113 1,1-Dichloroethylene	5,000,000,000	130 (0.6 drum)
Denver, Colorado	trainyard, airport	1,1,1-Trichloroethane Trichloroethylene Dibromochloropropane	4,500,000,000	80 (0.4 drum)

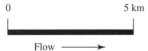

0   5 km

Flow ———▶

considered, it appears highly likely that much larger amounts still remain in DNAPL form in the source zones. Mass calculations for many other plumes in granular aquifers in the U.S. provide results that are similar to those in Table 2.1.

At a given site, a number that may be of greater interest than plume mass is the mass **flux** of dissolved contaminants. This flux can be estimated by multiplying the plume concentrations by the groundwater fluxes through cross sections orthogonal to the mean flow direction. The plume flux, expressed in equivalent drums per year, is a small fraction of the total plume mass for the plumes in Table 2.1, and also for the many other plumes that have been assessed in this manner. Plume fluxes range from less than 0.1 equivalent drum per year to approximately 10 equivalent drums per year.

Near a DNAPL source zone, the plume flux equals the mass rate of dissolution of the DNAPL. Farther downgradient, the plume flux should generally be similar, perhaps with some decline due to transformations. Therefore, the ultimate impact of plumes emanating from solvent DNAPL source zones can be evaluated in terms of impact of relatively small annual mass fluxes to the receptor such as water-supply wells or surface waters. In some cases, the fluxes present significant risk to human health and/or the environment, and extensive remedial action is warranted. In other cases, the fluxes are insignificant, and remedial action would provide little or no actual environmental risk reduction.

2.5.4 Ultimate Fate

In preceding sections of this chapter, we have presented general conceptual models for DNAPL sites that include subsurface source zones feeding dissolved contaminants to plumes. The considerable masses of DNAPL that typically exist in the sources and the small dissolved mass fluxes from the sources mean that such source zones will persist for many decades or centuries. Therefore, in cases where remedial measures are not imposed on the plume, the plume front will advance in the direction of groundwater flow until the plume encounters a natural **hydrologic boundary** such as a river, lake, or wetland, or until it enters the capture zone of a water supply well (Figure 2.16). In some cases, the concentrations of dissolved contaminants leaving the source zone may be sufficiently low to allow dispersion in the aquifer to diminish plume concentrations below regulatory MCLs prior to arrival of the plume at water supply wells or at natural hydrologic boundaries. However, this is an unlikely scenario. Therefore, it should be assumed that plume fronts (including unknown fronts) that have not yet been observed at natural hydrologic boundaries are still advancing towards these boundaries.

Many plumes from solvent DNAPL source zones reached their natural hydrologic boundaries long ago, and have therefore already attained their ultimate sizes. The contaminant flux may cross the interface between the groundwater zone and surface water without alteration or attenuation. The ultimate fate of the contaminants then depends on processes in the surface water systems. Some plumes enter surface waters by moving up through organic-rich sediments at the bottoms of streams or lakes, or up through organic-rich soils in wetlands. Little is known about the influence of such layers on plume chemistry or aquatic ecology. Scientific literature pertaining specifically to the behavior and fate of solvents in surface water bodies is limited. However, it is known that mixing as well as subsequent escape by volatilization to the atmosphere are normally rapid. Solvent concentrations above drinking water MCLs or even above very low detection levels are rarely observed in streams or lakes downgradient of plume discharge zones. Nevertheless, in Canada and in the northern part of the U.S., winter ice cover can temporarily prevent escape to the atmosphere. Whether or not ice cover results in significant adverse impacts on stream or lake ecology has not been determined.

Figure 2.16.a shows a plume that extends to a nearby river. In this case, the plume travels in a local-scale groundwater flow system that is bounded laterally by the river. At many sites, however, the deepest part of the DNAPL zone extends below the bottom boundary of the groundwater flow for the local watershed. Flowpaths in such a system can transport dissolved contamination towards natural hydrologic boundaries that are situated at great distances from the site, often in a different watershed. For this to occur in a system like that represented in Figure 2.16.a, the deep part of the plume must travel beneath the river to the more distant boundary while the shallow part of the plume discharges to the river (or to a local lake).

Many plumes are captured (and therefore contained) by water supply wells, thereby causing contamination of the supplies (see Figure 2.16.b). If the wells are shut down, plume containment ceases, and the plume begins to advance towards other boundaries. Some plumes that cause contamination of supply wells are only partly captured by the wells. The uncaptured part advances beyond the wells towards other wells or natural boundaries.

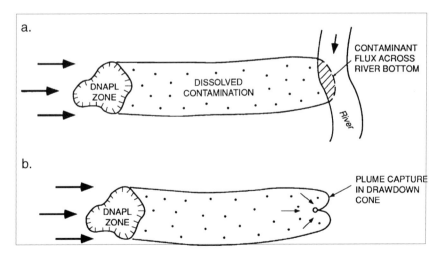

Figure 2.16   Two containment scenarios for a plume from a DNAPL source: a) plume encounters a hydrologic boundary (river); and b) plume front is captured by a pumping well.

Monitoring required by the U.S. federal regulatory frameworks of Superfund and RCRA has caused discovery of many thousands of solvent plumes in granular aquifers and fractured bedrock. The average groundwater velocity in the horizontal direction in sand or gravel is usually between 400 to 4,000 m/decade. The retardation of the common solvents such as TCE, PCE, TCA, and DCM is generally small in such aquifers. Therefore, plume fronts typically advance at rates close to the groundwater velocity, although other chemical constituents of the plume may move more slowly. Plumes in fractured rock, particularly those in relatively non-porous rock such as granite, or those in rock with large fractures such as karstic limestone, can advance much more rapidly than in granular aquifers. In large regional aquifers, particularly in southwestern U.S., the distances between recharge and discharge areas are tens to hundreds of kilometers. Ultimately, solvent plumes in these aquifers can become immense if not contained by extraction wells or other control systems.

2.6 IMPLICATIONS FOR SITE CHARACTERIZATION AND MONITORING

A site investigation should provide the data necessary to determine whether the site is a DNAPL site, and further, provide the data necessary to form technically-sound decisions on remediation. Site characterization and monitoring at nearly all DNAPL sites has been done using **conventional methods** previously developed and widely applied to non-NAPL sites. The need to proceed rapidly with many site investigations in the 1980s, as driven by Superfund and RCRA regulations, contributed to this preference for conventional methods: innovation requires time and flexibility. However, it is now known that the task of delineating contamination at DNAPL sites presents unprecedented difficulties to the scientific, engineering, and regulatory communities, and that these difficulties can often be exacerbated when conventional methods are used. Drilling into or through DNAPL zones poses hazards for DNAPL **remobilization**, and **uncertainty** in the validity of sampling results.

Determination of the "nature and extent" of contamination is a demand inherent in many regulations or guidelines for site investigations. Strictly speaking, however, this is only very rarely accomplished at DNAPL solvent sites because DNAPL distributions are so complex. The rarity of direct detections of residual or free-phase DNAPL in the groundwater zone at the many intensely investigated DNAPL solvent sites is testimony to this subsurface complexity.

Shelby-tube or split-spoon soil samples taken at selected depth levels, together with permanent monitoring wells installed in clusters of two to four at different depths, are common components of site investigations. For non-NAPL sites, these techniques are often effective. For DNAPL sites, however, even after great expense has been invested in the site investigation, they rarely provide the level of detail needed to provide a reliable picture of the nature and extent of solvent DNAPL below the water table. In recent years, new strategies and investigative technologies have been developed for DNAPL sites, and their performances are being assessed at the present time.

2.7 IMPLICATIONS FOR SITE REMEDIATION

In the 1980s, decisions were made at thousands of DNAPL sites across North America to restore aquifers using groundwater extraction wells, above-ground water treatment, then surface disposal of the treated water. This is the **pump-and-treat** method. At many sites, the plumes are contained hydraulically in this approach, but the DNAPL source zones persist with no apparent reduction in long-term concentrations in the source-zone. The common **futility** of pump-and-treat for restoration of DNAPL source zones is now well established.

In some hydrogeologic situations, pump-and-treat can restore the plume portion of the aquifer to drinking water standards. However, for the restoration to be permanent, the source zone must be isolated to prevent further contribution of dissolved contamination to the plume. This can be done by positioning groundwater extraction wells within or close to the source zone for hydraulic containment of the source. In order to prevent plume re-growth, these wells must operate for as long as the DNAPL source zone exists, which can be many decades, or probably longer at nearly all DNAPL sites.

An alternative to pump-and-treat for source zone containment is the construction of an impervious enclosure around the entire source to prevent groundwater flow through the source zone. Several technologies are now available for such enclosures in unconsolidated deposits, some of which can be installed to depths of 50 to 100 m. Enclosures around DNAPL source zones in most types of fractured bedrock are much more difficult and expensive to construct because very closely-spaced boreholes must be used for injection of sealants into the fractures.

Much effort in the field of groundwater remediation has been directed at cleaning up surface soil and deeper parts of the vadose zone. This is commonly done in order to prevent contaminants from leaching into the groundwater zone. However, at DNAPL sites the contaminant mass flux to the groundwater zone from the vadose zone is typically small relative to the flux contributed to the plume from the DNAPL situated below the water table. Thus, DNAPL sites are distinct from non-NAPL sites in that remedial efforts in the vadose zone generally contribute little or no reduction of risk resulting from the groundwater contamination. At some DNAPL sites, however, removal or remediation of surface soil is needed to reduce the risk at the surface to land users (*e.g.*, homeowners), or to remove the potential hazards that would be caused by soil erosion or vapor emission.

The recent recognition that pump-and-treat is generally not effective for remediating DNAPL source zones has prompted intense research and development efforts aimed at identifying and developing new technologies. Some of these technologies are directed at source zone restoration, and others at plume containment. Chapter 14 describes some of these new and emerging technologies and indicates their current development status.

2.8 CONCLUSIONS

The retention capacity of geologic media for DNAPLs in the vadose zone, particularly chlorinated solvent DNAPLs, is typically small. Therefore, even small releases of DNAPL commonly result in the movement of DNAPL all the way through the vadose zone and into the groundwater zone. Repetitive small releases at the same location (as beneath a leaky tank or distribution pipe) can cause penetration as deep or deeper than a single sudden release of the same total spill volume. In some cases a water table of 50 or 100 m is not too deep to prevent DNAPL entry into the groundwater zone if solvent leakage or disposal has occurred for many years. Lateral DNAPL movement from the input location can also be large. We also note that low-permeability layers, either above or below the water table, commonly contain fractures, root holes or other small openings that allow DNAPL to move through aquitards into underlying aquifers. The DNAPL retention capacity of most fractured rock is particularly small. This can result in very deep DNAPL penetration, in some cases hundreds of meters or more.

Once the release of DNAPL into the subsurface ceases, subsurface movement of DNAPL also ceases soon thereafter, perhaps within weeks or months at solvent sites. The resulting immobile DNAPL then exists in the DNAPL source zone as "residual" non-aqueous liquid and also possibly as "free-product" accumulations ponded on lower permeability layers within aquifers, or on the tops of aquitards. The free-product DNAPL will not become mobile again unless a release of more DNAPL causes further accumulation in the same zones, or unless there are changes in pressure in the surrounding water phase due to groundwater pumping or injection.

Subsurface DNAPL can act as a persistent source for contaminant plumes in both the vadose and groundwater zones. In fractured porous media, much or all of the DNAPL in the fractures can dissolve and diffuse into the low-permeability material surrounding the fractures. DNAPL source zones are often persistent because the majority of the entire subsurface contaminant mass is usually still situated in the source zone, and the release of contaminants from the source is slow, often diffusion controlled. Source depletion mechanisms include diffusive loss to the vadose zone and diffusive loss to flowing groundwater.

Plumes of groundwater contamination from chlorinated solvent source zones commonly extend great distances (kilometers or more) because: 1) these compounds exhibit generally weak sorption affinity for most aquifer materials; 2) they usually undergo little dilution; and 3) the contaminants degrade slowly or not at all. Plumes at DNAPL sites have complex shapes. Multiple plumes can occur where shallow dissolved contaminant migrates in one direction and deeper contamination in another direction, or where the source zone has multiple DNAPL input locations. Plume size is often increased by lateral spreading of vapor-phase contamination. Natural attenuation is usually not sufficient to cause the fronts of chlorinated solvent plumes to stabilize at steady-state positions. Many such plumes are ultimately destined to reach water supply wells. If no wells exist in the path of a plume, hydrologic boundaries such as rivers or lakes, where dilution and volatilization will occur, often tend to minimize the severity of the environmental impact.

The overall size and internal anatomy of a DNAPL source zone and the plume(s) caused by such a source zone will depend on many factors. These factors include the type of DNAPL, the volume of the release, the depth to the water table, and the general geologic and topographic settings. What normally distinguishes the degree of complexity of a DNAPL source zone from other contaminant sources is the considerable influence of small-scale variabilities, geologic structure, and/or bedding. The scale at which geological variability affects DNAPL flow and distribution is much smaller than can be studied by current field techniques. Thus, there is a critical need to develop and depend on conceptual models which can guide decisions regarding the nature of this problem, as well as the suitability and practicality of various options for corrective action.

The release of a given volume of DNAPL will produce much different results from one hydrogeologic situation to the next because the retention capacity properties of the subsurface will vary greatly from site to site and within sites. The determination of feasible cleanup levels, time frames, and ultimate costs depend on estimates of the total contaminant mass and the distribution of that mass in the subsurface. It is particularly important to understand how much of the chlorinated solvent is present in slow release zones, fast release zones, and/or present as free-product accumulations. Usually, these estimates must be based on conceptual models: direct answers to such questions are generally not attainable because of the excessive cost of field investigations at the relevant scales. The examination and interpretation of site data requires the perceptual framework of hypotheses represented by conceptual models. It is the responsibility of practicing groundwater scientists and engineers to further refine these conceptual models by building site-specific conceptual models for actual sites. The more tested our conceptual models become through data acquisition and analysis, the more effective and less risky will be our decisions regarding corrective actions.

This chapter has provided an overview of a broad range of geological conditions and conceptual models so as to serve as the basis for organizing the subsequent chapters of this book, and to help the reader integrate the details presented in each of the subsequent chapters into an overall paradigm for the behavior of DNAPLs in the subsurface. The methods that are available for the investigation of DNAPL sites as well as the mathematical models that are available for representing subsurface DNAPL behavior are improving rapidly. We expect that new information will permit further refinement of the DNAPL paradigm.

ACKNOWLEDGEMENTS

The concepts and interpretations described in this chapter were developed during the past ten years as a result of many discussions with our numerous colleagues in industry, academia, consulting, and regulatory agencies; we offer these colleagues our sincere thanks. We also acknowledge the pioneering research on chlorinated solvents conducted by Dr. Friedrich Schwille, and thank him for the advice and encouragement he provided to the solvent research group at the Waterloo Centre for Groundwater Research.

Funding support for this research was provided in part by the University Consortium Solvents-in-Groundwater Research Program. Sponsors of the Program between 1988 and 1994 have included: The Boeing Company, Ciba-Geigy Corporation, Dow Chemical Canada/USA, Eastman Kodak Co., General Electric Co., Laidlaw Environmental Systems Ltd., Mitre Corporation, The Natural Sciences and Engineering Research Council of Canada, and the Ontario University Research Incentive Fund.

2.9 REFERENCES

Hughes, B. M, R. W. Gillham, and C. A. Mendoza (1992) "Transport of trichloroethylene vapors in the unsaturated zone: A field experiment". In: *Proceedings: Conference on Subsurface Contamination by Immiscible Fluids*, International Association of Hydrogeologists, Calgary, Alberta, April 18-20, 1990.

Imhoff, P. T., P. R. Jaffe, and G. F. Pinder (1989) "Experimental investigation of the dissolution dynamics of chlorinated hydrocarbons in porous media". In: *Proceedings: Symposium on Processes Governing the Movement and Fate of Contaminants in the Subsurface Environment*, Stanford, California.

Johnson, R. L. and J. F. Pankow (1992) "Dissolution of dense chlorinated solvents into groundwater. 2. Source functions for pools of solvent", *Environ. Sci. Technol.*, **26**, 896-901.

Kueper, B. H. and D. B. McWhorter (1991) "The behavior of dense non-aqueous phase liquids in fractured clay and rock", *Ground Water*, **29**, 716-728.

Kueper, B. H., W. Abbot, and G. J. Farquhar (1989) "Experimental observations of multiphase flow in heterogeneous porous media", *J. Contaminant Hydrology*, **5**, 83-95.

Mackay, D. M. and J. A. Cherry (1989) "Groundwater contamination: Limits of pump-and-treat remediation", *Environ. Sci. Technol.*, **23**, 630-636.

Mendoza, C. A. and E. O. Frind (1990a) "Advective-dispersive transport of dense organic vapors in the unsaturated zone. 1. Model development", *Water Resources Research*, **26**, 379-387.

Mendoza, C. A. and E. O. Frind (1990b) Advective-dispersive transport of dense organic vapors in the unsaturated zone. 2. Sensitivity analysis", *Water Resources Research*, **26**, 388-398.

Parker, B. L., R. W. Gillham, and J. A. Cherry (1994) "Diffusive disappearance of immiscible phase organic liquids in fractured geologic media", *Ground Water*, **32**, 805-820.

Poulsen, M. and B. H. Kueper (1992) "A field experiment to study the behavior of tetrachloroethylene in unsaturated porous media", *Environ. Sci. Technol.*, **26**, 889-895.

Rivett, M. O. (1995) "Soil-gas signatures from volatile chlorinated solvents: Borden field experiments", *Ground Water*, **33**, 84-98.

Schwille, F. (1988) *Dense Chlorinated Solvents in Porous and Fractured Media - Model Experiments*, translated from the German by J. F. Pankow, Lewis Publishers, Boca Raton, Florida.

Vogel, T. M, C. S. Criddle, and P. L. McCarty (1987) "Transformations of halogenated aliphatic compounds", *Environ. Sci. Technol.*, **21**, 722-736.

Wilson, J. L. and S. H. Conrad (1984) "Is physical displacement of residual hydrocarbons a realistic possibility in aquifer restoration?", In: *Proceedings: National Water Well Assoc. Conference on Petroleum Hydrocarbons and Organic Chemicals in Groundwater*, Houston, Texas, November 5-7, pp. 274-298.

3

Mechanics and Mathematics of the Movement of Dense Non-Aqueous Phase Liquids (DNAPLs) in Porous Media

David B. McWhorter[1] and Bernard H. Kueper[2]

[1] Department of Chemical and Bioresource Engineering, Colorado State University, Fort Collins, Colorado, 80523

[2] Department of Civil Engineering, Queen's University, Kingston, Ontario, Canada, K7L 3N6.

ABSTRACT

The fundamental principles governing multi-phase flow in porous media are presented. Topics addressed include interfacial tension, capillary pressure, fluid contents, entry pressure, wettability, residual and pool formation, and relative permeability. The equations governing the static distribution and movement of non-aqueous phase liquids (NAPLs) in the subsurface are also outlined. Simple applications involving each of these topics is provided, including the height of dense non-aqueous phase liquid (DNAPL) in a well, the distribution of DNAPL in unsteady horizontal flow, the Buckley-Leverett solution, and DNAPL displacement by waterflooding.

3.1 INTRODUCTION

Chlorinated solvents entering the subsurface from a spill, leak, or other release often do so as constituents of a **nonaqueous phase liquid (NAPL)**. When a significant fraction of the NAPL is made up of one or more chlorinated solvents, the specific gravity will be greater than unity. The term **dense nonaqueous phase liquid (DNAPL)** is then used to describe the fluid. DNAPLs are often described as being **"immiscible"** with soil gas and subsurface waters because they can retain their identity as a separate phase, distinguishable from contiguous fluids by distinct interfaces. Actually, no fluid can ever be totally immiscible with another, and the constituents of a DNAPL can partition into the gaseous and aqueous phases, and will sometimes form extensive vapor and dissolved plumes. Indeed, a primary motivation for the study of DNAPLs in aquifers is the fact that they can function as enduring sources for soil-gas and aqueous-phase contamination.

A working knowledge of the way in which DNAPLs migrate and distribute themselves at equilibrium in geologic materials is an essential ingredient of informed decisions concerning the characterization, diagnosis, and remediation of DNAPL sites. This chapter presents the physical principles regarding such knowledge. The connection between theoretical concepts and practical considerations is demonstrated and emphasized by application of the principles to several specific types of situations that arise at DNAPL sites. Of course, we must do this in a rather generic way, and the practitioner is likely to find applications confounded by heterogeneity, lack of data, and other complicating factors. Nevertheless, the physical principles embedded in our examples form reliable guides for appropriate transfer of experience from one site to another.

3.2 CAPILLARY PRESSURE AND FLUID CONTENTS

3.2.1 General

The invasion of groundwater by a DNAPL is a process in which previously-existing pore waters are displaced by the invading DNAPL. Consider, for example, the **pool** of DNAPL that has accumulated on the bedrock in Figure 3.1. The upper surface of the pool is a macroscopic interface that corresponds to the interface separating water and DNAPL in any ordinary vessel, say a beaker in the laboratory. However, in contrast to the situation in a beaker, the water and DNAPL coexist in the pore spaces located below the macroscopic surface of the DNAPL pool. In fact, water is continuous throughout the thickness of the aquifer, including through the DNAPL pool.

Pore-scale interfaces separate the water and DNAPL at points below the macroscopic interface. Unlike the macroscopic interface, whose orientation is controlled by *gravity*, the pore-scale interfaces are primarily affected by **interfacial forces** that exist between the two fluids and among the fluids and the solid. Interfaces at the pore scale may be randomly oriented with respect to the gravitational field. Furthermore, the relative amounts of water and DNAPL in a representative volume of the porous medium is not constant below the macroscopic interface. The relative amounts of water and DNAPL will depend upon the difference in pressure between the two fluids.

Based on the above discussion, we see that the intuitively appealing notion of separate water and DNAPL bodies that interact only on their macroscopic boundaries, as in a beaker or pipe, is inappropriate. In the remainder of this section, we explore these

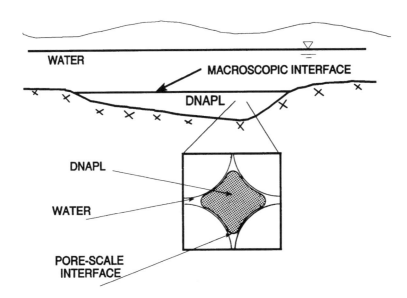

Figure 3.1 Macroscopic and pore-scale interfaces between DNAPL and water in a porous medium.

matters in more detail. While much of the foregoing discussion has been framed in the specific context of a static DNAPL pool, the principles involved apply in both static and dynamic situations.

3.2.2 Interfacial Tension, Wettability and Capillarity

The interface between two contiguous immiscible fluids experiences a tension that is similar to that in a stretched membrane. This tension is called the **interfacial tension** and arises because of unbalanced cohesional forces on molecules at the interface (Adam, 1968). The tension causes the interface between the two fluids to contract and form an area that is as small as possible. Interfacial tension is usually expressed as a force per unit length, but can also be thought of as energy per unit area. The tendency to contract minimizes the excess free energy of the interface.

A force balance on a curved interface between two fluids (Corey, 1986) leads to the conclusion that the pressures in the fluids on either side of the interface are not equal; the difference being given by

$$\Delta P = \sigma \left[\frac{1}{r_1} + \frac{1}{r_2} \right] \quad , \qquad (3.1)$$

where ΔP is the pressure difference across the interface, σ is the interfacial tension, and r_1 and r_2 are the principal radii of curvature of the interface. The fluid on the concave side of the interface is at the higher pressure. If the interface forms a subsection of a sphere, then $r_1 = r_2 = r$, and the more familiar

$$\Delta P = 2\sigma/r \qquad (3.2)$$

is obtained. Interfacial tension is seen to be the property that permits two fluids to exist in contact at different pressures. Values of interfacial tension range from about 20 to 50 dynes/cm for most water-DNAPL fluid pairs (Mercer and Cohen, 1990). However, DNAPLs encountered at field sites are often mixtures of organic liquids and have undergone aging processes that may have altered the interfacial properties. The interfacial tension of field DNAPL-water systems should therefore be measured whenever possible.

When two fluids are in contact with a solid, one usually has a greater affinity for the solid than the other. The fluid with the greater affinity for the solid is said to be the **wetting fluid**, the other being the **non-wetting fluid**. The wetting fluid preferentially spreads over the solid. The relative affinity of the two fluids for the solid (wettability) is manifested in a **contact angle**, which is the angle that the fluid-fluid interface makes with the solid. Wettability depends upon the chemical properties of the two fluids, and upon the composition of the solid surface. Anderson (1986) has reviewed the ways in which wettability can be measured.

The concept of contact angle permits one to relate the pressure difference across an interface not only to the interfacial tension and interface geometry as in Eq.(3.1), but also to the geometry of the opening across which the interface is positioned. For example, the pressure difference across an interface in a capillary tube with a circular cross-section of radius a is

$$\Delta P = 2\sigma \frac{\cos \alpha}{a} \quad , \tag{3.3}$$

where α is the contact angle. This result follows from Eq.(3.2) upon recognition that the radius of the interface is $a/\cos \alpha$.

Organic solvents are often observed to be the nonwetting fluid when present in aquifers. For this reason, DNAPLs preferentially occupy the larger openings, while water tends to coat the solids and occupy the smaller, more constricted portions of the pore space. This pore-scale arrangement of fluids is illustrated in Figure 3.1 where the DNAPL is found on the concave side of the pore-scale interfaces and is the fluid at the higher pressure. The difference between the nonwetting-fluid (DNAPL) pressure and the wetting-fluid (water) pressure is called the **capillary pressure** P_c

$$P_c = \Delta P = P_{nw} - P_w \quad , \tag{3.4}$$

where P_{nw} is the pressure of the nonwetting fluid and P_w is the pressure of the wetting fluid. Throughout this chapter we will assume that water is wetting with respect to a DNAPL.

The geometry of an interstitial pore space is obviously highly complex. Nevertheless, it is possible to conceive of a network of interstitial spaces connected by **pore throats** of a smaller characteristic dimension. To the extent that Eq.(3.3) applies in such a complex geometry, it predicts the **threshold value** of the capillary pressure that must be exceeded for DNAPL to pass through a pore throat of radius a. Thus, DNAPL is denied access to an interstitial pore until the capillary pressure exceeds the threshold value associated with the **largest throat** already in contact with the DNAPL. Once entry has been achieved, the DNAPL moves into the pore. The water-DNAPL interfaces then position themselves across regions of the pore space that support radii of curvature consistent with the prevailing capillary pressure. As the capillary pressure is increased, successively smaller pore throats are invaded by the DNAPL.

3.2.3 Dependence of Fluid Content on Capillary Pressure

The foregoing conceptualization of DNAPL invasion into a previously water-filled porous medium suggests that there should exist a relationship between capillary pressure and the relative amounts of DNAPL and water in a porous medium. Indeed, this is the case, but the complex geometry of the pore space precludes direct computation of the relationship: it must be measured for a given medium. The measured relationship is known as the **capillary pressure-saturation function** or, sometimes, simply as the **capillary pressure curve**. This macroscopic function is defined only for volume elements of a porous medium that are very large relative to the volume of individual grains.

It is convenient to express the fluid contents in terms of the fraction of the total interstitial void volume occupied by each fluid. Let V_v be the void volume in a representative element of bulk porous medium. Then

$$S_w = V_w/V_v \quad , \tag{3.5}$$

$$S_{nw} = V_{nw}/V_v \quad , \tag{3.6}$$

$$S_w + S_{nw} = 1 \quad , \tag{3.7}$$

where V_w and V_{nw} are the volumes of wetting and nonwetting fluids, respectively, and S_w and S_{nw} are the relative volumes of wetting and nonwetting fluids expressed as a fraction of the pore volume. The relative volumes are referred to as saturations (*e.g.*, the **"wetting-fluid saturation"**).

The capillary pressure-saturation function $P_c(S_w)$ is often measured in a cell similar to that shown in Figure 3.2. This cell was used by Kueper (1989) to measure the capillary pressure curve for tetrachloroethylene (PCE) and water in several sands. Such a test is initiated with all of the pore space filled with water; the DNAPL pressure is then increased incrementally. Each step-increase in DNAPL pressure causes increased invasion of the pore space by DNAPL. The volume of DNAPL injected and/or the volume of water displaced is measured and used to calculate the fluid content after equilibrium has been

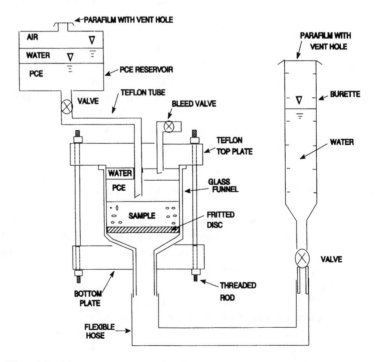

Figure 3.2   Schematic of a capillary pressure-saturation cell. (Reprinted with permission from Kueper, 1989.)

established at each pressure level. The porous plate on which the porous medium rests allows the displaced water to leave the cell, but prevents DNAPL from doing so. It is usually constructed of porous ceramic. The water pressure is indicated by the water level in the outflow burette, and the DNAPL pressure is calculated from the fluid levels in the DNAPL reservoir. Therefore, the capillary pressure corresponding to each equilibrium fluid content is known. More sophisticated devices employing pressure transducers and utilizing prescribed increments of injected volume instead of increments of pressure are also available.

Data obtained by the method described above are shown in Figure 3.3. These data were utilized in a numerical modeling study by Kueper and Frind (1991b). The capillary pressure at a given water saturation was found to be greater in the sands with lower hydraulic conductivity. This is consistent with Eq.(3.3) in that the sands with smaller hydraulic conductivity are comprised of smaller pores and pore throats. Also, little or no DNAPL was found to invade the samples until the capillary pressure reached a threshold value determined by the largest pore throat (or throats) exposed to the DNAPL on the exterior surface, and providing access to the interior of the sample. While some invasion of DNAPL occurred at capillary pressures equal to or slightly above the threshold, it is not likely that DNAPL became continuous throughout the sample until an even greater capillary pressure was exerted. The capillary pressure at which the DNAPL becomes continuous in the macroscopic sense and is capable of flowing through the material is known as the **entry pressure** (Corey, 1986). For most materials, the entry pressure corresponds to a water saturation in the range of 0.8 to 0.95.

Another characteristic capillary pressure that has found widespread use is the **displacement pressure** (P_d). The displacement pressure is described in Figure 3.4, and is the minimum capillary pressure required to initiate invasion of a water saturated porous medium by a DNAPL. The value of P_d is obtained from the capillary pressure curve by drawing a tangent to the curve at the inflection point, and extrapolating that tangent to $S_w = 1$. Often, there is little numerical difference between the entry pressure and the displacement pressure.

Insofar as the displacement pressure must be exceeded in order that DNAPL invasion occur, it should not be surprising that the **subsurface distribution** of P_d plays a central role in determining the paths of DNAPL migration (Kueper and Frind, 1991a, 1991b). Indeed, it is a key factor in the **diversion** of DNAPL around fine-grained lenses and in the formation of DNAPL pools. These subjects are taken up in more detail below. However, before doing so, we must first address the fact that the capillary pressure-saturation function is not unique, even for a particular porous medium and fluid pair.

3.2.4 Hysteresis and Residual DNAPL

The capillary pressure-saturation curves shown in Figure 3.3 were measured under conditions in which the water saturation decreased and the capillary pressure increased as the result of invasion of DNAPL into previously water-saturated media. This phenomena is known as **drainage** and corresponds to field situations in which the DNAPL advances into ground water from some type of source. Once the source is exhausted, the DNAPL

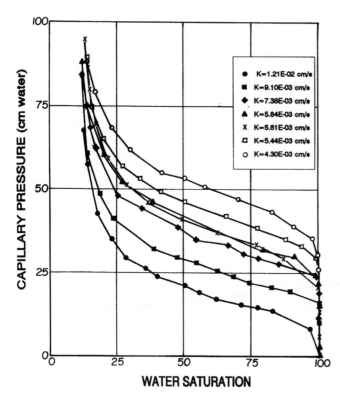

Figure 3.3 Measured capillary pressure-saturation curves for a perchloroethylene-water system. (Reprinted with permission from Kueper and Frind, 1991b.)

will continue to migrate away from the source and will be replaced in that zone by water. The situation is now one of increasing water saturation and decreasing capillary pressure, referred to as **wetting**. Injection of water to displace DNAPL in remediation efforts is another example of a circumstance in which the water saturation increases and capillary pressure decreases.

Unfortunately, the $P_c(S_w)$ relationship is not the same for decreasing S_w as for increasing S_w. Figure 3.4 shows the type of **hysteresis** that is commonly observed. The water saturation at any particular capillary pressure is less during the wetting process than during drainage. Of particular importance is the fact that the **maximum water saturation** (S_m) achievable during the wetting process is less than unity. The quantity $(1 - S_m)$ is known as the **residual DNAPL saturation**. Residual DNAPL is comprised of blobs and fingers (ganglia) of DNAPL that have been cutoff and disconnected from the continuous DNAPL body by the invading water. It can be said that residual DNAPL is **occluded** by water.

A body of DNAPL issuing from a source continues to sink following the elimination or exhaustion of the source. As water replaces the draining DNAPL, residual DNAPL is formed on the trailing surface of the DNAPL body. In the absence of an obstructing geologic feature, most of the DNAPL eventually will be converted into residual, and DNAPL migration will cease. At the pore scale, the reinvasion of water and the conse-

CAPILLARY PRESSURE CURVE

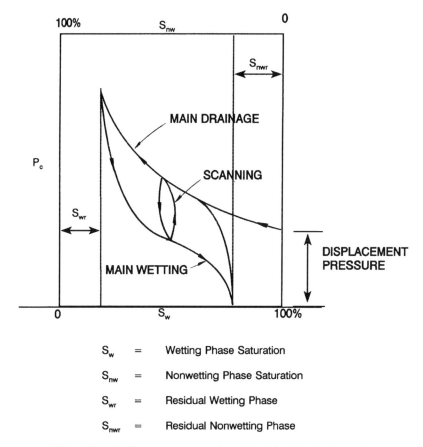

S_w	=	Wetting Phase Saturation
S_{nw}	=	Nonwetting Phase Saturation
S_{wr}	=	Residual Wetting Phase
S_{nwr}	=	Residual Nonwetting Phase

Figure 3.4 Capillary pressure-saturation relationships showing hysteresis.

quent displacement of DNAPL occurs as a sequence of **menisci advancement** in pore bulges by jumps and the consequent rupture and choke-off of menisci positioned across pore necks. The result is a rupture of nonwetting-fluid connections and the isolation of fingers of nonwetting fluid. The pore doublet model (*e.g.*, Morel-Seytoux, 1969; Stegemeier, 1974) is a popular explanation for the entrapment of nonwetting fluid by the invasion of a wetting fluid. Chatzis and Dullien (1983) show that pore doublet models must include a neck-bulge-neck type of pore geometry in order to explain the entrapment of the nonwetting fluid. According to Mohanty *et al.* (1987), the amount of nonwetting fluid isolated from the connected fluid body depends upon the local pore geometry, pore topology, fluid properties, the externally imposed pressure gradient, and the amount of nonwetting fluid present prior to displacement.

Residual DNAPL does not move with the flowing ground water. Instead, it forms a distributed, **immobile source** for dissolved-phase partitioning into the contiguous ground water. The solubilities of most organic solvents are orders of magnitude greater than the concentrations at which there is concern for human health. Thus, since residual DNAPL will initially be present virtually everywhere there was once continuous DNAPL, it will be an instrumental feature in the creation of dissolved-phase groundwater plumes. Typical values of residual DNAPL saturation in the field are presently unknown; in cases where small-scale heterogeneities are present, they are a function of the scale of measurement. In a field experiment conducted in a sand aquifer, Kueper *et al.* (1993) observed residual DNAPL saturations below the water table that ranged from 0.01 to 0.15. In homogeneous sands, Schwille (1988) reports laboratory values on the order of 0.02 to 0.15. In coarse Ottawa sand, residual saturations of DNAPL in the range 0.15 to 0.4 were observed (Anderson, 1988).

Once the DNAPL ceases to flow downward, there will remain a connected body of DNAPL of height $P_d / \Delta\rho g$. This is the thickness required to generate the minimum capillary pressure for DNAPL penetration. Thus, it is expected that all DNAPL sites will have some pools, even in very homogeneous media.

3.2.5 Algebraic $P_c(S_w)$ Relationships

In virtually all calculations of two-phase phenomena in porous media, it is convenient to use algebraic expressions for $P_c(S_w)$ as opposed to the experimental data themselves. Many algebraic formulae have been proposed for this purpose. Among the most popular is the **Brooks-Corey** (1966) equation:

$$
\begin{aligned}
S_e &= 1 & , \quad P_c \geq P_d \\
P_c &= P_d S_e^{-1/\lambda} & , \quad P_c \geq P_d
\end{aligned}
\tag{3.8}
$$

where P_d is the displacement pressure for the medium, and λ is a pore-size distribution index. Another popular expression is the van Genuchten (1980) equation

$$
P_c = P_o(S_e^{-1/m} - 1)^{1-m} \quad , \quad P_c \geq 0 \quad ,
\tag{3.9}
$$

where P_o is the characteristic capillary pressure and m is a fitting parameter determined by the pore-size distribution. In both of these expressions, S_e is a normalized wetting-fluid saturation defined by

$$
S_e = \frac{S_w - S_r}{S_m - S_r} \quad .
\tag{3.10}
$$

We recall that S_m is unity when DNAPL is invading into a water-saturated porous medium; it is less than unity when water displaces DNAPL because of the entrapment of DNAPL.

The parameters P_d, λ, and S_r for the Brooks-Corey equation are evaluated by fitting the equation to experimental data. The values of m (note that $0 < m < 1$), P_o, and S_r in the van Genuchten equation are similarly determined. The wetting-fluid saturation S_r is often called the residual saturation. It is approximately the wetting-fluid saturation at which the $P_c(S_w)$ curve appears to approach a vertical asymptotic value (see Figure 3.4). It is not to be confused with the residual saturation for the DNAPL. Parameter values (particularly P_d and P_o) will be different when determined from wetting data and drying data. Other algebraic $P_c(S_w)$ relationships such as that obtained by Luckner *et al.* (1989) account for "scanning curves" between the main drainage and main wetting limbs.

3.2.6 Summary

The replacement of groundwater in the pores of an aquifer by invading DNAPL never becomes complete. Thus, water and DNAPL will coexist in the interstitial pore space anywhere that DNAPL is present[†]. Interfacial tension, a property of two adjacent fluid phases, permits adjacent fluid phases to be under different pressures. The pressure difference across pore-scale interfaces is balanced by the interfacial forces acting tangent to the curved interfaces. Because water is usually the wetting fluid in saturated subsurface systems, it preferentially occupies the smaller, more constricted regions of the pore spaces. A DNAPL solvent, being the nonwetting fluid, resides and moves through the larger regions of the pore network and is the fluid at the higher pressure. The dependence of the pressure difference across the curved interface yields the macroscopic relationship between capillary pressure and fluid content that is the capillary pressure-saturation function. This function enables one to quantitatively relate the relative volume of water and DNAPL in a representative volume element of porous medium to the pressure difference between the DNAPL and water in that element. The capillary pressure-saturation function has been shown to apply for both static and dynamic problems in many situations of practical interest.

3.3 DISTRIBUTION OF DNAPL IN A POOL ABOVE AN AQUITARD

3.3.1 General

In Section 3.2.4 we found that there exist relationships between capillary pressure and fluid saturations. Thus, given knowledge of the capillary pressure curve and the value of capillary pressure, one can determine the water and DNAPL saturation values. How one might know the capillary pressure in the first place has remained unexplained to this point. In the most general case, the capillary pressure must be determined by solution of the differential equations for flow of both water and DNAPL (see below).

The capillary-pressure distribution and, therefore, the fluid-content distribution, is calculated most easily for a case when neither fluid is in motion. The downward migration of DNAPL from a large source may be arrested by an aquitard. Upon encountering a stratum that it is unable to penetrate, the DNAPL will accumulate and spread laterally to form a pool. The accumulation of DNAPL will be accompanied by an increasing capillary pressure. Eventually, the pool thickness may cease to increase with the system then becoming static. Alternatively, the DNAPL may accumulate to the point where penetration of the aquitard occurs. The distributions of capillary pressure and the fluid

---

[†]The context here is that invading DNAPL can never *physically* force out all of the water in the pore space. Nevertheless, DNAPL can come to occupy 100% of the pore space when the percent of the pore space occupied by the invading DNAPL is high enough that all of the remaining water can *dissolve* into the DNAPL.

saturations in a static pool and the conditions for **incipient penetration** of the aquitard may be determined as follows.

3.3.2 Distribution of Capillary Pressure

A pool of DNAPL with thickness T is shown perched on an aquitard in Figure 3.5. Such a pool might be formed by a gradual thickening due to lateral migration of DNAPL from a remote source. During formation of the pool, the DNAPL is advancing into a previously water-saturated porous medium and the relevant capillary pressure-saturation relation is the drainage curve shown in Figure 3.4. Once the source is exhausted, some DNAPL drainage from the pool interior occurs as the pool continues to expand laterally. The result is a recession (lowering) of the upper surface of the pool, accompanied by re-invasion of water and the formation of a halo of residual DNAPL. Because the recession is a wetting process, the capillary pressure on the upper surface of the connected DNAPL is approximately zero.

The water pressure increases with depth below the water table in the usual way, namely

$$P_w = -\rho_w g Z + C_1 \quad , \tag{3.11}$$

where ρ_w is the density of water, g is the gravitational constant, and Z is a vertical coordinate which is measured positively upward. The constant C_1 can be evaluated from the knowledge that $P_w = 0$ on the water table at a known value of Z. Eq.(3.11) is the familiar equation of hydrostatics and applies in the aquifer just as it does in a body of standing surface water. It also applies in the portion of the aquifer where DNAPL is

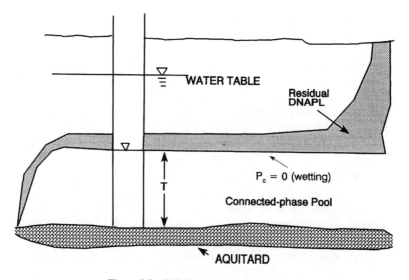

Figure 3.5   DNAPL pool above an aquitard.

present. For the variation in DNAPL pressure within the DNAPL pool we have

$$P_{nw} = -\rho_{nw}gZ + C_2 \quad , \tag{3.12}$$

where ρ_{nw} is the DNAPL density ($\rho_{nw} > \rho_w$).

Eqs.(3.11) and (3.12) are substituted into the definition of capillary pressure (Eq.(3.4)) to obtain

$$P_c = -\Delta\rho gZ + C \quad , \tag{3.13}$$

where $\Delta\rho$ is the positive quantity $\rho_{nw} - \rho_w$. The constant C is evaluated by noting that $P_c = 0$ at $Z = T$. Therefore, the distribution of capillary pressure within the DNAPL pool is given by

$$P_c = \Delta\rho g(T - Z) \quad , \quad Z \leq T \quad . \tag{3.14}$$

Eqs.(3.11) and (3.12) are shown graphically in Figure 3.6. It is apparent from this figure that the capillary pressure increases with depth in the pool because the DNAPL pressure increases more rapidly with depth than does the pressure in the water. This is due, of course, to the fact that $\rho_{nw} > \rho_w$. Note that the capillary pressure in the pool is independent of the depth of the pool below the water table.

Clearly, the maximum capillary pressure occurs at the base of the DNAPL pool, and is directly proportional to both the density difference and the pool thickness. That the DNAPL has not penetrated the underlying aquitard and dissipated the pool is directly attributable to the condition that the displacement pressure of the aquitard exceeds the capillary pressure imposed by the pool. Incipient invasion of the aquitard is given by the

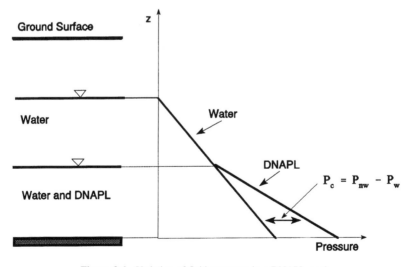

Figure 3.6   Variation of fluid pressures in a DNAPL pool.

condition

$$\Delta \rho g T = P_d \quad , \qquad (3.15)$$

where P_d refers to the aquitard, not the medium in which the pool resides.

As we have already observed, P_d depends upon the size of the pore throats, as does the **hydraulic conductivity**. A close relationship between P_d and hydraulic conductivity might therefore be anticipated. Leverett (1941) assumed that P_d as well as all other capillary pressures are inversely proportional to the square root of the intrinsic permeability and, therefore, of the hydraulic conductivity. Laliberte *et al.* (1968) showed from theoretical considerations that P_d should be inversely proportional to the square root of the hydraulic conductivity. McWhorter and Nelson (1979) report a correlation of P_d with hydraulic conductivity that can be expressed as

$$P_d = 9.6 \left(\frac{\sigma}{\sigma_{aw}} \right) \left(\frac{K}{\Phi} \right)^{-0.403} \quad , \qquad (3.16)$$

where Φ is the porosity, σ is the interfacial tension of the fluid pair of interest, and σ_{aw} is the interfacial tension of water against air. Other investigators have found similar correlations (*e.g.*, see Thomas *et al.*, 1968). The hydraulic conductivity K in Eq.(3.16) is commonly expressed in units of cm/s. Common units for the displacement pressure are cm of water equivalent.

By combining Eqs.(3.15) and (3.16), one obtains the simple formula

$$T = 9.6 \left(\frac{\rho_w}{\Delta \rho} \right) \left(\frac{\sigma}{\sigma_{aw}} \right) \left(\frac{K}{\Phi} \right)^{-0.403} \quad , \qquad (3.17)$$

from which the pool thickness (cm) required to initiate DNAPL entry into a stratum with hydraulic conductivity K (cm/s) can be computed. For example, a pool thickness of 106 cm is required for entry of TCE into a stratum for which $K = 0.001$ cm/s and $\Phi = 0.3$. We have assumed interfacial tensions of 34 dynes/cm and 65 dynes/cm for TCE/water and air/water, respectively. The value of $\Delta \rho$ for TCE and water is 0.47 g/cm^3.

It is clear from calculations with Eq.(3.17) that **stratigraphic features** with K values which are only moderately low relative to the surrounding materials can halt and/or redirect the downward migration of DNAPLs. Eq.(3.17) also indicates that DNAPLs with large specific gravities are less likely to form large pools than are DNAPLs with specific gravities near unity, other factors being equal. Indeed, it is the authors' experience that chlorinated solvents with their high densities form thick pools only rarely. (In contrast, creosote and coal tars, which are DNAPLs with lower densities, often occur in pools of substantial thickness.)

3.3.3 Vertical Distribution of DNAPL in a Pool

The variation of capillary pressure through the DNAPL pool, as described by Eq.(3.14), is readily translated into a vertical distribution of fluid saturations by use of the capillary pressure-saturation function. For example, the capillary pressure given by Eq.(3.14) can be substituted for capillary pressure in Eq.(3.8) or Eq.(3.9) to arrive at explicit expressions for water saturation as a function of Z. Using Eq.(3.9), the result is

$$Z = T - \frac{P_o}{\Delta \rho g} \left[\left(\frac{S_w - S_r}{S_m - S_r} \right)^{-1/m} - 1 \right]^{1-m} . \qquad (3.18)$$

Distributions of water and DNAPL for pool thicknesses of 0.5 m and 0.3 m were calculated using Eq.(3.18) and are shown in Figure 3.7. The parameter values used for these calculations are $P_o/\Delta \rho g = 0.2$ m, $m = 0.75$, $S_m = 0.9$, and $S_r = 0.2$.

It is apparent from Figure 3.7 that thick pools result in greater DNAPL saturations than do thin pools. DNAPL saturations are similarly sensitive to the parameter $P_o/\Delta \rho g$. The important parameter actually is $T \Delta \rho g / P_o$. Significant DNAPL saturations exist only in pools for which this ratio is greater than unity. For any given pool thickness, the ratio is large when $\Delta \rho$ is large and/or P_o is small. Small values of P_o are associated with porous media with large hydraulic conductivity (see Section 3.3.2). The ability of a DNAPL to flow from a pool into a drain or a well will be seen below to be critically dependent upon the DNAPL saturation in the pool. The greater the DNAPL saturation, the more readily the DNAPL will move under an applied driving force. Thus, thick pools of DNAPL with high specific gravity located in highly permeable material will be the most amenable to **direct recovery** by drains or wells.

If investigations eventually establish the thickness and area of a given DNAPL pool, it will be possible to estimate the volume of DNAPL in the pool. This is accomplished

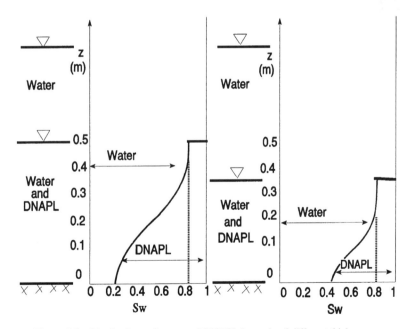

Figure 3.7 Distributions of water and DNAPL in pools of different thicknesses.

by evaluating

$$V_{nw} = \Phi \int_0^T (1 - S_w) dZ \tag{3.19}$$

with the use of Eq.(3.14) and either Eq.(3.8) or Eq.(3.9). Here, V_{nw} is the volume of DNAPL per unit area. The integral in Eq.(3.19) evaluates the area labeled "DNAPL" in the saturation distributions shown in Figure 3.7.

3.3.4 DNAPL in a Monitoring Well

Upon construction of a monitoring well, a DNAPL may enter the well. If such entry occurs, the DNAPL will seek a height such that the DNAPL pressure in the well is equal to that in the adjacent aquifer at all elevations. The water-DNAPL interface in the monitoring well will establish itself at an elevation equal to or greater than the upper surface of the connected-phase pool, depending upon the capillary pressure at the top of the pool.

The monitoring well shown in Figure 3.5 penetrates a pool that has experienced a recession following the halt of DNAPL input. Under this circumstance, the capillary pressure on the upper surface of the pool is approximately zero, as previously explained. In this case, the water-DNAPL interface in the monitoring well is at the same elevation as the upper surface of the connected-phase pool.

In the case of a pool that has undergone no recession, the capillary pressure will equal the displacement pressure on the upper surface of the pool. Now, the DNAPL pressure in the well at the elevation $Z = T$ must exceed the water pressure in the adjacent aquifer by P_d. This is possible only if the DNAPL in the well rises to an elevation that is $P_d/\Delta\rho g$ above the top of the pool. Thus, the difference in elevation (ΔE) between the DNAPL-water interface in the monitoring well and the top of the pool in the aquifer is given by

$$\Delta E = P_d/\Delta\rho g \quad , \tag{3.20}$$

with the top of the pool in the aquifer being at the lower elevation. It is as if the DNAPL forms a negative capillary fringe.

Implicit in Eq.(3.20) is the assumption that the capillary pressure-saturation function is such that the saturation of connected DNAPL is zero at a nonzero capillary pressure (*i.e.*, a Brooks-Corey function). In some cases the van Genuchten function, which considers DNAPL to be continuous at all P_c as given in Eq.(3.9), may be more appropriate. Examples include soils containing preferential pathways such as root and worm holes. In a van Genuchten material, the DNAPL/water interface in a monitoring well will be at the elevation of the top of the DNAPL pool in the aquifer, with $\Delta E = 0$.

DNAPL will fill an observation well to a height dictated by the DNAPL pressure in the aquifer only if DNAPL cannot escape the well bore at some point below the level of DNAPL entry. For example, DNAPL entering a well bore from a lens or pool located high in the screened section will have the opportunity to again flow out through the screen at a lower level. Also, the length of the DNAPL column in the well is rarely related to the thickness of the DNAPL pool in the aquifer. Only if the well is terminated at the base of the pool will the DNAPL thickness in the well correspond to the thickness of the DNAPL pool in the aquifer. We can conclude that a great deal of caution should be associated with the interpretation of DNAPL column heights in wells.

3.4 DARCY'S LAW AND RELATIVE PERMEABILITY

3.4.1 General

As in our previous considerations, our goal is to know the distribution of DNAPL saturations, but now under circumstances in which one or both of the fluids is in **motion**. For static fluids, a balance of the forces due to pressure gradient and gravity in each fluid, coupled with the function $P_c(S_w)$, was all that was required. In the case of fluid motion, the capillary pressure is no longer linearly related to the vertical space coordinate. The distribution of capillary pressure must be calculated from equations that fully account for fluid flow. Just as in a single-fluid system, Darcy's Law is the starting point for analyzing multi-fluid flow. Darcy's Law is written twice for a two-fluid problem; once for each fluid. Also, the concept of permeability must be generalized to account for the presence of two fluids in the pore space.

3.4.2 The Darcy Equations

The motion of individual fluid elements in porous media is extremely complex owing to the highly irregular geometry of the pores in which motion can occur. The intractable complexities associated with a pore-scale description of fluid flow are largely eliminated by use of a macroscale relationship between the rate of flow and the driving forces on the fluid. This is Darcy's Law. Variables such as density and pressure that refer to fluid elements in traditional fluid mechanics now denote values averaged over a representative volume of porous medium.

Darcy's Law is an empirical constitutive equation that forms the basis for practically all quantitative work with fluid motion in porous media. One consequence of passing from the pore-scale to the macroscale view is the introduction of the **permeability** parameter. The permeability of a porous medium to a particular fluid strongly depends upon the size, geometry and fluid content of the pores. Also, one cannot properly speak of fluid velocity at the macroscale since the velocity of fluid elements is described only in some average sense. It has become common to use the term "volume flux" or "flux density" to denote the volume of fluid passing a macroscopic unit area of porous medium per unit time.

Fluid motion in a porous medium is impelled by the gradient of fluid pressure and the body force due to gravity. Motion is resisted by viscous shear which, in turn, depends upon the rate of motion, the fluid viscosity, and the size, shape and tortuosity of each opening through which the fluid passes. The latter are characterized by the **intrinsic permeability**, k, of the porous medium when a single fluid is present. The coexistence of another fluid in the pores reduces the area available for flow of either fluid and increases the tortuosity of the flow path which fluid elements must traverse. These effects are incorporated in the **relative permeabilities** to each fluid and are strong functions of the fluid saturations.

We use the tensor notation that has become common in subsurface hydrology to write Darcy's Law for the individual fluids as

$$q_{wi} = -\frac{k_{ij}k_{rw}}{\mu_w}\left(\frac{\partial P_w}{\partial x_j} - \rho_w g_j\right) \quad , \tag{3.21}$$

$$q_{nwi} = -\frac{k_{ij}k_{rnw}}{\mu_w}\left(\frac{\partial P_{nw}}{\partial x_j} - \rho_{nw}g_j\right) \quad , \tag{3.22}$$

where i and j are indices that extend over the three Cartesian coordinates. In Eqs.(3.21) and (3.22), q is the volume flux, k is the intrinsic permeability, k_r is the relative permeability, P is the pressure, ρ is the density, μ is the dynamic viscosity, and the subscripts w and nw denote the wetting fluid (water) and nonwetting fluid (DNAPL), respectively. By convention, the repeated index, j, implies a summation over $j = 1$, 2, and 3.

At first glance, Eqs.(3.21) and (3.22) appear to be uncoupled. Such is not the case, however, because the relative permeabilities k_{rw} and k_{rnw} are strong functions of the saturations. It was previously pointed out that fluid saturation is a function of capillary pressure. Therefore, the relative permeabilities are functions of $P_c = P_{nw} - P_w$, and Eqs.(3.21) and (3.22) are **strongly coupled**. Explicit demonstrations of the importance of that coupling are provided by the example applications discussed later in this chapter.

3.4.3 Relative Permeabilities

Typical relative permeability functions are shown in Figure 3.8. By definition, these functions range from zero to unity. The relative permeability to the wetting phase (water) is thought to be practically free of hysteresis. On the other hand, the saturations at which k_{rnw} is zero in a wetting or draining process are not the same because of entrapment of nonwetting fluid during the wetting process. It is usual to assume that k_{rnw} is greater than zero in a draining process for all $S_w < 1$. In reality there will be a **threshold saturation** of nonwetting phase required to bring about an initial network of connected pore and pore throats across the sample volume of interest. This threshold value of saturation at which the nonwetting phase first becomes continuous corresponds to the entry pressure discussed in Section 3.2.3. During wetting, the relative permeability to DNAPL becomes zero at $S_w = 1 - S_m$. Also, it is worth noting that the relative permeability to water during wetting does not become unity because of the presence of residual DNAPL.

While it is possible to measure the relative permeability functions in the laboratory (*e.g.*, Johnson, *et al.*, 1959; Jones and Roszelle, 1978; Sigmund and McCaffery, 1979; Honarpour and Mahmood, 1988), it is often found convenient to calculate them from $P_c(S_w)$ data. Burdine (1953) and Mualem (1976) developed models that connect relative permeability to the capillary pressure-saturation function. These models can be used in conjunction with Eqs.(3.8) and (3.9) to derive closed-form expressions for $k_{rw}(S_w)$ and $k_{rnw}(S_w)$. Brooks and Corey (1966) used Eq.(3.8) in the model of Burdine (1953) to

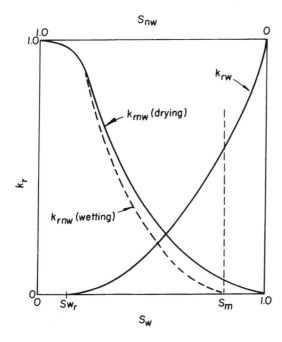

Figure 3.8 Typical relative permeability curves.

derive

$$k_{rw} = S_e^{(2+3\lambda)/\lambda} \tag{3.23}$$

and

$$k_{rnw} = (1 - S_e)^2 (1 - S_e^{\frac{2+\lambda}{\lambda}}) \quad . \tag{3.24}$$

By evaluating the Mualem (1976) model with Eq.(3.9), van Genuchten (1980) derived

$$k_{rw} = S_e^{1/2} [1 - (1 - S_e^{1/m})^m]^2 \quad . \tag{3.25}$$

For the relative permeability of the nonwetting phase, Parker *et al.* (1987) used the same procedure to write

$$K_{rnw} = (1 - S_e)^{1/2} (1 - S_e^{1/m})^{2m} \quad . \tag{3.26}$$

Still other forms can be obtained by using the Brooks-Corey equation (Eq.(3.8)) in the Mualem model, or the van Genuchten equation (Eq.(3.9)) in the Burdine model.

As noted above, the parameters λ, m, and S_r are determined by fitting Eq.(3.8) or Eq.(3.9) to $P_c(S_w)$ data. Thus, the rather difficult task of measuring the relative permeability functions is avoided. Values for λ typically range from about 0.5 for materials with a large range of pore sizes (*e.g.*, aggregated clay) to perhaps 4.0 for very uniform materials. A value of $\lambda = 2$ is typical for sandy aquifer material. The corresponding range for m is approximately 0.35 to 0.80. From a theoretical point of view, λ can be any number greater than zero, but m must be between zero and unity.

3.5 THE EFFECT OF GROUNDWATER FLOW ON DNAPL MIGRATION

3.5.1 General

The **migration** of DNAPL is affected by gravity, the pressure gradients in both the DNAPL and water phases, and the distributions of capillary and hydraulic properties of the porous medium. Owing to the density of a DNAPL, the tendency is for the migration path to be generally **downward**. However, heterogeneity has a marked influence on the direction of DNAPL migration. A random distribution of permeability and displacement pressure will result in a **highly erratic** pattern of DNAPL flow (Kueper and Frind, 1991a and 1991b); lateral spreading well beyond the extent of the source area has been a striking feature observed by these workers.

Paths of DNAPL migration which are readily-definable are created by permeability and displacement pressure contrasts of regular geometry. For example, downward-moving DNAPL may encounter a dipping stratum that it is unable to penetrate, so that it moves downdip along the contact. Also, DNAPL pooled on the subcrop of an aquifer with dipping bedding planes will preferentially enter the layers with low displacement pressure. The result is downdip DNAPL migration in a series of distinct layers separated by intervals entirely free of DNAPL (Figure 3.9). Such distributions of DNAPL have been observed in rock cores, and also in porous media by Poulsen and Kueper (1992) and Kueper *et al.* (1993).

Calculating the migration path of a DNAPL, even along a 1-D flow path, requires the solution of the full set of governing equations. However, results with significant

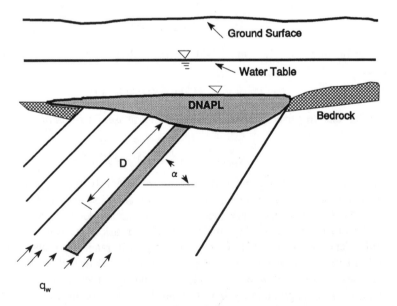

Figure 3.9 Migration of DNAPL in a sloping stratum subcropping in a pool of DNAPL.

practical utility are obtained by examining situations in which groundwater flow and capillary forces cause migration of DNAPL to cease. Similar analyses by Arthur D. Little, Inc. (1982), Villaume (1985) and Hunt *et al.* (1988) are summarized by Mercer and Cohen (1990).

3.5.2 Forces Acting on a DNAPL in Flowing Groundwater

The forces acting on a DNAPL may sometimes combine to cause the DNAPL to cease migrating. We have already encountered one such circumstance when neither the DNAPL nor the groundwater was in motion. It was necessary for the DNAPL to accumulate on a low-permeability stratum in order for that situation to develop. The force on a DNAPL due to flowing groundwater is now considered. One of the conclusions will be that groundwater flow alone can arrest the motion of DNAPL.

We begin by re-writing Eq.(3.22) for DNAPL flow along a 1-D path in an isotropic medium, obtaining

$$q_{nwi} = -\frac{kk_{rnw}}{\mu_{nw}}\left(\frac{dP_{nw}}{dx_i} + \rho_{nw}g\frac{dZ}{dx_i}\right) \quad , \tag{3.27}$$

where Z is the vertical coordinate, measured positively upward. No flow of DNAPL occurs when the forces in parentheses add to zero. Since the effect of groundwater flow is somewhat difficult to discern from Eq.(3.27), it is useful to replace P_{nw} with the equivalent $P_c + P_w$. Then, upon noting that $P_w = \rho_w g(H\text{-}Z)$, one obtains

$$q_{nwi} = -\frac{kk_{rnw}\rho_w g}{\mu_{nw}}\frac{d}{dx_i}\left(H + \frac{P_c}{\rho_w g} + \frac{\Delta\rho}{\rho_w}Z\right) \quad , \tag{3.28}$$

wherein H is the familiar hydraulic head for water.

The quantity in parentheses is given the symbol Φ:

$$\Phi = H + \frac{P_c}{\rho_w g} + \frac{\Delta\rho}{\rho_w}Z \quad . \tag{3.29}$$

Eq.(3.29) defines a **force potential** (Hubbert, 1940), the constancy of which means that no DNAPL will flow. The negative gradient of Φ is the net driving force on the DNAPL. Situations in which Φ is constant are examined in the following sections.

3.5.3 Static DNAPL in a Sloping Bed

The downdip migration of DNAPL along a sloping contact or in laminae associated with bedding planes may be arrested by updip groundwater flow. The situation to be considered is one in which DNAPL has entered a sloping layer that subcrops in pooled DNAPL as shown in Figure 3.9. The DNAPL has migrated to a distance, D, at which point further downward motion is arrested by updip groundwater flow. Our purpose is to compute the hydraulic gradient required to achieve this result and to calculate D.

Once DNAPL motion has ceased, the requirement that Φ be constant translates to

$$q_w = \frac{kk_{rw}}{\mu_w}\left(\frac{dP_c}{d\ell} - \Delta\rho g\sin\alpha\right) \quad , \tag{3.30}$$

in which q_w is the groundwater flux and is a constant because we assume the flow to be steady. The spatial coordinate ℓ is measured positive downward along the bed with dip angle α. Because the groundwater flux is constant, q_w is the same within and downdip of the DNAPL body. However, the hydraulic gradient is constant only in the zone downdip of the DNAPL. Variable water saturation and, therefore, variable relative permeability to water results in a spatially variable hydraulic gradient within the DNAPL body.

The groundwater flux, evaluated with the hydraulic gradient as measured downdip of the DNAPL is

$$q_w = -K \frac{\Delta H}{\Delta \ell} = -\frac{k \rho_w g}{\mu_w} \frac{\Delta H}{\Delta \ell} \quad , \tag{3.31}$$

where K is the hydraulic conductivity and $\Delta H/\Delta \ell$ is the constant hydraulic gradient downdip of the DNAPL. An equation for the migration distance D is obtained by combining Eqs.(3.30) and and (3.31), followed by the integration

$$D = \frac{1}{\rho_w g} \int_{P_d}^{P_c(0)} \frac{dp_c}{\frac{\Delta H}{\Delta \ell} k_{rw}^{-1} - \frac{\Delta \rho}{\rho_w} \sin \alpha} \quad . \tag{3.32}$$

The lower limit of integration is the displacement pressure of the layer in which the DNAPL is present and is the capillary pressure at the downdip extent of the DNAPL body. The capillary pressure at the source is $P_c(0)$ and is determined by the thickness of the source pool.

Eq.(3.32) makes physical sense only when

$$\frac{\Delta H}{\Delta \ell} > \frac{\Delta \rho}{\rho_w} \sin \alpha \quad . \tag{3.33}$$

This inequality constitutes the condition that must be satisfied if the motion of DNAPL is to be arrested by the updip flow of groundwater. The result for vertical flow is obtained of course with $\sin \alpha = 1$.

The calculation indicated in Eq.(3.32) is performed by expressing k_{rw} as a function of P_c and carrying out the integration numerically or graphically. Figure 3.10 is a dimensionless graph resulting from evaluation of Eq.(3.32) using

$$k_{rw} = \left(\frac{P_c}{P_d} \right)^{-5} \quad . \tag{3.34}$$

The use of Figure 3.10 can be demonstrated by a specific numerical example. Suppose the DNAPL in question has a density of 1.2 g/cm^3, and is pooled to a depth of 1.0 m on the subcrop of a stratum with $P_d = 0.15$ m of water. From Eq.(3.14) it is determined that the capillary pressure at the base of the pool and on the face of the subcropping stratum is $P_c(0) = 0.2$ m of water. Thus the ordinate value in Figure 3.10 is $P_c(0)/P_d = 1.33$. We will assume that the stratum dips at an angle of 3 degrees and that the updip hydraulic gradient is 0.011. Then,

$$\frac{\Delta H}{\Delta \ell} \left(\frac{\rho_w}{\Delta \rho \sin \alpha} \right) = 0.011 \left(\frac{1.0}{0.2 \times 0.0523} \right) = 1.05 \quad .$$

Figure 3.10 gives

$$\frac{D \Delta \rho g \sin \alpha}{P_d} = 0.615 \quad .$$

from which D is determined to be about 9 m. Note that the minimum updip hydraulic gradient that would arrest the DNAPL migration is 0.0105. This shows that an updip gradient only slightly greater than the critical value is sufficient to greatly limit the extent to which the DNAPL will migrate downdip.

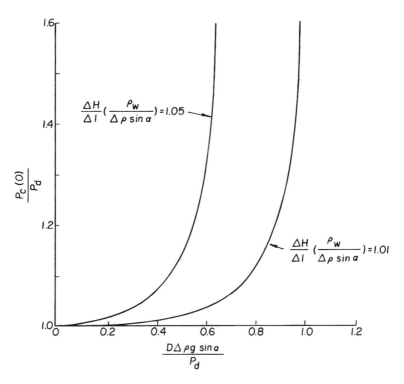

Figure 3.10 Dependence of depth of DNAPL penetration on the upward hydraulic gradient and capillary pressure on top of bedrock.

3.5.4 Incipient Motion of DNAPL Fingers (Ganglia)

For the circumstances assumed in the previous section, the migration of the DNAPL will be promoted by both gravity and a capillary pressure gradient. Once the DNAPL source is depleted, however, the gradient of capillary pressure is reversed and opposes DNAPL flow. DNAPL motion may now cease, even if groundwater flow is downward along the migration path. Again, the constancy of the force potential leads to a force balance on a static **finger** (ganglion) of length D residing in a sloping fracture or thin stratum. The force balance is expressed as

$$\frac{\Delta\rho\sin\alpha}{\rho_w} - \frac{P_c(D)}{\rho_w g D} - \frac{\Delta H}{D} = 0 \quad . \tag{3.35}$$

The quantity ΔH is the difference in hydraulic head across the finger and is positive when the groundwater flow is updip. It has been assumed that the capillary pressure is zero on the trailing end of the DNAPL body. The capillary pressure on the leading end is $P_c(D)$.

Fingers of DNAPL that have migrated to positions of static equilibrium can be **remobilized** by pumping groundwater. For example, suppose a 5 m long finger of DNAPL ($\rho_{nw} = 1.2$ g/cm^3) has come to rest in a thin stratum ($\alpha = 10$ degrees) as a consequence of encountering a medium with $P_d = 0.2$ m of water. Suppose, also, that the groundwater is static. According to Eq.(3.35), the capillary pressure at the leading edge is 0.174 m of water. If nearby pumping of groundwater then induces downdip flow of water in the stratum, a corresponding increase in capillary pressure will occur on the leading end of the finger due to the reduction of the water pressure. Incipient remobilization of the DNAPL will occur when $P_c(D) = 0.2$ m of water (*i.e.*, $P_c(D) = P_d$). Eq.(3.35) predicts that the finger will be remobilized by any downdip gradient ($\Delta H/D$) greater than 0.0053.

The DNAPL fingers considered above are large relative to the representative element of volume for the porous media in which they reside. Residual DNAPL, which is entrapped at a much smaller scale, is very difficult to mobilize by hydrodynamic forces. The ratio of capillary forces opposing mobilization to the viscous forces promoting the movement of residual is called the **capillary number** N_c where

$$N_c = \frac{k\rho_w g}{\sigma}\frac{\Delta H}{\Delta\ell} \quad . \tag{3.36}$$

Wilson and Conrad (1984) reported that residual phase can begin to be mobilized at $N_c \sim 2 \times 10^{-5}$ and that practically all residual becomes mobilized at $N_c \sim 1.3 \times 10^{-3}$. These values can be used to conclude that the hydraulic gradients required to mobilize significant quantities of residual DNAPL in most types of porous media are **unachievably large**.

3.6 DISTRIBUTION OF DNAPL IN UNSTEADY, HORIZONTAL FLOWS

3.6.1 General

The simultaneous, horizontal flow of water and DNAPL is discussed in this section. The design and performance assessment of well and drain fields intended for the recovery of pooled DNAPL is one application of the type of analysis presented here. However, such applications are not yet fully developed and remain an area of active research. Analyses of the type discussed in this section have also found use for the verification of numerical models. Because the flows discussed in this section are **unsteady**, their analysis is substantially more complicated than for the problems of fluid statics and steady flow discussed above. The capillary pressure-saturation function, relative permeabilities, and Darcy's Law remain applicable, but now two additional equations are required. These equations express the conservation of mass for water and DNAPL.

3.6.2 The Differential Equations for Two-Fluid Flow

The mathematical basis for the calculation of the simultaneous flow of DNAPL and water in an aquifer is completed by the introduction of the relevant conservation laws. A conservation law for each fluid, together with the flux equations of Section 3.4, result in two strongly coupled partial differential equations. Considering the relations $P_c(S_w)$, $k_{rw}(S_w)$, $k_{rnw}(S_w)$, and the identity $S_w + S_{nw} = 1$, the mathematical statement consists of eight equations and eight unknowns. These must be solved simultaneously subject to the appropriate boundary and initial conditions.

In the present development, both the DNAPL and water are considered to be incompressible and the porous medium is regarded as rigid. Furthermore, it is assumed that DNAPL solubility is slight such that component partitioning across phase boundaries can be neglected. Under these conditions, the conservation laws are

$$\frac{\partial q_{wi}}{\partial x_i} = -\Phi \frac{\partial S_w}{\partial t} \quad , \quad i = 1, \ 2, \ 3, \tag{3.37}$$

and

$$\frac{\partial q_{nwi}}{\partial x_i} = -\Phi \frac{\partial S_{nw}}{\partial t} \quad , \quad i = 1, \ 2, \ 3. \tag{3.38}$$

As before, the repeated index i implies a summation over all i.

The left sides of these equations represents the divergence of the fluid flux and consists of three terms in each case. Explicit reference to the fluid fluxes is eliminated by simply combining the conservation laws with the fluxes given by Eqs.(3.21) and (3.22). For example, by combining Eqs.(3.21) and (3.37), one obtains

$$\frac{\partial}{\partial x_i} \left[\frac{k_{ij}k_{rw}}{\mu_w} \left(\frac{\partial P_w}{\partial x_j} - \rho_w g_j \right) \right] = \Phi \frac{\partial S_w}{\partial t} \quad . \tag{3.39}$$

An identical result with the subscript w replaced by nw is obtained from Eqs.(3.22) and (3.38). These results are supplemented by the auxiliary relations $P_c = P_{nw} - P_w$, $P_c(S_w)$, $k_{rw}(S_w)$, $k_{rnw}(S_w)$, and $S_w + S_{nw} = 1$.

Addition of Eqs.(3.17) and (3.18) yields

$$\frac{\partial}{\partial x_i}(q_{wi} + q_{nwi}) = 0 \quad , \tag{3.40}$$

which requires that the sum $q_{wi} + q_{nwi}$ be space invariant. This can be thought of as the conservation law for the combined fluid system. The quantity $q_w + q_{nw}$ is known as the **total volume flux**, q_t, and is at most a function of time. Any time dependency in q_t must derive from the boundary conditions imposed on the solution domain.

While perhaps not apparent upon casual inspection, all of the problems analyzed so far in this chapter are special cases of the above general flow equations. Specialization for horizontal, unsteady flow is accomplished by eliminating the terms involving gravity. The general differential equations reduce to (Fokas and Yortsos, 1982; McWhorter and Sunada, 1990):

$$\frac{\partial}{\partial x}\left(D\frac{\partial S_w}{\partial x}\right) - q_t d\frac{f}{dS_w}\frac{\partial S_w}{\partial x} = \Phi\frac{\partial S_w}{\partial t} \quad , \tag{3.41}$$

wherein

$$f(S_w) = \left(1 + \frac{k_{rnw}\mu_w}{k_{rw}\mu_{nw}}\right)^{-1} \quad , \tag{3.42}$$

$$D(S_w) = -\frac{kk_{rnw}f}{\mu_{nw}}\frac{dP_c}{dS_w} \quad , \tag{3.43}$$

$$q(t) = q_w(x,t) + q_{nw}(x,t) \quad . \tag{3.44}$$

Eq.(3.41) is written with the water saturation as the dependent variable. It can be written, also, with DNAPL saturation or capillary pressure as the dependent variable.

The total flux q_t must be prescribed (known) or, alternatively, calculated from the boundary conditions. In the latter case, the required formula is

$$q_t(t) = \frac{P_w(0) - P_w(L) - \int_{P_c(0)}^{P_c(L)}(1-f)dP_c}{\int_0^L\left(\frac{k_w}{\mu_w} + \frac{k_{nw}}{\mu_{nw}}\right)^{-1}dx} \quad , \tag{3.45}$$

where L is the length of the flow domain, $P_w(0)$ is the water pressure at $x = 0$, $P_w(L)$ is the water pressure at $x = L$, and $P_c(0)$ and $P_c(L)$ are the corresponding capillary pressures. The derivation of Eq.(3.45) proceeds by substituting Darcy's Law into Eq.(3.44) and integrating the result over the flow domain (Morel-Seytoux and Khanji, 1974). Evaluation of the denominator in Eq.(3.45) requires knowledge of the saturation distribution because both k_w and k_{nw} depend upon S_w. Thus, Eqs.(3.41) and (3.45) must be solved simultaneously.

3.6.3 The Buckley-Leverett Solution

The classical solution for unsteady, horizontal flow was presented by Buckley and Leverett (1942). These authors were interested in the calculation of oil displacement by injection of water. Buckley and Leverett (1942) recognized that when the injection rate is large, the second term in Eq.(3.41) is dominant. They neglected the second order term and solved the resulting first-order, partial differential equation to obtain

$$x(S_w,t) = \frac{f'}{\Phi}\int_0^t q_t(\tau)d\tau = \frac{f'V_w}{\Phi} \quad , \tag{3.46}$$

where f is the function defined by Eq.(3.42), $f' = df/dS_w$, V_w is the volume of water injected, and Φ is porosity. The quantity $x(S_w, t)$ denotes the coordinate of saturation S_w at time t.

The function f is typically S-shaped, so f' is not single valued. Eq.(3.46) thus predicts two different saturations for the same location x. This physically untenable result is circumvented by the Welge (1952) tangent construction in which f is replaced by the two part function:

$$f = \left(1 + \frac{k_{rnw}\mu_w}{k_{rw}\mu_{nw}}\right)^{-1} \quad , \quad S_w \geq S_b \quad , \tag{3.47a}$$

$$f = F(S_b)\left(\frac{S_w - S_i}{S_b - S_i}\right) \quad , \quad S_i \leq S_w \leq S_b \quad , \tag{3.47b}$$

where S_i is the uniform initial saturation. Accordingly, all saturations between S_i and S_b propagate at the same velocity given by $q_t f(S_b)/\Phi(S_b - S_i)$. This propagation is in the form of a **shock front** as shown in Figure 3.11 as the sudden drop in S_w at some distance x.

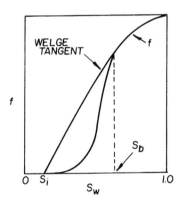

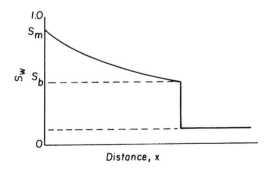

Figure 3.11   Buckley-Leverett profile.

The Buckley-Leverett solution is the limiting condition achieved when the impelling forces due to gradients of capillary pressure are negligible relative to the overall gradient of fluid pressure induced by fluid injection on the boundary. Morel-Seytoux (1969) presented a thorough discussion of the Buckley-Leverett analysis and demonstrated its use for oil recovery predictions. However, rarely will conditions of interest to hydrogeologists dealing with DNAPL problems be similar to those in which the Buckley-Leverett equation applies. Nevertheless, the Buckley-Leverett solution remains important for historical perspective and as a limiting case.

3.6.4 Lateral Migration of DNAPL

Eq.(3.41) is a highly nonlinear differential equation, and few exact solutions are available. Fokas and Yortsos (1982) have presented an exact closed-form solution subject to constant q_t and uniform initial saturation. Their solution was enabled by restricting $f(S_w)$ such that $f' = aD$ with $D = (bS_w + c)^{-2}$, and a, b, and c are arbitrary constants. Unfortunately, these forms do not exhibit some of the important features of real porous media, and the resulting solutions are of limited use for the study of DNAPL invasion in aquifers.

Exact integral solutions for arbitrary $D(S_w)$ and $f(S_w)$ were derived by McWhorter and Sunada (1990) for 1-D and also for radial flows. Their solution for 1-D invasion of DNAPL into water saturated porous media is

$$x(S_w, t) = -\frac{V_{nw}}{\Phi} F'_{nw}(S_w) \quad , \tag{3.48}$$

where V_{nw} is the accumulated volume of DNAPL in the porous medium, $F'_{nw} = dF_{nw}/dS_w$, and the fractional-flow function F_{nw} is given by

$$F_{nw}(S_w) = 1 - \frac{\displaystyle\int_{S_w}^{S_o} \frac{(\beta - S_w)D(\beta)}{F_{nw}(\beta) - f_n(\beta)} d\beta}{\displaystyle\int_{1}^{S_o} \frac{(S_w - 1)D}{F_{nw} - f_n} dS_w} \quad , \tag{3.49}$$

where $f_n = 1 - f$. The saturation S_o is the water saturation on the inflow boundary (*i.e.*, at $x = 0$) and is constant. However, the value of S_o depends upon the prescribed value of A through the implicit relation

$$A^2 = \frac{\Phi}{2} \int_{1}^{S_o} \frac{(s_w - 1)D}{F_{nw} - f_n} dS_w \quad . \tag{3.50}$$

As before, x is the coordinate of saturation S_w at time t. Eq.(3.48) is exact if V_{nw} varies with time according to

$$V_{nw} = 2At^{1/2} \quad , \tag{3.51}$$

where A is an arbitrary constant.

While the solution as expressed in Eq.(3.48) is quite simple, the computation of F_{nw} from Eq.(3.49) is not a trivial matter. The computation proceeds by selecting a value for S_o and evaluating the integrals on the right side using $F_{nw} = 1$ as a first iteration. The result is a second estimate for $F_{nw}(S_w)$ which is again used on the right side to produce a third estimate of the fractional-flow function. The process is continued until convergence is achieved. The integration is accomplished by a suitable numerical procedure.

The solution outlined above is useful in the exploration of the factors affecting the extent and rate of lateral migration of a DNAPL. Figure 3.12 shows the fluid distributions calculated using Eqs.(3.8), (3.23), and (3.24) (a Brooks-Corey porous medium) and using Eqs.(3.9), (3.25), and (3.26) (a van Genuchten porous medium). It is evident that prescribing $S_o = 0.8$ for van Genuchten porous media with different values of m results in greatly different distributions of DNAPL. Penetration of DNAPL in a van Genuchten medium with uniform pore size (large m) is not nearly as great as for a wide distribution of pore size (small m). It is observed that the DNAPL tends to penetrate in **narrow elongated distributions**. The more blunt penetrations in Brooks-Corey media result because the ratio k_{rnw}/k_{rw} is much smaller at large S_w than in van Genuchten media.

The sensitivity of DNAPL penetration to the capillary-hydraulic properties is also revealed by computation of the injection constant A as a function of m with $S_o = $ constant. The results of such a computation are shown in Figure 3.13, indicating that the rate of DNAPL invasion ranges over an order of magnitude, depending upon the value of m. A small value of m results in a large value of A, other factors being equal.

Because the invasion of DNAPL into groundwater occurs in elongated distributions, the invasion of even small volumes can result in **extensive spreading**. Also, the rate of penetration given by $q_{nw}/\Phi S_{nw}$ is inordinately large owing to the small values of S_{nw}

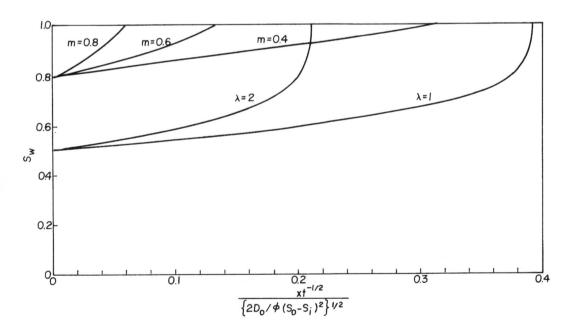

Figure 3.12 Penetration of a non-wetting phase affected by the pore-size distribution, with $\mu_w/\mu_{nw} = 2$.

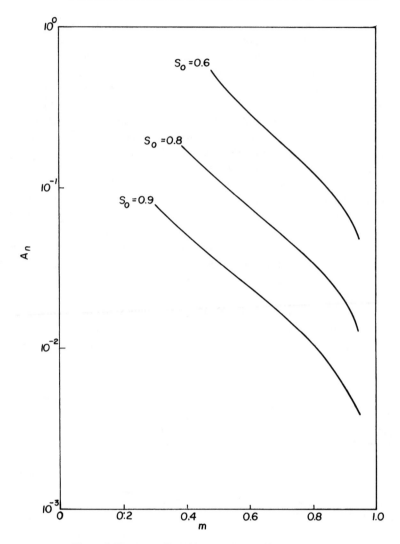

Figure 3.13 A_n as affected by m and S_o, with $\mu_w/\mu_{nw} = 2$.

that prevail. Both the rate and extent of penetration are greater in porous media with features that cause k_{rnw}/k_{rw} to be large near $S_w = 1$.

The remarkable sensitivity of DNAPL penetration to the capillary-hydraulic properties can be expected to result in **highly complex, seemingly chaotic**, saturation distributions in heterogeneous media. For example, consider a porous medium comprised of thin strata, each with different permeability, characteristic capillary pressure, and pore-size distribution. The penetration of DNAPL in the individual layers will differ greatly, much more so than would be the case for the penetration of a wetting phase. As noted above, DNAPL in thin laminae separated by intervals of DNAPL-free media have been observed in cores. The distribution of DNAPL determined by averaging the saturation across many such layers will appear especially diffuse.

3.6.5 Displacement of DNAPL by a Linear Water Flood

In the petroleum industry, the **injection of water** ("water flood") to force oil to recovery wells is a common practice. A similar process utilizing subsurface drains for the recovery of DNAPLs is described by Sale *et al.* (1988). One-dimensional displacement such as that described by Sale *et al.* (1988) can be analyzed with a mathematical solution for water invasion that closely parallels that given above for DNAPL invasion. Of particular interest is the recovery efficiency as indicated by the DNAPL fraction in the total produced fluid, and the cumulative volume of DNAPL recovered as a function of volume injected.

A solution of Eq.(3.41) presented by McWhorter and Sunada (1990) that forms a basis for analyzing the efficiency of a linear (1-D) water flood is

$$x(S_w, t) = \frac{V_w(1 - f_i)}{\Phi} F'_w(S_w) \quad, \tag{3.52}$$

where V_w is the volume of water injected. As before, the function $F'_w(S_w)$ is the derivative of $F_w(S_w)$ with respect to S_w where F_w is now defined as

$$F_w = \frac{q_w/q_t - f_i}{1 - f_i} \quad, \tag{3.53}$$

with $f_i = f(S_i)$ and S_i = the initial water saturation. The fractional flow function F_w is calculated by iteration using

$$F_w(S_w) = 1 - \frac{\displaystyle\int_{S_w}^{S_o} \frac{(\beta - S_w)D(\beta)}{F_w(\beta) - f_n(\beta)} d\beta}{\displaystyle\int_1^{S_o} \frac{(S_w - S_i)D}{F_w(\beta) - f_n(\beta)} dS_w} \quad, \tag{3.54}$$

with $f_n = (f - f_i)/(1 - f_i)$.

We consider an injection plane located a constant distance L from a recovery plane. The volume of DNAPL displaced across the recovery plane is

$$V_{nw} = \Phi \int_0^L (S_w - S_i) dx \quad. \tag{3.55}$$

Substituting Eq.(3.52) into Eq.(3.55) followed by an integration by parts eventually yields

$$\frac{V_{nw}}{\Phi(1 - S_i)L} = \left(\frac{V_w}{\Phi L}\right)\left(\frac{1 - f_i}{1 - S_i}\right)\left(1 + (S_w - S_i)F'_w - F_w\right) \quad, \tag{3.56}$$

in which it is understood that S_w is the water saturation at $x = L$. The volume of water injected is related implicitly to S_w at $x = L$ by

$$\frac{V_w}{\Phi L} = \frac{1}{(1 - f_i)F'_w(S_w)} \quad. \tag{3.57}$$

Finally, the fraction of DNAPL in the total produced fluid is obtained from a rearrangement of Eq.(3.53) so that

$$\frac{q_{nw}}{q_t} = (1 - f_i)(1 - F(S_w)) \quad . \tag{3.58}$$

Table 3.1 contains results of calculations obtained by the above procedure for the performance of a water flood. The functions $F_w(S_w)$ and $F'(S_w)$ were calculated as described in detail by McWhorter and Sunada (1990). The values of $V_w/(\Phi (1 - S_i) L)$ in Table 1 are the injected water volumes expressed as a fraction of the pore volume. The volume of DNAPL recovered as a fraction of the total volume initially present is $V_{nw}/(\Phi(1 - s_i)L)$. Recovery of 100% of the initial DNAPL will never be possible because of entrapment of some residual DNAPL by the invading water. The theoretically-recoverable volume per unit area is $\Phi(S_m - S_i)L$, where $S_m < 1$ because of the entrapped residual DNAPL.

TABLE 3.1   Performance of DNAPL Recovery by Water Flood. Input Data: $S_m = 0.90$; $S_i = 0.75$; $S_r = 0.2$; $m = 0.5$ in Eqs.(3.9), (3.25), and (3.26); $\mu_w/\mu_{nw} = 2$; residual DNAPL = $1 - S_m = 0.10$.

S_w	$F_w(S_w)$	$F'_w(S_w)$	$V_w/\Phi L$	$V_{nw}/\Phi(1-S_i)L$	q_{nw}/q_t
0.750	0	-	0	0	0.733
0.753	0.044	14.59	0.094	0.276	0.701
0.764	0.189	11.99	0.114	0.327	0.595
0.778	0.346	10.48	0.130	0.361	0.479
0.792	0.484	9.33	0.146	0.389	0.378
0.814	0.674	7.66	0.178	0.426	0.239
0.848	0.887	4.91	0.278	0.485	0.083
0.876	0.985	1.96	0.695	0.534	0.011
0.882	0.995	0.257	1.091	0.544	0.004

The data in Table 3.1 show that initially, the produced fluid contains about 73% DNAPL. However, by the time about one-third pore volume of water has been injected, the produced fluid contains less than 10% DNAPL. At one pore volume of injected water, the produced fluid contains less than 0.5 percent DNAPL. About 54% of the total DNAPL and about 90% of the theoretically-recoverable DNAPL have been recovered by injection of one pore volume of water. The ~10% of the theoretically recoverable DNAPL remaining is virtually unrecoverable because of the large injection volumes required to displace it. In other words, the displacement efficiency falls to essentially zero for injected volumes greater than one pore volume.

The performance of a water flood for the purposes of DNAPL recovery is rather sensitive to the pore-size distribution parameter m in Eqs.(3.9), (3.25), and (3.26). The sensitivity derives from the strong dependence of the relative-permeability ratio k_{rnw}/k_{rw} upon m. McWhorter and Sunada (1990) show that this ratio is about one order-of-magnitude greater for $m = 0.5$ than for $m = 0.8$ in the saturation range of relevance for

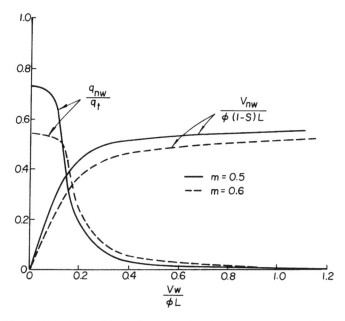

Figure 3.14   The sensitivity of water flood performance to pore-size distribution.

DNAPL recovery by water flood. Figure 3.14 depicts the substantial change in performance that is caused by increasing m from 0.5 to 0.6.

3.6.6 Displacement of DNAPL by Radial Water Flood

Injection of water through wells for the purpose of displacing DNAPL to recovery wells is an alternative to the 1-D water flood discussed above. Injection and recovery wells are easier to install and operate than are the horizontal drains required to effect 1-D displacements. The expected recovery efficiency under various operating conditions can be calculated as follows.

The water saturation at any radial distance, r, from an injection well is given by (McWhorter and Sunada, 1990)

$$r(S_w, t) = \left(\frac{Q_t(1 - f_i)}{\pi b \Phi} F_w'(S_w)t \right)^{1/2} \quad , \qquad (3.59)$$

in which Q_t is the injection rate at the well, b is the thickness of the injection zone, and the fractional flow function $F_w(S_w)$ is defined by

$$F_w = \frac{Q_w - f_i Q_t}{Q_t(1 - f_i)} \quad . \qquad (3.60)$$

The discharge of water across the lateral surface of a cylinder of radius r and height b is Q_w. The value of Q_w ranges from Q_t at the well to $f_i Q_t$ at large distances from the injection well. Thus, the fractional-flow function ranges from 0 to 1.

The fractional-flow function is calculated by iteration in

$$
F_w(S_w) = \frac{\int_{S_i}^{S} \exp\left(\frac{-4\pi b}{Q_t(1 - f_i)} \int_{S_i}^{\beta} \frac{D(\beta)}{F_w(\beta) - f_n(\beta)} dS_w\right) d\beta}{\int_{S_i}^{S_m} \exp\left(\frac{-4\pi b}{Q_t(1 - f_i) \int_{S_i}^{\beta} \frac{D(\beta)}{F_w(\beta) - f_n(\beta)} dS_w}\right) d\beta} .
\tag{3.61}
$$

As before, $f_n = (f - f_i)/(1 - f_i)$, f, and D are calculated from the capillary-hydraulic properties as indicated in Eqs.(3.42) and (3.43).

The above equations represent an exact solution for the differential equation that is Eq.(3.41) as modified for radial flow. The injection rate is a constant in this case. The volume of DNAPL V_{nw} that is displaced across a surface of radius R is calculated from

$$
\frac{V_{nw}}{\Phi(1 - S_i)\pi R^2 b} = \left(\frac{1 - f_i}{1 - S_i}\right)\left(\frac{V_w}{\Phi\pi R^2 b}\right)\left(1 + (S_w - S_i)F_w' - F_w\right) ,
\tag{3.62}
$$

with

$$
\frac{V_w}{\Phi\pi R^2 b} = \left[(1 - f_i)F_w'\right]^{-1} .
\tag{3.63}
$$

Again we have expressed the volume of displaced DNAPL as a fraction of the initial DNAPL volume, and the injected volume as a fraction of the pore volume. In this respect, Eqs.(3.62) and (3.63) are identical to Eqs.(3.56) and (3.57) for a 1-D water flood; the numerical values of F_w are different, of course, for the two cases.

The performances of two water floods conducted under identical conditions except for injection rate are represented in Figure 3.15. The dimensionless injection rates indicated on the figure refer to

$$
Q_n = \frac{Q_t(1 - f_i)\mu_w}{(S_m - S_i)kP_o} .
\tag{3.64}
$$

where k is the intrinsic permeability and P_o is a characteristic capillary pressure. The parameter Q_n has the physical significance of being the ratio of viscous forces to the capillary forces. It has been observed that water flood performs better when this ratio is large (*i.e.*, large injection rates).

For a given aquifer, the injection rate that can be achieved is dictated by the pressure difference between the injection and recovery wells and the well spacing. The relationship among these factors is given to a rough approximation by

$$
Q_t = \frac{2\pi kbk_{rw}(S_i)\Delta P}{\mu_w \ln(R/r_w)} ,
\tag{3.65}
$$

where $k_{rw}(S_i)$ is the relative permeability to water at the initial water saturation and ΔP is the pressure difference. The magnitude of ΔP, expressed as a height of water, will be on the order of the thickness of the DNAPL layer. One can then adjust the spacing R to achieve a target injection rate that will promote an efficient displacement process.

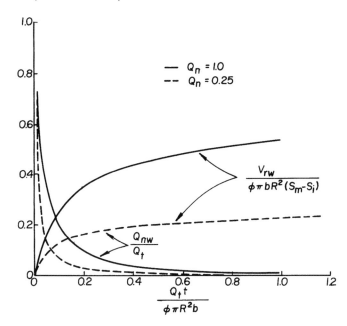

Figure 3.15   The performance of two radial water floods.

The above remarks include no consideration of costs. Small spacing will promote efficient displacement, but will cost more than a large spacing. A computation of performance with different values of R and an expression of cost as a function of R will permit the computation of a performance *vs.* cost curve. A decision on spacing that strikes a reasonable balance between performance and cost is then possible.

3.7 STABILITY OF TWO-FLUID DISPLACEMENTS

When a DNAPL penetrates the water table, water is displaced by a liquid which is denser and often less viscous than water. Such displacements give rise to a gravity and/or viscosity induced instability we have referred to as "fingering", and results in a chaotic and unpredictable propagation of the macroscopic interface separating the fluids of interest. Figure 3.16 illustrates the fingering process for the displacement of a more viscous liquid by a less viscous liquid. As shown, the originally planar interface separating the two liquids becomes increasingly distorted with travel distance. In general, the fingering process occurs whenever the displacement is characterized by an unfavorable density ratio such as the downward displacement of a light liquid by a heavier liquid, or the upward displacement of a heavy liquid by a lighter liquid, and in cases where the viscosity of the displacing fluid is less than that of the displaced fluid. In cases where one of either the density ratio or viscosity ratio is favorable and the other is not, a critical velocity determines whether or not the displacement will be stable.

It is generally accepted that the fingering process is triggered by microscopic heterogeneities such as those encountered at the pore scale. Studies illustrate that the spacing

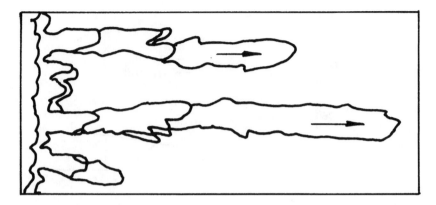

Figure 3.16   Fingering in a Hele-Shaw cell. The initial planar interface originated at the left side of the cell. Shown are four subsequent locations of the advancing interface. (Reprinted with permission from Perkins and Johnston, 1969.)

of fingers evolving in homogeneous media is a function of the porous medium properties, the fluid properties, and the velocity of the advancing interface. The fingering model, first introduced by Chuoke *et al.* (1959), assumes that the medium through which the fluids are moving is perfectly homogeneous. This may well be approximated in the laboratory, but in the field such media rarely exist. Within heterogeneous media, macroscopically planar interfaces will not exist between the fluids of concern. Stability analyses yielding optimum wavelengths of finger initiation will be invalid since heterogeneous media do not provide an infinite number of wavelengths from which to initiate fingering. Fingering will simply be initiated in the most permeable regions which exhibit the least resistance to the advancing front.

Exactly what degree of permeability variation is required to invalidate the homogeneous instability model is unclear, but experiments (Gupta *et al.*, 1973; Schwille, 1988) seem to indicate that it is very slight. If the porous medium of interest has macroscopic heterogeneities of a length scale equal to or less than the scale of the critical wavelengths required to initiate fingering, then no fingering by definition actually takes place. The highly irregular fluid distributions that result are due to local permeability variations, and should perhaps be termed **channeling** to distinguish them from similar fluid distributions that can arise in theoretically homogeneous media.

It should be noted that situations may occur where gravity- and viscosity-induced instabilities dominate over the influence of heterogeneity in determining the migration pathways of an immiscible contaminant. One such situation involves the case of low or negligible interfacial tension. Under such conditions, for a given set of fluid parameters and flow conditions, it would be expected that there will be a threshold degree of heterogeneity characterized by the variance and structure of the permeability field below which the fingering process dominates. Also, in situations where the fluid properties of interest and the prevailing flow conditions bring about a fingering wavelength below the scale of heterogeneity present, then the fingering process may be influential in determining the fate of an immiscible contaminant. One such situation may arise in a stratified porous medium having individual beds of a much larger horizontal extent than vertical extent. In such a case a great deal of lateral flow may occur above finer grained lenses, and this flow process would be subject to viscosity-induced instability along the plane of bedding. The fingering process is described further by Kueper and Frind (1988).

In this chapter we have assumed that interfacial tension forces are not negligible and that the length scale of heterogeneity in the porous medium of interest is on the order of the wavelengths of fingering. This allows use of the governing equations presented without modification to account for possible fluid instabilities. In practice, it is likely that the effects of heterogeneity will dominate the fate of DNAPL in field situations. When performing laboratory experiments in homogeneous media, however, explicit account of possible fluid instability should be taken.

3.8 CONCLUSIONS

The displacement of groundwater in the pores of an aquifer by an invading DNAPL can never be accomplished completely by physical means alone: unless there is enough DNAPL to allow all of the residual water to dissolve into that DNAPL, water and DNAPL will coexist in the interstitial pore space where DNAPL is present. The volumes of DNAPL and water present in the aquifer per unit of pore volume is characterized by the empirical capillary-pressure curve for the medium. This relationship is of fundamental importance to understanding and quantifying the movement and distribution of DNAPLs in aquifer systems.

A threshold capillary pressure, termed the entry pressure, must be attained for a DNAPL to become continuous and capable of flow through a porous medium that is otherwise saturated with water. The entry pressure is highly variable in heterogeneous aquifers, and results in seemingly-chaotic patterns of flow, as well as randomly-distributed pools and trails of residual DNAPL. A pool will form on top of a textural discontinuity when the capillary pressure is insufficient to exceed the entry pressure of the next material encountered. The thickness of a DNAPL pool required to initiate penetration of an obstructing stratum is inversely proportional to the buoyant density of the DNAPL. Fluids with densities near that of water are likely to form thick pools. The relative rarity of thick pools of chlorinated solvents is explained by the fact that even thin pools of these very dense liquids can result in significant capillary pressure.

Analyses of flow problems involving DNAPL are based on Darcy's Law written for each fluid. The permeability to the individual fluids is a strong function of the fluid contents, and therefore of the capillary pressures. Forces acting to cause DNAPL flow can be expressed in terms of the familiar gradient hydraulic head in the aqueous phase, the gradient of capillary pressure, and the buoyant density of the DNAPL. This approach for expressing the driving forces on a DNAPL phase leads to a particularly simple and general expression of the conditions under which upward hydraulic gradients in groundwater are sufficient to halt the downward migration of DNAPL that would otherwise occur. The same concept sets out the conditions under which a static DNAPL ganglion may be mobilized by modifying the gradient in the groundwater.

Calculation of unsteady flow of DNAPL can show the remarkable sensitivity of such flow to the capillary-hydraulic properties of the porous medium. Even in the idealized case of a perfectly homogeneous medium, DNAPL can be expected to penetrate in the form of narrow, elongated distributions in which the mean saturation of DNAPL is small. The result is that even small volumes of DNAPL can be expected to result in extensive spreading. Also, the small DNAPL saturation behind the advancing front results in large DNAPL seepage velocities. This, in combination with a large density and low viscosity, can cause rapid DNAPL migration.

ACKNOWLEDGEMENTS

Funding support for this research was provided in part by the University Consortium Solvents-in-Groundwater Research Program. Sponsors of the Program between 1988 and 1994 have included: The Boeing Company, Ciba-Geigy Corporation, Dow Chemical Canada/USA, Eastman Kodak Co., General Electric Co., Laidlaw Environmental Systems Ltd., Mitre Corporation, The Natural Sciences and Engineering Research Council of Canada, and the Ontario University Research Incentive Fund.

3.9 REFERENCES

Adam, N. K. (1968) *The Physics and Chemistry of Surfaces*, Dover Publications, N.Y., Unabridged and corrected republication of the third (1941) edition.

Anderson, M. R. (1988) *The Dissolution and Transport of Dense Nonaqueous Phase Liquids In Saturated Porous Media*, Ph.D. Thesis, Oregon Graduate Institute, Portland, Oregon.

Anderson, W. G. (1986) "Wettability literature survey. Wettability measurements', *J. Petrol. Technol.*, **38**, 1246-1262.

Arthur D. Little, Inc. (1982) *Capillary Pressure and its Effect on Non-Aqueous Phase Liquid Migration and Containment*. Report to Wald, Harkrader & Ross, Washington, D.C., prepared for the Environmental Protection Agency by Arthur D. Little, Cambridge, Massachusetts, March.

Buckley, S. E. and M. C. Leverett (1942) "Mechanism of fluid displacement in sands", *Trans. AIME*, **146**, 107-116.

Burdine, N. T. (1953) "Relative permeability calculations from pore-size distribution data", *Trans. AIME*, **198**, 71-77.

Brooks, R. H. and A. T. Corey (1966) "Properties of porous media affecting fluid flow", *J. Irrig. Drain. Div., Am. Soc. Civil Eng.*, **92**, 61-88.

Chatzis, I. and F. A. Dullien (1983) "Dynamic immiscible displacement mechanisms in pore doublets: theory *vs.* experiment", *J. Colloid and Interface Sci.*, **91**, 199-222.

Chuoke, R. L., P. van Meurs, and C. van der Poel (1959) "The instability of slow, immiscible, viscous liquid-liquid displacements in permeable media", *Trans. AIME*, **216**, 188-194.

Corey, A. T. (1986) *Mechanics of Immiscible Fluids In Porous Media*, Water Resources Publications, Littleton, Colorado, 259 p.

Fokas, A. S. and Y. C. Yortsos (1982) "On the exactly solvable equation occurring in two-phase flow in porous media. *SIAM J. Appl. Math.*, **42**, 318-332.

Gupta, S. P., J. E. Varnon, and R. A. Greenkorn (1973) "Viscous finger wavelength degeneration in Hele-Shaw models", *Water Resources Research*, **9**, 1039-1046.

Honarpour, M. and S. M. Mahmood (1988) "Relative permeability measurements: an overview", *J. Petrol. Technol.*, **40**, 903-966.

Hubbert, M. K. (1940) "The theory of groundwater motion", *J. Geology*, **48**, 785-943.

Hunt, J. R., N. Sitar, and K. S. Udell (1988) "Non-aqueous phase liquid transport and cleanup 1. Analysis of mechanisms", *Water Resources Research*, **24**, 1247-1258.

Johnson, E. F., D. P. Bossler, and V. O. Nauman (1959) "Calculations of relative permeability from displacement experiments", *Trans. AIME*, **216**, 370-372.

Jones, S. C. and W. O. Roszelle (1978) "Graphical techniques for determining relative permeability from displacement experiments", Society of Petroleum Engineers, 6045, SPE-AIME Meeting, New Orleans, Oct. 3-6.

Kueper, B. H. and E. O. Frind (1988) "An overview of immiscible fingering in porous media", *J. Contaminant Hydrology*, **2**, 95-110.

Kueper, B. H. (1989) *The Behaviour of Dense, Non-Aqueous Phase Liquid Contaminants in Heterogeneous Porous Media*, Ph.D. Thesis, University of Waterloo, Waterloo, Ontario.

Kueper, B. H. and E. O. Frind (1991a) "Two-phase flow in heterogeneous porous media, 1. Model development", *Water Resources Research*, **27**, 1049-1057.

Kueper, B. H. and E. O. Frind (1991b) "Two-phase flow in heterogeneous porous media, 2. Model application", *Water Resources Research*, **27**, 1059-1070.

Kueper, B. H., D. Redman, R. C. Starr, and S. Reitsma (1993) "A field experiment to study the behaviour of tetrachloroethylene below the water table, *Ground Water*, **31**, 756-766.

Laliberte, G. E., R. H. Brooks, and A. T. Corey (1968) "Permeability calculated from desaturation data", *J. Irrig. and Drainage Div., Am. Soc. Civil Eng.*, **94**, Proc. Paper 5843, 57-71.

Leverett, M. C. (1941) "Capillary behavior in porous solids", *Trans. AIME*, **142**, 152-169.

Luckner, L., M.Th. van Genuchten, and D. R. Nielsen (1989) "A consistent set of parametric models for the two-phase flow of immiscible fluids in the subsurface", *Water Resources Research*, **25**, 2187-2193.

Mualem, Y. (1976) "A new model for predicting the hydraulic conductivity of unsaturated porous media", *Water Resources Research*, **12**, 513-522.

McWhorter, D. B. and D. K. Sunada (1990) "Exact integral solutions for two-phase flow", *Water Resources Research*, **26**, 399-413.

McWhorter, D. B. and J. D. Nelson (1980) "Seepage in the partially saturated zone beneath tailings impoundments", *Mining Eng.*, April, 432-439.

Mercer, J. W. and Cohen, R. M. (1990) "A review of immiscible fluids in the subsurface: properties, models, characterization and remediation", *J. Contaminant Hydrology*, **6**, 107-163.

Mohanty, K. K., H. T. Davis, and L. E. Scriven (1987) Physics of oil entrapment in water-wet rock", *Society of Petrol. Engineers, Reservoir Eng.*, **2**, 113-128.

Morel-Seytoux, H. J. (1969) "Introduction to flow of immiscible liquids in porous media in flow through porous media". Chapter 11 in *Flow Through Porous Media*, R. J. M. de Wiest (Ed.), Academic Press, New York, New York, pp. 456-516.

Morel-Seytoux, H. J. and J. Khanji (1974) "Derivation of an equation of infiltration", *Water Resources Research*, **10**, 795-800.

Parker, J. C., R. J. Lenhard, and T. Kuppansamy (1987) "A parametric model for constitutive properties governing multiphase flow in porous media", *Water Resources Research*, **23**, 618-624.

Perkins, T. K. and O. C. Johnston (1969) "A study of immiscible fingering in linear models", *Soc. Petrol. Eng. J.*, March, 39-46.

Poulsen, M. and Kueper, B. H. (1992) "A field experiment to study the behaviour of tetrachloroethylene in unsaturated porous media", *Environ. Sci. Technol.*, **26**, 889-895.

Sale, T., D. Steib, K. Piontek, and R. Kuhn (1988) "Recovery of wood-treating oils from an alluvial aquifer using dual drainlines". In: *Proceedings: Conference on Petroleum Hydrocarbons and Organic Chemicals in Ground Water: Prevention, Detection and Restoration*, National Water Well Assoc./American Petroleum Institute, Nov. 9-11, Houston, Texas.

Schwille, F. (1988) *Dense Chlorinated Solvents In Porous and Fractured Media - Model Experiments*, translated by J. F. Pankow, Lewis Publishers Inc., Boca Raton, Florida.

Sigmund, P. M. and F. G. McCaffery (1979) "An improved unsteady-state procedure for determining the relative permeability characteristics of heterogeneous porous media", *Soc. Petrol. Eng., Journal*, **19**, 15-28.

Stegmeir, G. L. (1974) "Relationship of trapped oil saturation to petrophysical properties of porous media", Society of Petroleum Engineers, 4754, Improved Oil Recovery Symposium, Tulsa, Oklahoma, April.

Thomas, L. K., D. L. Katz and M. R. Tek (1968) "Threshold pressure phenomena in porous media", *Soc. Petrol. Eng. J.*, **8**, 174-184.

van Genuchten, M. Th. (1980) "A closed-form equation for predicting the hydraulic conductivity of unsaturated soils", *Soil Sci. Soc. Am. J.*, **44**, 892-898.

Villaume, J. F. (1985) "Investigations at sites contaminated with dense nonaqueous phase liquids", *Ground Water Monitoring Review*, **5**, 60-75.

Welge, H. J. (1952) "A simplified method for computing oil recovery by gas or water drive", *Trans. AIME*, **195**, 91-98.

Wilson, J. L. and S. H. Conrad (1984) "Is physical displacement of residual hydrocarbons a realistic possibility in aquifer restoration?". In: *Proceedings: NWAA/API Conference on Petroleum Hydrocarbons and Organic Chemicals In Groundwater*, Houston, Texas, National Water Well Association, Worthington, Ohio, pp. 274-298.

4

Numerical Simulation of the Migration of Dense Non-Aqueous Phase Liquids (DNAPLs) in Porous Media

Bernard H. Kueper[1] and Emil O. Frind[2]

[1]Department of Civil Engineering
Queen's University Kingston, Ontario, Canada K7L 3N6

[2]Waterloo Centre for Groundwater Research
University of Waterloo, Waterloo, Ontario, Canada N2L 3G1

ABSTRACT

Numerical models provide an essential tool for decision making, assessment, and design of remediation systems at hazardous waste sites. The steps of the modeling process, from conceptual design to modeling implementation are described including examples and a case history. The reliability and usefulness of model results are dependent upon the degree of site characterization. In most cases, a single, site-specific prediction cannot be obtained, but rather an envelope of possible behavior.

4.1 INTRODUCTION

Upon release at the ground surface, a **dense non-aqueous phase liquid (DNAPL)** will migrate through the subsurface according to a variety of complex and inter-related processes. In both saturated and unsaturated deposits, a DNAPL can distribute itself in **"residual"** form as disconnected blobs and ganglia, and also as larger accumulations referred to as pools. Residual DNAPL is formed at the trailing edge of a migrating DNAPL body due to pore-scale snap-off and trapping mechanisms, and is extremely difficult to displace by hydraulic means alone (see Chapter 3). DNAPL pools, on the other hand, form on top of capillary barriers and are relatively easily mobilized through either manipulation of hydraulic gradients, or by a lowering of the DNAPL/water interfacial tension. It is known that the migration pathways of DNAPL are governed primarily by **heterogeneity** and porous media structure, with subtle variations in permeability capable of causing significant degrees of lateral spreading, and migration patterns which are both sparse and tortuous.

Below the water table, residual and pooled DNAPL will slowly **dissolve** into flowing groundwater, giving rise to evolving plumes of contaminated groundwater. The magnitude of the concentrations arising in these plumes is a function of the chemical composition of the DNAPL phase, as well as the degree of surface area available for interphase mass transfer. It is known that residual and pooled DNAPL may not always be directly accessible to flowing groundwater, in which case the dissolution process becomes **diffusion limited**. This results in an inherently slow mass transfer process, and is often the cause of the well-known **tailing** phenomenon observed in remediation efforts. Above the water table, residual and pooled DNAPL will lead to the evolution of a vapor plume, which can in turn transfer contaminants directly to the water table, or to infiltrating water. In cases where DNAPL is trapped in layers of high water content, or in fine-grained material, the transfer of components to the air phase may also be diffusion controlled.

The above processes can be described through **numerical simulation**. A numerical model is a tool that allows integration of all the processes which are relevant in a given situation, and allows analysis of the behavior of a system under a wide range of conditions. Since field experimentation with hazardous immiscible liquids is prohibited by law in many regulatory jurisdictions, numerical modeling may offer the only means of gaining insight into field-scale processes and remedial actions at real sites. Some parameters, such as field-scale dispersivities and mass transfer coefficients, are difficult to measure directly and must be determined by fitting field data to models. Also, through the use of a numerical model, a variety of "what if" scenarios and worst case conditions can be examined for a particular system. Individual processes can be turned on and off to determine their importance. Moreover, by means of **Monte Carlo** methods and similar statistical approaches, the uncertainty associated with a given event can be estimated.

The understanding which can be gained from modeling can assist in anticipating the consequences of a spill, and can help judge the prospect of being able to clean it up. Modeling, by virtue of the integrated insight it provides, can be an important component of the overall regulatory, environmental, economic, and political decision making process at a particular site.

4.2 THE MODELING PROCESS

The modeling process begins by defining the modeling **objectives**. The specific objectives to be met will be site specific and may seek to answer one or more of the following questions:

- What is the relative importance of the various processes and parameters?
- What are the possible worst-case scenarios?

- What are the possible migration paths and travel times of contaminants?
- What are the arrival curves of contaminant concentration at critical points under various scenarios?
- Will the contaminant be cleaned up in a reasonable time frame by natural processes alone?
- How effective will remediation efforts be in cleaning up the aquifer, and could attempts at remediation actually worsen the extent of contamination?

Once the modeling objectives have been clearly identified, a **conceptual model** must be formulated. A conceptual model is an idealization of the real system incorporating the relevant processes and degree of coupling required between these processes. The underlying assumptions for including certain processes and excluding others should be carefully considered and the implications of these assumptions should be fully understood by the model user. For example, if the tailing associated with a soil vacuum extraction system is of interest, then the possible presence of low permeability lenses and DNAPL in zones of high water content must be incorporated; conceptualizing such a site as a homogeneous domain would be inappropriate.

The conceptual model underlying a given numerical model incorporates information on the extent, configuration, variability, and properties of both the contaminant and the hydrogeological units. This information is obtained from field investigations, and must be of sufficient quality and quantity so that a valid conceptual model can be formulated. The conceptual model determines what spatial dimensions are necessary to meet the modeling objectives. Since all real sites are three-dimensional and a DNAPL can spread in three dimensions, a 3D model will in almost all cases provide the most complete representation. However, 3D models are expensive to operate, and it is therefore desirable to choose the fewest dimensions that will satisfy the stated objectives. A model incorporating DNAPL migration, for example, should always include the vertical dimension to account for the action of gravity. Complex aquifers and a desire to study the influence of small-scale heterogeneity will require a full 3D model. If the spill in question is small and the aquifer is relatively homogeneous, a 2D axisymmetric model including the radial and vertical dimensions may suffice. Similarly, to simulate the overall migration of a plume of *dissolved* DNAPL in a thin confined aquifer, a 2D plane model may be adequate.

The time scale of the various processes of interest must also be considered in the selection of an appropriate conceptual model. At many sites, downward DNAPL migration and the formation of residual and pooled DNAPL may take place within days or months, while the dissolution process may carry on for decades and possibly centuries. In such situations it would be appropriate to decouple the migration of the immiscible phase from the evolution of a dissolved plume, with a separate numerical model used to describe each. The decoupling of processes will, in virtually all cases, greatly simplify the modeling effort, leading to cost savings.

Once a conceptual model has been formulated, a **mathematical model** must be created. At this step, physical processes are formulated in the form of a boundary value problem which comprises the governing partial differential equations, relevant constitutive relationships, material properties, boundary conditions, and initial conditions. In the most general case, the equations governing the migration of DNAPL, air, and water, subject to mass transfer across phase boundaries, can be assembled from the following mass balance equation for chemical component k in phase α:

$$\frac{\partial}{\partial t}(\varepsilon_\alpha \rho_\alpha \omega_k^\alpha) + \frac{\partial}{\partial x_i}(\varepsilon_\alpha \rho_\alpha \omega_k^\alpha v_{\alpha,i}) - \frac{\partial}{\partial x_i} J_{k,i}^\alpha = I_k^\alpha + E_k^\alpha \quad , \qquad (4.1)$$

where ε_α is the fraction of bulk volume occupied by the α phase, ρ_α is the average mass density of the α phase, ω_k^α is the mass fraction of component k in the α phase, $v_{\alpha,i}$ is the velocity of the α phase in the i-th direction, $J_{k,i}^\alpha$ is the non-advective flux of k in the α phase in the i-th direction, I_k^α represents the transfer of k due to phase change and diffusion across phase boundaries, and E_k^α is the external supply of k to the α phase through biotic and abiotic transformations. It follows from Eq.(4.1) that the mass fractions within a given phase must sum to unity, $i.e.$,

$$\sum_{k=1}^{n} \omega_k^\alpha = 1 \quad , \qquad (4.2)$$

where n is the total number of components comprising phase α. It also follows that the fractional phase volumes sum to unity, $i.e.$,

$$\sum_{\alpha=1}^{N} \varepsilon_\alpha = 1 \quad , \qquad (4.3)$$

where N is the total number of phases, in the most general case being four (air, water, DNAPL, and solid). The following expresses the conservation of mass of a given component distributed amongst the phases:

$$\sum_{\alpha=1}^{N} I_k^\alpha = 1 \quad . \qquad (4.4)$$

Eq.(4.1) requires that the phase velocities, $v_{\alpha,i}$, be defined. For saturated groundwater flow these are usually obtained from **Darcy's Law**. Based on laboratory experiments performed in the petroleum industry (Wyckoff and Botset, 1936; Leverett, 1938), it has been suggested that Darcy's Law can be extended to DNAPL systems as well. Others (*e.g.* Allen, 1985) have shown that Darcy's Law can be extended to multiphase systems by considering a momentum balance for each phase of interest. Such studies show Darcy's Law to be valid if inertial effects are negligible and there is no transfer of momentum between phases. It appears that in most cases an extended form of Darcy's Law is applicable to DNAPL systems in order to define the phase velocities required in Eq.(4.1). Darcy's Law extended to multiphase systems may be expressed as

$$v_{\alpha,i} = -\frac{K_{i,j}^\alpha}{\varepsilon_\alpha}\left(\frac{\partial P_\alpha}{\partial x_j} + \rho_\alpha g \frac{\partial z}{\partial x_j}\right) \quad , \qquad (4.5)$$

where P_α is the pressure of the α phase, g is the gravitational constant, z the vertical direction, and $K_{i,j}^\alpha$ a second rank mobility tensor given by

$$K_{i,j}^\alpha = \frac{k_{i,j}k_{r,\alpha}}{\mu_\alpha} \quad , \tag{4.6}$$

where μ_α is the dynamic viscosity of the α phase, $k_{i,j}$ is a second rank intrinsic permeability tensor, and $k_{r,\alpha}$ the relative permeability to the α phase accounting for the reduction in permeability due to the presence of other phases.

Equation (4.1) requires that the non-advective flux vector, $J_{k,i}^\alpha$, be defined. This vector accounts for the molecular diffusion and mechanical dispersion of component k within a given phase. It is often assumed that both of these are **Fickian** in nature in which case the processes are additive leading to

$$J_{k,i}^\alpha = -\varepsilon_\alpha \tau_{\alpha,ij} D_o^{k,\alpha} \frac{\partial(\rho_\alpha \omega_k^\alpha)}{\partial x_j} - \varepsilon_\alpha D_{m,ij}^{k,\alpha} \frac{\partial(\rho_\alpha \omega_k^\alpha)}{\partial x_j} \quad , \tag{4.7}$$

where $\tau_{\alpha,ij}$ is a tensor of phase tortuosity coefficients, $D_o^{k,\alpha}$ is the free-solution molecular diffusion coefficient of k in α, and $D_{m,ij}^{k,\alpha}$ a mechanical dispersion tensor of k in α. The proper form of the mechanical dispersion tensor for a given scale of interest, flow conditions, and saturation distribution is not always obvious. For solute transport in groundwater, various forms of the dispersion tensor have been proposed as discussed by Bear (1972) and Gelhar (1986).

In order to complete the set of equations required to represent DNAPL migration in the subsurface, the various phase pressures must be coupled through **capillary pressure relationships**. For a general air-water-DNAPL system, the following capillary pressures can be defined:

$$P_C^{a,w}(S_a, S_w) = P_a - P_w \quad , \tag{4.8}$$

$$P_C^{a,n}(S_a, S_n) = P_a - P_n \quad , \tag{4.9}$$

$$P_C^{n,w}(S_n, S_w) = P_n - P_w \quad , \tag{4.10}$$

where the scripts a, n and w are taken to represent air, NAPL, and water, respectively. The phase saturations, S_α, are expressed as a fraction of pore space and are related to the phase volume fractions by $S_\alpha = \varepsilon_\alpha / \phi$ where ϕ is the porosity of the medium.

The relationships in Eqs.(4.8)-(4.10) are typically determined experimentally for the media and fluids of interest. It is known that these relationships vary spatially at real sites, often at the scale of centimeters (*e.g.* see Poulsen and Kueper, 1992). For the case of two-phase flow, various workers have proposed empirical relationships allowing a mathematical function to be fit to experimental data (*e.g.* Brooks and Corey, 1966; van Genuchten, 1980). Leverett (1941) presented a relationship demonstrating that capillary pressure curves can be scaled as functions of hydraulic conductivity and interfacial tension. The use of interfacial tensions to scale capillary pressure curves has also been demonstrated by Schiegg (1984) and Parker *et al.* (1987).

Where three fluid phases are present, it has been suggested that two-phase capillary pressure relationships can be used to approximate three-phase capillary pressures (*e.g.* Leverett, 1941). These studies assume that the total liquid saturation given by $S_T = S_N +$

S_W is a function of the air-DNAPL capillary pressure only, and that water saturation is a function of DNAPL-water capillary pressure only. This assumes that water is wetting with respect to DNAPL, and that DNAPL is wetting with respect to air. Although validated under certain specific flow conditions (*e.g.* Lenhard and Parker, 1988), the use of two-phase capillary pressure relationships to represent three-phase systems has not yet been experimentally validated for a wide set of flow conditions. Since most three-phase flow models available at the present time adopt this approximation, they should be used in three-phase flow situations with caution until further experimental validation is obtained.

As with the capillary pressure relations in Eqs.(4.8)-(4.10), the relative permeability relationships in Eq.(4.6) are path-dependent functions of fluid saturation that vary spatially at real sites. Because relative permeability curves are difficult to measure in practice, they are often predicted from measured capillary pressure data (*e.g.* Brooks and Corey, 1966). This is justified by recognizing that the distribution of pore and throat sizes which largely determine the shape of a capillary pressure curve also largely determine the nature of the relative permeability curve. In three-phase systems it has been demonstrated that water-relative permeability and air-relative permeability are dependent mostly on water and air saturation, respectively (*e.g.* see Leverett and Lewis, 1941). As a result, various methods have been proposed to predict three-phase relative permeabilities from two-phase data (e.g. Stone, 1970; Lenhard and Parker, 1987). As with capillary pressures, these extensions have been validated for selected flow conditions.

In cases where the transfer of components across phase boundaries is of interest, such as the vaporization of a DNAPL in the unsaturated zone, or DNAPL dissolution below the water table, it must be decided whether or not the mass transfer terms appearing in Eq.(4.1) will be treated on the basis of **local equilibrium**. The local equilibrium assumption assumes that the transfer of components between phases occurs *instantaneously* relative to the bulk phase flow rates. This implies that equilibrium mass fractions of components are uniformly distributed within all phases at all times. Commonly adopted equilibrium relations include Henry's Law for the partitioning of components between water and air, linear sorption isotherms for partitioning of components between water and solid phases, and Raoult's Law for partitioning from a multicomponent DNAPL phase to another phase.

For many situations, it is known that the local equilibrium assumption is not valid, in which case a **kinetic** (*i.e.*, rate-limited) approach must be adopted. These situations often occur when describing a particular process at the field scale; examples include the diffusion of components out of low permeability zones leading to tailing in soil vacuum extraction systems, and the dependence of solubilization on flow rate in a solubilizing surfactant flood.

Once a mathematical formulation has been arrived at for a given problem of interest, a solution technique must be used to solve the governing equations. Because the equations governing multiphase/multicomponent flow and transport are typically non-linear, and since material properties vary spatially, exact analytical solutions are available only for simplified cases. The majority of situations require that a **numerical solution** technique such as finite difference, finite element, or finite volume be employed. Numerical techniques require that the problem domain be discretized into a grid, with the governing equations approximated at the cells or nodes of the grid by means of algebraic equations which link the cells or nodes together. The unknowns of interest, such as DNAPL saturation or contaminant concentration, are then solved for at these node locations or cell centroids. Typical solution methods are described in textbooks such as Huyakorn and Pinder (1983).

In many situations of interest, an implicit, iterative solution scheme will be required to treat the non-linear nature of the governing equations. Typical non-linearities include the dependence of relative permeability and capillary pressure on fluid saturation, and the dependence of mass transfer rates on chemical concentration. In some systems the non-linearity of the governing equations may be weak, allowing a simple iterative or time-lagging scheme to be adopted. In other cases, such as the migration of a DNAPL, the governing equations can be highly non-linear, in which case a Newton-Raphson approach is usually adopted. Given a set of non-linear algebraic equations, $F(\mathbf{X}) = 0$, the Newton Raphson approach leads to a linearized matrix equation of the form

$$\frac{\partial F(\mathbf{X})^n}{\partial \mathbf{X}} \partial \mathbf{X} = -F(\mathbf{X})^n \quad , \tag{4.11}$$

where $\frac{\partial F(\mathbf{X})^n}{\partial \mathbf{X}}$ is a square matrix of Jacobian derivative terms, $F(\mathbf{X})^n$ is a vector of residual values, n the iteration level, and $\partial \mathbf{X}$ a vector of incremental unknowns given by:

$$\partial \mathbf{X} = \mathbf{X}^{n+1} - \mathbf{X}^n \tag{4.12}$$

where $\mathbf{X}$ is a vector of discrete unknowns. The algorithm in Eq.(4.11) is repeated until the residual vector has converged to within a prescribed tolerance.

The set of algebraic equations arising through the application of a numerical technique must be solved for each iteration and/or time step. The simplest matrix solution techniques involve the use of Gaussian elimination. For large sets of equations, direct solvers utilizing Gaussian elimination will be prohibitively slow and prone to machine round-off errors. Computer storage may also be a problem. Iterative solvers have been shown to be more efficient at solving large sets of equations, and offer an additional advantage that only the bands of non-zero elements of the coefficient matrix need to be stored in memory. Letniowski (1989) gives an excellent review of preconditioned iterative methods for solving sparse matrix equations.

Once a numerical solution technique has been applied to discretize the governing partial differential equations, a **computational algorithm** is created by transposing the numerical technique into a computer code through the use of a chosen computer language. The resulting computer code is often referred to as "the model", but it should be clear from the preceding discussion that this is merely one stage of the overall modeling process.

In order to apply a given computer code to a site-specific situation, the user must decide upon an appropriate scale of nodal discretization. For example, if the individual migration pathways of DNAPL through heterogeneous sands is of interest, this may require discretization at the centimeter scale (*e.g.* Kueper and Frind, 1991b). In a three-dimensional model this may lead to the use of hundreds of thousands of nodal points, leading to an extremely CPU- and memory-intensive effort. In recent years there has been much attention given to the development of effective, large-scale parameters for multiphase/multicomponent flow and transport (*e.g.* Mantoglou and Gelhar, 1987; Kueper and McWhorter, 1992). These parameters would allow much coarser computational grids to be employed, but the resulting simulations would provide only the average behavior of the system. It is important to realize, however, that effective, large-scale parameters currently exist only for certain simplified situations. The unfortunate implication is that reliable field-scale numerical simulation of certain DNAPL processes can at the present time only be carried out using small-scale nodal discretization.

Figure 4.1 presents a numerical simulation of trichloroethylene (TCE) migration through a heterogeneous sand aquifer where small-scale variability of hydraulic conductivity has been accounted for (Gerhard, 1993). A total of 32,000 nodal points has been incorporated into the solution domain, with horizontal and vertical node spacings of 25 cm and 12.5 cm, respectively. A spatially correlated, random hydraulic conductivity field was generated using a log-normal distribution as input (mean $\ln(K) = -4.6$, variance $\ln(K) = 2.0$). An exponential autocorrelation function was assumed with horizontal and vertical correlation lengths of 5.0 m and 0.5 m, respectively. As can be seen, the TCE spreads laterally across various lower permeability horizons, with a significant degree of lateral spreading at the upper elevations. Simulations presented by Kueper *et al.* (1990) have demonstrated that the use of an equivalent homogeneous domain incorporating a large-scale hydraulic conductivity as might be obtained from a pump-test, does not yield the proper infiltration rates and degree of lateral spreading for point releases of this nature.

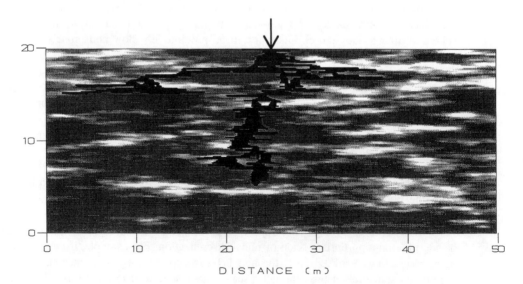

Figure 4.1   Trichloroethylene (TCE) migration through a heterogeneous sand aquifer from a point release. (Reproduced with permission from Gerhard (1993).)

Once a computer code has been created, it must be **verified** to confirm that the governing equations have been solved correctly and that the code is free of errors. Verification is carried out by running test problems and comparing results to those obtained independently with an exact method such as an analytical solution. Since analytical solutions are only available for idealized situations with simple boundary conditions, it is in general extremely difficult to completely verify a multiphase/multicomponent flow and transport model. A less stringent method of verification is to compare the results of a model with those of a previous, independently created numerical model. While there is still the possibility that both models are making the same errors, the exercise should nevertheless be carried out. Under no circumstances should a numerical model be used if it has not been at least partially verified against an analytical solution, or compared to the results of a previously published model.

Even if a computer code has been verified to ensure that the chosen numerical method has been properly implemented, it remains to be seen whether or not the governing equations upon which the model is based have been correctly formulated. To ensure this, the computer code should be **validated** through comparison to a controlled laboratory or field experiment. Validation is carried out by independently measuring all model input parameters and comparing the model output to that of the controlled experiment. This provides a complete check of not only whether the appropriate governing equations have been employed, but also whether adequate constitutive relationships and material property definition has been incorporated. From a strict scientific point of view, however, agreement of the model results with those from a given experiment simply implies that the model is capable of simulating that particular experiment. According to Konikow and Bredehoeft (1992), a computer model cannot be shown to be valid, it can only be shown to be invalid. This is a particularly important distinction where complex processes are concerned such as those associated with the behavior of a DNAPL in the subsurface. We recommend the use of the term "model testing" to avoid the misleading notion of unconditional validity and even infallibility.

Calibration involves fitting the model output to a set of observed data while adjusting the input. Once the input parameters have been adjusted to produce a satisfactory fit, these are deemed to be the proper input parameters so that the model can be used for predictive purposes. A pump test may be an opportunity to calibrate a groundwater flow model, for example, so that it can be used for future prediction of the performance of a full-scale pump-and-treat system. For complex situations where not all controlling input parameters can be obtained by independent measurement, model calibration may be the only practical way to obtain certain parameters such as dispersivity or a large-scale mass transfer coefficient. In theory, only one parameter should be fitted to a given set of data in order to obtain a unique solution. In practice, if different parameters affect the solution in distinctly different ways, more than one parameter can be fitted. The possibility of non-uniqueness, however, where more than one combination of parameters give an equally good fit, increases with the number of parameters fitted. It may be determined during the model calibration stage that additional field work is necessary to constrain certain input parameters in order to reduce the uncertainty associated with the model output.

4.3 MODEL USAGE

For the typical model user, the mathematical solution, numerical solution, computational algorithm, and verification steps of creating a model will have been completed by the model author. The task therefore simplifies to formulation of the conceptual model, the choice of proper scale and dimensionality, and the obvious task of selecting an appropriate computer code. **Model testing** will still be necessary to demonstrate that an appropriate model has been selected, and model calibration will in most cases be needed to determine uncertain parameters. It should be emphasized that the task of selecting an appropriate computer code can only be carried out successfully if the model user fully understands the mathematical formulation upon which the model is based. There are numerous assumptions and simplifications that can be implemented at the mathematical formulation stage, and one must carefully examine the final set of partial differential equations which are solved to determine exactly what physics the model represents.

Once an appropriate model has been selected, tested, and calibrated, the user is in the position to carry out a variety of tasks. For complex systems, the best way to understand the interaction and relevance of various processes is to carry out a **sensitivity analysis**. This involves varying key input parameters one at a time within a physically realistic range and observing the response of the model. The parameter ranges are usually known to the experienced hydrogeologist and in many cases may be narrowly defined. A sensitivity analysis is an excellent means of educating those involved with a particular site or class of contaminants, and is often the only "experimental" method available to gain insight into specific processes.

Once the calibration of a numerical model has been completed, in many cases the model can be used for **design** purposes. Examples may include selecting the number and location of pumping wells in a pump-and-treat remediation scenario, determining the hourly mass removal rate from a soil vacuum extraction system so that an above ground treatment system can be designed, or selecting the spacing and number of wells to use in a surfactant or alcohol flood designed to remove DNAPL. Whenever used for design purposes, however, it must be kept in mind that all model output is subject to uncertainty. A proper design exercise will involve producing a probable range of system behavior, with the final design having enough flexibility to accommodate the full range of possible system behavior.

In certain circumstances a numerical model can be run to examine a variety of "**what-if**" situations. An example may be the loss of capture in a pump-and-treat system upon failure of one well, or the rate at which a vapor plume will resume spreading upon accidental shut-down of a soil vacuum extraction system. A model can also be utilized to study the uncertainty associated with a given process. This is often done with a **Monte Carlo** analysis, which is simply a sensitivity analysis in which parameter values are selected at random from their respective ranges. The suite of model outputs can then be analyzed and described in statistical terms to yield the most probable behavior of the system, along with the uncertainty associated with that behavior.

Whenever a model is used for purposes of site specific prediction, it must be kept in mind that multiphase/multicomponent flow and transport models are highly sensitive to site-specific factors such as heterogeneities, the scale of discretization, and mass transfer parameters. In addition, it must be kept in mind that some controlling processes are still imperfectly understood. The possibilities for full validation at real sites are therefore limited. The prudent approach to numerical modeling at DNAPL sites is to utilize a numerical model for education purposes, and to produce a **range of possible system behavior** rather than one individual prediction that is claimed to be a perfect representation of site conditions.

4.4 EXAMPLE

To demonstrate the use of a DNAPL migration model, the two-phase flow model developed by Kueper and Frind (1991a,b) was utilized to examine the possible rates of DNAPL leakage from a waste lagoon located at Ville Mercier, Quebec. These lagoons were operational from 1968 through to 1972 and received a variety of oils, sludges and other debris (Poulin, 1977). Because exact records were not kept, it is unknown at present exactly how much DNAPL could have leaked out of the base of the lagoons, and at what rates. Figure 4.2 presents a vertical cross section through the site illustrating the subsurface conditions. As can be seen, the unlined lagoon was situated in a sand and gravel unit ($K = 5 \times 10^{-3}$ cm/s) underlain by a discontinuous upper silty sand till ($K = 1 \times 10^{-3}$ cm/s). This till is in turn underlain by a discontinuous basal till ($K = 1 \times 10^{-4}$ cm/s) situated above fractured bedrock. For the purposes of modeling, the lagoon was attributed a total area of 8,400 m^2. Examination of aerial photographs taken during the operating period of the lagoon suggests that this area is a minimum.

The specific objective of the modeling was to determine what possible rates of DNAPL leakage could have occurred through the base of the lagoon during the first two years of operation. The conceptual model assumed that DNAPL acted as a non-wetting liquid in the presence of water, and that DNAPL dissolution did not significantly influence leakage rates over the four year period of operation. It was also noted that the base of the lagoon was below the water table during the entire operating period. The migration process of interest was therefore DNAPL displacing water in the absence of mass transfer by dissolution. On the basis of site history, it was further conceptualized that the level of DNAPL in the lagoon was maintained at a relatively constant level over the four year period, but that a sludge layer built up with time. It was also decided that spatial variability of geological properties within each of the major lithologic units would not be influential in governing the overall rate of leakage since the size of the lagoon was large relative to the scale of heterogeneity.

The mathematical model required to simulate DNAPL displacing water in the absence of mass transfer is based on the following partial differential equations, which can be created by summing Eq.(4.1) over all components comprising a given phase:

$$\frac{\partial}{\partial x_i}\left(\frac{k_{i,j}k_{r,\alpha}}{\mu_\alpha}\left[\frac{\partial P_\alpha}{\partial x_j} - \rho_\alpha g \frac{\partial z}{\partial x_j}\right]\right) = \phi\frac{\partial S_\alpha}{\partial t}, \quad \alpha = w, n \qquad (4.13)$$

where the subscripts w and n denote water and DNAPL, respectively. The pair of equations represented by Eq.(4.13) are coupled through the capillary pressure relation

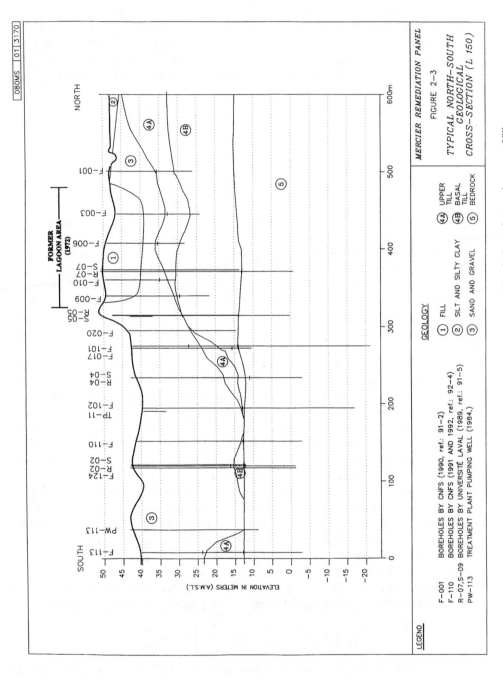

Figure 4.2 Vertical cross-section illustrating major geological units beneath waste lagoons at Ville

in Eq.(4.10) and are subject to the constraint that the two phase saturations sum to unity.

The finite difference model developed by Kueper and Frind (1991a) solves Eq.(4.13) fully implicitly using full Newton Raphson iteration. A sparse matrix solver based on the ORTHOMIN technique (Vinsome, 1976) is employed to minimize CPU time and computer storage requirements. The computational algorithm was created using the FORTRAN language, with all simulations carried out on an IBM 6000 Risc based workstation. As described in Kueper and Frind (1991a), the model was verified in one dimension against an exact analytical solution by McWhorter and Sunada (1989), and was tested through comparison with a controlled laboratory experiment (Kueper *et al.,* 1989) involving the migration of tetrachloroethylene through a heterogeneous sand pack.

For the modeling task under consideration here, all model input parameters were estimated from various previous studies completed at the site. These studies, as well as further details of the numerical modeling, are found in Mercier (1993). Although large amounts of data are available for many hydrological parameters, certain model input parameters such as DNAPL density, interfacial tension, and viscosity were not readily available. To account for this uncertainty, these properties were varied within expected ranges. In addition, the properties of the sludge layer across the lagoon bottom were not precisely defined, demanding that these also be varied over an expected range.

It was decided to adopt a two-dimensional vertical cross-section grid with vertical and horizontal nodal spacings of 1.0 m and 2.0 m, respectively. This resulted in adequate resolution of the geological features in Figure 4.2, and resulted in a total of 8,000 nodes in a 40 m high by 400 m wide solution domain. To account for the uncertainty in various input parameters, a total of 12 simulations were performed. Figure 4.3 presents both

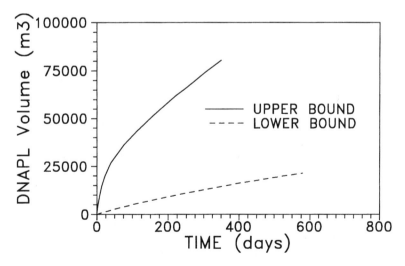

Figure 4.3   Maximum and minimum DNAPL leakage rates through base of lagoon estimated using numerical simulation. (Reproduced with permission from Mercier (1993).)

the maximum and minimum rates of leakage from this suite of simulations. The bottom curve in this figure represents a DNAPL having a density of 1100 kg/m^3, a viscosity of 0.050 Pa-sec, an interfacial tension of 0.045 N/m, and a 0.50 m accumulated DNAPL pool height. The upper curve represents a DNAPL having a density of 1300 kg/m^3, a viscosity of 0.002 Pa-sec, an interfacial tension of 0.015 N/m, and an accumulated DNAPL pool height of 0.50 m.

The overall conclusion of this modeling assignment was that the geological conditions beneath the lagoons at Mercier were such that **significant volumes of DNAPL likely escaped** the lagoon during its operating period. Additional simulations (not shown), however, have demonstrated that a silting of the lagoon bottom could have completely arrested DNAPL leakage after an initial period. Even with such silting, the initial infiltration rates were found to be significant. Further details of the modeling are presented in Mercier (1993).

4.5 CONCLUSIONS

Numerical modeling offers an **efficient and cost-effective** means of gaining insight into the various processes which govern multiphase/multicomponent flow and transport in a variety of geological environments. Used properly, modeling can be a useful component of the design and decision making process at most sites. In regulatory jurisdictions where it is prohibited by law to introduce contaminants into the subsurface for research purposes, numerical modeling may be the only experimental technique available to study and assess the behavior and clean-up of DNAPLs at the field scale.

The modeling process begins by clearly stating the modeling objectives. Following this, an appropriate conceptual model must be formed for the problem at hand. The conceptual model will include identification of the relevant physical and chemical processes, possible decoupling of time scales, a clear definition of the spatial scales and dimensionality required, and definition of relevant material and fluid properties. The conceptual model then leads to formulation of a mathematical model, which includes the governing partial differential equations, boundary conditions, and necessary constitutive relationships. Through the use of a numerical solution technique such as finite differences or finite elements, the governing equations are solved and a computational algorithm is created. This computer code must in turn be verified to ensure that the numerical solution technique has been properly implemented and tested to ensure that the governing partial differential equations have been selected properly.

Once a numerical model has been chosen, the model user will likely calibrate the model to a known set of data from a site in order that certain input parameters can be constrained. The model can then be used to perform sensitivity and uncertainty analyses, to assist in the design process, and to examine a variety of "what if" scenarios. While much can be gained from the proper use of a numerical model, it must be remembered that failing to pay attention to critical issues (*e.g.* the scale of discretization and the proper choice of input parameters) can result in a completely misleading interpretation of site conditions. This is particularly true for multiphase/multicomponent flow and transport modeling where the physical and chemical processes involved are an order of magnitude more complex than those associated with traditional groundwater flow and solute transport modeling.

ACKNOWLEDGEMENTS

Funding support for this research was provided in part by the University Consortium Solvents-in-Groundwater Research Program. Sponsors of the Program between 1988 and 1994 have included: The Boeing Company, Ciba-Geigy Corporation, Dow Chemical Canada/USA, Eastman Kodak Co., General Electric Co., Laidlaw Environmental Systems Ltd., Mitre Corporation, The Natural Sciences and Engineering Research Council of Canada, and the Ontario University Research Incentive Fund.

4.6 REFERENCES

Allen, M. B. (1985) "Numerical modelling of multiphase flow in porous media", *Advances in Water Resources*, **8**, 162-187.

Bear, J. (1972) *Dynamics of Fluids in Porous Media*, Elsevier, New York.

Brooks, R. H. and A. T. Corey (1966) "Properties of porous media affecting fluid flow", *Journal Irrigation Drainage Division, American Society of Civil Engineers*, **92** (IR2), 61-88.

Gelhar, L.W. (1986) "Stochastic subsurface hydrology form theory to applications", *Water Resources Research*, **22**, 135S-145S.

Gerhard, J. (1993) B.A.Sc. Thesis, Queen's University, Kingston, Ontario, Canada.

Huyakorn, P. S. and G. F. Pinder (1983) *Computational Methods in Subsurface Flow*, Academic Press.

Konikow, L. F. and Bredehoeft, J. D. (1992) "Groundwater models cannot be validated", *Advances in Water Resources*, **15**, 75-83.

Kueper, B. H., W. Abbot, and G. Farquhar (1989) "Experimental observations of multiphase flow in heterogeneous porous media", *Journal of Contaminant Hydrology*, **5**, 83-95.

Kueper, B. H. and E. O. Frind (1991a) "Two-phase flow in heterogeneous porous media, 1. Model development", Water Resources Research, **27**, 1049-1057.

Kueper, B. H. and E. O. Frind (1991b) "Two-phase flow in heterogeneous porous media, 2. Model application", *Water Resources Research*, **27**, 1059-1070.

Kueper, B. H., E. O. Frind, and D. B. McWhorter (1990) "Application of a numerical model and laboratory parameter measurement to the movement of dense, immiscible phase liquids in a heterogeneous sand aquifer", In: *Proceedings: IAH Conference on Subsurface Contamination by Immiscible Liquids*, Calgary, Alberta, April 18-20.

Kueper, B. H. and D. B. McWhorter (1992) "The use of macroscopic percolation theory to construct large-scale capillary pressure curves", *Water Resources Research*, **28**, 2425-2436.

Lenhard, R. J. and J. C. Parker (1987) "A model for hysteretic constitutive relations governing multiphase flow. 2: Permeability-saturation relations", *Water Resources Research*, **23**, 2197-2206.

Lenhard, R. J. and J. C. Parker (1988) "Experimental validation of the theory of extending two-phase saturation-pressure relations to three-phase systems for monotonic drainage paths", *Water Resources Research*, **24**, 373-380.

Letniowski, F. W. (1989) "An overview of preconditioned iterative methods for sparse matrix equations", Research report CS-89-26, Faculty of Mathematics, University of Waterloo, Waterloo, Ontario.

Leverett, M. C., (1938) "Flow of oil-water mixtures through unconsolidated sands", *Trans. A.I.M.E.*, **132**, 149-171.

Leverett, M. C. (1941) "Capillary behaviour in porous solids", *Trans. Soc. Pet. Eng. A.I.M.E.*, **142**, 152-169.

Leverett, M. C. and W. B. Lewis (1941) "Steady flow of gas-oil-water mixtures through unconsolidated sands", *Trans. A.I.M.E.*, **142**, 107.

Mantoglou, A. and L. W. Gelhar (1987) "Stochastic modelling of large-scale transient unsaturated flow systems", *Water Resources Research*, **23**, 37-46.

McWhorter, D. B. and D. K. Sunada (1990) "Exact integral solution for two-phase flow", *Water Resources Research*, **26**, 399-414.

Mercier Remediation Panel (1993) "Evaluation of remedial measures for the subsurface contamination associated with the former mercier lagoons at Ville Mercier, Quebec", Final report submitted to Laidlaw Environmental Services (Mercier) Ltd.

Parker, J.C., R. J. Lenhard and T. Kuppusamy (1987) "A parametric model for constitutive properties governing multiphase flow in porous media", *Water Resources Research*, **23**, 618-624.

Poulin, M. (1977) "Groundwater contamination near a liquid waste lagoon, Ville Mercier, Quebec", M.Sc. Thesis, University of Waterloo, Waterloo, Ontario, Canada.

Poulsen, M. and B. H. Kueper (1992) "A field experiment to study the behaviour of tetrachloroethylene in unsaturated porous media", *Environmental Science and Technology*, **26**, 889-895.

Schiegg, H. O. (1984) "Considerations on water, oil and air in porous media", *Wat. Sci. Tech.*, **17**, 467-476.

Stone, H. L. (1970) "Probability model for estimating three-phase relative permeability", *J. Pet. Tech.*, 214-218.

van Genuchten, M. Th. (1980) "A closed form equation for predicting the hydraulic conductivity of unsaturated soils", *Soil Sci. Am. J.*, **44**, 892-898.

Vinsome, P. K. W. (1976) "ORTHOMIN, an iterative method for solving sparse sets of simultaneous linear equations", SPE Symposium on Numerical Simulation of Reservoir Performance, Society of Petroleum Engineers, Los Angeles, Feb. 19-20.

Wyckoff, R. D. and H. G. Botset (1936) Physics, **7**, 325.

5

Experimental Studies of the Movement of Chlorinated Solvent Compounds and other DNAPLs in the Vadose, Capillary, and Groundwater Zones

Richard L. Johnson[1] **and Bernard H. Kueper**[2]

[1]Department of Environmental Science and Engineering
Oregon Graduate Institute
Beaverton, OR 97006

[2]Department of Civil Engineering
Queen's University
Kingston, Ontario, Canada K7L 3N6

ABSTRACT

The behavior of dense non-aqueous phase liquids (DNAPLs) in naturally heterogeneous porous media is extremely complex and difficult to predict. Physical model experiments have therefore played and continue to play an important role in understanding that complexity. They provide a means to incorporate all of the physics and chemistry which are important for DNAPL behavior while also providing a great deal of experimental control. Perhaps most importantly, physical model experiments can be conducted and insights can be gained without an *a priori* understanding of all of the relevant processes. Physical model experiments are therefore excellent for developing conceptual models of how DNAPLs behave in the subsurface.

Physical model experiments can be used to examine all aspects of DNAPL behavior in the subsurface, including DNAPL flow, dissolution, vaporization, and remediation. As with numerical models, an important strength of physical models is that experimental conditions can be reproduced. For example, the effects of different release conditions can be studied in the same physical setting. In the same way, different remediation strategies can be compared directly using a series of similar releases. The experiments can be conducted using a variety of media and DNAPLs, and can be conducted under both saturated and unsaturated conditions.

Perhaps the most important long term benefit of physical model experiments is in the validation of numerical models. The experimental data reported here are of use in evaluating the performance of the models which provide the basis for decisions regarding the design and implementation of remediation systems.

5.1 INTRODUCTION

The pioneering **laboratory experiments** of Schwille (1984a, 1984b, 1988a,b) and others on the movement of dense chlorinated solvents in porous media has resulted in the conceptualizations of dense chlorinated solvent behavior presented in Chapter 2. As discussed in Chapter 4, **numerical modeling** offers an alternative means of predicting the behavior of chlorinated solvents and other dense non-aqueous phase liquids (DNAPLs) in complex systems. However, although some modeling successes have been achieved, such efforts are still limited by difficulties in characterizing the systems of interest in sufficient detail that meaningful predictions can be obtained. Conducting **field experiments** with DNAPLs in the subsurface may be a preferable means of investigation in some cases, but the associated drawbacks usually include high costs, difficulties in reproducing experiments, and regulatory restrictions. Thus, physical model experiments remain important for the development of an improved understanding of chlorinated solvent behavior in both porous and fractured media.

The fundamentals of multi-phase flow and transport as well as the factors which control chlorinated solvent movement in the subsurface are discussed in Chapters 2, 3, and 11. In this chapter, the microscopic and macroscopic behavior of chlorinated solvents are discussed based on the results of various laboratory and field experiments. To date, the majority of experimental work has concerned flow through homogeneous porous media. Since most chlorinated solvent spills occur in media where **heterogeneity** controls the pathways of infiltration, the current trend is towards experiments on DNAPL behavior in more complex, heterogeneous media.

For the purpose of this discussion, it is convenient to divide the subsurface into three general domains: 1) the **vadose or unsaturated zone**; 2) the **capillary zone**; and 3) the **saturated or groundwater zone**. The vadose zone is defined here as that portion of the soil which is near or at residual water saturation. DNAPL migration in the vadose zone concerns primarily the displacement of air by DNAPL. The capillary zone spans the region over which the water content rises from the residual value to full saturation of the pore space by water. It is in this region that three-phase flow can take place, with DNAPL acting both as a wetting fluid displacing air and as a non-wetting fluid displacing water. The groundwater zone is, of course, below the free water table, and most DNAPLs there typically act as non-wetting fluids with respect to water, though exceptions to this generalization do occur in practice.

As the above discussion indicates, the primary change that occurs in a porous medium when moving downwards from ground surface is an increase in the water content. Moving from the vadose zone to the saturated zone represents a change from a system in which two immiscible fluids (air and water) initially share the pore space, to a system where water occupies the entire pore space. When a liquid chlorinated solvent is introduced, the relationships between the fluids and the porous medium become considerably more complex. Thus, at a spill site, a portion of the unsaturated zone can contain up to three fluids; below the water table, two fluids may be present.

5.2 DNAPL MOVEMENT IN THE VADOSE ZONE

The laboratory experiments conducted by Schwille (1988a) in homogeneous sand under conditions of a point source demonstrated that, within the vadose zone, chlorinated solvent DNAPLs are **well behaved**. Tetrachloroethylene (PCE) was observed to move downwards as a uniform front and drain to an apparently homogeneous residual distribution. In these experiments, liquid solvents were found to penetrate relatively quickly due to their low viscosity and high density; there was little tendency for the solvent body to spread laterally as it sank. Figure 5.1 shows the behavior observed in a typical small spill of PCE in a column of fine-grained silica sand ($K = 1.2 \times 10^{-4}$ m/s). Note that the infiltration body remained very thin as it penetrated through the unsaturated portion of the column (the zone above the open inverted triangle is at residual water saturation and therefore represents the vadose zone).

Schwille (1988a) and others have observed that within the vadose zone, chlorinated solvents behave in ways that are similar to petroleum-derived organic liquids. The behavior of the latter group has been studied in considerable detail (*e.g.*, see: Van Dam, 1967; Dracos, 1978; Van der Waarden *et al.*, 1971 and 1977; Dietz, 1967; and Eckberg and Sunada, 1984). The experiments of Eckberg and Sunada (1984), in which oil was spilled into a column of glass beads initially under drainage conditions, demonstrate the

18   DENSE CHLORINATED SOLVENTS

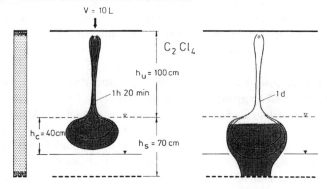

Figure 5.1   Infiltration of 10 L of tetrachloroethylene (PCE) into a fine-grained sand $(K = 1$ to 2×10^{-4} m/s). (Reprinted with permission from Schwille (1988a).)

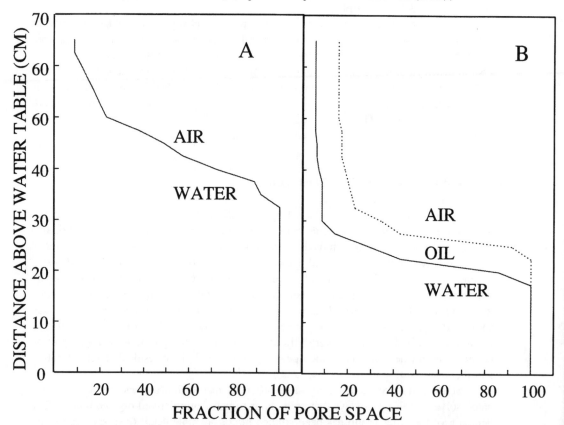

Figure 5.2   Distribution of water and oil before and after oil is spilled into a column of glass beads under drainage conditions. (Adapted with permission from Eckberg and Sunada (1984).)

type of three-phase interactions which can be expected between air, water, and solvent. Figure 5.2 depicts the distribution of fluid phases before and after the addition of the oil. Both air and water were displaced by the infiltrating liquid. Air was displaced by the more-viscous, more-wetting NAPL. Water was mobilized in part because the **capillary pressure** across the water/oil interface is less than that across the original air/water interface (oil is wetting with respect to air on a water surface, and therefore preferentially situates itself between the water and air phases). Some water is also mobilized because of the downward pressure exerted by the oil body on the water phase.

In homogeneous media, infiltration through the unsaturated zone can occur in the form of "**fingers**" caused an inherent instability in the advancing front. As discussed in Kueper and Frind (1989), this instability can arise from an unfavorable density and/or viscosity ratio between the displacing and displaced fluids. Schwille's (1988a) experiments with "sheet-like" spills of solvent show preferential penetration along such fingers (Figure 5.3). It is important to note that a fingered front will, in general, not arise from a point source release of solvent when the size of the release point is less than the **critical wavelengths** required to initiate fingering. In addition to the density and viscosity ratios, the velocity of the displacement and permeability of the medium influence the spacing of the fingers formed. Similar results have been obtained for water infiltrating into homogeneous, unsaturated sand. For example, Glass *et al.* (1989) showed that the extent to which the wetting front was unstable could be predicted based on the properties of the medium and the fluid. In general, as the permeability of the medium decreases, the importance of preferential or "fingered" flow through the unsaturated zone will increase.

Unsaturated zone experiments have demonstrated that when the medium is heterogeneous, DNAPL flow is controlled by those heterogeneities. Johnson (1990) conducted an experiment in a large cylindrical column which contained a single layer of lower permeability sand ($K = 1.7 \times 10^{-4}$ m/s) within a medium sand ($K = 3.8 \times 10^{-4}$ m/s, Figure 5.4). The fine lens was characterized by a water content higher than the host sand. A release at the surface of 100 mL of dyed PCE moved downwards through the medium sand as a relatively uniform front. When it reached the finer-grained layer, it **pooled** and spread over nearly the entire cross-section of the column. The solvent then fingered into the finer layer at a number of points; these fingers terminated within the first few centimeters due to the limited volume of the spill. Although the permeabilities of the two sands differed by only a factor of two, that difference controlled the initial water distribution. The solvent spread laterally along the fine layer because that layer did not contain enough air to allow the solvent to continue to imbibe and displace air. Since it was easier for the solvent to imbibe laterally and displace air rather than displace water vertically as a non-wetting fluid, lateral flow took place. Had the fine-grained layer been primarily saturated with air, spontaneous imbibition of solvent into the layer would have taken place. Since permeability contrasts between layers of an order of magnitude or more are common at field sites, it is likely that solvent flow in the unsaturated zone will be strongly affected by such heterogeneities.

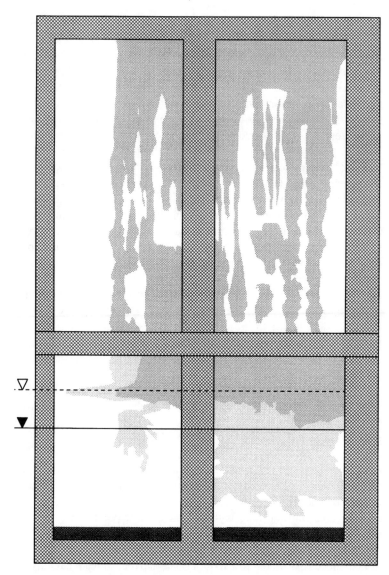

Figure 5.3 Finger formation during a "sheet-like" infiltration of tetrachloroethylene (PCE) into unsaturated sand. (Reprinted with permission from Schwille (1988a).)

5.3 DNAPL MOVEMENT IN THE CAPILLARY ZONE

Chlorinated solvent behavior within the capillary zone is greatly complicated by the fact that up to **three fluid phases** can be actively flowing at one time. Also, as discussed above, the relative permeability to liquid chlorinated solvents is lower in regions of higher water content. We note then that even within relatively homogeneous media,

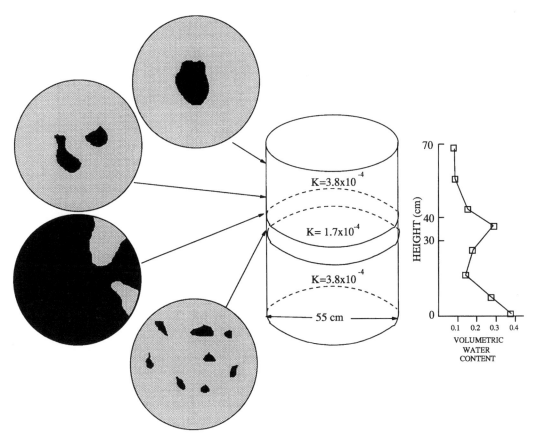

Figure 5.4 Horizontal excavations of a cylindrical physical model showing the infiltration of trichloroethylene (TCE) into a medium sand ($K = 3.8 \times 10^{-4}$ m/s) containing a single lower-permeability layer ($K = 1.7 \times 10^{-4}$ m/s).

spatial variations in water content in the capillary zone can be large. Thus, in many cases, water-content-induced **permeability contrasts** in the capillary zone are sufficient to control the infiltration pathways of a liquid solvent.

Anderson (1988) conducted 3-D model experiments to examine solvent movement through the capillary zone in fine sand. The dimensions of the model were 50 cm long by 25 cm wide by 30 cm high. Under drainage conditions, spills of 75 mL of PCE caused 100 to 500 mL of water to be displaced out of the tank. This was in part the result of a **collapse of the capillary fringe** brought about by the lower capillary pressures that existed across the solvent/water interfaces as compared to the original air/water interfaces. (Eckberg and Sunada (1984) observed an identical effect.) The release of water was also affected by the fact that in regions of high water content, PCE must displace water in order to undergo gravity-driven migration. Excavation of the tank following the spill revealed that when the DNAPL reached the capillary zone, the infiltration front became unstable and fingers formed (Figure 5.5). The fingers had many geometries, some being vertically very thin and laterally extensive. Others penetrated downward into the saturated zone and were in places only millimeters in diameter. This irregular behavior existed despite the fact that the tank had been carefully packed with very homogeneous sand.

In another set of experiments, Anderson (1988) released PCE into a 60 cm high by 30 cm wide by 2 cm thick tank (Figure 5.6). The tank had again been packed with a fine sand ($K = 2 \times 10^{-4}$ cm/s) and existed under drainage conditions prior to the

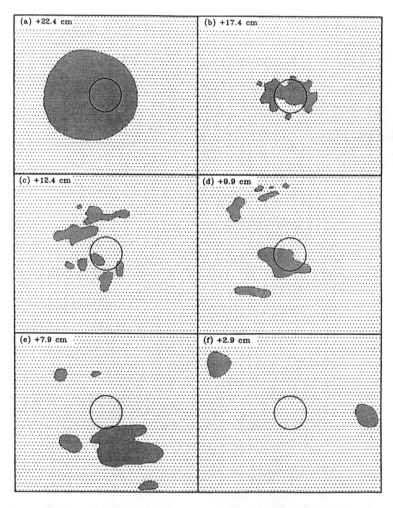

Figure 5.5 Distribution of PCE at various elevations above the water table during the excavation of a 75 mL release into a three dimensional sand tank. (Reprinted with permission from Anderson (1988).)

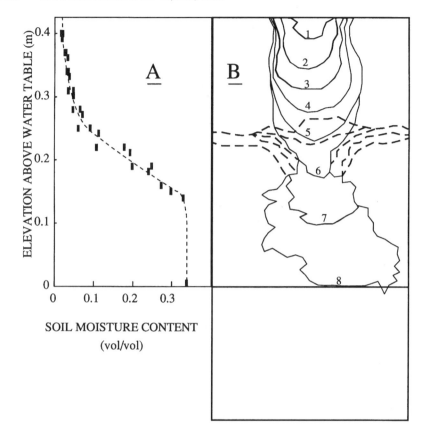

Figure 5.6 a. Soil moisture profile prior to a tetrachloroethylene (PCE) release; b. Infiltration of PCE into a fine-grained sand showing the depression of the capillary zone caused by the solvent. (Reprinted with permission from Anderson (1988).)

spill. The spill was made across the entire thickness so that the DNAPL movement could be monitored through the transparent walls of the tank. As the solvent moved into the capillary zone, it again appeared to cause a collapse of the capillary zone in the region ahead of the main DNAPL body. This resulted in a "**funneling**" effect that focused the DNAPL body as it approached the water table. This promoted the build-up of DNAPL head such that, in this case, the **entry pressure** of the underlying water-saturated sands could be overcome.

As a DNAPL moves into the tension-saturated portion of the capillary zone, it must displace water if continued downward migration is to occur. Since it is generally a non-wetting fluid with respect to water, there must be a sufficient build-up of capillary pressure to allow the solvent to overcome the entry pressure of the nearly water-saturated medium. In the case of imbibition conditions for which there is a sharp increase in water content at the top of the capillary zone, some simultaneous lateral spreading of DNAPL may take place due to imbibition of air-filled pores. If sufficient solvent reaches the top of the capillary zone, the zone can be breached and the solvent can continue downward into the saturated zone. Within the capillary zone as well as in the underlying saturated zone, the infiltration of DNAPL is accompanied by the displacement of water. This process is **unstable** due to the fact that the displacement is by a less-viscous, more-dense fluid. If the width of the solvent front exceeds the **critical wavelength** for finger initiation, continued solvent infiltration will proceed in the form of fingers. (In cases where the solvent viscosity is greater than that of water, a velocity threshold will exist beyond which the displacement is unstable.)

Fingers form in homogeneous porous media within pore-scale zones of higher permeability. Once fingers have been established, the DNAPL permeability within the fingers is greatly increased such that the fingers act as **conduits** for subsequent DNAPL movement. In heterogeneous porous media, solvent migration through the capillary zone will proceed through the higher permeability regions, again giving the appearance of fingers. In this case, however, these "channels" of solvent are simply due to the fact that higher permeability migration pathways exist, and are independent of the fact that an unstable displacement process may be taking place (Kueper and Frind, 1988).

5.4 DNAPL MOVEMENT IN THE GROUNDWATER ZONE

5.4.1 General

Interest in the behavior of solvents in the subsurface usually stems from concern over the potential impact of the solvents on groundwater quality. In that context, the behavior of solvents within the saturated zone is often of greatest interest. There are many case histories in which spills of chlorinated solvents and other DNAPLs have penetrated all three subsurface zones and resulted in wide-spread contamination (*e.g.*, see Kueper *et al.* 1992). In many cases, however, the evidence of contamination is limited to the detection of dissolved compounds. Direct observation of "**free-product**" solvents in the subsurface is the exception rather than the rule.

The behavior of chlorinated solvents as they penetrate the saturated zone has been followed visually in the large tank experiments of Schwille (1988a), and also in smaller tank experiments at the Oregon Graduate Institute and at the University of Waterloo. Two important conclusions have been drawn from these saturated-zone observations: 1) as in other zones, subtle permeability contrasts can have a controlling influence on the movement of a DNAPL; and 2) typical groundwater flows do not have much effect on the flow behavior of a DNAPL. The latter point is clearly demonstrated in Schwille's (1988a) large tank experiments (see Figure 5.7) where under conditions of a relatively high groundwater velocity ($v > 1$ m/day), there was essentially no distortion of the penetrating solvent body.

Once having crossed the water table, the downward migration of a chlorinated solvent may continue until the **bottom** of the aquifer is reached. In general, a barrier to groundwater flow will also be a barrier to solvent migration. DNAPL solvent that reaches an aquitard will tend to form a flat pool, and/or collect in local depressions on the top

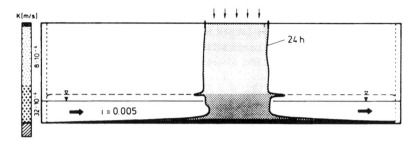

Figure 5.7 Infiltration pattern of an areal spill of tetrachloroethylene (PCE) into a medium sand. (Reprinted with permission from Schwille (1988a).)

of the aquitard. In the case of a chlorinated solvent having even a moderate interfacial tension with water, lateral flow and pooling will also occur above regions (*e.g.*, lenses) of only slightly lower permeability (Kueper and Frind, 1991a,b).

5.4.2 The Role of Aquifer Heterogeneity in DNAPL Movement

As discussed above and also in Chapter 3, a DNAPL which is migrating below the water table will spread **laterally** whenever a horizon of lower permeability is encountered. A DNAPL will accumulate on top of that horizon until the entry pressure of the lower permeability material is exceeded. As demonstrated by Kueper and Frind (1991b), lateral spreading can continue even after a lower permeability lens has been penetrated. This is due to the fact that a higher relative permeability to the DNAPL exists above the lens as compared to within. This follows from the fact that a **saturation discontinuity** exists whenever a permeability contrast exists, leading to higher DNAPL saturations in the more permeable material. The net result is that solvents will also be spreading sideways if they are migrating vertically through horizontally-stratified porous media. The numerical simulations presented in Chapter 4 suggest that a DNAPL solvent can spread laterally several meters below a point source before even having migrated one or two meters vertically.

Kueper *et al.* (1989) studied the influence of porous media heterogeneity on DNAPL migration in an initially water-saturated, sand-packed cell. The experimental device and the arrangement of the four types of sand used to pack the cell are illustrated in Figure 5.8. The source area for the injection of PCE was located along the top boundary; lateral outflow of water occurred at the side boundaries. The sand pack had a depth in the third dimension of 0.6 cm, which is significantly less than the wavelengths for fingering that would be expected for this system. Drainage PCE-water capillary pressure curves measured for each of the four sands are presented in Figure 5.9. As expected, the curves for the lower permeability sands are shifted vertically upwards. A Brooks-Corey (Brooks and Corey, 1966) capillary pressure function was fitted to each of the four measured curves. The best fit Brooks-Corey parameters and the results of falling-head permeameter testing are presented in Table 5.1.

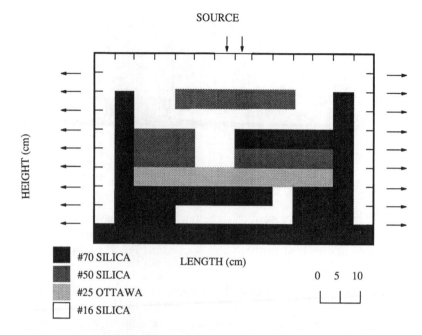

Figure 5.8   Schematic drawing of the physical model used by Kueper *et al.* (1989) for tetrachloroethylene (PCE) spills into saturated heterogeneous porous media. (Adapted with permission from Kueper *et al.* (1989).)

Throughout the duration of the Kueper *et al.* (1989) experiment, the source area was subjected to a constant head of 4 cm of PCE. Figure 5.10.a illustrates the fluid distribution in the cell 126 seconds after initial PCE penetration. The PCE is seen to be pooling and cascading off of the finer sand (#50 silica) just below the source area. The inability to penetrate this lens is due to the fact that the capillary pressure immediately above the lens is less than the 13.5 cm **displacement pressure** for the sand in the lens. Figure 5.10.b illustrates the fluid distribution in the cell after 220 seconds. The PCE is continuing to cascade off the finer sands (#50 and #70 silica) it has encountered, and is seen to have just reached the #25 Ottawa sand lens. Figure 5.10.c corresponds to the point in time at which the PCE first penetrated the #25 sand lens. However, because the displacement pressure of the #25 sand is higher than that of the #16 sand, lateral flow occurred above the #25 sand lens prior to penetration. This lateral flow and associated pooling allowed the capillary pressure above the lens to build up and exceed the displacement pressure of the lens. The build-up of capillary pressure is accompanied by an increasing DNAPL saturation.

Figure 5.10.d gives the status of the Kueper *et al.* (1989) experiment after 313 seconds. The PCE has now fully penetrated into the #25 Ottawa sand lens, but is also continuing to build above that lens. This is an example of how a non-wetting fluid will continue to pool and flow laterally above a finer-grained lens even after penetration of that lens. It is clear that: 1) in a natural aquifer, significant degrees of lateral flow will be

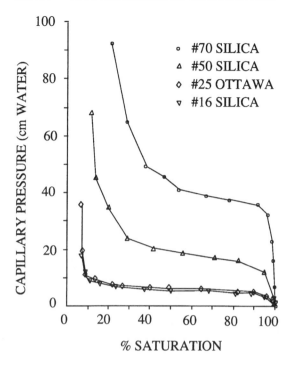

Figure 5.9 Measured capillary pressure curves of the tetrachloroethylene-water system for the four sands used by Kueper *et al.* (1989). (Adapted with permission from Kueper *et al.* (1989).)

TABLE 5.1 Best-fit Brooks-Corey parameters and the results of permeameter test for the four sands used in the physical model of Kueper *et al.* (1989).

Sand	Permeability (m^2)	P_d (cm H_2O)	λ	S_r
#16 Silica	5.0×10^{-10}	3.77	3.86	0.078
#25 Ottawa	2.1×10^{-10}	4.43	3.51	0.069
#50 Silica	5.3×10^{-11}	13.5	2.49	0.098
#70 Silica	8.2×10^{-12}	33.1	3.30	0.189

caused by permeability variations; and 2) vertical migration of a DNAPL in heterogeneous materials will not occur without some associated degree of lateral spreading.

The observation that NAPLs are often not able to cross capillary zones has been used to advantage by the oil pipeline industry. When an underground pipe is sited in fine-grained media, the pipe is often installed within a bed of very coarse-grained materials. As the result of the capillary contrast between those materials and the surrounding media, oil which leaks from the pipeline will often be collected and contained exclusively within the coarser-grained medium.

Within the saturated zone, DNAPL movement can be affected by heterogeneities which are not observable even with careful inspection. A most striking example of this is the microscopic investigation of flow through a bed of glass beads conducted by Schwille

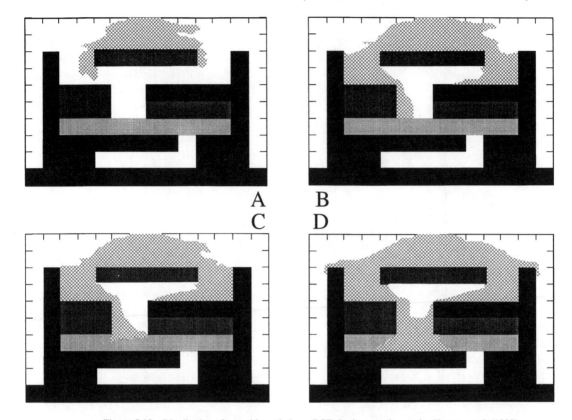

Figure 5.10 Distribution of tetrachloroethylene (PCE) in the experiments by Kueper *et al.* (1989). a. 126 seconds after initiation of the release; b. 220 seconds after initiation of the release; c. 245 seconds after the initiation of the release, at the point in time at which the PCE first penetrates the #25 Ottawa sand lens; and d. 313 seconds after initiation of the release. (Adapted with permission from Kueper *et al.* (1989).)

(1988a). In real-world aquifers, where it is possible only to characterize large-scale aquifer properties, the small-scale heterogeneities which may control DNAPL behavior will be difficult if not impossible to detect. Schwille's (1988a) experiments showed that a permeability decrease of only a factor of four can be sufficient to completely halt the inflow of solvent. Within many naturally-occurring porous media, much greater local permeability contrasts are to be expected. The parameters governing infiltration will in this case be the lateral extent, bedding angle, and continuity of the low permeability layers.

5.5 DNAPL RETENTION CAPACITY OF POROUS MEDIA

The ability of a porous medium to exhibit a **retention capacity** for an infiltrating spill is important in determining the spatial distribution of the solvent within the medium. The retention capacity of a medium for a solvent (R_s) is defined here as the average volume of solvent which is retained per unit volume of the aquifer, regardless of whether certain lenses within the overall region are accessible to DNAPL or not. R_s differs from the **residual saturation** for a solvent in that the latter refers to the fraction of the pore space which is occupied by solvent. Also, the term residual saturation is typically reserved for regions of porous media through which actual solvent migration has taken place. The R_s concept is frequently used along with spill volume and cross-sectional area to predict the depth of penetration of a spill. Since heterogeneities in real systems can lead to uneven flow patterns, simple models using R_s values derived from small-scale laboratory tests should always be used with considerable caution. In heterogeneous media, flow may occur preferentially in a few channels, and result in penetration depths which are much larger than would be expected based on laboratory-estimated R_s values.

Mercer and Cohen (1990) have reviewed the R_s values documented in the literature, and report a range of 3 to 30 L/m^3 for unsaturated sandy porous materials and 5 to 50 L/m^3 for sandy materials below the water table. Kueper *et al.* (1993) report a value of 8.6 L/m^3 for PCE below the water table in sandy deposits, while Brewster (1993) reports a value of 3.2 L/m^3 for PCE in the same aquifer. Poulsen and Kueper (1992) report R_s values ranging from 4.9 L/m^3 to 12.6 L/m^3 for point releases of PCE in unsaturated sandy deposits. The study by Poulsen and Kueper (1992) demonstrated that both R_s and the ultimate depth of migration can be expected to be functions of the release rate at ground surface. Wilson and Conrad (1984) provide an extensive summary of the mechanisms leading to residual formation as well as the porous media and fluid factors which govern residual values in typical sands and gravels.

5.6 SOLVENT MIGRATION IN FRACTURED MEDIA

As with porous media flow, the movement of solvents within **fractured media** is controlled by the density and viscosity of the solvent, as well as the capillary pressures in the system of interest (see also Chapters 4, 11, and 12). Once again, Schwille's (1988a,b) experiments represent pioneering work in this area. They involved spilling small volumes of chlorinated solvents between closely-spaced (0.1 or 0.3 mm separation) glass plates. The opposing faces of the plates were either smooth, or roughened by sandblasting. Releases were conducted into saturated as well as partially-saturated fractures. In hydraulically-rough, unsaturated fractures, a substantial quantity of solvent was retained as **droplets and films** within both the unsaturated and saturated zones (Figure 5.11). This retention of solvent was both increased and more widely dispersed when the width of the fracture was reduced from 0.3 mm to 0.1 mm. Schwille (1988b) also conducted a series of experiments using a network of vertical fractures mounted in a near-horizontal network. Most of the published data on these experiments were obtained with both DNAPL solvents and miscible fluids. These experiments with idealized fractures demonstrated that substantial amounts of a non-wetting DNAPL fluid can be retained within fractures. This conclusion has important ramifications for the cleanup of fractures contaminated with chlorinated solvents (see also Chapter 12).

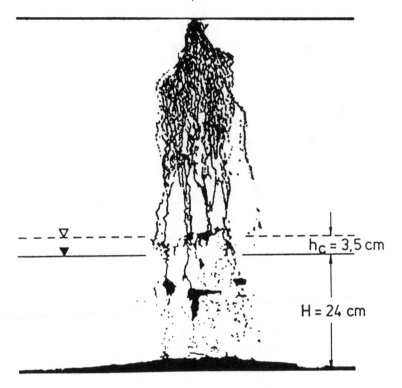

Figure 5.11   Tetrachloroethylene (PCE) release into a rough, unsaturated "fracture" with
aperture 0.2 mm. (Reprinted with permission from Schwille (1988a).)

In naturally-occurring fracture systems, **variations in fracture aperture** will have
a significant influence on DNAPL movement. Tsang and Tsang (1987) found significant
spatial variation in the aperture dimension in sections of individual fractures. They
concluded that water flow in many fractures will occur in channels as opposed to
occurring uniformly across the fractures. It can be anticipated that solvent flow will
be even more heterogeneous than water flow, due to the strong influence of capillary
effects. It will generally not be possible to characterize a real fracture system in sufficient detail to allow deterministic predictions of solvent behavior within a fractured
medium. Kueper and McWhorter (1991) outline the conditions necessary for a DNAPL
to enter a water-saturated fracture, and demonstrate the influence of a spatially-variable
aperture.

5.7 STUDIES USING MICROSCOPIC MODELS OF POROUS MEDIA

Schwille (1988a) conducted a series of **microscopic experiments** to examine the behavior
of chlorinated solvents in porous media. The media in these experiments were glass beads
of two different size ranges. One or more layers of beads was placed between two glass
sheets, and the model was placed into an outer trough which was used to control water

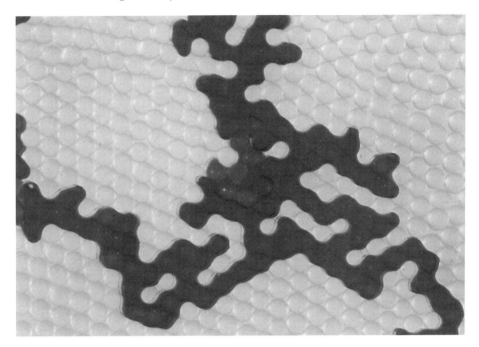

Figure 5.12   Distribution of PCE after infiltration into a saturated glass bead micro-model (bead diameter ∼1 mm). (Reprinted with permission from Schwille (1988).)

level and content. Experiments were conducted under both unsaturated and saturated conditions. Figure 5.12 shows the results obtained when the infiltration of PCE took place under saturated conditions. The PCE is the non-wetting fluid with respect to water; the result is infiltration into the medium as small fingers.

Figure 5.13 shows the microscopic behavior of PCE observed by Schwille (1988a) when the PCE encountered a lower-permeability zone (*i.e.*, smaller grains). Penetration of that zone did not occur initially because the entry pressure for the non-wetting PCE is greater in those zones. As has been noted above in related contexts, once the thickness of the overlying pool becomes sufficiently large, then the PCE could begin to penetrate into the lower zone. When doing so, it once again moves in **preferential pathways** or channels. As is seen in the figure, these pathways often have dimensions similar to the grain size. In some cases, the channels are widely separated. As has been observed in sand models, once a preferential pathway is formed, the relative permeability of that zone for the chlorinated solvent substantially greater than for the bulk of the medium. Consequently, continued solvent flow may be limited largely to those channels, leading to a substantial increase in the depth of penetration into the groundwater zone.

Wilson *et al.* (1990) carried out an extensive examination of NAPL movement using microscopic models. Their physical models consisted of etched glass plates which were fused together. Because of the construction technique, the "pore structure" within

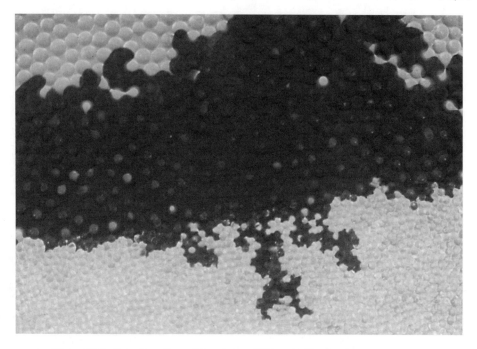

Figure 5.13 Retention of tetrachloroethylene PCE at the interface between two glass bead layers in a saturated glass-bead micro-model. (Reprinted with permission from Schwille (1988a).)

these models (Figure 5.14) was more variable than in Schwille's (1988a) models. Figure 5.15 shows the movement of a NAPL (Soltrol) through an initially water-saturated medium. As with Schwille's (1988a) experiments, infiltration occurred by the formation of many channels of solvent. As a consequence, only a fraction of the pore space in the medium actually contained NAPL. During the subsequent infiltration of additional NAPL, the pattern shown in the figure remained constant, resulting in a state of residual saturation for the water (the wetting phase). When the NAPL flow was stopped and water flow was induced in the opposite direction, the water displaced a substantial fraction of the NAPL (Figure 5.16). The result was a stable state of residual saturation for the NAPL (the non-wetting phase).

In addition to the work discussed above, Wilson *et al.* (1990) conducted micro-model experiments which contained zones of larger diameter pores. During NAPL infiltration, because of their lower entry pressures, they observed that the NAPLs spread more quickly in the coarser zones. In experiments where coarser-grained zones extended across the length of the model, Wilson *et al.* (1990) report that the bulk of the NAPL flow occurred in those zones, and that most of the surrounding, finer-grained zones were bypassed. After the infiltration of NAPL had stopped, water flow in the opposite direction was initiated at a water velocity of ~14 cm/day. Little of the NAPL in the coarser zones was removed, while a significant fraction of the NAPL in the finer zones was removed.

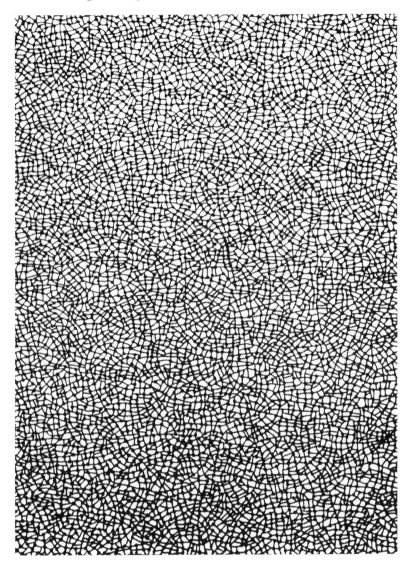

Figure 5.14 Pore structure of one of the micro-models used by Wilson *et al.* (1990). (Reprinted with permission from Wilson *et al.* (1990).)

This is due to the fact that, at this velocity, **capillary forces** dominated over **viscous forces** and the water was preferentially drawn into the finer pores. At a velocity of ∼140 cm/day, viscous forces played a much larger role, and a substantial fraction of the NAPL was displaced from the coarser zones.

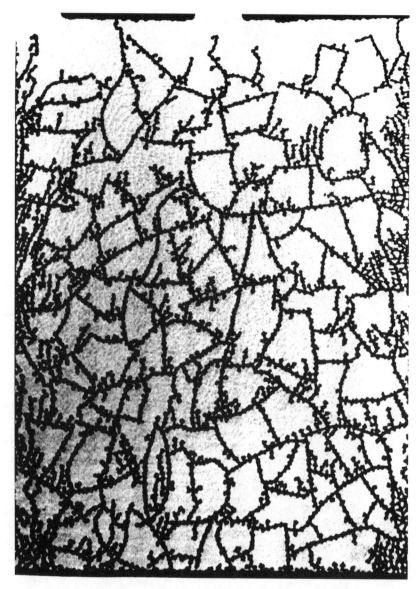

Figure 5.15   NAPL movement through an initially water-saturated medium in a micro-scale model. (Reprinted with permission from Wilson *et al.* (1990).)

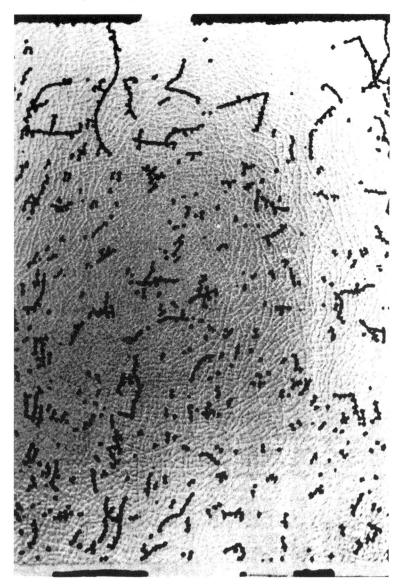

Figure 5.16   Non-wetting (NAPL) residual saturation resulting from water displacement of the NAPL in Figure 5.15. (Reprinted with permission from Wilson *et al.* (1990).)

5.8 EXPERIMENTAL RELEASES OF CHLORINATED SOLVENTS IN THE FIELD

5.8.1 General

As has been discussed above, it is very difficult to characterize the movement of chlorinated solvents at actual spill sites. At the same time, it is very difficult to reproduce naturally-occurring micro- and macro-scale heterogeneities in laboratory models. Thus, well-controlled field experiments can be an invaluable means of confirming how chlorinated solvents behave in the "real world". To date, the best-characterized field experiments have been conducted at the Canadian Forces Base Borden site in Ontario, Canada (Poulsen and Kueper, 1992; Greenhouse *et al.*, 1993; Kueper *et al.*, 1993). These experiments include liquid chlorinated solvent releases in both the vadose and groundwater zones.

The Borden site has been described in a number of previous publications (MacFarlane *et al.*, 1983; Mackay *et al.*, 1986; Sudicky, 1986; and Brewster, 1993). Briefly, the Borden site is an unconfined aquifer consisting of fine to medium grained beach sands. The water table in the vicinity of the field experiments described here ranges areally from ground surface to a depth of 3 to 4 m, depending upon local topography. The aquifer is relatively homogeneous, with small and medium scale (millimeters to meters) variations in permeability of up to three orders of magnitude. Bedding in the sand ranges from near horizontal to steeply dipping. Groundwater flow velocity at the site is on the order of 10 cm/day, and the organic carbon content of the sand is quite low. Laboratory studies show that in Borden sand, chlorinated solvents are non-wetting fluids with respect to water.

5.8.2 Vadose Zone Releases

Two releases of small volumes of PCE (6 liters) into the vadose zone of the Borden aquifer have recently been described by Poulsen and Kueper (1992). These releases took place at a location where the aquifer exhibits a total thickness of approximately 9 m, with the water table ~3.5 m below ground surface. The first release, referred to as the "**ponded release**", involved the rapid release of 6 L of PCE over a period of 90 seconds. In this release, the solvent ponded before it was able to infiltrate fully. The second release, referred to as the "**drip release**", was carried out at a site 4.5 m away from the ponded release and involved the slow release of 6 L of PCE over a period of 100 minutes.

After allowing for re-distribution, excavation of each release was carried out in small lifts. It was noted for both releases that PCE had migrated through individual sand laminations ranging in thickness from a few millimeters to a few centimeters. PCE was found to be distinctly present in certain laminations and not in others. It was noted that angled bedding existed at the site, and that PCE had migrated parallel to the bedding at all times. This provided evidence that the migration process was governed to a large degree by capillary forces. The ponded release migrated to a total depth of 2.1 m, and the drip release to a depth of 3.2 m.

Figures 5.17 and 5.18 illustrate the overall volumes within which the PCE migration pathways occurred. The greater depth achieved in the drip release is attributed to the fact that relative to the ponded release, higher capillary pressures were maintained on average throughout the release. The overall average bulk solvent retention capacity (R_s) values for the ponded and drip releases were 12.6 and 4.9 L/m^3, respectively. These values are lower than most estimates derived from laboratory experiments. The low values are due to the influence of heterogeneity and the fact that only certain lenses and laminations below the release points were invaded by PCE. Detailed permeability measurements revealed that the hydraulic conductivities of those invaded lenses and laminations were generally less than a factor of 1.7 different from adjacent, PCE-free lenses and laminations.

Figure 5.19 presents a plot of depth of PCE migration *vs.* volume released based on the bulk R_s values measured for the ponded and drip releases. The plot indicates that a slow release of 200 L of PCE into Borden-type sand could reach a depth of 100 m. These results have serious implications for the many slow releases of chlorinated solvents which have occurred during the past 50 years at industrial sites. It must be concluded from these experiments that even small releases of chlorinated solvents have the potential to reach even deep water tables.

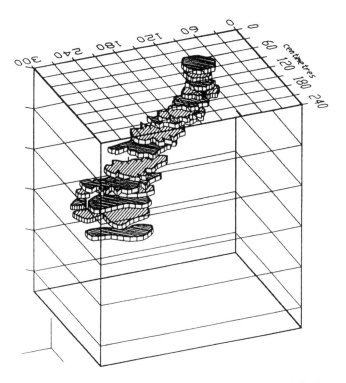

Figure 5.17   Rapid ("ponded") infiltration of PCE into unsaturated Borden sand. (Reprinted with permission from Poulsen and Kueper (1992).)

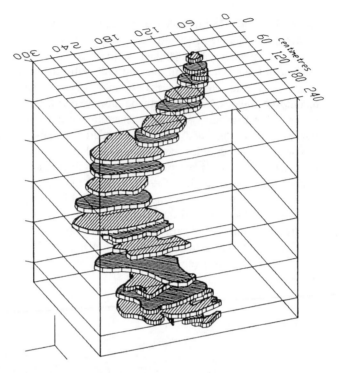

Figure 5.18 "Drip-like" infiltration of tetrachloroethylene (PCE) into Borden sand. (Reprinted with permission from Poulsen and Kueper (1992).)

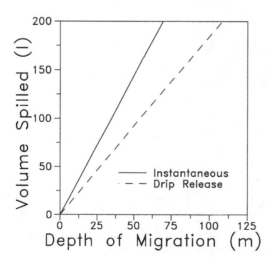

Figure 5.19 Depth of migration *vs.* volume spilled at ground surface using cross-sectional area of migration and overall bulk residual contents. (Reprinted with permission from Poulsen and Kueper (1992).)

5.8.3 Groundwater Zone Releases

Two large-scale releases of PCE into the groundwater zone have been conducted at the Borden site. The first of these was the release of 231 L of PCE at the water table into a 3 m × 3 m × 3.4 m deep sheet-pile cell (Kueper *et al.*, 1993). As in the vadose zone releases, the PCE was dyed red with SUDAN IV to aid in visual location of the PCE during excavation and coring.

During and after the 231 L release, the movement of the PCE was followed using time-domain reflectometry (TDR). Following cessation of DNAPL movement, the upper 0.9 m of the cell was excavated in shallow lifts, and three continuous cores were taken through the remaining thickness of the cell. During both the excavation and coring processes, small samples were taken and analyzed for PCE content. A histogram of PCE saturation for all samples is presented in Figure 5.20. Note that the saturation distribution is highly variable, with a high frequency of low values. Laboratory measurements presented in Kueper *et al.* (1993) suggest that all saturation values above 15% represent pooled PCE, and that values less than that represent residual DNAPL. During excavation it was noted that the PCE was found to be present in certain laminations and distinctly absent from others, with what appeared to be subtle variations in texture controlling migration pathways. The PCE migrated preferentially through the relatively coarser-grained

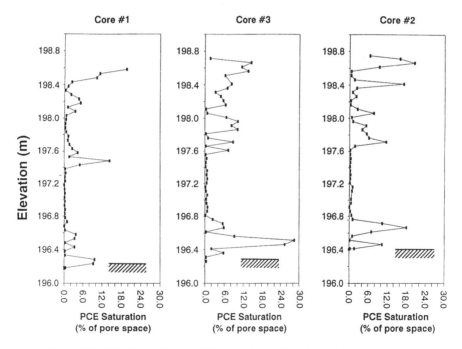

Figure 5.20 Tetrachloroethylene (PCE) saturation profiles obtained from subsampling of three vertical cores. (Reprinted with permission from Kueper *et al.* (1992).)

laminations, consistent with the fact that PCE is non-wetting with respect to water in Borden sand. Lateral spreading of the PCE allowed the liquid PCE to reach the cell walls at numerous locations.

In the second large-scale release of PCE at Borden, 770 L of PCE was spilled into a 9 m × 9 m × 3.3 m deep, sheet-pile cell near the site of the first release. The release took place from a point source at the water table over a 70 hour period. The primary purpose of this release was to assess the extent to which a variety of geophysical methods could characterize the movement and final distribution of PCE in the aquifer. The methods included ground-penetrating radar, neutron probe, TDR, gamma-gamma logging, and electrical resistance logging. All of these techniques, with the possible exception of gamma-gamma logging, were able to track the progress of the PCE into the groundwater zone. They were able to confirm that the PCE front moved relatively quickly (*i.e.*, in a matter of hours) down through the medium. They also indicated that there was significant lateral movement of the PCE due to the presence of subtle structures within the aquifer, and that the PCE encountered the side walls of the cell at a depth of approximately 1 m. A significant portion of the PCE became immobilized in pools on top of lower-permeability zones and in slightly coarser lenses within the medium. As in the 231 L release, coring confirmed that the PCE migration paths were governed by centimeter-scale variations in hydraulic conductivity.

The success of the geophysical monitoring of PCE in the 770 L release was due in large part to the availability of pre-spill data for the site. Thus, it can be concluded that after-the-fact use of surface and borehole measurements to detect where solvents are located at actual sites will likely be difficult due to the inherent variabilities in the geology at most sites. On the other hand, the potential for using geophysical monitoring to follow the progress of the remediation of subsurface chlorinated solvent contamination is quite good: the initial "pre-cleanup" data for a site can be compared to changes observed as the remediation progresses.

5.9 CHLORINATED SOLVENT VAPOR TRANSPORT IN THE VADOSE ZONE

Residual solvents left behind in the vadose and groundwater zones can act as **long-term sources** of contamination in the subsurface. In the vadose zone, the solvents can dissolve into infiltrating water, or they can volatilize into pore air. The volatilities of most of the common chlorinated solvents are sufficiently high that **vapor transport** in the vadose zone is important. Vapor transport can occur both by molecular diffusion and by advection. Both of these processes have been examined using large-scale physical models. Advection can arise due to density effects caused by the presence of the organic vapors in the air, and due to external pressure gradients. Only **density-driven** advective flow as might occur near source zones will be discussed here. Numerical modeling of vapor transport is discussed in Chapter 6.

The diffusive transport of contaminants has been investigated in several large-scale experiments. Hughes *et al.* (1992) observed the diffusion of trichloroethylene (TCE) from a residual source in the vadose zone at the Borden field site. In their experiments, the source consisted of a cylindrical zone (~1 m in diameter and 1 m high, and located near ground surface) into which was placed sand containing 4% TCE by volume. The depth to the water table was 3 to 4 m. The moisture content for most of the soil profile was near field capacity (~10% of the total soil volume). They observed that TCE vapors moved more than 5 m in ~20 days. Numerical modeling of the experiments indicated that this was consistent with the rates expected due to molecular diffusion.

    MacPherson (1991) also conducted large-scale diffusion experiments in a medium sand. In their work, a liquid mixture of organic contaminants was allowed to vaporize and diffuse into the vadose zone from a simulated pool of organic liquid near the water table. Subsurface conditions were quite similar to those described by Hughes *et al.* (1992). The MacPherson (1991) data show large differences in the diffusion rates of the various compounds (Figure 5.21); the differences can be explained based on differences in partitioning of the organics to the soil and to the pore water. The results obtained with

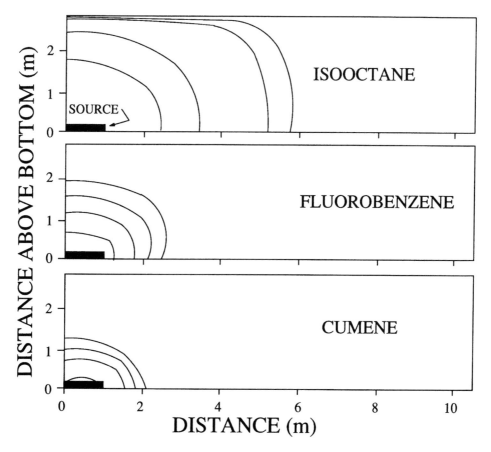

Figure 5.21 Diffusion of isooctane, cumene, and 1,2-dichlorobenzene in a large sand model. (Adapted with permission from MacPherson (1991).)

numerical models which focussed on the role of molecular diffusion compared well with the experimental data.

Many chlorinated solvents have both sufficient volatility and molecular weight that **density-driven** advective flow can be important in coarse media. This has been examined by Schwille and Weber (1991) and Johnson *et al.* (1992). Johnson *et al.* (1992) conducted experiments with TCE and with dichlorfluoromethane (Freon 22) in both medium sand and pea gravel. For TCE, density-driven flow was found to be very important in the pea gravel, but played only a minor role in the sand (Figure 5.22). For Freon 22, which has a vapor density three times that of air, density-driven flow was found to be significant even in the sand. Johnson *et al.* (1992) found that the numerical model developed by Mendoza and Frind (1990a,b) supported their conclusions regarding the behavior of both TCE and Freon 22.

Diffusive and advective transport can carry chlorinated solvent vapors towards the **capillary zone** (and therefore the groundwater zone) over areally-extensive regions. Once at the capillary zone, the vapors can be transported across the water table by infiltration, water-table fluctuations, and/or diffusive/dispersion. Movement of TCE across the water table has been examined using both physical and numerical models by McCarthy and

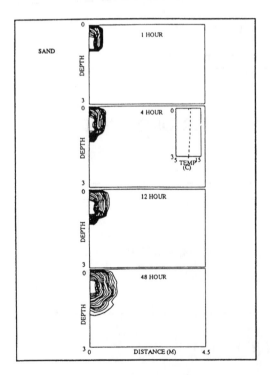
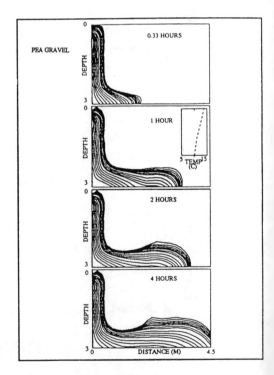

Figure 5.22 Diffusion and density-driven vapor transport of trichloroethylene (TCE) in sand and pea gravel. (Adapted with permission from Johnson *et al.* (1992).)

Johnson (1993). They examined TCE movement from groundwater under conditions of steady groundwater flow with both a stationary and a fluctuating water table. In a sand with an hydraulic conductivity of ~0.1 cm/s and at a groundwater velocity of 0.1 m/d, they concluded that mass transfer was controlled by **vertical dispersion** in the groundwater zone, and that the dispersion was very small (on the same order as aqueous diffusion). Nevertheless, given the potentially large areal extent of many vapor plumes, and the very low drinking water limits for many chlorinated solvents, movement of vapors into the groundwater zone may be a significant mechanism for the contamination of shallow groundwater.

5.10 CHLORINATED SOLVENT DISSOLUTION IN THE GROUNDWATER ZONE

In the groundwater zone, chlorinated solvents become immobilized as residual droplets or ganglia, and as pools perched on top of lower-permeability zones. The effects of groundwater flow and solubility limits cause residual and pooled solvent to dissolve at significantly different rates. Dissolution from both residual and pools has been examined experimentally. Van der Waarden *et al.* (1971), Fried *et al.* (1979), and Miller *et al.* (1990) examined dissolution from residual solvent in porous media. These experiments were carried out in 1-D columns where the medium was first mixed with residual-levels of the solvent, then packed into a column. Two unrealistic features of these experiments were that: 1) the residual was distributed very uniformly within the medium; 2) the 1-D geometry of the column forced the water to flow through the residual zone.

   In order to avoid the limitations of a 1-D column model as discussed above, Anderson *et al.* (1992a) conducted experiments in a 3-D physical model. Solvent was emplaced by spilling PCE inside of a cylindrical, sand-containing column situated inside of a larger tank of sand. Dissolution from this zone was allowed to begin when the cylinder was pulled out and water was allowed to begin to flow around and through the residual zone. The water flow through the residual zone was somewhat reduced (by 20%) due to the presence of the residual solvent. The water that did flow through the residual zone attained **saturation concentrations** quickly. At actual sites, residual zones may be relatively small and widely separated from one another. As a consequence, with increasing distance from the source, the initially saturated concentrations from the residual zones may become **diluted** significantly. This may be one reason why the concentrations of chlorinated solvents in contaminated groundwater are often **far below saturation**, even at sites where a pure "free-product" solvent is known to be present in the groundwater zone (Anderson *et al.*, 1992b).

   As discussed above, experimental data suggest that at many sites, a significant portion of the mass of the chlorinated solvent(s) in the groundwater zone is present in pools. Unlike solvent that is suspended in a state of residual saturation, the solvent in long, flat pools will have limited contact with the flowing groundwater. Consequently, the rate of dissolution will be limited by vertical dispersion of the dissolved solvent up into the flowing groundwater. Schwille (1988a) studied this process experimentally. Johnson and Pankow (1992) examined Schwille's (1988a) data and concluded that because vertical mixing process is quite weak, the **lifetimes of pools** chlorinated solvents will usually be measured in **decades to centuries** (Figure 5.23). They also concluded that increasing the groundwater flow rate over the pools (*e.g.* by pumping) might be only marginally successful at shortening pool lifetimes.

Rivett *et al.* (1991) conducted a large-scale dissolution experiment at the Borden site. The source zone for the experiment consisted of a three-component mixture of solvents which was emplaced below the water table in a rectangular volume. The source chemicals were mixed with sand at a value below residual saturation just before emplacement. Groundwater concentrations of the dissolved solvent chemicals were monitored in a 3-D array of point samplers. Dispersion in the transverse directions was weak, and as a result a long, thin groundwater plume developed. Once the **multicomponent** nature of the source liquid was taken into consideration, the concentrations observed in the heart of the plume were found to be near the values expected for saturation with that source.

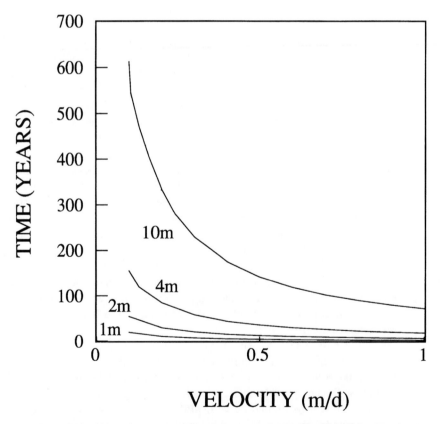

Figure 5.23   Dissolution time for TCE *vs.* groundwater velocity for pool lengths. (Reprinted with permission from Johnson and Pankow (1992).)

5.11 CONCLUSIONS

The physical model studies discussed in this chapter demonstrate the complexity of chlorinated solvent movement in porous and fractured media. The results show that very subtle changes in permeability can greatly affect the subsurface distribution of chlorinated solvents, with differences in permeability of a factor of two or less capable of completely redirecting solvent movement. Thus, the past movement of solvents at industrial sites probably cannot be calculated in a deterministic manner. There can be significant pooling on the tops of lower-permeability lenses in the saturated zone. This type of distribution can substantially limit the rate at which dissolution will occur, leading to very long lifetimes of chlorinated solvents in the subsurface (see also Chapter 7).

The complex nature of chlorinated solvent migration in the subsurface makes it very difficult to predict the depth to which solvents will penetrate the subsurface at a given site. Factors such as bedding angle, length scales of layers, release rate, permeability contrasts, and water content all affect the retention capacity. Since all of these parameters will usually not be known for a particular site of interest, it is clear that estimates of depth of penetration will have a significant degree of uncertainty associated with them.

Physical model studies obviously comprise an important component of DNAPL research. However, to date, most controlled experiments have been conducted using well-sorted sands and gravels. This is the case because of the relative ease of working with these media. The result, though, is a relatively incomplete picture of solvent behavior. Model studies in fine-grained and/or heterogeneous media, as well as in fractured rock, should be viewed as important research activities for the next decade.

ACKNOWLEDGEMENTS

Funding support for this research was provided in part by the University Consortium Solvents-in-Groundwater Research Program. Sponsors of the Program between 1988 and 1994 have included: The Boeing Company, Ciba-Geigy Corporation, Dow Chemical Canada/USA, Eastman Kodak Co., General Electric Co., Laidlaw Environmental Systems Ltd., Mitre Corporation, The Natural Sciences and Engineering Research Council of Canada, and the Ontario University Research Incentive Fund.

5.12 REFERENCES

Anderson, M. R. (1988) Ph.D. Thesis, *The Dissolution and Transport of Dense Non-Aqueous Phase Liquids in Saturated Porous Media*, Oregon Graduate Institute, Portland, Oregon.

Anderson, M. A., R. L. Johnson, and J. F. Pankow (1992a) "Dissolution of dense chlorinated solvents into groundwater: 1. Dissolution from a well-defined source geometry", *Ground Water*, **30**, 250-256.

Anderson, M. A., R. L. Johnson, and J. F. Pankow (1992b) "Dissolution of dense chlorinated solvents into groundwater. "3. Modeling contaminant plumes from fingers and pools of solvent", *Environ. Sci. Technol.*, **26**, 901-908.

Brewster, M. L. (1993) *Observed migration of a controlled DNAPL release by ground penetrating radar*, M.Sc. Thesis, University of Waterloo, Waterloo, Ontario.

Brooks, R. H. and A. T. Corey (1966) "Properties of porous media affecting fluid flow", *J. Irrig. and Drainage Div., Am. Soc. Civil Eng.*, **92(IR2)**, 61-88.

Dietz, D. N. (1967) "Pollution of permeable strata by oil components". In: *Joint Problems of the Oil and Water Industries*, P. Hepple (Ed.), Institute of Petroleum, London.

Dracos, T. (1978) "Theoretical considerations and practical implications on the infiltration of hydrocarbons in aquifers". In: *Proceedings: International Symposium on Ground Water Pollution by Oil Hydrocarbons*, Prague, Czechoslovakia, 127-137.

Eckberg, D. K. and D. K. Sunada (1984) "Nonsteady three-phase immiscible fluid distribution in porous media", *Water Resources Research*, **20**, 1891-1897.

Fried, J. J., P. Muntzer, and L. Zilliox (1979) "Ground-water pollution by transfer of oil hydro-carbons", *Ground Water*, **17**, 586-592.

Glass, R. J., J. Y. Parlange, and T. S. Steenhuis (1989) "Wetting front instability. 1. Theoretical discussion and dimensional analysis", *Water Resources Research*, **25**, 1187-1194.

Greenhouse, J., M. Brewster, G. Schneider, D. Redman, P. Annan, G. Olhoeft, J. Lucius, K. Sander and A. Mazzella (1993) "Geophysics and solvents: The Borden experiment", *The Leading Edge*, April, 261-267.

Hughes, B. M., R. W. Gillham, and C. A. Mendoza (1992) "Transport of trichloroethylene vapours in the unsaturated zone: A field experiment". In: *Proceedings: Subsurface Contamination by Immiscible Fluids*, Calgary, Alberta, April 18–20, 1990. K. U. Weyer (Ed.) A. A Balkema, Rotterdam. 588 pp. Order from A. A. Balkema, Old Post Road, Brookfield, Vermont 05026.

Johnson, R. L. (1990) Unpublished data. Oregon Graduate Institute, Portland, Oregon.

Johnson, R. L. and J. F. Pankow (1992) "Dissolution of dense chlorinated solvents into groundwater. 2. Source functions for pools of solvent", *Environ. Sci. Technol.*, **26**, 896-901.

Johnson, R. L., K. A. McCarthy, M. Perrott, and C. A. Mendoza (1992) "Density-driven va-por transport: Physical and numerical modeling". In: *Subsurface Contamination by Immiscible Fluids*, K. U. Weyer (Ed.), A. A Balkema, Rotterdam. 576 pp.

Kueper, B. H., W. Abbott, and G. Farquhar (1989) "Experimental observations of multiphase flow in heterogeneous porous media", *J. Contaminant Hydrology*, **5**, 83-95.

Kueper, B. H. and E. O Frind (1988) "An overview of immiscible fingering in porous media", *J. Contaminant Hydrology*, **2**, 95-110.

Kueper, B. H. and E. O Frind (1989) "An overview of immiscible fingering in porous media", *J. Contaminant Hydrology*, **5**, 83-95.

Kueper, B. H. and E. O. Frind (1991a) "Two-phase flow in heterogeneous porous media, 1. Model development", *Water Resources Research*, **27**, 1049-1057.

Kueper, B. H. and E. O. Frind (1991b) "Two-phase flow in heterogeneous porous media, 2. Model application", *Water Resources Research*, **27**, 1059-1070.

Kueper, B. H. and D. B. McWhorter (1991) "The behavior of dense non-aqueous phase liquids in fractured clay and rock", *Ground Water*, **29**, 716-728.

Kueper, B. H., C. S. Haase, and H. King (1992) "Leakage of DNAPL from waste impound-ments constructed in fractured rock and clay: Theory and case history", *Canadian Geotechnical Journal*, **29**, 234-244.

Kueper, B. H., D. Redman, R. C. Starr, S. Reitsma, and M. Mah (1993), "A field experiment to study the behavior of tetrachloroethylene below the water table: Spatial distribution of residual and pooled DNAPL" *Ground Water*, **31**, 756-766.

MacFarlane, D. S. J. A. Cherry, R. W. Gillham, E. A. Sudicky (1983) "Migration of contaminants in groundwater at a landfill: a case study. 1. Groundwater flow and plume delineation", *J. Hydrology*, **63**, 1-29.

Mackay, D. M., D. L. Freyberg, P. V. Roberts, and J. A. Cherry (1986) "A natural gradient experiment on solute transport in a sand aquifer", *Water Resources Research*, **22**, 2017-2030.

MacPherson, J. R. (1991) *Gas Phase Diffusion of Organic Compounds in Porous Media: Physical and Numerical Modeling*, Ph.D. Thesis, Oregon Graduate Institute, Portland, Oregon.

McCarthy, K. A. and R. L. Johnson (1993) "Transport of volatile organic compounds across the capillary fringe", *Water Resources Research*, **29**, 1675-1683.

Mendoza C. A. and E. O. Frind (1990a) "Advective-dispersive transport of dense organic vapors in the unsaturated zone. 1. Model development", *Water Resources Research*, **26**, 378-387.

Mendoza C. A. and E. O. Frind (1990b) "Advective-dispersive transport of dense organic vapors in the unsaturated zone. 2. Sensitivity analysis", *Water Resources Research*, **26**, 388-398.

Miller, C. T., M. M. Poirier-McNeill, and A. S. Mayer (1990) "Dissolution of trapped nonaqueous phase liquids: Mass transfer characteristics", *Water Resources Research*, **26**, 2783-2986.

Mercer, J. W. and R. M. Cohen (1990) "A review of immiscible fluids in the subsurface: Properties, models, characterization and remediation", *J. Contaminant Hydrology*, **6**, 107-163.

Poulsen, M. M. and B. H. Kueper (1992) "A field experiment to study the behavior of tetra-chloroethylene in unsaturated porous media", *Environ. Sci. Technol.*, **26**, 889-895.

Rivett, M., S. Feenstra, and J. Cherry (1991) "Field experimental studies of a residual solvent source emplaced in the groundwater zone". In: *Proceedings: Petroleum Hydrocarbons and Organic Chemicals in Ground Water Conference*, 20-22 November, 1991, Houston, Texas, 283-299.

Schwille, F. (1984a) *Leichtflüchtige Chlorkohlenwasserstoffe in Porösen and Klüftigen Medien-Modelversuche*, Besondere Mittellungen zum Deutschen Gewässerkundlichen Jahrbuch, Nr.46, Herausgegeben von der Bundesanstadt für Gewässerkunde in Koblenz.

Schwille, F. (1984b) "Migration of organic fluids immiscible with water in the unsaturated zone". In: *Pollutants in Porous Media*, Ecological Studies, **47**, Springer-Verlag, 27-48.

Schwille, F. (1988a) *Dense Chlorinated Solvents in Porous and Fractured Media: Model Experiments*, translated from the German by J. F. Pankow, Lewis Publishers, Boca Raton, Florida.

Schwille, F. (1988b) "Fluid-mechanical aspects of the migration of chemicals in fractured media". In: *Groundwater Flow and Quality Monitoring*, E. Custodio *et al.*, (Eds.), D. Reidel Publishing Co., 515-537.

Schwille, F. and D. Weber (1991) "Model experiments on gravity spreading of heavy organic vapors in the zone of aeration", *Schr. Angew. Geol. Karlsruhe*, **12**, 153-211.

Sudicky, E. A. (1986) "A natural gradient experiment on solute transport in a sand aquifer: Spatial variability of hydraulic conductivity and its role in the dispersion process", *Water Resources Research*, **22**, 2069-2082.

Tsang, Y. W. and C. F. Tsang (1987) "Channel model of flow through fractured media", *Water Resources Research*, **23**, 467-479.

Van Dam, J. (1967) "Migration of hydrocarbons in a water bearing stratum". In: *Joint Problems of the Oil and Water Industries*, P. Hepple (Ed.), Institute of Petroleum, London, 55-95.

Van der Waarden, M., A. L. A. M. Bridie, and W. M. Groenewoud (1971) "Transport of mineral oil components to groundwater. I. Model experiments on the transfer of hydrocarbons from a residual oil zone to trickling water", *Water Research*, **5**, 213-226.

Van der Waarden, M., W. M. Groenwoud, and A. L. A. M. Bridie (1977) "Transport of mineral oil components to groundwater. II. Influence of lime, clay, and organic soil components on the rate of transfer", *Water Research*, **11**, 359-365.

Wilson, J. L. and S. H. Conrad (1984) "Is physical displacement of residual hydrocarbons a realistic possibility in aquifer restoration?", In: *Proceedings of the NWWA/API Conference on Petroleum Hydrocarbons and Organic Chemicals in Ground Water-Prevention, Detection and Restoration*, National Water Well Association, November 5-7, 1984, Houston, Texas.

Wilson, J. L., S. H. Conrad, W. R. Mason, W. Peplinski, and E. Hagan (1990) *Laboratory Investigation of Residual Liquid Organics*, EPA/600/6-90/004, Cincinnati, Ohio.

6
Vapor Migration in the Vadose Zone

Carl A. Mendoza[1], Richard L. Johnson[2], and Robert W. Gillham[3]

[1]Department of Geology
University of Alberta
Edmonton, Alberta
Canada,T6G 2E3

[2]Department of Environmental Science and Engineering
Oregon Graduate Institute
P.O. Box 91000
Portland, Oregon
U.S.A. 97291-1000

[3]Waterloo Centre for Groundwater Research
University of Waterloo
Waterloo, Ontario
Canada N2L 3G1

ABSTRACT

When a dense non-aqueous phase liquid (DNAPL) is released to the unsaturated zone, it will migrate downwards and capillary forces will immobilize some of the liquid in the pore spaces as residual. Pools of DNAPL may also accumulate on lenses of lower permeability and on top of the capillary zone. This DNAPL will then begin to vaporize into the gas phase and migrate by diffusion away from the source. Gaseous advection due to pressure or density gradients can also play a role in the overall transport process. As the vapors migrate, they will partition into the aqueous and solid phases. These partitioning processes will tend to retard the rate of vapor migration. Partitioning into soil water will also make contaminants readily available for aqueous-phase transport. Eventually, the contaminants will reach the capillary fringe and dissolved DNAPL will be transported into groundwater by diffusion across the water table, by infiltrating water, and as the result of water-table fluctuations. At the ground surface, vapors can be lost to the atmosphere if no impermeable cover is present; alternatively, a cover will retain vapors and may lead to increased lateral migration. Since vapor transport by diffusion is commonly a rapid process that acts in all directions away from a residual source, groundwater contamination may occur over a wider area and much more quickly than if infiltration of either water or free-product were the only processes transporting DNAPL-related contaminants into the saturated zone. Groundwater contamination may even occur hydraulically up- or cross-gradient from a residual source. Failure to recognize the role of vapor transport can therefore lead to serious misinterpretations of the groundwater contamination at a given site.

6.1 INTRODUCTION

As a group, the dense chlorinated solvents are quite **volatile**, and can thus partition into the gas phase and migrate great distances as vapors in the unsaturated zone. Because these vapors can also partition into any soil moisture that is present, vapor transport processes have the potential to **contaminate** underlying groundwater resources. In this way, even if the residual source is completely contained within the vadose zone, vapor transport can cause rapid and widespread groundwater contamination. A conceptual model illustrating some of the processes that are responsible for vapor transport and subsequent groundwater contamination is presented in Figure 6.1.

As has been discussed in prior chapters, the dense chlorinated solvents are dense non-aqueous phase liquid (DNAPLs). As a DNAPL moves downwards in the unsaturated zone, some of the liquid will be immobilized by capillary forces in the pore spaces as residual. Pools of DNAPL may also form on the tops of lower permeability lenses. In the vadose zone, a DNAPL solvent will vaporize into the gas phase and migrate by **gaseous diffusion** in all directions away from the source. Gaseous **advection** due to pressure or density gradients may also play a role in the transport process. As the vapors migrate, the partitioning into the aqueous and solid phases that occurs will tend to retard the rate of vapor migration. Eventually the contaminants will reach the top of

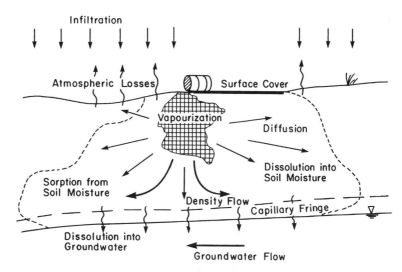

Figure 6.1 Conceptual model of vapor transport processes from a residual DNAPL source in the unsaturated zone. (Reprinted with permission from Mendoza and Frind, 1990a.)

the capillary fringe. Contaminants in the dissolved phase can then be transported into groundwater by diffusion across the water table, by infiltrating water, and as the result of water-table fluctuations. At the ground surface, vapors may be lost to the atmosphere if no impermeable cover is present. On the other hand, if a cover is present, it will retain vapors and may lead to increased lateral migration.

Since vapor transport by diffusion is commonly a **rapid** process that acts in all directions away from a residual source, groundwater contamination may occur over a wider area, and much more quickly, than if infiltration of water and/or the chlorinated solvent itself were the only mechanisms transporting contaminants from a release in the unsaturated zone. Groundwater contamination may even occur hydraulically up- or cross-gradient from the residual source. Thus, at many sites, failure to recognize the role of vapor transport could lead to serious misinterpretations of the potential for groundwater contamination. This chapter discusses all of the above aspects of passive vapor transport in the vadose zone. Although this discussion is oriented towards the behavior of vapors derived from dense chlorinated solvents, many of the same principles apply to the vapors of other volatile organic compounds and mixtures (*e.g.*, gasoline).

When dealing with flow and transport in several phases, as we are here, the notation can become cumbersome. To simplify that notation, most parameters that apply to the gas (air) phase have not been given the subscript a. All other parameters have w, l, or s subscripts to show that they pertain to the aqueous (water), liquid (DNAPL), or solid phases, respectively. In addition, it is implicitly assumed that mixtures of compounds are being discussed, and so subscripts are not generally used to distinguish between constituents.

6.2 PHASE PARTITIONING

6.2.1 General

The **partitioning** of contaminants between the different phases in the unsaturated zone
plays an important role in vapor transport. It is, in fact, the process of partitioning
between the organic liquid phase and the gas phase that provides the source necessary
for vapor migration. One-dimensional screening models, such as that developed by Jury
et al. (1990), use phase partitioning concepts to indicate the likely fate of contaminants in
the unsaturated zone. For given site conditions, these models indicate whether a particular
organic constituent is more likely to: 1) be transported to groundwater in the gas phase
or the aqueous phase; 2) be lost to the atmosphere; or 3) remain more-or-less in place.

6.2.2 Vaporization

The extent to which a compound vaporizes is determined by both its **vapor pressure**
and the **composition** of the liquid from which the vapors are derived. For a liquid that
contains only one constituent, the equilibrium vapor concentration is given simply by the
pure compound vapor pressure, expressed in appropriate units. However, if the residual
liquid is a **mixture** of different constituents, the equilibrium vapor concentration of each
constituent can be approximated by **Raoult's Law** which states that

$$c = X_t \frac{P^o}{RT} \quad , \tag{6.1}$$

where P^o is the pure compound vapor pressure of a particular constituent at the temperature T (Kelvin) of interest, X_l is the mole fraction of the compound in the source
liquid, and R is the gas constant. The vapor concentration c is expressed in units of mols
per unit volume.

Since the vapor concentration of a given compound at the source depends on the
mole fraction of that compound in the liquid phase, the source vapor concentration will
change over time as the compound is **depleted** or **enriched** relative to other compounds
in the source liquid. If the different compounds in the original liquid-phase source are
in equal proportions, the more volatile constituents will preferentially vaporize and become depleted relative to the less volatile compounds. In general, then, the source vapor
composition over time will be a function not only of the values of P^o for the various
constituents, but also of the values of X_l for those constituents.

Bloes *et al.* (1992) described a laboratory column experiment in which a medium-
grained sand was brought to residual saturation with an organic liquid consisting of
approximately equal mass fractions of benzene, trichloroethylene (TCE) and toluene. A
constant flow of air was then passed through the column. Figure 6.2 shows experimentally-
measured and model-simulated vapor concentrations in the effluent. Applicable experimental parameters and chemical properties are given in Table 6.1. The vapor concentrations for all three compounds that were observed initially are seen to be: 1) less than their
pure phase equilibrium concentrations; and 2) consistent with Raoult's Law. As the most
volatile compound (benzene) was depleted, the concentration of the next-most volatile

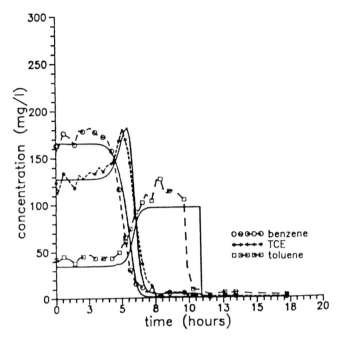

Figure 6.2 Breakthrough curves for vapor extraction of a residual mixture of organic liquids in a one-dimensional laboratory column. Points are measured values; solid lines are predicted values based on Raoult's Law. (Reprinted with permission from Bloes *et al.*, 1992.)

TABLE 6.1 Experimental Parameters for Column Study of Bloes *et al.* (1992).

| Compound | Measured initial residual fractions | | Vapor concentrations (mg/L) | | |
| | | | Pure compound | Initial column value | |
	Mass	Mole	Literature value	Calculated by Eq. (6.1)	Measured
benzene	0.351	0.432	379	164	158
TCE	0.349	0.255	497	127	114
toluene	0.300	0.313	117	37	43

compound (TCE) increased to a maximum, reflecting its enrichment in the remaining liquid mixture. Similar behavior was observed for toluene as the TCE was depleted in the source liquid. A comparison of the experimental data with the solid lines in Figure 6.2 indicates good agreement between the observed results and the predictions of a mathematical model based on Raoult's Law. Analogous behavior is to be expected in the vadose zone as vapors passively migrate away from a multicomponent residual source.

Kinetic mass-transfer effects do not appear to play a significant role in the vaporization of residual organic chemicals during passive migration. This statement is supported by observations from vapor extraction experiments where air was constrained to flow through porous media containing residual organic liquids (*e.g.*, Johnson *et al.*, 1987; McClellan and Gillham, 1990; and Bloes *et al.*, 1992). Because any kinetic partitioning limitations should be accentuated under forced advection, and because saturated vapors were nevertheless observed in the presence of free-product during these studies, we conclude that kinetic limitations are not likely to be important under passive migration circumstances.

In each of the studies referred to above, it is probable that the source liquid was in **direct contact** with the gas phase. Direct contact will occur in any organic liquid/soil system, and in any organic liquid/water/soil system in which the organic liquid is non-wetting (of the soil phase) relative to water. However, in a system of the latter type in which the organic liquid is the wetting phase (relative to water), such a liquid would be restricted to the smaller pores and might have a film of water between it and the gas phase. In such a case, it is conceivable that non-equilibrium (*i.e.*, kinetic effects) related to rate-limiting diffusion through the aqueous phase might be observed; to our knowledge a system of this type has not been investigated.

The vapor pressures of the chlorinated solvents increase significantly with increasing **temperature**. Figure 6.3 illustrates this dependence on temperature for TCE. The temperature dependence of the vapor pressure of a given compound is commonly calculated from the Antoine Equation whose regression coefficients are tabulated in standard chemistry reference texts (*e.g.*, Stephenson and Malanowski, 1987; Dean, 1985; and Weast, 1987).

The strong dependence of vapor pressure on temperature has several consequences for vapor transport. Firstly, the temperature will control the vapor concentrations in the source area and thus the vapor concentrations throughout the unsaturated zone. Secondly,

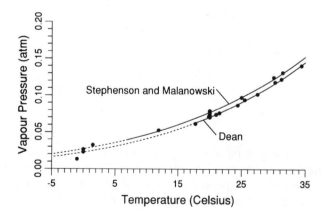

Figure 6.3   Temperature-dependent relationships and literature data values for the vapor pressure of trichloroethylene (TCE). (Adapted with permission from Mendoza *et al.*, 1990.)

if the porous medium is sufficiently coarse that density-induced advection is important, increased temperature will increase the propensity for gas-phase advection by increasing the source concentrations and thus the density gradients in the source area (see Section 6.3.3).

Vapor sampling in the field commonly indicates that the concentrations observed within suspected chlorinated solvent source areas are not as high as might have been expected based on equilibrium partitioning. The possible reasons for this may include one or more of the following:

- heterogeneity in both porous media properties and residual fluid distribution (see Chapter 5);
- uncertainty concerning the actual location of the residual source;
- not accounting for mixtures of compounds;
- poor sampler installation or sampling techniques;
- recent gas-phase advection caused by vapor extraction systems; and
- not correcting concentrations for temperature variations.

6.2.3 Gaseous-Aqueous Partitioning

In the absence of forced advection, the assumption of **equilibrium partitioning** between the gaseous and aqueous phase appears to be valid for chlorinated solvent compounds in the unsaturated zone (Johnson *et al.*, 1987). This equilibrium partitioning process is represented by **Henry's Law** as

$$H = \frac{c}{c_w} \quad , \tag{6.2}$$

where c and c_w are the concentrations in the gaseous and aqueous phases, respectively, in units of mols per unit volume. The parameter H is then the dimensionless Henry's Law constant expressed on a molar basis (*i.e.*, mol/volume per mol/volume). For compounds which are only slightly soluble in water, common means for estimating the Henry's Law constant is (Mackay *et al.*, 1979)

$$H = \frac{P^o/S}{RT} \quad , \tag{6.3}$$

where S is the solubility of the compound in water in units of mols per volume.

As is indicated in Eq.(6.3), the Henry's Law constant for a given compound depends on both the compound's vapor pressure and its solubility. Because vapor pressures generally increase strongly with temperature (see Figure 6.3), and solubilities increase moderately with temperature, Henry's Law constants increase moderately with temperature. The reader should be aware that there are several alternate sets of units used for H values. When the level in the gas phase is expressed in units of pressure, H is often reported in units of atm-m^3/mol, or in units of kPa-m^3/mol. Alternatively, some texts define H to be the dimensionless ratio of the gas concentration to the water concentration. Thus, care must be taken in the use of H values that are reported in the literature.

6.2.4 Aqueous-Solid Partitioning

Aqueous-solid partitioning at equilibrium in the unsaturated zone is commonly described using a distribution coefficient K_d approach which assumes **linear, instantaneous, and reversible partitioning** between the water and the soil phases. This description is identical to that often used in saturated groundwater transport. As is discussed in detail in Chapter 8, for organic contaminants, K_d is often predicted using

$$K_d = K_{oc} f_{oc} \tag{6.4}$$

where K_{oc} is the water/organic carbon partitioning coefficient and f_{oc} is the fraction of organic carbon in the soils. The level of uncertainty associated with using Eq.(6.4) to predict K_d values is discussed in Chapter 8.

6.2.5 Gaseous-Solid Partitioning

If the unsaturated zone is very dry, as can occur in soils immediately adjacent to the ground surface, it may be possible for contaminants to partition from the gaseous phase to the solid phase in a manner that is different than when liquid water is present. Although the mechanisms are not currently well understood, the available evidence suggests that this mode of partitioning can be **strong as well as highly non-linear** (Chiou and Shoup, 1985). This type of gaseous-solid partitioning can be important only when the relative humidity in the unsaturated zone is less than about 90%. At humidities of 90% and greater, the soil grains become completely covered with a very thin film of water, and the sorption properties of the soil tend towards what is expected when macroscopic amounts of water are present (Chiou and Shoup, 1985). Because completely dry soils rarely exist to any significant depth in the unsaturated zone, this type of enhanced sorption is generally not important for passive vapor migration.

6.2.6 Retardation Factor

The equilibrium phase partitioning concepts discussed above lead to a **retardation factor** that can be defined as (Baehr, 1987)

$$R = 1 + \frac{\theta_w}{\theta_a}\frac{1}{H} + \frac{\rho_b K_d}{\theta_a H} \quad , \tag{6.5}$$

where θ_a and θ_w are the volumetric soil-gas and soil-moisture contents, respectively, and ρ_b is the bulk density of the porous medium. It should be noted that R is a strong function of θ_w since the soil-gas and soil-moisture contents are related through the expression $\theta = \theta_w + \theta_a$, where θ is the porosity.

The terms that comprise R describe the relative masses of contaminant that occupy each of the three phases at any particular point in space. The retardation factor also describes the rate of vapor plume migration relative to a vapor plume that does not partition to the aqueous or solid phases. This retardation factor is analogous to that used in groundwater transport modeling, except that the pore water *as well as* the solids act as immobile phases. The middle term on the right hand side of Eq.(6.5) represents partitioning between the gaseous and aqueous phases while the last term represents partitioning between the aqueous and solid phases. A thin film of soil moisture is assumed to be present on all the soil grains so that the type of enhanced sorption by the solid phase discussed in Section 6.2.5 is not important.

6.3 GASEOUS TRANSPORT

6.3.1 General

Although diffusion due to chemical concentration gradients is usually the primary transport mechanism in the unsaturated zone, vapors may also be transported by advection in that zone. Passive vapor transport can thus be described using the **advection-dispersion equation**

$$\frac{\partial}{\partial x_i}\left[\theta_a D_{ij}\frac{\partial c}{\partial x_j}\right] - \theta_a v_i \frac{\partial c}{\partial x_i} = \theta_a R \frac{\partial c}{\partial t} \quad , \qquad i, j = 1, 2, 3 \quad , \tag{6.6}$$

where i and j represent the three coordinate directions, and t is time. The average linear gas-phase velocity (v_i) is determined from the Darcy Equation.

The terms in Eq.(6.6) are similar to those for contaminant transport by groundwater in the saturated zone. The first term on the left represents transport by dispersion (including diffusion), while the second represents transport by bulk gas-phase advection. The change in concentration over time is described by the term on the right. For simplicity, no terms have been included for external sources or sinks.

The **dispersion coefficient** is a second rank tensor that has components describing both mechanical dispersion and chemical diffusion so that

$$D_{ij} = \alpha_T |v| \, \delta_{ij} + (\alpha_L - \alpha_T)\frac{v_i v_j}{|v|} + D_e \delta_{ij} \quad , \qquad i, j = 1, 2, 3 \quad , \tag{6.7}$$

where a_L and a_T are the longitudinal and transverse dispersivities respectively, D_e is the **effective gaseous diffusion coefficient**,[†] and δ_{ij} is the Kronecker delta (Bear, 1972).

Concentrations here are in units of mols per unit volume. Often, however, gaseous concentrations are reported in a wide variety of units that include volume fraction units (*e.g.*, parts-per-million-by-volume (ppmV) and percent (%)), pressure units (*e.g.*, atm and Pa), or mass concentration units (*e.g.*, mg/L and μg/L). Using the Ideal Gas Law, the temperature, and the molecular weight of the contaminant of interest, conversions can be made between these various units.

Eq.(6.6) has been written in three-dimensional Cartesian coordinates. Often, however, releases of volatile organic compounds to the subsurface can be confined within a relatively small lateral area. In such cases, especially if diffusion is the primary transport

---

[†]The effective diffusion coefficient is sometimes also referred to as D^*.

mechanism, a two-dimensional axisymmetric representation of the transport equation may
be valid because the vapors will then be migrating in all directions from a centralized
residual source. The axisymmetric formulation of Eq.(6.6) may be written as

$$\frac{1}{r}\frac{\partial}{\partial x_i}\left[r\theta_a D_{ij}\frac{\partial c}{\partial x_j}\right] - \theta_a v_i \frac{\partial c}{\partial x_i} = \theta_a R \frac{\partial c}{\partial t} \quad , \qquad i, j = 1, 2 \quad , \tag{6.8}$$

where the coordinate axes are oriented in the radial and vertical directions and have their
origin at the center of the residual source. The radius from the center of the spill is also
denoted by r.

6.3.2 Diffusion

Transport by **diffusion** occurs in response to a chemical activity gradient. As written in
Eq.(6.6), it is assumed that the activity gradient can be represented by the concentration
gradient and that diffusion can be described by Fick's Laws. Ideally, Fick's Laws apply
only to scenarios involving isothermal transport in dilute binary systems where the compounds have similar molecular weights. Nevertheless, in practice, Fick's Laws appear to
be reasonable approximations under a wide range of conditions.

In very fine-grained materials and at low absolute pressures, interference with the
pore walls may limit the applicability of Fick's Laws, and Knudsen diffusion may provide
a more appropriate description (Thorstenson and Pollock, 1989). The Knudsen diffusion
model is not, however, generally used.

The effective gas phase diffusion coefficient in Eq.(6.7) may be described by

$$D_e = \tau D \tag{6.9}$$

where τ is the **tortuosity** of the porous medium and D is the **free-air diffusion coefficient**. The tortuosity, which lies between 0.0 and 1.0, accounts for the increased distance
that contaminant molecules must travel in a porous medium relative to the straight line
distance that is possible in a free gas phase.

Free-air diffusion coefficients are typically several orders of magnitude greater
than aqueous diffusion coefficients. For example, the free-air diffusion coefficient for
TCE and similar chlorinated solvents is slightly less than 10^{-5} m²/s at 20 °C, while the
aqueous phase diffusion coefficient for TCE is on the order of 10^{-9} m²/s at 20 °C. This
large difference commonly leads to gas phase diffusion dominating over aqueous phase
diffusion as a transport mechanism in the unsaturated zone.

Free-air diffusion coefficients have been measured for a wide range of different
compounds and are tabulated in chemistry reference texts (*e.g.*, Weast, 1987). Alternatively, they can be estimated using empirical relationships (*e.g.*, see, Lyman *et al.*,
1984). These estimation equations are also useful for determining the dependence of D
on temperature. However, in general, D values increase only slightly with increasing
temperature. Between 10 °C and 20 °C, the values for D for the common chlorinated
solvents increase by an average of less than 5% (Mendoza and Frind, 1990b).

Several empirical estimates have been developed for the tortuosity of porous media. The most widely used approximation is that usually attributed to Millington and Quirk (1961)

$$\tau = \theta_a^{7/3}/\theta^2 \quad , \tag{6.10}$$

where θ is the bulk (effective) porosity of the medium. Similar relationships have been developed by Currie (1970) and Grable and Siemer (1968), among others. These models are applicable to sandy materials whose soil-moisture saturation (θ_w/θ) is less than about 70% (Weeks et al., 1982). At higher water saturations, a continuous air phase may cease to exist and aqueous diffusion begins to play a relatively more important role in controlling the diffusion process. Also, these tortuosity relations tend to breakdown in silty and clayey materials due to the absence of a continuous air phase.

Eq.(6.10) illustrates the strong dependence of the effective diffusion coefficient on soil moisture content: as moisture content increases, D_e decreases dramatically. However, even at relatively high moisture contents, D_e may still be several orders of magnitude greater than effective aqueous diffusion coefficients.

Effective diffusion coefficients can be measured in the laboratory or in the field. In the laboratory, they are measured by monitoring the migration of gases diffusing through a column filled with soil with different moisture contents. The data analysis may be either transient or steady-state. In the field, compounds are allowed to diffuse through the medium of interest in its natural state (e.g., Kreamer et al., 1988). Numerical or analytical models are then used to back-calculate the diffusion coefficients. Typically, transient methods yield effective reactive diffusion coefficients which implicitly include retardation factors, with the quantity that is being measured directly being D_e/R. A separate measurement of R then allows calculation of D_e.

6.3.3 Advection

Because diffusion in the gas phase can be such an important transport process, it commonly dominates over **advection**. Nevertheless, advection can be important under some circumstances because the low viscosity of gases causes them to be highly mobile even when the pressure or density gradients are very low.

For coarse-grained materials, advective flow in the gas phase may be described using the gas-phase continuity equation and the Darcy Equation. If density effects are known to be negligible, a pressure-based formulation may be appropriate:

$$\frac{\partial}{\partial x_i}\left[k_r \frac{k_{ij}}{\mu}\frac{\partial P}{\partial x_j}\right] = \theta_a \beta \frac{\partial P}{\partial t} \quad , \qquad i,j = 1,2,3 \quad . \tag{6.11}$$

However, in some cases, density gradients may contribute significantly to vapor transport. One form of the flow equation that includes density is the equivalent fresh-air head formulation (Mendoza and Frind, 1990a):

$$\frac{\partial}{\partial x_i}\left[k_r k_{ij}\frac{\rho_0 g}{\mu}\left(\frac{\partial h^*}{\partial x_j} + \frac{\rho - \rho_0}{\rho_0}\frac{\partial z}{\partial x_j}\right)\right] = \theta_a \rho_0 g \beta \frac{\partial h^*}{\partial t} \quad , \qquad i,j = 1,2,3 \quad . \tag{6.12}$$

In the above equations, P is the pressure, μ is the gas viscosity, β is the gas-phase compressibility, k_{ij} is the intrinsic permeability of the medium, and k_r is the relative gas permeability. The relative permeability, which depends on the soil and its moisture content, may be described by the Brooks and Corey (1964) relationships, or may be measured in the laboratory. In the equivalent head formulation, ρ is the actual density of the gas phase, ρ_0 is the density of pure air, and g is the gravitational constant. The equivalent fresh-air head is defined by the equation

$$h^* = \frac{P}{\rho_0 g} + z \quad , \tag{6.13}$$

where z is the elevation above some datum. Since the most significant contribution to variations in density is usually caused by changes in concentration, Eq.(6.12) and the vapor transport equation (Eq.(6.6)) form a coupled pair of non-linear partial differential equations. As with the advection-dispersion equation, axisymmetric formulations may also be written for these equations.

In fine-grained materials, especially under the influence of a strong applied pressure gradient, the Darcy Equation may no longer strictly apply. This is due to the Klinkenberg effect where the assumption of no-slip along the pore walls is no longer valid and the flow of gases will exceed that predicted by the Darcy Equation. However, for the passive migration of gases in unsaturated, fine-grained media, this effect is rarely of consequence because the driving forces that commonly arise are not sufficient to cause significant advection.

As written, Eqs.(6.11) and (6.12) require that the gas phase be essentially **incompressible**. Strictly speaking, gases do not satisfy this requirement since their compressibilities are on the order of 10^{-5} Pa^{-1}, compared to 4.4×10^{-10} Pa^{-1} for water. However, Massmann (1989) has shown that the assumption of incompressibility is applicable for pressure differentials up to about 20,000 Pa (0.2 atm). Pressure differences of this magnitude are not expected for passive vapor migration, and so the assumption of an essentially incompressible gas phase is appropriate for such situations.

Pressure and density gradients that are sufficiently large to cause advective transport in the unsaturated zone may arise from several causes, including density gradients due to the heavy nature of chlorinated solvent vapors, and pressure gradients due to: 1) barometric pressure variations; 2) vaporization from the liquid product; 3) landfill gas generation; and 4) the movement of water in the unsaturated zone.

A common characteristic of many chlorinated solvents is that their saturated vapors are much **denser** than air. This is because they have high molecular weights (commonly three to four times greater than the mean molecular weight for air), and they are very volatile (saturated vapor concentrations of up to several tens of percent of 1 atmosphere). As a result, large density gradients may exist near a residual source if the vapor source approaches saturation. These density gradients may cause downward advection with velocities on the order of meters per day (Mendoza and Frind, 1990b; Johnson et al., 1992).

The effects of density-induced transport have been investigated in numerical modeling studies by several researchers, including Sleep and Sykes (1989), Falta et al. (1989),

Mendoza and Frind (1990a,b) and Mendoza and McAlary (1990). These studies show that in high permeability environments, density-induced advection can be a significant transport mechanism that equals or exceeds the effect of diffusion. The threshold permeability above which density-induced advection becomes important for the chlorinated solvents appears to be on the order of 10^{-11} m^2 (equivalent to a hydraulic conductivity of 10^{-2} cm/s). The vapor source must be maintained at a high concentration in order to maintain high density gradients. Also, the greater the thickness of the unsaturated zone, the greater the advective effects due to density gradients. Temperature can have a strong effect on the density of the gas phase through its influence on the vapor pressure.

The **atmospheric pressure** fluctuates according to global and regional weather patterns. This means that the pressure along the upper boundary of the unsaturated zone (*i.e.*, the ground surface) is changing constantly. Although these pressure variations are generally relatively small, they can exceed 5 kPa (0.05 atm). If the ground surface is open to the atmosphere, these pressure variations are applied uniformly over the entire boundary and so act in the same manner over the whole domain, either retaining vapors (high pressure zone) or enhancing vapor removal (low pressure zone). However, this effect will only be significant if the depth to groundwater is very large. If the ground surface is restricted by a cover, vapors will be pumped out of, or confined within, the area beneath the cover as barometric pressure changes act along the edges of the cover. Massmann and Farrier (1992) showed that the net effect of barometric pumping is to increase the apparent dispersion of vapors in the unsaturated zone and that the advective effects of barometric pumping beneath a cover can be significant. Thibodeaux *et al.* (1982), Nilson and Lie (1990), and Nilson *et al.* (1991) considered the effects of barometric pumping on contaminants located below a fractured impermeable cover. These analyses showed that the transport of vapors through cracks could be significantly enhanced by barometric pressure fluctuations.

The mixture of wastes placed in landfills commonly leads to **microbial action** that produces large amounts of carbon dioxide and methane gas. In generating this gas, pressure gradients may be established towards the exterior of the landfill. Although these gradients are typically low (on the order of a few Pa/m), they can be large enough to cause significant bulk movement of gas from the landfill. If volatile organic wastes are also present in the landfill, their vapors will migrate along with this bulk gas flow (Metcalfe and Farquhar, 1987).

Even in the absence of biologically-produced gases, **vaporization** from a residual source can result in bulk gas migration by advection away from the source (Bird, 1956). For chlorinated solvents, this aspect of vapor transport was considered by Mendoza and Frind (1990b) who showed that while it may be of secondary importance in some cases, transport of volatilized solvents is generally dominated by diffusion and other advective effects.

Regional movement of the water table may also result in advection in the gas phase. If the water table drops, air is drawn into the unsaturated zone to fill the newly desaturated pore space. Similarly, if the water table rises, gas is expelled to the atmosphere. This movement of the gas phase will transport whatever contaminants are in the vapor phase. Weeks *et al.* (1982) document a regional case study where long-term declines in water table elevation have drawn contaminants further into the unsaturated zone than would have been expected based on diffusion alone.

6.4 AQUEOUS TRANSPORT

Contaminants can be transported in the aqueous phase in the unsaturated zone just as they can be transported in the gas phase. In fact, some form of transport in the aqueous phase is necessary for the creation of groundwater contamination from vapor plumes since vapors themselves cannot enter the saturated zone. Transport in the aqueous phase may be due to either advection or diffusion. If we consider equilibrium between the gaseous and aqueous phases, Eq.(6.6) can be modified to include aqueous transport by writing

$$\frac{\partial}{\partial x_i}\left[\left(\theta_a D_{ij} + \frac{\theta_w}{H} D_{w_{ij}}\right)\frac{\partial c}{\partial x_j}\right] - \left(\theta_a v_i + \frac{\theta_w}{H} v_{w_i}\right)\frac{\partial c}{\partial x_i} = \theta_a R \frac{\partial c}{\partial t} \quad , \quad i, j = 1, 2, 3 \quad .$$

(6.14)

Here v_w is the velocity of water due to infiltration. The aqueous dispersion tensor ($D_{w_{ij}}$) may be written in a form analogous to Eq.(6.7).

By assuming **equilibrium** between the gaseous and aqueous phases, aqueous concentrations can be written in terms of gaseous concentrations using Henry's Law. Thus, aqueous concentrations do not appear in Eq.(6.14). If equilibrium between the gaseous and aqueous phases is not assumed, two equations need to be written, one for the concentration in each of the two phases. Because the physics of aqueous flow and transport in the unsaturated zone is the topic of many texts (*e.g.*, Hillel, 1980), it is not discussed in detail here.

6.5 INTERACTIONS WITH THE ATMOSPHERE

The nature of the ground surface may have a great influence over the distribution and fate of chlorinated solvent vapors in the unsaturated zone. If the ground surface is **open** to the atmosphere, vapors will be transported by diffusion from the unsaturated zone to the atmosphere: having essentially zero concentrations of these compounds, the atmosphere acts as a sink. Kimball and Lemon (1971) found that wind passing across the surface of a coarse porous medium resulted in greater losses of heptane vapors from shallow depths than in the absence of the wind. If the ground surface is covered with a **finer-grained layer** or with **vegetation**, atmospheric losses will be restricted due to the resistance to flow and diffusion caused by such covers. The ground surface may be covered by pavement or a building foundation which is impermeable to both gas flow and vapor diffusion. Cracks or small open sections in such a cover may, however, allow the loss of significant vapor mass to the atmosphere (Thibodeaux *et al.*, 1982; Nilson *et al.*, 1991).

The character of the ground surface also affects the extent of **lateral migration** in the unsaturated zone. If diffusive transport is the primary vapor transport mechanism, an open ground surface results in less lateral transport than beneath a covered ground surface. This is due to the mass losses through the open ground surface. However, if density-induced transport is a significant transport mechanism, the opposite effect may be observed due to higher gas-phase velocities in the absence of a cover (Mendoza and Frind, 1990b).

Obviously, the nature of the ground surface boundary also affects the **infiltration** of water. An impermeable cover at the ground surface will prevent infiltration, whereas an open ground surface will allow infiltratation. In the latter case, water can pass through contaminated zones, including the residual source area, ultimately allowing contaminated water to recharge the groundwater zone.

6.6 INTERACTIONS WITH GROUNDWATER

As the interface between the unsaturated and groundwater zones, the **capillary fringe** is the boundary through which contaminants must move if contamination in the vadose zone is to cause groundwater contamination. Conversely, contaminants may migrate from an established plume in the groundwater zone into the unsaturated zone; this mode of transport is required for the successful mapping of groundwater plumes by vapor sampling.

Because the capillary fringe does not contain a connected gas phase, transport of contaminants through this zone must occur in the aqueous phase. The three main mechanisms for contaminants to migrate through the capillary fringe are diffusion and dispersion, advection, and fluctuations in the elevation of the water table. The plume of groundwater contamination caused by these processes is expected to be confined to the regions of the saturated flow regime that are near the water table.

In the unsaturated zone, contaminants can rapidly reach the top of the capillary fringe by vapor transport processes. At the top of the capillary fringe, the contaminants will partition into the aqueous phase and an aqueous-phase concentration gradient will be established into the saturated zone. Such a gradient will result in transport through the capillary fringe by molecular diffusion or dispersion. However, McCarthy and Johnson (1992) have shown that vertical dispersion within the capillary fringe is a weak process. Moreover, aqueous-phase diffusion is typically weak due to the small magnitude of aqueous-phase diffusion coefficients. Thus, advective transport due to infiltrating water is likely to be a more significant mechanism for transporting contaminants downwards through the capillary fringe.

Another important mechanism which can contribute to groundwater contamination involves the upward and downward movements of the **water table** in response to changes in regional infiltration. As noted above, if the water table drops, the unsaturated zone will be enlarged and contaminant vapors will be drawn deeper into the domain. The vapors will then be able to partition to the soil moisture in the newly exposed section of the unsaturated zone. If the water table later rises, this contaminated soil moisture will be incorporated into the groundwater flow system and a groundwater plume will be created.

6.7 SOIL-GAS SURVEYS

6.7.1 General

Soil-gas surveys provide a rapid and inexpensive method of **detecting and mapping** vapor concentrations in the unsaturated zone. These surveys can be useful as preliminary surveys to plan more costly operations such as coring or piezometer installation. Possible sources of the vapors to be delineated include free-product liquid in the unsaturated zone, vapor plumes, and aqueous plumes in the saturated zone underlying the site of interest.

6.7.2 Sampling

In general, vapor sampling methods may be classified as being either **active** or **passive**. Active sampling involves analyzing vapor samples drawn from a temporary or permanent access tube; passive sampling involves the analysis of vapors collected by a sorbent detector buried in the subsurface for some period of time. Active sampling appears to be the preferred method of conducting soil-gas surveys. The reasons for this are that the vapor concentration values can be obtained directly and rapidly. Consequently, a soil-gas survey can easily be modified before it is completed. A disadvantage of active sampling may be that the vapor distribution in the unsaturated zone can be disturbed by sample withdrawal. Active soil-gas sampling is discussed in detail by Kerfoot (1988), Tillman *et al.* (1989), and Hughes *et al.* (1990), among others.

The primary advantages of passive sampling are that it is less costly than active sampling and that time-averaged results are obtained. Disadvantages include the fact that longer periods of time (typically a few weeks) are required to obtain results, the survey cannot be modified in-progress, and only relative concentrations are obtained. With regard to the last point, the measured concentrations are not absolute concentrations in the soil gas; rather, they give an indication of relative amounts of different chemicals at a particular location and between locations from the same survey. Passive sampling techniques have been discussed by Voorhees *et al.* (1984), Malley *et al.* (1985), and Kerfoot and Mayer (1986).

6.7.3 Contaminant Detection

In principle, with a properly-conducted soil-gas survey, it is straightforward to delineate a **vapor plume** in the unsaturated zone. It is, however, not always as simple to determine whether free product is also present. Interpretation problems generally arise because saturated vapor concentrations are rarely observed, even if free product is present. The primary reasons for this are outlined in Section 6.2.2. In these cases, good judgement, experience, and alternative indicators must be used to interpret the data.

The idea of detection of a **groundwater plume** by vapor sampling in the unsaturated zone (see Figure 6.4) has become popular in the past few years, and a number of successful demonstrations have been reported (e.g., Marrin and Thompson, 1987; Kerfoot, 1987; Marrin and Kerfoot, 1988; Bishop *et al.*, 1990). However, because several

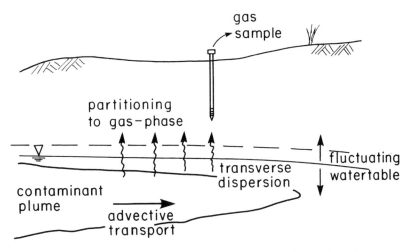

Figure 6.4   Conceptual model for processes involved in groundwater plume detection using soil-gas sampling techniques.

interrelated factors control mass transfer across the capillary fringe, it seems likely that, at most, soil gas surveys can only provide qualitative information about groundwater contamination. In particular, because dispersion transverse to flow is a weak process, *only plumes that are immediately adjacent to the water table* will be detected by a soil gas survey. In addition, the presence of any source of vapors (*e.g.*, small undetected pools or pockets of residual within the unsaturated zone) will greatly complicate the delineation of groundwater plumes. Active infiltration due to precipitation may make such a delineation impossible.

6.8 A PAIR OF FIELD EXPERIMENTS

A pair of detailed field experiments involving the transport of TCE vapors at the Borden field site were reported by Hughes (1991) and Hughes *et al.* (1992). The unsaturated zone at the site consists of a medium-grained sand with moisture contents at field capacity and organic carbon contents that are generally low ($\sim$0.02%). The upper section of the unsaturated domain is heterogeneous, with increased organic carbon contents (see Figure 6.5). The first experiment was conducted in the winter and had a covered ground surface to limit vapor losses to the atmosphere. The second experiment was conducted in the summer and had an open ground surface, except for immediately above the residual source. Variations in temperature greatly affected the experimental results; temperature profiles are shown in Figure 6.5.

A residual source of TCE was prepared by mixing liquid TCE with excavated native sand at near residual saturation, and placing it in the ground. Vapor distributions were obtained using active sampling techniques along an array of sampling probes extending radially outwards from the source. Between the two experiments, vapor extraction was used to reduce TCE vapor concentrations to less than 20 ppmV.

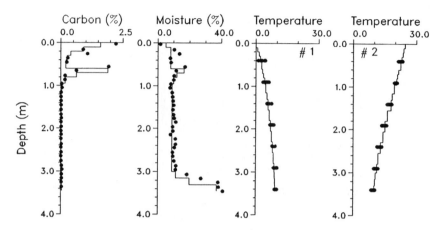

Figure 6.5 Physical parameters measured at the Borden vapor transport site: a) soil organic carbon content; b) soil moisture content; c) temperature distribution for the first experiment, and d) temperature distribution for the second experiment. (Reprinted with permission from Mendoza *et al.*, 1990.)

Field observations of the vapor plumes for each experiment after 18 days are shown in Figure 6.6. In both cases, the plumes migrated a considerable distance in a short period of time. However, in the second experiment, the overall concentrations were higher and the leading edge of the plume extended farther from the source zone.

Sensitivity analyses were performed using a numerical model (Mendoza *et al.*, 1990, 1992). The overall differences in concentration between the two experiments are primarily attributable to the different temperature regimes in the two experiments: the first experiment had lower vapor concentrations (by a third) due to lower temperatures in the source area. In addition, the lower temperatures near the ground surface resulted in a higher degree of partitioning to the aqueous phase, and so led to increased retardation. The higher organic carbon contents near the ground surface, in particular a continuous layer at about 0.8 m depth, were shown to exhibit high retardation factors which led to slower transport in this region in both experiments, and tended to limit vapor losses to

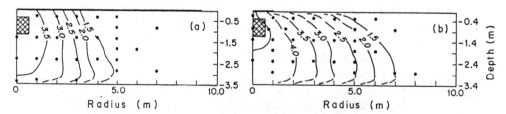

Figure 6.6 Measured vapor concentrations after 18 days in the Borden vapor transport experiments: a) covered experiment; b) uncovered experiment. Contours are logarithms of concentration expressed in parts-per-million-by-volume (ppmV). (Reprinted with permission from Mendoza *et al.*, 1992.)

the atmosphere in the second experiment. This led to the similar plume shapes despite the different ground surface boundary conditions.

The sensitivity analyses also indicated that density-induced advection played a small role in the experiments, with the effect being greater in the second experiment where the source concentrations were higher. The average permeability (1.2×10^{-11} m^2) of the sands is in the range where density-induced advection can begin to become a significant transport process, providing that the vapor density is sufficiently high (Mendoza and Frind, 1990b).

A thin, but laterally extensive, groundwater plume developed beneath the portion of the vadose zone used in the two experiments (Rivett and Cherry, 1991). Although TCE was used for other experiments at the site, it is felt that this contamination is primarily a result of the vapor migration experiments. Annual water table fluctuations on the order of 1 m and precipitation appear to be responsible for the development of this plume.

6.9 CONCLUSIONS

Vapor transport from residual or pooled chlorinated solvents in the vadose zone can have a significant impact on groundwater quality. The primary reasons for this are that vapor transport is often very rapid relative to aqueous transport, and that vapors tend to migrate in all directions from the source. Thus, contamination from a spill of chlorinated solvents may quickly reach the water table over a wide area and in a manner that is not controlled by the hydraulic gradients in the saturated zone.

Vapor transport can be described by equations that are similar in form to groundwater transport equations. They are conceptually easy to understand and existing groundwater transport models may be modified to simulate vapor transport. The greatest difference between the behavior of contaminants in the two zones is that diffusion tends to be the dominant transport process in the unsaturated zone, while advection is commonly the primary transport mechanism in the saturated zone.

In high-permeability porous media, density-driven advective flow can play an important role in transport if the vapor concentrations are high. Initial velocities on the order of meters per day are possible, and the result can be high gaseous and aqueous concentrations in the vicinity of the water table. Advective transport due to pressure gradients arising from barometric pressure fluctuations may also increase dispersion and lead to a wider distribution of contaminants.

The rate of vapor transport is strongly dependent on the soil-moisture content of the unsaturated zone because the effective diffusion coefficient and the retardation factor are both functions of the soil-moisture content. Temperature variations in the subsurface can affect vapor concentrations and migration rates through their influence on vapor pressures and Henry's Law constants (Kerfoot, 1991).

The character of the ground surface often controls the degree of vapor losses to the atmosphere and the degree of infiltration into the unsaturated zone. Losses to the atmosphere remove contaminants that might otherwise reach the water table, while infiltration can transport contaminants to the water table.

While vapor transport mechanisms are responsible for distributing contaminant vapors throughout the unsaturated zone, aqueous-phase transport mechanisms cause groundwater contamination in the saturated zone. The primary aqueous-phase transport processes involved are advection due to the movement of infiltrating water, diffusion across the capillary fringe, and regional fluctuations in the elevation of the water table. These transport processes typically result in thin plumes of contaminated groundwater immediately adjacent to the water table.

ACKNOWLEDGEMENTS

Funding support for this research was provided in part by the University Consortium Solvents-in-Groundwater Research Program. Sponsors of the Program between 1988 and 1994 have included: The Boeing Company, Ciba-Geigy Corporation, Dow Chemical Canada/USA, Eastman Kodak Co., General Electric Co., Laidlaw Environmental Systems Ltd., Mitre Corporation, The Natural Sciences and Engineering Research Council of Canada, and the Ontario University Research Incentive Fund.

6.10 REFERENCES

Bear, J. (1972) *Dynamics of Fluids in Porous Media*, Elsevier, New York.

Baehr, A. L. (1987) "Selective transport of hydrocarbons in the unsaturated zone due to aqueous and vapor phase partitioning", *Water Resources Research*, **23**, 1926-1938.

Bird, R. B. (1956) "Theory of diffusion", in *Advances Chem. Eng.*, T. B. Drew and J. W. Hoopes, Jr. (Eds.), Academic, San Diego, 155-239.

Bishop, P. K., M. W. Burston, D. N. Lerner, and P. R. Eastwood (1990) "Soil gas surveying of chlorinated solvents in relation to groundwater pollution studies", *Quarterly J. Eng. Geol.*, **23**, 255-265.

Bloes, M. B., K. M. Rathfelder, and D. M. Mackay (1992) "Laboratory studies of vapor extraction for remediation of contaminated soil". In: *Proceedings: Conference on Subsurface Contamination by Immiscible Fluids*, K. U. Weyer (Ed.) International Association of Hydrogeologists, Calgary, April 18-20. Order from A. A. Balkema, Old Post Road, Brookfield, Vermont 05036.

Brooks, R. H. and A. T. Corey (1964) "Hydraulic properties of porous media", *Hydrology Papers*, **3**, Colorado State University, Fort Collins.

Chiou, C. T. and T. D. Shoup (1985) "Soil sorption of organic vapors and effects of humidity on sorptive mechanism and capacity", *Environ. Sci. Technol.*, **19**, 1196-1200.

Currie, J. A. (1970) "Movement of gases in soil respiration", In: *Sorption and Transport Processes in Soils*, SCI Monographs, **37**, Rothamsted Experimental Station, Harpenden, England.

Dean, J. A. (Ed.) (1985) *Lange's Handbook of Chemistry*, 13th Edition, McGraw-Hill, New York.

Falta, R. W., I. Javandel, K. Pruess, and P. A. Witherspoon (1989) "Density-driven flow of gas in the unsaturated zone due to the evaporation of volatile organic compounds", *Water Resources Research*, **25**, 2159-2169.

Grable, A. R. and E. G. Siemer (1968) "Effects of bulk density, aggregate size, and soil water suction on oxygen diffusion, redox potentials, and elongation of corn roots", *Soil Sci. Soc. Amer. Proc.*, **32**, 180-186.

Hillel, D. (1980) *Fundamentals of Soil Physics*, Academic Press, New York.

Hughes, B. M. (1991) *Vapour Transport of Trichloroethylene in the Unsaturated Zone: A Field Experiment*, M.Sc. Thesis, Dept. Earth Sciences, University of Waterloo, Waterloo, Ontario.

Hughes, B. M., R. W. Gillham, and C. A. Mendoza (1992) "Transport of trichloroethylene vapours in the unsaturated zone: A field experiment". In: *Proceedings: Conference on Subsurface Contamination by Immiscible Fluids*, K. U. Weyer (Ed.), International Association of Hydrogeologists, Calgary, April 18-20. Order from A. A. Balkema, Old Post Road, Brookfield, Vermont 05036.

Hughes, B. M., R. D. McClellan, and R. W. Gillham (1990) "Application of soil-gas sampling technology to studies of trichloroethylene vapour transport in the unsaturated zone", In: *Groundwater Quality and Analysis at Hazardous Waste Sites*, S. Lesage and R. E. Jackson (Eds.), Marcel Dekker.

Johnson, R. L., K. A. McCarthy, M. Perrott, and C. A. Mendoza (1992) "Density-driven vapor transport: Physical and numerical modeling". In: *Proceedings: Conference on Subsurface Contamination by Immiscible Fluids*, K. U. Weyer (Ed.), International Association of Hydrogeologists, Calgary, April 18-20. Order from A.A. Balkema, Old Post Road, Brookfield, Vermont 05036.

Johnson, R. L., C. D. Palmer, and J. F. Keely (1987) "Mass transfer of organics between soil, water and vapor phases: Implications for monitoring, biodegradation and remediation". In: *Proceedings: NWWA/API Conference on Petroleum Hydrocarbons and Organic Chemicals in Ground Water: Prevention, Detection, Restoration*, November 17-19, Houston, Texas.

Jury, W. A., D. Russo, G. Streile, and H. El Abd (1990) "Evaluation of volatilization by organic chemicals residing below the soil surface", *Water Resources Research*, **26**, 13-20.

Kerfoot, H. B. (1987) "Shallow-probe soil-gas sampling for indication of ground-water contamination by chloroform", *Int. J. Environ. Anal. Chem.*, **30**, 167-181.

Kerfoot, H. B. (1988) "Is soil-gas analysis an effective means of tracking contaminant plumes in ground water? What are the limitations of the technology currently employed?", *Ground Water Monitoring Review*, Spring, 54-57.

Kerfoot, H. B. (1991) "Subsurface partitioning of volatile organic compounds: Effects of temperature and pore-water content", *Ground Water*, **29**, 678-684.

Kerfoot, H. B. and C. L. Mayer (1986) "The use of industrial hygiene samplers for soil-gas surveying", *Ground Water Monitoring Review*, Fall, 74-78.

Kimball, B. A. and E. R. Lemon (1971) "Air turbulence effects upon soil gas exchange", *Soil Sci. Soc. Amer. Proc.*, **35**, 16-21.

Kreamer, D. K., E. P. Weeks, and G. M. Thompson (1988) "A field technique to measure the toruosity and sorption-affected porosity for gaseous diffusion of materials in the unsaturated zone with experimental results from near Barnwell, South Carolina", *Water Resources Research*, **24**, 331-341.

Lyman, W. J., W. F. Reehl, and D. H. Rosenblatt (1984) *Handbook of Chemical Property Estimation Methods*, McGraw-Hill, New York, New York.

Mackay, D., W. Y. Shiu, and R. P. Sutherland (1979) "Determination of air-water Henry's constants for hydrophobic pollutants", *Environ. Sci. Technol.*, **13**, 333-337.

Malley, M. J., W. W. Bath, and L. H. Bongers (1985) "A case history: Surface static collection and analysis of chlorinated hydrocarbons from contaminated ground water", In: *Proceedings:*

NWWA/API Conference on Petroleum Hydrocarbons and Organic Chemicals in Ground Water: Prevention, Detection, Restoration, November 13-15, Houston, Texas.

Marrin, D. L. and G. M. Thompson (1987) "Gaseous behavior of TCE overlying a contaminated aquifer", *Ground Water*, **25**, 21-27.

Marrin, D. L. and H. B. Kerfoot (1988) "Soil-gas surveying techniques", *Environ. Sci. Technol.*, **22**, 740-745.

Massmann, J. W. (1989) "Applying groundwater flow models in vapor extraction system design", *J. Environ. Eng.*, **115**, 129-149.

Massmann, J. W. and D. F. Farrier (1992) "Effects of atmospheric pressures on gas transport in the vadose zone", *Water Resources Research*, **28**, 777-791.

McCarthy, K. A. and R. L. Johnson (1992) "Transport of volatile organic compounds across the capillary fringe", *Water Resources Research*, **29**, 1675-1683.

McClellan, R. D. and R. W. Gillham (1990) "Vapour extraction of trichloroethylene under controlled field conditions". In: *Proceedings: Conference on Subsurface Contamination by Immiscible Fluids*, International Association of Hydrogeologists, Calgary, April 18-20.

Mendoza, C. A. and E. O. Frind (1990a) "Advective-dispersive transport of dense organic vapors in the unsaturated zone. 1. Model development", *Water Resources Research*, **26**, 379-387.

Mendoza, C. A. and E. O. Frind (1990b) "Advective-dispersive transport of dense organic vapors in the unsaturated zone. 2. Sensitivity analysis", *Water Resources Research*, **26**, 388-398.

Mendoza, C. A. and T. A. McAlary (1990) "Modeling of groundwater contamination caused by organic solvent vapors", *Ground Water*, **28**, 199-206.

Mendoza, C. A., E. O. Frind and B. M. Hughes (1990) "Vapour transport of organic compounds: Simulation of a field experiment and model validation", In: *Calibration and Reliability in Groundwater Modelling*, K. Kovar (Ed.) International Association of Hydrological Sciences, Publication 195, pp. 331-340.

Mendoza, C. A., B. M. Hughes, and E. O. Frind (1992) "Transport of trichloroethylene vapours in the unsaturated zone: Numerical analysis of a field experiment". In: *Proceedings: Conference on Subsurface Contamination by Immiscible Fluids*, K. U. Weyer (Ed.), International Association of Hydrogeologists, Calgary, April 18-20. Order from A. A. Balkema, Old Post Road, Brookfield, Vermont 05036.

Metcalfe, D. E. and G. J. Farquhar (1987) "Modeling gas migration through unsaturated soils from waste disposal sites", *Water, Air, and Soil Pollution*, **32**, 247-259.

Millington, R. J. and J. M. Quirk (1961) "Permeability of porous solids", *Trans. Faraday Soc.*, **57**, 1200-1207.

Nilson, R. H. and K. H. Lie (1990) "Double-porosity modelling of oscillatory gas motion and contaminant transport in a fractured medium", *Int. J. Numerical and Analytical Methods in Geomechanics*, **14**, 565-585.

Nilson, R. H., E. W. Peterson, K. H. Lie, N. R. Burkhard, and J. R. Hearst (1991) "Atmospheric pumping: A mechanism causing vertical transport of contaminated gases through fractured permeable media", *J. Geophysical Research*, **96**, 21,933-21,948.

Rivett, M. O. and J. A. Cherry (1991) "The effectiveness of soil gas surveys in delineation of groundwater contamination: Controlled experiments at the Borden field site". In: *Proceedings: NWWA/API Conference on Petroleum Hydrocarbons and Organic Chemicals in Ground Water*, November 20-22, Houston, Texas.

Sleep, B. E. and J. F. Sykes (1989) "Modeling of transport of volatile organics in variably saturated media", *Water Resources Research*, **25**, 81-92.

Stephenson, R. M. and S. Malanowski (1987) *Handbook of the Thermodynamics of Organic Compounds*, Elsevier, New York.

Thibodeaux, L. J., C. Springer, and L. M. Riley (1982) "Models of mechanisms for the vapor phase emission of hazardous chemicals from landfills", *J. Hazardous Materials*, **7**, 63-74.

Thorstenson, D. C. and D. W. Pollock (1989) "Gas transport in unsaturated porous media: The adequacy of Fick's Law", *Rev. Geophysics*, **27**, 61-78.

Tillman, N., K. Ranlet and T. J. Meyer (1989) "Soil gas surveys: Part II/Procedures," *Pollution Eng.*, **21**, 79-84.

Voorhees, K. J., J. C. Hickey, and R. W. Klusman (1984) "Analysis of groundwater contamination by a new surface static trapping/mass spectrometry technique", *Anal. Chem.*, **56**, 2602-2604.

Weast, R. C. (Ed.) (1987) *Handbook of Chemistry and Physics*, 68th Edition, CRC Press, Boca Raton, Florida.

Weeks, E. P., D. E. Earp, and G. M. Thompson (1982) "Use of atmospheric fluorocarbons F-11 and F-12 to determine the diffusion parameters of the unsaturated zone in the southern high plains of Texas", *Water Resources Research*, **18**, 1365-1378.

7

Dissolution of Dense Non-aqueous Phase Liquids (DNAPLs) in the Subsurface

Stan Feenstra[1] and Nilson Guiguer[2]

[1]Applied Groundwater Research Ltd.
The Pentagon Building, Suite 207
2550 Argentia Rd.
Mississauga, Ontario
Canada L5N 5R1
and
Waterloo Centre for Groundwater Research,
University of Waterloo
Waterloo, Ontario
Canada, N2L 3G1

[2]Waterloo Hydrogeologic Inc.
200 Candlewood Cr.
Waterloo, Ontario
Canada N2L 5Y9

ABSTRACT

The magnitude of the concentrations of dissolved contaminants in groundwater and the length of time that associated DNAPL source zones will cause groundwater contamination are determined by the rate of DNAPL dissolution. In porous media, under typical subsurface flow conditions, laboratory and computer modeling studies indicate that groundwater that exits residual DNAPL zones does so at saturation with the DNAPL. This is due to the intimate contact that exists between residual DNAPL and groundwater. In contrast, studies show that dissolved concentrations derived from pools of DNAPL will typically be considerably lower than saturation when the concentration is averaged over a vertical distance of 0.5 or more above the pool. At field sites where DNAPL is present, saturated dissolved concentrations are not frequently observed in groundwater. This is the result of the variability in the spatial distribution of the DNAPL residual zones and pools, dilution in monitoring wells with long intakes, and dispersion processes in the aquifer. For a multi-component DNAPL, the effective solubility of a given compound will be given by the product of the pure-phase solubility of that compound with the mole fraction of the compound in the mixture. During dissolution of such a mixture, the compound(s) having the highest effective solubility(ies) will be removed preferentially, and both the DNAPL composition and the dissolved concentrations will change with time. At a site contaminated with a multi-component DNAPL, an examination of changes in the dissolved concentrations with time may provide a method for determining the degree to which the DNAPL source mass has been depleted by dissolution.

7.1 INTRODUCTION

The rate of dissolution of a **dense non-aqueous phase liquid (DNAPL)** from the source zone at a contaminated site will influence the magnitude of the dissolved chemical concentrations in the groundwater as well as the length of time that the DNAPL zone will persist. An understanding of DNAPL **dissolution rates** is therefore required when evaluating existing sources of dissolved chemical plumes with respect to future plume migration, as well as the effectiveness of pumping to remove dissolved plumes. This chapter describes conceptual models for the dissolution of DNAPLs in the subsurface. The models consider: 1) the solubility of organic compounds in water; 2) the theory of mass transfer from DNAPL phases into water; and 3) the dynamic dissolution behavior of DNAPLs as observed in laboratory experiments. Understanding the implications of these conceptual models will allow assessments of what concentration data for dissolved contaminants at a site might indicate regarding: 1) the possible presence of a DNAPL phase in the subsurface at the site; 2) the degree of mass depletion of such a DNAPL source by dissolution; and 3) the nature of the groundwater transport of chemicals away from such a DNAPL source.

7.2 SOLUBILITY FROM PURE DNAPLS AND FROM DNAPL MIXTURES

The mass dissolution rate of a DNAPL in the subsurface is a function of the **solubil-ity**(ies) of the compound(s) in the DNAPL, the **groundwater velocity**, the **mass and**

distribution of the DNAPL material in the subsurface, the **pore distribution** of the medium, the aqueous-phase **diffusion coefficient**(s) of the compound(s) in question, and the effects of other chemical constituents in the system. A DNAPL can be comprised of a **single compound**, or it can be a **mixture**. In their pure forms, chlorinated organic solvents are liquids which exhibit a wide range of solubilities in water. These water solubilities are not very temperature dependent over the ambient groundwater temperature range.

The available solubility data for chlorinated solvent compounds have been obtained in studies conducted for a variety of purposes, over a span of several decades, using reagents of varying purity, and using a variety of analytical techniques. The result is that there is disagreement in the published solubility data for these compounds. For example, the solubility values for trichloroethylene (TCE) reported in Horvath (1982) for 20-25 °C vary from 700 to 1470 mg/L. For some other compounds, the range in reported values is even larger. This situation has made it difficult for practicing hydrogeologists to determine what value is best when assessing the dissolution processes for a given chlorinated solvent compound. In general, it can be assumed that the most reliable values are those that have been measured recently using good analytical methods (see Table 7.1 and Appendix I).

TABLE 7.1 Measured Solubilities (mg/L) of Four Chlorinated Solvent Compounds at 23 to 25 °C.

Compound	Broholm and Feenstra (1995) (23-24 °C)	Horvath (1982) (25 °C)	Mackay and Shiu (1981) (25 °C)
Chloroform	8700	7920	7925
Carbon Tetrachloride	780	793	1000
1,1,1-Trichloroethane	1250	1495	720
Trichloroethylene	1400	1100	1050

For an organic NAPL mixture, the aqueous-phase concentration of each component that is in equilibrium with the mixture can be approximated using a **solubility analog of Raoult's Law** for vapor pressure. This analog is

$$C_{sat,m} = X_m C_{sat}^o \quad , \tag{7.1}$$

where $C_{sat,m}$ is the aqueous solubility of component m from the mixture (also sometimes referred to as the "**effective solubility**" from the mixture), X_m is the mole fraction of component m of interest in the NAPL mixture, and C_{sat}^o is the solubility of the pure compound.

Laboratory experimental studies (*e.g.*, Banerjee, 1984, and Broholm and Feenstra, 1995) suggest that Eq.(7.1) is a reasonable approximation for mixtures of structurally-similar hydrophobic organic liquids, such as mixtures of chlorinated solvents. Broholm and Feenstra (1995) conducted experiments with mixtures of chloroform, carbon tetrachloride, 1,1,1-trichloroethane (1,1,1-TCA), trichloroethylene (TCE), and tetrachloro-ethylene (PCE). They concluded that Eq.(7.1) works well when predicting the effective aqueous solubilities of binary mixtures of these compounds. An example of the results obtained in that study is shown in Figure 7.1. Laboratory studies (*e.g.*, Leinonen and Mackay, 1973) have shown that use of Eq.(7.1) may cause some error with complex mixtures of certain structurally-dissimilar compounds (*e.g.*, alkanes dissolved in aromatics). However, the error is usually smaller than a factor of 2. Such deviations from ideal behavior are small enough that they may usually be safely ignored in environmental studies where there are often much larger uncertainties[†].

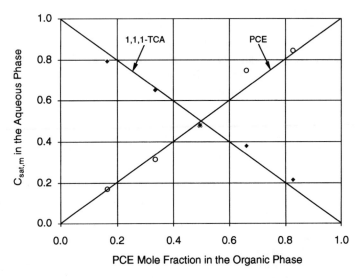

Figure 7.1   Solubility as a function of mole fraction for mixtures of 1,1,1-TCA and PCE.

The DNAPLs encountered at waste disposal sites are commonly mixtures of chemicals that are liquids in their pure forms at ambient temperatures. However, DNAPLs at waste sites also sometimes contain dissolved compounds that are **solids in their pure forms** at ambient temperatures, *e.g.*, some chlorinated benzenes, polychlorinated biphenyls (PCBs), and polycyclic aromatic hydrocarbons (PAHs) (see Table 7.2). For such a compound, its **"sub-cooled" liquid solubility** (*i.e.*, also referred to as its "super-cooled" liquid solubility) must be used as C_{sat}^o in Eq.(7.1). For relatively rigid molecules of the type that are of interest here, the sub-cooled liquid solubility ($C_{sat,liq}$) at a given temperature (T, K) of interest can be estimated based on the solid-phase solubility ($C_{sat,sol}$)

[†]Examples of exceptions to this rule include: 1) an alcohol dissolved in a largely alkane (non-polar) mixture (as occurs with alcohol additives in gasoline); 2) an alkane (non-polar) dissolved in one or more alcohols; and 3) a chlorinated solvent dissolved in an alcohol.

and the melting point (T_m, K) of the compound of interest according to (Shiu *et al.*, 1988)

$$C_{sat,liq} = C_{sat,sol} \exp[6.8(T_m/T - 1)] \quad . \tag{7.2}$$

Sub-cooled liquid solubilities can be considerably higher than the corresponding solid-phase solubilities, and the difference increases as T_m increases (see Table 7.2).

A comparison of observed groundwater concentrations with calculated effective solubility values can be carried out based on data from a Superfund site in Pennsylvania where DNAPL has been found in numerous wells in a fractured sandstone aquifer (ERM, 1987). Two samples of DNAPL recovered from wells were analysed and found to contain the same compounds, though at different concentrations (see Table 7.3). This type of variability is likely to be common at many multi-component DNAPL sites. Because the DNAPL composition varies at the Pennsylvania site, the dissolved concentrations in the groundwater would be expected to vary to a similar degree. For each DNAPL sample, the effective solubilities of the four principal components were calculated and are given in Table 7.3 along with data for the groundwater. For groundwater collected close to the DNAPL source, the dissolved concentrations are comparable to the calculated effective solubilities, and follow the expected concentration trend of 1,2,3-trichloropropane > xylenes > toluene > ethylbenzene.

As implied in the heading for Table 7.3, a significant fraction of the organic DNAPL phase at the Pennsylvania site could not be identified or quantified. This type of situation has been encountered at other sites. However, when estimating the mole fractions of the compounds of interest in a given DNAPL sample, one requires an estimate of the weight percent of the unidentified fraction as well as an estimate of the average molecular weight (MW) of the compounds making up the unidentified fraction. The type of uncertainty which arises when making such assumptions is indicated in Table 7.4 for one of the two DNAPL samples considered in Table 7.3. Increasing the estimate of the average MW of the unidentified fraction causes the estimated effective solubilities for the known contaminants to increase: for a given weight % of unidentified fraction, a higher

TABLE 7.2 Melting Points, Solid-Phase Solubilities at 25 °C, and Estimated Sub-Cooled Liquid Solubilities of Selected Compounds in Water at 25 °C.

PAH Compounds	Melting point (°C)	Melting point (T_m, K)	Solid-phase solubility (μg/L, 25 °C)	Estimated sub-cooled liquid solub. (μg/L, 25 °C)
p-Dichlorobenzene	53	326	79,000	150,000
Naphthalene	80	353	31,000	110,000
Fluorene	117	390	1,900	16,000
Anthracene	217	510	730	92,000
Benzo[a]pyrene	179	452	3.8	130
Biphenyl	71	344	7,000	20,000
2,2′,5,5′-Tetrachlorobiphenyl	87	360	103	423
Decachlorobiphenyl	306	579	0.0012	0.73

TABLE 7.3 Pure Compound Properties, Weight Percent Composition Values for Two DNAPL Samples from a Superfund Site in Pennsylvania, Calculated Effective Solubility Values for those Compositions, and Observed Dissolved Groundwater Concentrations at the Site. (The average molecular weight (*MW*) of the unidentified portions of the two DNAPL samples was assumed to be 150 g/mol.)

Property	1,2,3-Trichloro-propane	Toluene	Xylenes	Ethyl benzene
Pure Compound Solubility (mg/L)	1,900	580	200	190
Molecular Weight (g/mol)	146	92	106	106
Weight %, DNAPL Sample 1	23	4.2	17	3.8
Effective Solubility (mg/L)	400	35	43	9.1
Weight %, DNAPL Sample 2	73	0.9	5.8	0.9
Effective Solubility (mg/L)	1,400	8.1	16	2.3
Observed Groundwater Conc.				
Lower Value (mg/L)	220	2.1	7.3	1.1
Upper Value (mg/L)	1,200	53	74	12

TABLE 7.4 Calculated Effective Solubilities at 25 °C for Components of DNAPL Sample 1 from a Superfund Site in Pennsylvania for Different Assumed Molecular Weight (*MW*) Values for the Unidentified Fraction.

Compound	Wt.%	*MW* (g/mol)	C_{sat}^o (mg/L)	Effective solubility (mg/L) Assumed *MW* of unidentified fraction		
				$MW = 100$	$MW = 200$	$MW = 300$
1,2,3-Trichloro-propane	23	146	1900	325	450	520
Toluene	4.2	92	580	29	40	46
Xylenes	17	106	200	33	46	53
Ethyl Benzene	3.8	106	190	7.4	10	12

average *MW* results in a lower calculated mole fraction for the unidentified fraction, and correspondingly higher mole fractions for the identified contaminants.

7.3 DISSOLUTION PROCESSES

7.3.1 Theory and Conceptual Models

7.3.1.1 General

In the subsurface, DNAPL will occur in **residual zones**, in **layers** above an underlying aquitard, and in **pools** on top of an underlying aquitard. In residual zones, DNAPL is present as immobile blobs and ganglia that may occupy 10% or less of the pore space.

Groundwater flow occurs through the remaining pore space, although the presence of the DNAPL does reduce the relative permeability of the medium to water. Dissolution of the DNAPL occurs as groundwater flows through the residual zone. Within layers or pools of free-phase DNAPL, the DNAPL may occupy as much as 50 to 70% of the pore space and may substantially reduce groundwater flow through these zones. Dissolution of the DNAPL then occurs predominantly along the tops, lateral margins of the layers and pools. Flow may also occur beneath layers of DNAPL.

The rate of dissolution of DNAPL in the subsurface will depend on the effective solubilities and diffusivities of the DNAPL components, the physical distribution of the DNAPL in the porous or fractured medium (*e.g.*, the contact area between the DNAPL and the groundwater), and the rate of groundwater flow through and around the DNAPL. These fundamental relationships are illustrated on a sub-pore scale and a pore scale in Figure 7.2. At the interface between the DNAPL and the groundwater, the concentration in the groundwater approaches the solubility or effective solubility of each of the components. Dissolved chemicals are transferred into the flowing groundwater by molecular diffusion.

It is necessary to express the rate of dissolution mathematically in order to quantify the dissolution process. The rate of mass transfer from a DNAPL to the water phase is typically expressed as a function of a **mass transfer coefficient**, a **driving force**, and the **interfacial contact area** between the two phases of interest so that

$$
\begin{array}{ccccc}
\text{Rate of} & \text{Mass Transfer} & \text{Concentration} & \text{Contact} & \\
\text{Mass Transfer} & \text{Coefficent} & \text{Difference} & \text{Area} & \\
= & \times & \times & & (7.3) \\
(M/T) & (L/T) & (M/L^3) & (L^3) &
\end{array}
$$

The driving force for mass transfer is the concentration difference across the mass transfer boundary layer, and is usually defined as the difference between the effective solubility of the component and the dissolved concentration in the bulk water flowing past the

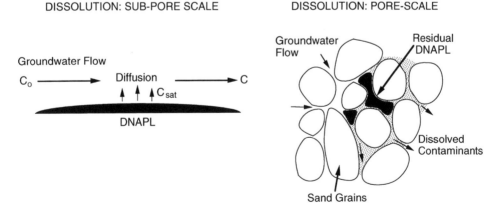

Figure 7.2   Schematic representation of dissolution processes on a sub-pore and pore scale.

DNAPL. The rate of mass transfer will determine the dissolved-phase concentrations that will occur in the groundwater as well as the persistence of the DNAPL zone in the subsurface. The mass transfer coefficient is a parameter determined largely by the water flow conditions. Several models have been used in the field of chemical engineering to describe mass transfer coefficients for the dissolution of an immiscible phase. The three most common models are the stagnant film model, the film penetration model, and the random surface renewal model (Cussler, 1984).

7.3.1.2 Stagnant film model

In the stagnant film model, all the resistance to mass transfer is assumed to reside in a stagnant layer of thickness δ adjacent to the interface, as shown in Figure 7.3. The concentration at the interface is taken to be equal to C_{sat}: it is assumed that the rate of equilibration across the fluid-fluid interface is rapid, and that the slower rate of molecular diffusion in the water phase coupled with advective flow determines the overall rate of mass transfer (Levich, 1962; Turitto, 1975). The aqueous-phase concentration of the same species in the bulk water is represented as C_w. Burris and MacIntyre (1986) measured the dissolution of a four-component liquid hydrocarbon layer overlying a stirred aqueous phase. Their results suggest that chemical equilibrium likely existed at the interface in that system.

For 1-D diffusion, the flux of a species is given by Fick's First Law as

$$N = -D\frac{\partial c}{\partial x} \qquad (7.4)$$

where: $N =$ flux of the species (units of M/L^2T); $D =$ diffusion coefficient of species A (units of L^2/T); and $\partial c/\partial x =$ concentration gradient of the species in the water near the interface (units of ML^{-3}/L). In the stagnant film model, it is assumed that the **concentration gradient is linear** over the boundary layer thickness δ as shown by the dashed line in Figure 7.3 so that

$$\frac{\partial}{\partial x} \simeq \frac{C_w - C_{sat}}{\delta} \qquad (7.5)$$

and the particular form of Equation (7.4) becomes

$$N = K_c(C_w - C_{sat}) \qquad (7.6)$$

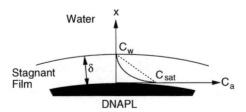

Figure 7.3 Stagnant film model for dissolution mass transfer.

where $K_c = D/\delta$ is the mass transfer coefficient. Although the stagnant film model assumes that the concentration decreases linearly over the distance δ, the concentration dependence may in fact be more like that given by the solid line in Figure 7.3.

The stagnant film model predicts that the mass transfer coefficient is directly proportional to the diffusion coefficient. Hence, doubling the diffusion coefficient should double the rate of mass transfer. This mass transfer coefficient also depends on variables such as the fluid viscosity and local water velocity (both of which depend strongly on the heterogeneity of the porous medium): the effects of these variables are lumped into the film thickness δ.

In porous media, it is useful to define a mass transfer rate per volume of porous medium N^* by multiplying the mass flux by the ratio of DNAPL surface contact area A_n to the unit volume of porous medium V so that

$$N^* = N\frac{A_n}{V} = K_c\frac{A_n}{V}(C_w - C_{sat}) = \lambda(C_w - C_{sat}) \tag{7.7}$$

where λ has dimensions of 1/T and is defined as the lumped mass transfer coefficient such that $\lambda = K_c A_n/V$. The use of such a lumped mass transfer coefficient in porous media is a common practice (Miller *et al.*, 1990; Sleep and Sykes, 1989; Zilliox *et al.*, 1978).

If a multi-component DNAPL is present, the mass transfer rate for each individual component within the DNAPL mixture can be calculated according to

$$N_m^* = \lambda_m(C_{w,m} - C_{sat,m}) \tag{7.8}$$

where λ_m is the lumped mass transfer coefficient for the component m and $C_{w,m}$ is the concentration of component m in the bulk aqueous phase. $C_{sat,m}$ is the effective solubility of component m which can be calculated using Eq.(7.1).

7.3.1.3 Penetration model

This model, proposed by Higbie (1935), was the earliest attempt to find an alternative for the stagnant film model. Higbie (1935) felt that it was unreasonable to assume that a liquid film could remain static, and not mix at all with the adjacent turbulent bulk liquid. Higbie (1935) pictured a small **fluid element** moving from the bulk phase (in this case the water phase) to the interface where it remains for a time period t, after which it returns to the bulk phase. During the time t, **transient diffusion** is assumed to take place between the interface and the element so that

$$K_c = 2\sqrt{\frac{D}{\pi t}} \tag{7.9}$$

Although it has been suggested that a square root relationship between K_c and D may be more reasonable than the direct proportionality suggested by the stagnant film model, the characteristic penetration time t is not known for situations of practical interest.

7.3.1.4 Random surface renewal model

The random surface renewal model was proposed by Dankwerts (1951) who basically adopted Higbie's (1935) approach, but instead of assuming that all the elements have the same contact time t, assigned a **random distribution** to t. The mass transfer coefficient then becomes:

$$K_c = \sqrt{sD} \qquad (7.10)$$

where s is the rate of surface renewal.

The three mass transfer models discussed above all relate K_c for a compound to its diffusion coefficient in water and to an empirical parameter (*i.e.*, the stagnant layer thickness, the contact time, or the rate of surface renewal) which in each case is a function of the flow conditions and fluid properties. The mass transfer coefficient is therefore usually treated as a fitting parameter in models used to examine the results of lab or field experiments. This is particularly true in groundwater systems where one must also contend with other complicating factors such as the distribution of residual DNAPL in the pores, the effective contact area, and the degree of aquifer heterogeneity. Thus, although such models provide the basis for the description of mass transfer coefficients, at the present time there is no evidence that one particular model works better than another when predicting DNAPL dissolution in groundwater. Since the stagnant film model is the simplest of the available mass transfer models, it has been the model used in most practical applications.

7.3.1.5 Dimensionless numbers

In the chemical engineering literature, experimental mass transfer data are seldom reported directly. Rather, the results are expressed as **correlations equations** between different dimensionless numbers. These numbers are useful because they allow the prediction of mass transfer coefficients under a wider range of conditions than would otherwise be possible. The dimensionless numbers commonly used in mass transfer correlations are given in Table 7.5 (Cussler, 1984; Wakao and Kaguei, 1982; Sherwood *et al.*, 1975). The Sherwood and Stanton numbers involve the mass transfer coefficient. The Schmidt and Lewis numbers involve different kinds of diffusion. The Reynolds, Grashöf, and Péclet numbers involve flow considerations. The Damköhler number involves diffusion and chemical reaction.

A key point about each of the numbers in Table 7.5 is that its exact definition implies a specific physical system. For example, the characteristic length l in the Sherwood number (Sh) could be the stagnant layer thickness for a liquid-to-liquid transfer, or the average grain size of a porous medium (Powers *et al.*, 1992; Miller *et al.*, 1990). Some correlations involving the mass transfer coefficient (expressed in terms of Sh) that have been used in previous works involving NAPL dissolution are given in Table 7.6 (Powers *et al.*, 1991; Miller *et al.*, 1990; Powers *et al.*, 1992; Geller and Hunt, 1993). In that table, $Sh = K_c l/D$ everywhere except for the study of Miller *et al.* (1990) for which $Sh = \lambda d_p^2/D$ where λ is the lumped mass transfer coefficient and d_p is the mean diameter of the sand grains.

TABLE 7.5   Dimensionless Numbers Relating to Dissolution of DNAPLs in the Subsurface.

Group	Physical meaning	Used in
Sherwood number $Sh = \dfrac{K_c l}{D}$	$\dfrac{\textit{mass transfer rate}}{\textit{diffusion rate}}$	Usual dependent variable
Stanton number $St = \dfrac{K_c}{v}$	$\dfrac{\textit{mass transfer rate}}{\textit{flow rate}}$	Occasional dependent variable
Schmidt number $Sc = \dfrac{v}{D}$	$\dfrac{\textit{diffusivity of momentum}}{\textit{diffusivity of mass}}$	Correlations of gas and liquid data
Lewis number $Le = \dfrac{\alpha}{D}$	$\dfrac{\textit{diffusivity of energy}}{\textit{diffusivity of mass}}$	Simultaneous heat and mass transfer
Reynolds number $Re = \dfrac{l v}{v}$	$\dfrac{\textit{inertial forces}}{\textit{viscous forces}}$ $\quad or \quad$ $\dfrac{\textit{flow velocity}}{\textit{momentum velocity}}$	Forced convection
Grashöf number $Gr = \dfrac{l^3 g \Delta\rho/\rho}{v^2}$	$\dfrac{\textit{buoyancy forces}}{\textit{viscous forces}}$	Free convection
Péclet number $Pe = \dfrac{v l}{D}$	$\dfrac{\textit{flow velocity}}{\textit{diffusion rate}}$	Correlations of gas or liquid data
Damköhler number $\omega = \dfrac{k l^2}{D}$	$\dfrac{\textit{reaction rate}}{\textit{diffusion rate}}$	Correlation involving reactions

D = diffusion coefficient [L^2/T]

g = acceleration due to gravity [L/T^2]

K_c = mass transfer coefficient [L/T]

l = characteristic length [L]

v = fluid velocity [L/T]

α = thermal diffusivity [L^2/T]

k = first-order reaction rate constant [1/T]

v = kinematic viscosity [L^2/T]

$\Delta\rho/\rho$ = fractional density change

    The published correlations confirm that the mass transfer coefficient is a function of the flow conditions and the diffusion coefficient. Usually, once a correlation equation is fitted to laboratory data, the predictions of the mass transfer coefficient are very reliable (Cussler, 1984). For example, Miller *et al.* (1990) and Powers *et al.* (1992) were able to simulate their experimental results using correlations given in Table 7.6. However, this

TABLE 7.6   A Selection of Mass Transfer Correlations Previously Used in NAPL Dissolution Studies.

Dissolution of:	Basic equation	Characteristic length	Reference
oil in porous media	$Sh = 0.55 + 0.25 Pe^{1.5}$	sand grain diameter	Pfannkuch (1984)
solid spheres in fluidized beds	$Sh = 2 + 1.1 Re^{0.6} Sc^{0.33}$	mean sphere diameter	Wakao & Kaguei (1982)
solid spheres in packed beds	$Sh = 1.09(\theta S_w)^{-1} Pe^{0.33}$	mean sphere diameter	Wilson & Geankoplis (1966)
flow around single spheres	$Sh = 0.978 Pe^{0.33}(\theta S_w)^{-0.33}$ $(Pe > 10)$ or $Sh = 2$ $(Pe < 1)$	sphere diameter	Bowman et al. (1961)
TCE in sand column	$Sh = 37.2 Re^{0.656}$	mean sand grain diameter	Powers et al. (1992)
toluene in sand column	$Sh = 12 Re^{0.75} S_n^{0.6} Sc^{0.5}$	mean sand grain diameter	Miller et al. (1990)

θ = porosity; S_w = water saturation; S_n = NAPL saturation.

type of success can only be expected within the range of experimental conditions (flow, compound type, etc.) used in the experiments underlying the correlations. To date, there is no evidence that these correlations can be made even more general.

7.3.2 Laboratory Studies

Under most circumstances, the difficulty in predicting mass transfer coefficients may not be a large problem when evaluating DNAPL dissolution rates into groundwater. Indeed, theoretical studies and the review of laboratory dissolution experiments by Pfannkuch (1984) suggest that the applicable mass transfer coefficients may often be sufficiently large to result in **saturated aqueous concentrations** in DNAPL zones at typical residual contents and typical groundwater velocities. (At high groundwater velocities, several laboratory studies have found that mass transfer coefficients can become dependent on groundwater velocity resulting in a reduction in the dissolved concentrations.)

Laboratory batch experiments indicate that for water in contact with a NAPL, the dissolved concentrations often approach effective solubility values in minutes to hours, depending on the NAPL/water volume ratio (Shiu et al., 1988; Poulsen et al., 1992). Laboratory column and tank experiments (Schwille 1988; Anderson et al., 1992; Imhoff et al., 1994) suggest that for groundwater flow at up to 1 m/day (linear velocity) through DNAPL zones at typical residual contents, saturated concentrations will be attained after contact times of ~ 30 min. Under such conditions, DNAPL dissolution is not limited by the rate of interphase mass transfer. (Theoretical and laboratory studies have shown, however, that dissolution may become mass transfer rate limited at high groundwater velocities (>1 m/day) as can be found in the immediate vicinity of pumping wells (Pfannkuch, 1984; Geller and Hunt, 1993)).

In situations where the DNAPL is present in layers and pools, theoretical and laboratory experiments suggest that **less-than-saturated dissolved concentrations** are often observed (Schwille, 1988; Geller and Hunt, 1993). Within a DNAPL layer or pool, the DNAPL may occupy a large proportion of the pore space and substantially reduce the groundwater flow through such a zone. In addition, horizontal layers or pools present a very **small cross-sectional area** of DNAPL zone to horizontal groundwater flow. Thus, dissolution of DNAPL from a layer on a low permeability lens or from a pool occurs predominantly along the margins of the lens or pool. Consequently, the rate of dissolution may be much lower than for a residual zone.

A laboratory experiment was performed by Schwille (1988) to illustrate the dissolution of a TCE pool measuring 1.5 m in length and 0.5 m in width (Figure 7.4). The pool was formed in a tank containing medium-grained sand. Water flow through the tank passed over the TCE pool at different velocities and the dissolved TCE concentrations were measured in the tank effluent. The results of the experiment are given in Table 7.7. The dissolved concentrations were found to be well below saturation levels, even when dissolved concentrations are averaged over a short vertical distance above the pool.

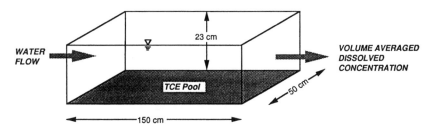

Figure 7.4 TCE pool experiment of Schwille (1988).

TABLE 7.7   Results of TCE Pool Dissolution Experiment by Schwille (1988).

Linear velocity (m/d)	Concentration (mg/L)	Percent saturation
2.3	67	6.1%
1.1	90	8.2%
2.3	87	7.9%
4.5	73	6.6%
6.8	77	7.0%

7.3.3 Modeling Studies

Over the past three decades, many models have been developed that describe some aspect of multi-phase transport (see Abriola, 1989; Kueper and Frind, 1991; and Guiguer,

1993). Several of these models address the dissolution of NAPLs in the saturated zone. Whether it incorporates NAPL movement or not, such a model is usually known as a **compositional model**, since at some point the model utilizes mass balance equations in some form for each species m in each phase (soil, gas, water, or DNAPL). A species can be defined as a specific chemical component that is present in one or more phases, or can be considered as a group of such components if average characteristics can be defined. In the case of dissolution of DNAPLs by percolating water, the mass balance equation for the water phase can be written as:

$$\frac{\partial}{\partial t}(S_w, C_{w,m}) \; + \; \frac{\partial}{\partial x_i}(S_w v_i, C_{w,m}) \; - \; \frac{\partial}{\partial x_i}\left(S_w D_{ij}\frac{\partial C_{w,m}}{\partial x_j}\right) \; - \; N_m \; = \; 0$$

change in mass   (7.11)
in dissolved   adjective   dispersive
phase   transport   transport   dissolution

where: v_i = average pore water velocity; S_w = average fraction of pore volume occupied by water; $C_{w,m}$ = concentration of component m in water; D_{ij} = dispersion coefficient; N_m = mass transfer of component m from DNAPL to water. In a multi-component model, the number of equations required depends on the number of chemical components of interest. A solution results not only in a quantification of the remaining residual saturation and its composition, but also in the delineation of the contaminant plume of each component at any point in space and time.

The mass transfer term N_m is generally treated in one of two ways: 1) local equilibrium is assumed between the phases, *i.e.*, the concentration of component m is always equal to its effective solubility; or 2) as a first order reaction given by

$$N_m = S_w \lambda_m (C_{sat,m} - C_{w,m}) \quad . \tag{7.12}$$

Abriola and Pinder (1985a, 1985b), Baehr and Corapcioglu (1987), and Kaluarachchi and Parker (1990) present 2-D models that solve for the migration of NAPL as an immiscible phase, while the dissolution process is taken into account using the local equilibrium assumption. Guiguer (1993) presents a 3-D model for the migration of NAPL where the dissolution process is considered as a first order reaction. Guiguer (1993) used that model to examine the effects of heterogeneities on the evolution of contaminant plumes emanating from residual zones. Powers *et al.* (1992) and Miller *et al.* (1990) developed 1-D models for a single component DNAPL trapped as immobile residual. Both studies assumed first order mass transfer; the mass transfer coefficients used were obtained as a function of dimensionless numbers determined in lab column experiments. Brusseau (1992) developed a 1-D solution for a single component NAPL. That model utilized a two-domain concept where mass transfer was assumed to be essentially instantaneous for some portion of the NAPL zone and rate limited with first order mass transfer for the remainder.

The mass transfer coefficient λ_m expresses the process of diffusive mass transfer from the surfaces of residual blobs to free-flowing groundwater. This parameter depends on the characteristics of the component of interest (through its aqueous phase diffusion coefficient), and on the nature of the porous medium. However, as dissolution progresses, λ_m can change due to a changing geometry of the residual zone, *e.g.*, a lengthening of the diffusion pathways from residual trapped in deadend pores. Guiguer and Frind (1994) incorporated this time-varying behavior by expressing λ_m in a general way as a nonlinear function of the DNAPL saturation so that $\lambda_m = \lambda_m^* Sn^\beta$ where the exponent β is a lumped parameter that accounts for the residual distribution and the soil characteristics (*e.g.*, the relative abundance of deadend pore zones). A property of the porous medium that would be expected to affect β is the pore size distribution of the medium. As a practical matter, β must be considered to be a fitting or calibrating parameter.

Analytical solutions for the **dissolution of DNAPL residual** in a 1-D column were developed by Hunt *et al.* (1988). They idealized the distribution of the residual DNAPL as spherical droplets of uniform size and showed that DNAPL residuals can persist for long periods releasing low concentrations because the mass transfer rate can decrease with time. Hunt *et al.* (1988) also developed an analytical solution for **dissolution of DNAPL pools**, considering that the dissolution occurred only along the edges of the pool and that the location of the interface did not change with time. The vertical profile of dissolved concentrations above the downgradient edge of a pool can then be expressed as (Johnson and Pankow, 1992)

$$C(z) = C_{sat}\,\text{erfc}\left(\frac{z}{2\left(\frac{D_v L}{V}\right)^{0.5}}\right) \tag{7.13}$$

where z is the vertical distance above the pool, $D_v = \alpha_v v + D_e$ is the dispersion coefficient in the vertical direction, α_v is the vertical dispersivity, v is the linear groundwater velocity, and D_e is the effective molecular diffusion coefficient in the porous medium. An example of the vertical concentration profile above a 25 m long pool in a sandy aquifer is given in Figure 7.5. The dissolved concentrations are expressed as a percentage of the saturated concentration. Saturated concentrations are found only very close to the top of the pool.

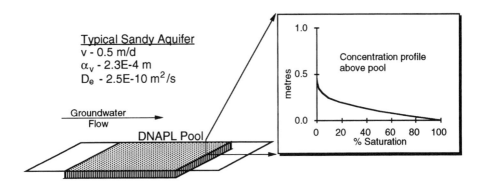

Figure 7.5 Example of dissolved concentration profile above a DNAPL pool.

The distance that dissolved concentrations extend upward from a pool will be greater for longer pool lengths, lower groundwater velocities, and larger coefficients of vertical dispersion. Concentration profiles above a pool in a typical sandy aquifer for various pool lengths are shown in Figure 7.6. In this case, the linear groundwater velocity was taken to be 0.5 m/d, and α_v was taken to be 0.00023 m. For these conditions, at the downgradient edge of the pool, the concentration profiles extend less than 1 m upward from the pool, even for pool lengths as great as 100 m. This result illustrates that the vertical concentration profile above a pool at the downgradient edge of the pool does not depend strongly on pool length.

Concentration profiles above a pool (at the downgradient edge) in a sandy aquifer are given in Figure 7.7 for a range of groundwater velocities. The pool length was taken to be 25 m, and α_v was assumed equal to 0.00023 m. At a groundwater velocity of 0.001 m/d, the concentration profile extends more than 2 m upward from the pool. However, at groundwater velocities 0.1 and 1 m/d, the concentration profile extends less than 0.5 m upward from the pool; the water is swept away before the contaminant can diffuse very far in the upward direction. These calculations suggest that the vertical concentration profile above a pool will be very thin for groundwater velocities in the range of 0.1 to 1 m/d, *i.e.*, for the range that is typical for sandy aquifers.

Calculated concentration profiles above a pool (at the downgradient edge) in a sandy aquifer for values of α_v in the range 0.00023 to 0.1 m are given in Figure 7.8 for a pool length of 25 m and a linear groundwater velocity of 0.5 m/d. Measurements of α_v for

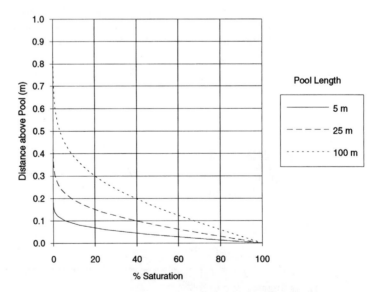

Figure 7.6 Dissolved concentration profiles at the downgradient edge of DNAPL pools of varying length when the linear groundwater velocity = 0.5 m/day and $\alpha_v = 0.00023$ m.

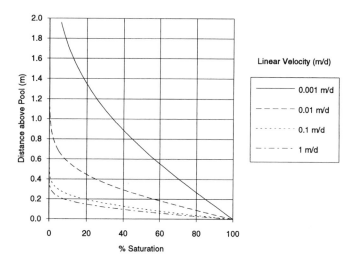

Figure 7.7   Dissolved concentration profiles at the downgradient edge of a 25 m long DNAPL pool for varying groundwater velocities when $\alpha_v = 0.00023$.

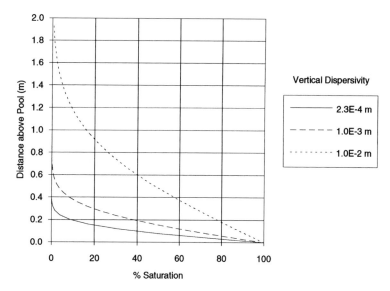

Figure 7.8   Dissolved concentration profiles at the downgradient edge of a 25 m long DNAPL pool for varying α_v values when groundwater velocity $= 0.5$ m/day.

sands derived from small-scale laboratory experiments suggest a value of ~ 0.00023 m (Johnson and Pankow, 1992). Large-scale field experiments such as those at the Borden test site (Rivett *et al.*, 1994), the Twin Lakes site (Moltyaner and Wills, 1991) and at Cape Cod (Garabedian *et al.*, 1991) suggest α_v values in the range 0.001 to 0.01 m. Therefore, in any given situation, there will be considerable uncertainty in the value of

α_v. Some of the vertical dispersion observed in large-scale tests is likely due to the effects of macro-scale heterogeneities and temporal fluctuations in groundwater flow direction that may not be relevant to the local process of dissolution from a pool. For the conditions in Figure 7.8, when $\alpha_v = 0.01$ m, the concentration profile at the downgradient edge extends more than 2 m upward from the pool; when $\alpha_v = 0.00023$ and 0.001 m, the concentration profile extends about 0.5 m upward from the pool.

The distance that significant dissolved concentrations extend upward from a pool into an aquifer will have a very large influence on the magnitude of the dissolved concentrations that are observed in monitoring wells in an aquifer. Wells with a short intake interval (*e.g.*, ~1.5 m) that are situated at the same elevation as a pool may exhibit dissolved concentrations that are 10% or more of the saturated concentration. However, wells with a longer intake interval that reach the same elevation as the pool may exhibit dissolved concentrations of less than 1% of saturation. Wells with an intake interval that does not reach close to the elevation of a pool may yield no measurable dissolved concentrations at all. The implications of these considerations for the diagnosis of the presence of DNAPL pools in the subsurface is discussed in Chapter 13.

7.3.4 Persistence of DNAPL Zones

Based on the results of laboratory and modeling studies of dissolution, it is possible to make estimates of the possible **longevity of DNAPL sources** in residual and pool form in the subsurface. For a residual source, consider a zone of residual DNAPL occupying 1 m^3 of a sandy aquifer and containing 30 L/m^3 of dichloromethane, TCE, or PCE. Groundwater is assumed to flow through this zone at a linear velocity of 0.14 m/day, reflecting a typical sandy aquifer with a hydraulic conductivity of 10^{-2} cm/s, a hydraulic gradient of 0.005, and a porosity of 0.3. If it is assumed that the dissolved concentration in the residual zone is at saturation and that this level is maintained until the source is completely dissolved, then the estimated minimum source-lives are: dichloromethane, 46 days; TCE, 2 years; and PCE, 13 years.

The above estimates are absolute minima, and will be considerably longer for several reasons: 1) the DNAPL within the residual zone may be heterogeneously distributed such that saturated dissolved concentrations may not be produced throughout the 1 m^3 residual zone; 2) the presence of DNAPL residual will reduce the permeability of the residual zone to groundwater flow, and this will reduce the mass flux out of the residual zone; and 3) saturated concentrations will not be maintained as the residual mass is depleted. Laboratory studies by Lamarche (1991) clearly illustrate (see Figure 7.9) that dissolved concentrations will decline as the mass of residual DNAPL is depleted. They also illustrate that low but significant dissolved concentrations can persist for very long times. Source-life calculations can also be performed for pools. For the TCE pool in the laboratory experiment of Schwille (1988), the pool was 1.5 m long, 0.5 m wide, and 0.2 m thick. For the mass transfer rate that can be extrapolated from the Schwille (1988) data when the groundwater velocity is 0.75 m/day (see Johnson and Pankow, 1992), the estimated source-life for such a pool is 50 to 100 years. These calculations suggest that zones of

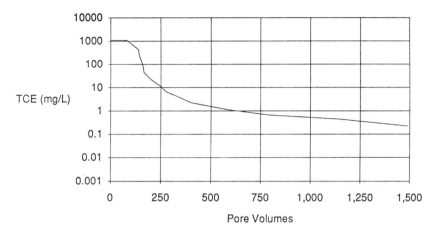

Figure 7.9   TCE concentration vs. time for a column experiment by Lamarche (1991).

residual DNAPL and especially pool DNAPL can persist in the subsurface and contribute to groundwater contamination for **decades to centuries**. These estimates are consistent with the observation of on-going groundwater contamination problems at waste disposal facilities and chemical spill sites which have existed since the 1940s, 1950s, and 1960s.

As noted above, as residual DNAPL dissolves into groundwater, the volume of DNAPL per volume of porous medium decreases, and the DNAPL interfacial area per volume of porous media also decreases. This decreases the value of λ. Powers *et al.* (1991) and Geller and Hunt (1993) used correlations between the volume of DNAPL remaining in the pores and the surface area in order to calibrate their lab column experiments. Very simplistic geometrical shapes of the DNAPL blobs, such as spheres and cylinders, had to be assumed. A more realistic idealization of the dynamic behavior of the mass transfer coefficient inside a representative elementary volume (REV) is illustrated in Figure 7.10.

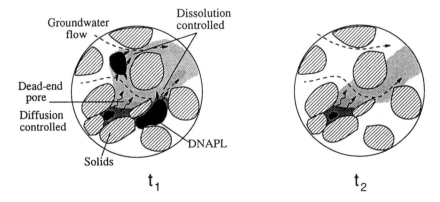

Figure 7.10   Dissolution processes at the pore scale.

In any given case, residual DNAPL will be located in pores with different geometries. When the dissolution process begins, some droplets will be in direct contact with the flowing water, some will be in partial contact with the flowing water, and some will be trapped in dead end pores with a stagnant layer of water separating them from the flowing water. Mass transfer from the droplets in direct contact with the flowing water will be dissolution-controlled (*i.e.*, occur at saturation) and will proceed more quickly. Mass transfer between the droplets in the dead end pores and the flowing water will be diffusion-controlled and will depend on the thickness of the layer of stagnant water. As the overall dissolution proceeds, the droplets in contact with the flowing water will become completely dissolved, and the only droplets remaining will be those trapped in the dead end pores. As the size of these droplets decreases, the thickness of the stagnant water layer will increase, and the dissolution rate of the remaining droplets will decline further. The concentrations of dissolved DNAPL in the groundwater leaving the DNAPL zone may then become substantially lower than saturation, but remain non-zero for long periods of time. Overall, it can be expected that as long as DNAPL residual is present, some mass transfer will be dissolution-controlled and some will be diffusion-controlled. As long as there is a diffusion component, the overall process will be naturally asymptotic. At the same time, we note that the decrease in the volume of the trapped DNAPL will open up some new flow paths, so that some blobs may become accessed by the flowing groundwater.

Finally, we note that the presence of **heterogeneity** in a porous medium can slow the dissolution rate of a DNAPL in that medium. Figure 7.11 illustrates a possible scenario. When the DNAPL moves downward through the saturated zone, it will first tend to invade the larger pores. Depending on the forces involved and the pore interconnections, it may also penetrate layers of lower permeability. Since more water will flow through the higher permeability zones, the residual DNAPL in these zones will be dissolved first. As less pore space is occupied by the DNAPL in these zones, the permeability will become even larger, and more water will be diverted away from the lower permeability zones. With less flow passing through the low permeability zones, the mass transfer rate there will decrease, and the residual DNAPL there will persist longer. When dilution by clean water passing through the system and into monitoring wells is considered, the overall result can be aquifer concentrations which are substantially lower than the solubility limit.

7.3.5 Field Observations of DNAPL Dissolution

Saturated dissolved concentrations are seldom observed in groundwater except in the immediate vicinity of large DNAPL sources. In the past, concentrations below saturation have commonly been interpreted to mean that DNAPL is not present. However, considerations such as those presented in the preceding sections indicate that such interpretations can be incorrect. Indeed, concentrations below saturation may be the result of: 1) **reduced effective solubilities** due to the DNAPL being multi-component in nature; 2) the **heterogeneous distribution of the DNAPL** as residuals, layers, or pools; 3) **dispersion** in the aquifer; and 4) **dilution** in monitoring wells having long intakes lengths. As a "rule-of-thumb", the finding of dissolved concentrations that **exceed 1% of the**

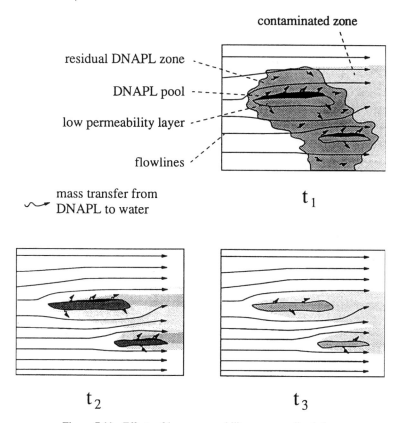

Figure 7.11   Effects of lower permeability zones on dissolution.

effective solubility should probably be cause for serious consideration of the presence of a DNAPL phase in the subsurface. Such a finding should stimulate the collection and evaluation of other lines of evidence to help confirm or disprove the presence of DNAPL in the subsurface at the site of interest.

7.4 MULTI-COMPONENT DNAPLS

7.4.1 Theory and Laboratory Studies

The preferential removal of the most soluble components from synthetic mixtures of aromatic hydrocarbons, mixtures of chlorobenzenes, diesel fuel, and crude oil has been examined in laboratory studies by Mackay *et al.* (1991). The results indicate that for a multi-component DNAPL, the compounds having the highest effective solubilities will be removed most quickly. The **preferential removal** of the most soluble compounds will change the composition of the DNAPL, thereby changing the effective solubilities of the remaining compounds.

Changes in the dissolved concentrations of constituent compounds can be predicted based on the effective solubilities of the compounds by simulating the incremental depletion of the DNAPL phase of interest (Shiu *et al.*, 1988; Mackay *et al.*, 1991). This concept is referred to here as the **Effective Solubility Model (ESM)**. Laboratory experiments on the dissolution of organic mixtures (Shiu *et al.*, 1988) found that the dissolved concentration changes predicted using the ESM compared favorably with the concentration changes that were observed (see Figure 7.12). These experiments were conducted at water flow rates low enough to yield saturated dissolved concentrations.

The results of a laboratory experiment conducted by Geller and Hunt (1993) can be used to show that the ESM can also simulate the **relative changes** in dissolved concentrations in situations when water velocities are high and dissolution is limited by the rate of mass transfer. In that experiment, a 50/50 mixture of benzene and toluene was used. (Although this mixture was not a DNAPL, the dissolution processes for such a mixture will be very similar to that expected for a DNAPL.) A known volume of the mixture was injected into the center of a column packed with 40-45 mesh glass beads. Water flowed through the column at a Darcy velocity of 10 m/day (linear velocity = 25 m/day). At this high flow rate, the initial dissolved concentrations in the column effluent were approximately 55 mg/L for benzene and 14 mg/L for toluene (see Figure 7.13). These values are well below the effective solubility saturation values of 900 and 250 mg/L, respectively. The low concentrations were due to mass transfer limitations resulting from the high water flow rates and from the limited extent of the residual zone.

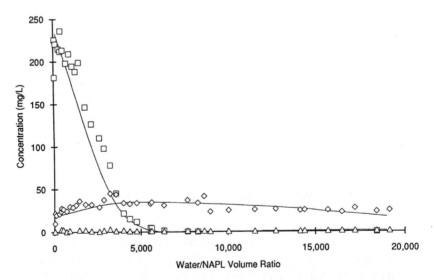

Figure 7.12 Results of dissolution experiment using a mixture of chlorobenzenes. Key: chlorobenzene, open squares; 1,2,4-trichlorobenzene, open diamonds; 1,2,3,5-tetrachlorobenzene, open triangles. The data are fitted according to predictions of the Effective Solubility Model (ESM). Data from Mackay *et al.* (1991).

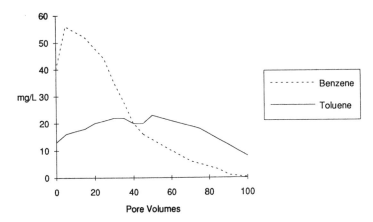

Figure 7.13 Changes in benzene and toluene concentrations as benzene is removed preferentially from a benzene/toluene mixture. Data from Geller and Hunt (1989).

As the benzene/toluene mixture dissolved, the dissolved concentrations changed as the more soluble benzene was removed preferentially. The results of the experiment are shown in Figure 7.14 as a plot of the toluene/benzene ratio in the water with the fraction of the source remaining in the column. The observed changes compare well with the changes predicted using the ESM. This is an expected result, even for high groundwater velocities. Indeed, all of the models used to predict mass transfer coefficients suggest that for a given set of water flow conditions, the mass transfer coefficients for different chemical components should depend principally on the aqueous diffusivities

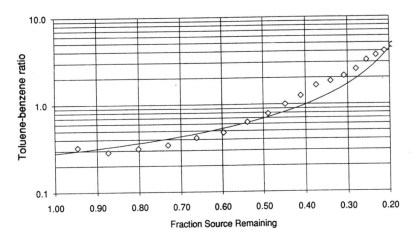

Figure 7.14 Change in toluene/benzene ratio in water during dissolution. Open diamonds give experimental results. The data are fitted according to predictions of the Effective Solubility Model (ESM). Data from Geller and Hunt (1989).

of the compounds of interest. Because the aqueous diffusivities of most organic chemicals of interest span a relatively small range (see Table 7.8), the mass transfer coefficients for the components of a multi-component DNAPL will remain similar one-to-another. Consequently, for a given groundwater flow regime and DNAPL residual zone, the relative rates of mass transfer of the components of a multi-component DNAPL, and therefore the concentration ratios should depend primarily on the effective solubilities of the components. The relative concentrations of dissolved constituents may therefore be useful in evaluating the dissolution history of subsurface multi-component DNAPL sources.

TABLE 7.8   Aqueous Diffusivity Values for Selected Organic Compounds. (Benzene data from Bonolli and Witherspoon (1968); correlation data for other compounds from Wilke and Chang (1955) as described in *Perry's Chemical Engineers Handbook* (1984).)

		10 °C	20 °C
Compound	MW (g/mol)	Diffusion coefficient cm²/s	Diffusion coefficient cm²/s
Toluene	92.1	6.7×10^{-6}	9.0×10^{-6}
Xylenes	106.2	6.2×10^{-6}	8.4×10^{-6}
Benzene	78.1	7.4×10^{-6}	1.0×10^{-5}
Ethylbenzene	106.2	6.1×10^{-6}	8.3×10^{-6}
Chlorobenzene	112.6	6.3×10^{-6}	8.5×10^{-6}
Trichloroethylene	131.4	7.4×10^{-6}	1.0×10^{-5}
Perchloroethylene	165.8	6.8×10^{-6}	9.3×10^{-6}
Dichloromethane	84.9	9.1×10^{-6}	1.2×10^{-5}
Chloroform	119.4	7.9×10^{-6}	1.1×10^{-5}
Carbon tetrachloride	153.8	7.1×10^{-6}	9.5×10^{-6}
1,1,1-Trichloroethane	133.4	7.0×10^{-6}	9.4×10^{-6}

7.4.2 Estimates of DNAPL Source Depletion

During the 1980s, groundwater purging operations were implemented at many waste disposal and chemical spill sites. When these purging operations began, the objective of most was aquifer restoration. Experience has now shown that clean-up of groundwater contamination by organic chemicals is often not possible when the goal is background conditions, or even satisfaction of drinking water criteria. At many sites, elevated dissolved chemical concentrations continue in the groundwater even after years of purging. This is most frequently the case near suspected source areas. We now understand that these cleanup failures have often been due to the presence of DNAPL sources, either in residual zones, or in pools.

Groundwater purging operations conducted within or close to a DNAPL source area will, of course, accelerate depletion of the source. However, the actual degree of depletion usually cannot be determined because the mass of DNAPL in the source zone is not known. Nevertheless, for a multi-component source, a consideration of the **relative**

concentrations of the dissolved contaminants may provide a method for evaluating the degree of depletion. The application of this method can be illustrated using the results of monitoring conducted during a groundwater purging operation at an industrial plant site in the eastern United States (Feenstra, 1992).

The site of interest is situated on the Atlantic Coastal Plain and is underlain by a sand and gravel aquifer approximately 15 m thick. In 1977, a dissolved plume of 1,1,1-TCA and PCE was identified in the shallow aquifer. The principal source of the contaminants is believed to have been the chemical transfer/storage area of the plant. In 1978, a groundwater purging system was implemented and operated until late 1984. During that time, up to 14 purge wells were operated throughout the plume area as well as close to the suspected source area. With the exception of the wells immediately adjacent to the source area, the dissolved 1,1,1-TCA and PCE concentrations in the groundwater were reduced from as high as several thousand μg/L to below the clean-up criteria of 50 μg/L; in some wells, the levels were reduced to below detection limits. In purge wells close to the source area, although the dissolved concentrations were reduced significantly during purging, they remained relatively high (see Figure 7.15). Approximately 60% of the total chemical mass removed by purging was removed from two wells close to the source.

The dissolved concentrations in the purge wells close to the source area were much lower than saturation, but still relatively high, suggesting that DNAPL remains in the subsurface in the source area. The dilution relative to saturation likely occurred due to the heterogeneous distribution of the DNAPL material, and the fact that the purge wells were screened over the full thickness of the aquifer. During the period of groundwater purging, the PCE/1,1,1-TCA ratio increased in the purge wells close to the suspected source. This trend was not observed in purge wells far from the source. The change in the PCE/1,1,1-TCA ratio is shown in Figure 7.16. Since 1,1,1-TCA is more soluble than PCE (see Table 7.1), this increase is consistent its preferential dissolution from the source DNAPL.

Based on the initial PCE/1,1,1-TCA ratio of $\sim$0.5 in the groundwater, the initial composition of the DNAPL is estimated to have been 88% PCE and 12% 1,1,1-TCA. Based on this value, the ESM can be used to predict subsequent changes in the PCE/1,1,1-TCA ratio as the DNAPL mass is depleted (see Figure 7.17). Although the PCE/1,1,1-TCA ratio in the groundwater shows fluctuations (see Figure 7.16), it is clear that the

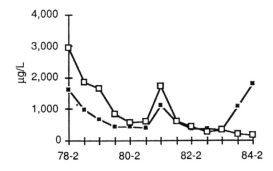

Figure 7.15 Dissolved concentrations in purge well GW-32 close to suspected source zone during pumping. Key: 1,1,1-TCA, open squares; PCE, solid squares.

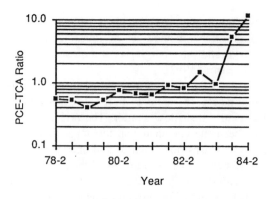

Figure 7.16 Change in PCE/1,1,1-TCA ratio in water in purge well GW-32 close to suspected source zone during pumping.

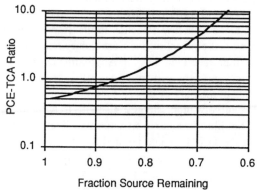

Figure 7.17 Predicted change in PCE/1,1,1-TCA ratio using the Effective Solubility Model (ESM) for dissolution of a DNAPL with an initial composition of 88% PCE and 12% 1,1,1-TCA.

ratio increased during the pumping from $\sim$0.5 up to $\sim$5. For such an increase, the ESM implies that $\sim$30% of the DNAPL phase was removed during the pumping.

7.5 CONCLUSIONS

The rate of dissolution of DNAPL to groundwater is commonly expressed as a function of a mass transfer coefficient and the contact area between the DNAPL and groundwater. A universal relationship between the mass transfer coefficient and groundwater velocity has not been established. Likewise, the typical dependencies of the dissolution rate on the contact area and DNAPL residual content have not been established. However, these uncertainties can be largely set aside by consideration of empirical observations of DNAPL dissolution from laboratory experimental studies. These observations suggest that the groundwater exiting DNAPL residual zones acquires saturated dissolved concentrations when the residual zones are at least several centimeters in length, and groundwater velocities are typical of natural groundwater conditions (< 1 m/day). For groundwater passing over DNAPL pools, studies (*e.g.*, Johnson and Pankow, 1992) indicate that concentrations that are considerably lower than saturation will be developed for typical pool lengths and sampling intervals over which the groundwater to be analyzed is acquired. For most chlorinated solvents, the rate of dissolution of pools will be sufficiently slow that the DNAPL zones will cause significant contamination of the groundwater for centuries or more (Johnson and Pankow, 1992).

Saturated dissolved concentrations are not frequently observed in groundwater except in the immediate vicinity of large DNAPL sources. In the past, concentrations below saturation have commonly been interpreted to mean that DNAPL is not present at a given site. In many cases, evidence of other types now indicate that such interpretations have often been incorrect. Concentrations below saturation may be a result of: 1) a multi-component rather than a single component DNAPL; 2) the heterogeneous distribution of DNAPL as residuals and layers or pools; 3) dilution in monitoring wells having long intakes lengths; and 4) dispersion in the aquifer. The importance of these various factors will be site specific. In most hydrogeologic situations, the finding of dissolved concentrations exceeding 1% of the effective solubility should be cause for serious consideration of the presence of DNAPL.

For multi-component DNAPLs, laboratory studies and field examples suggest that the effective solubility of a given constituent compound can be estimated as the product of the mole fraction of that compound in the DNAPL with its pure-phase solubility. The chemicals having the highest effective solubilities will be dissolved preferentially from the DNAPL. This will result in changes in the composition of the DNAPL, which in turn will change the effective solubilities. For a given DNAPL composition, it may be possible to relate the changes in the ratios of the dissolved concentrations derived from the DNAPL to the degree of mass depletion of the DNAPL source.

ACKNOWLEDGEMENTS

Funding support for this research was provided in part by the University Consortium Solvents-in-Groundwater Research Program. Sponsors of the Program between 1988 and 1994 have included: The Boeing Company, Ciba-Geigy Corporation, Dow Chemical Canada/USA, Eastman Kodak Co., General Electric Co., Laidlaw Environmental Systems Ltd., Mitre Corporation, The Natural Sciences and Engineering Research Council of Canada, and the Ontario University Research Incentive Fund.

7.6 REFERENCES

Abriola, L. M. and G. F. Pinder (1985a) "A multiphase approach to the modelling of porous media contamination by organic compounds. 1. Equation development", *Water Resources Research*, **21**, 11-18.

Abriola, L. M. and G. F. Pinder (1985b) "A multiphase approach to the modelling of porous media contamination by organic compounds. 2. Numerical simulation", *Water Resources Research*, **21**, 19-28.

Abriola, L. M. (1989) "Modeling multiphase migration of organic chemicals in groundwater systems - A review and assessment", *Environ. Health Perspectives*, **83**, 117-143.

Anderson, M. R., R. L. Johnson, and J. F. Pankow (1992) "Dissolution of dense chlorinated solvents into groundwater: 3. Modeling contaminant plumes from fingers and pools of solvent", *Environ. Sci. Technol.*, **26**, 901-908.

Baehr, A. L. and M. Y. Corapcioglu (1987) "A compositional multiphase model for groundwater contamination by petroleum products. 2. Numerical simulation", *Water Resources Research*, **23**, 201-203.

Banerjee, S. (1984) "Solubility of organic mixtures in water", *Environ. Sci. Technol.*, **18**, 587-591.

Bonolli, L. and P. A. Witherspoon (1968) "Diffusion of aromatic and cycloparaffin compounds in water at 20 °C to 60 °C", *J. Phys. Chem.*, **72**, 2532-2534.

Bowman, C. W., D. M. Ward, A. I. Johnson, and O. Trass (1961) "Mass transfer from fluid and solid spheres", *Canadian J. Chem. Eng.*, **39**, 9-13.

Broholm, K., and S. Feenstra (1995) "Laboratory measurements of the aqueous solubility of mixtures of chlorinated solvents", *Environmental Toxicology and Chemistry*, **14**, 9-15.

Brusseau, M. L. (1992) "Rate-limited mass transfer and transport of organic solutes in porous media that contain immobile immiscible organic liquid", *Water Resources Research*, **28**, 33-45.

Burris, D. R. and W. G. MacIntyre (1986) "Solution of hydrocarbons in a hydrocarbon-water system with changing phase composition due to evaporation", *Environ. Sci. Technol.*, **20**, 296-299.

Cussler, E. L. (1984) *Diffusion, Mass Transfer in Fluid Systems*, Cambridge University Press, New York, New York.

Danckwerts, P. W. (1951) "Significance of liquid-film coefficients in gas absorption", *Ind. Eng. Chem., Process Design Development*, **43**, 1460-1467.

ERM (1987) *Off-site Operable Unit Remedial Investigation Report - Volume 1. Tyson's Site, Montgomery County, Pennsylvania*. Submitted to U.S. EPA, Region III, Philadelphia on behalf of Ciba-Geigy Corporation, Ardsley, New York. Prepared by Environmental Resources Management, Inc., Exton, Pennsylvania.

Feenstra, S. (1992) "Evaluation of multi-component DNAPL source by monitoring of dissolved phase concentrations". In: *Proceedings: International Conf. on Subsurface Contamination by Immiscible Fluids*, K. U. Weyer (Ed.), International Association of Hydrologists, Calgary, Alberta, April 18-20, 1990. A. A. Balkema, Rotterdam, pp. 65-72.

Garabedian, S. P., D. R. LeBlanc, L. W. Gelhar, and M. A. Celia (1991) "Large-scale natural gradient tracer test in sand and gravel, Cape Cod, Massachusetts. 2. Analysis of spatial moments for a nonreactive tracer", *Water Resources Research*, **27**, 911-924.

Geller, J. T. and J. R. Hunt (1993) "Mass transfer for nonaqueous phase organic liquids in water-saturated porous media", *Water Resources Research*, **29**, 833-846.

Guiguer, N. (1993) *Dissolution and Mass Transfer Processes for Residual Organics in the Saturated Groundwater Zone: Numerical Modelling*. Ph.D. Thesis, Dept. of Earth Sciences, University of Waterloo, Waterloo, Ontario.

Guiguer, N. and E. O. Frind (1994) "Dissolution and mass transfer processes for residual organics in the saturated groundwater zone". In: *Proceedings: International Symposium on Transport and Reactive Processes in Aquifers*, International Association for Hydraulic Research. April 11-15, ETH Zurich.

Higbie, R. (1935) "The rate of absorption of a pure gas into a still liquid during short periods of exposure", *Trans. Amer. Inst. Chem. Eng.*, **31**, 365-385.

Horvath, A. L. (1982) *Halogenated Hydrocarbons: Solubility-Miscibility with Water*, Marcel-Dekker, Inc., New York, New York.

Hunt, J. R., N. Sitar and K. S. Udell (1988) "Nonaqueous phase liquid transport and cleanup. 1. Analysis of mechanisms", *Water Resources Research*, **24**, 1247-1259.

Imhoff, P. T., P. R. Jaffe and G. F. Pinder (1994) "An experimental study of complete dissolution of a nonaqueous phase liquid in saturated porous media", *Water Resources Research*, **30**, 307-320.

Johnson, R. L. and J. F. Pankow (1992) "Dissolution of dense chlorinated solvents into groundwater. 2. Source functions for pools of solvent", *Environ. Sci. Technol.*, **26**, 896-901.

Kaluarachchi, J. J. and J. C. Parker (1990) "Modeling multicomponent organic chemical transport in three-fluid phase porous media", *J. Contam. Hydrology*, **5**, 349-374.

Kueper, B. H. and E. O. Frind (1991) "Two-phase flow in heterogeneous porous media. 1. Model development", *Water Resources Research*, **27**, 1049-1057.

Lamarche, P. (1991) *Dissolution of Immiscible Organics in Porous Media*, Ph.D. Thesis, Dept. of Earth Sciences, University of Waterloo, Waterloo, Ontario.

Leinonen, P. J. and D. Mackay (1973) "The multicomponent solubility of hydrocarbons in water", *Canadian J. Chem. Eng.*, **51**, 230-233.

Levich, V. G. (1962) *Physicochemical Hydrodynamics*, Prentice Hall, New Jersey.

Mackay, D. M., W. Y. Shiu (1981) "A critical review of Henry's Law constants for chemicals of environmental interest", *J. Phys. Chem. Ref. Data*, **10**, 1175-1199.

Mackay, D. M., W. Y. Shiu, A. Maijanen and S. Feenstra (1991) "Dissolution of non-aqueous phase liquids in groundwater", *J. Contam. Hydrology*, **8**, 23-42.

Miller, C. T., M. M. Poirier-McNeill and A. S. Mayer (1990) "Dissolution of trapped nonaqueous phase liquids: Mass transfer characteristics", *Water Resources Research*, **26**, 2783-2796.

Moltyaner, G. L. and C. A. Wills (1991) "Local- and plume-scale dispersion in the Twin Lake 40- and 260-m natural-gradient tracer tests", *Water Resources Research*, **27**, 2007-2026.

Perry, R. H. (1984) *Perry's Handbook of Chemical Engineering*, Sixth Edition. McGraw-Hill, New York, New York.

Pfannkuch, H. O. (1984) "Determination of the contaminant source strength from mass exchange processes at the petroleum-groundwater interface in shallow aquifer systems". In: *Proceedings: Conference on Petroleum Hydrocarbons and Organic Chemicals in Groundwater*, National Water Well Association/American Petroleum Institute, Nov. 5-7, Houston, Texas, pp. 111-129.

Powers, S. E., C. E. Loureiro, L. M. Abriola, and W. J. Weber, Jr. (1991) "Theoretical study of the significance of nonequilibrium dissolution of nonaqueous phase liquids in subsurface systems", *Water Resources Research*, **27**, 463-477.

Powers, S. E., L. M. Abriola and W. J. Weber, Jr. (1992) "Development of phenomenological models for NAPL dissolution processes". In: *Proceedings: Subsurface Restoration Conference*, June 21-24, Dallas, Texas.

Poulsen, M. M., L. Lemon, and J. F. Barker (1992) "Dissolution of monoaromatic hydrocarbons into groundwater from gasoline-oxygenate mixtures", *Environ. Sci. Technol.*, **26**, 2483-2489.

Rivett, M. O., S. Feenstra, and J. A. Cherry (1994) "Comparison of Borden natural gradient tracer tests". In: *Proceedings: IAHR/AIRII Symposium on Transport and Reactive Processes in Aquifers*, Dracos, Th. & Stauffer (Eds.) A. A. Balkema, Rotterdam, pp. 283-288.

Schwille, F. (1988) *Dense Chlorinated Solvents in Porous and Fractured Media - Model Experiments*, Translated by J. F. Pankow, Lewis Publishers, Boca Raton, Florida.

Sherwood, T. K., R. L. Pigford, and C. R. Wilke (1975) *Mass Transfer*, McGraw-Hill, New York, New York.

Shiu, W. Y., A. Maijanen, A. L. Y. Ng, and D. Mackay (1988) "Preparation of aqueous solutions of sparingly soluble organic substances: II. Multicomponent systems - Hydrocarbon mixtures and petroleum products", *Environ. Toxicol. Chem.*, **7**, 125-137.

Sleep, B. E. and Sykes, J. F. (1989) "Modeling the transport of volatile organics in variably saturated media", *Water Resources Research*, **25**, 81-92.

Turitto, V. T. (1975) "Mass transfer in annulli under conditions of laminar flow", *Chem. Eng. Sci.*, **30**, 503-509.

Wakao, N. and S. Kaguei (1982) *Heat and Mass Transfer in Packed Beds*, Gordon and Breach, New York, New York.

Wilke, C. R. and P. Chang (1955) "Correlation of diffusion coefficients in dilute solutions", *American Inst. Chem. Eng. J.*, **1**, 264-270.

Wilson, E. J. and C. J. Geankoplis (1966) "Liquid mass transfer at very low Reynolds numbers", *Ind. Eng. Chem. Fund.*, **23**, 9-14.

Zilliox, L., P. Muntzer, and J. J. Menanteau (1978) "Probleme de l'Echange entre un Produit Petrolier Immobile et l'Eau en Movement dans un Millieu Poreux", *Revue de l'Institut Français du Pétrole*, **XXVIII**, 185-200.

8

Sorption of Dissolved Chlorinated Solvents to Aquifer Materials

Richelle M. Allen-King[1], **Robert W. Gillham**[2], **and Douglas M. Mackay**[2]

[1]Department of Geology
Washington State University
Pullman, Washington, USA 99164-2812

[2]Waterloo Centre for Groundwater Research
University of Waterloo
Waterloo, Ontario, Canada N2L 3G1

ABSTRACT

The sorption of dissolved chlorinated solvent compounds to aquifer materials reduces the rate of contaminant transport in aquifers, increases the pumping required to flush compounds out of an aquifer relative to non-sorbing compounds, and can affect transformation rates. The degree of sorption in a given circumstance depends on the chemical properties of the given compound and also on the nature of the aquifer solids. Sorption increases as hydrophobicity increases, as can be predicted based on the compound's water solubility and its octanol/water partition coefficient. The role of the aquifer solids can be predicted using the fraction of organic carbon (f_{oc}) of the solids. Such predictions do not account for: 1) sorption to minerals (which can be important in low f_{oc} aquifers); 2) variations in the sorptivity of the organic carbon in the aquifer solids; or 3) non-equilibrium or non-linear behavior. Variations in the natural geochemistry of groundwaters generally have a minimal effect on sorption. However, sorption can be decreased when surfactants, co-solvents, and/or large concentrations of organic carbon are present in the groundwater.

8.1 INTRODUCTION

Sorption is the general term used to describe the uptake by soil of dissolved or gaseous species without reference to a specific mechanism (Chiou, 1989). The movement of dissolved organic pollutants in the subsurface is **retarded** by sorptive interactions. The diminished mobility caused by sorption has the obvious advantage that the rate of migration of dissolved contaminants from a spill site is less than the velocity of the groundwater. Thus, the volume of the porous medium contacted by a plume in a given period of time is less for more highly sorbing compounds than for less sorbing species. In this manner, sorption provides a natural mechanism which reduces the size of a contaminant plume. At the same time, however, the retarded behavior of sorbing compounds can make them difficult to remove from the subsurface. In particular, when sorbing pollutants are involved, more effort will be required to remediate a site using "pump and treat" methods than would be required for a site contaminated with non-sorbing species (Mackay and Cherry, 1989).

In addition to affecting migration rates, sorption can reduce the rates at which organic contaminants are **biodegraded**. Laboratory studies have shown that in some cases, the portion of the compound that is sorbed to the solid phase is unavailable for biodegradation (Mihelcic and Luthy, 1991; Ogram *et al.*, 1985, Steen *et al.*, 1980). Thus, sorption can decrease the rate of biotransformation of an organic compound in soil by making a portion of the compound at least temporarily unavailable. Recent laboratory experiments have shown that biodegradation can be enhanced by adding a low concentration of a surfactant which will promote desorption (Aronstein *et al.*, 1991).

The degree of sorption in the subsurface depends on the **physical and chemical properties** of the dissolved contaminant, the solids, and the aqueous solution. The sorption of different compounds may differ by orders of magnitude in the same geologic material. Sorption can also vary significantly between sites for a single compound. In sand and gravel aquifers, typically the degree of sorption is low compared to sorption in silt, clay, or organic-rich sediments. We also note that the degree of sorption between different sand and gravel aquifers varies less than when sand and gravel aquifers are compared with silty, clayey, or organic-rich sediments.

Although the properties of the compound and the solids exhibit the greatest influence on the degree of retardation, system-specific properties (*i.e.*, pH, temperature, natural dissolved organic matter (DOM) concentration, co-solvent concentration, surfactant concentration, and the soil water content) can also affect the degree of sorption. In some cases, natural DOM can significantly reduce sorption; high concentrations of the contaminants themselves can also reduce sorption. The fact that surfactants and co-solvents in the groundwater can significantly decrease sorption has stimulated much current research. In some circumstances involving complex mixtures of dissolved contaminants, the degree of sorption of a particular compound can be decreased by the presence of other contaminant compounds though in cases involving relatively dilute levels of organic contaminants, the effect will usually be small.

In general, solid-aqueous interactions are not completely understood, and comprise an active area of research. However, a body of field and laboratory observations exists from which discernable trends can be obtained. With the appropriate degree of caution, predictions of sorption and retardation for dissolved organic solvents can be made from correlations derived from these empirical findings, and from laboratory and field methods developed to measure sorption or retardation directly. The goal of this chapter is to describe the underlying mechanisms of sorption of chlorinated solvents as we understand them, and to discuss the effects of various system properties on sorption.

8.2 EFFECTS OF SORPTION ON TRANSPORT

The Stanford-Waterloo **natural-gradient field tracer test** (Mackay *et al.*, 1986a) provides quantitative information demonstrating the effect of sorption on the transport of several dissolved chlorinated and brominated compounds under natural conditions. In this experiment, measured masses of several contaminants, including carbon tetrachloride (CTET), tetrachloroethylene (PCE), 1,2-dichlorobenzene (DCB), hexachloroethane (HCE), and bromoform (BROM) were dissolved together with two non-reactive tracers (chloride and bromide) in a known volume of water which was then injected into a sandy, low **fraction organic carbon** (f_{oc}) aquifer near the "Borden Landfill" at Canadian Forces Base Borden. The movements of these compounds and the non-reactive tracers were monitored as a function of time.

Figure 8.1 shows a plan view of the vertically-averaged concentration of chloride at four different sampling times (1, 85, 462, and 647 days) during the experiment. Chloride behaved conservatively, showing the transport of the injected plume of water. Figure 8.2 shows a plan view of the distributions of chloride, CTET and PCE approximately 21 months (633 to 645 days) after injection. CTET and PCE both lag behind chloride in terms of plume movement. Over the course of the experiment, the velocity of the PCE center of mass was observed to be a factor of 2.7 to 5.9 slower than the unretarded velocity of the chloride. The degree of decreased mobility of PCE, characterized by this factor of 2.7 to 5.9 in this particular example, is commonly referred to

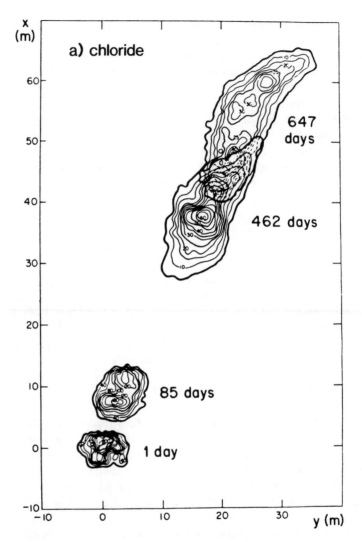

Figure 8.1 Chloride ion concentration (vertically averaged) in Stanford-Waterloo in-jection experiment, 1, 85, 462, and 647 days after injection. Contour interval is 5 mg/L. (Reprinted with permission from Mackay *et al.*, 1986.)

as the **retardation factor**. The retardation of CTET and PCE was due to sorption to the aquifer materials (Roberts *et al.*, 1986). For the various compounds injected, the retardation factors were generally proportional to the degree of **hydrophobicity** as given by the **octanol/water partitioning coefficient** (K_{ow}).

    Breakthrough curves of concentration in one piezometer over time through the experiment also show the effect of sorption on mobility (Figure 8.3). The chloride and bromide were the first to arrive at a given point down gradient. They were followed by

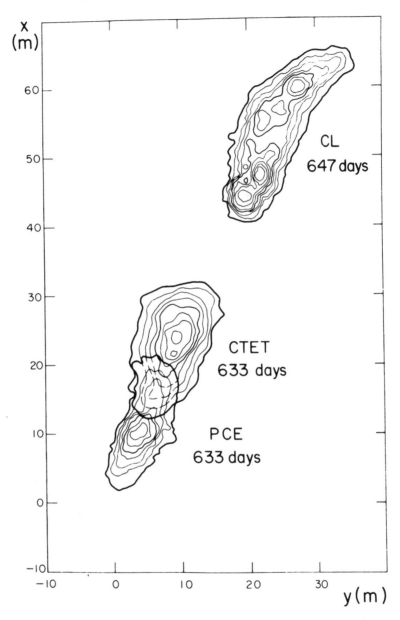

Figure 8.2   Separation of chloride, carbon tetrachloride (CTET), and tetrachloroethylene (PCE) plumes in Stanford-Waterloo injection experiment 21 months (633 or 647 days) after injection. The contour interval for chloride is 5 mg/L and for CTET and PCE is 0.1 μg/L. (Reprinted with permission from Roberts *et al.*, 1986.)

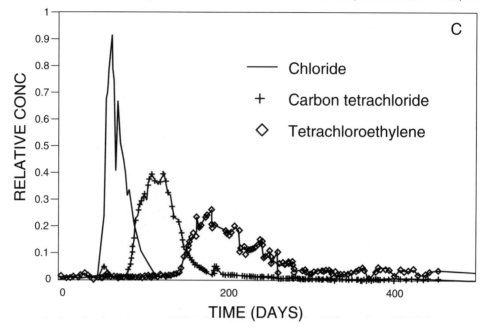

Figure 8.3 Breakthrough curves for chloride, carbon tetrachloride (CTET), and tetrachloroethylene (PCE) in Stanford-Waterloo injection experiment in a piezometer located 5 m from the injection point. (Reprinted with permission from Roberts *et al.*, 1986.)

the least hydrophobic (least sorbing) compounds, which were in turn followed by the more hydrophobic (more sorbing) compounds.

In the Stanford-Waterloo experiment, the retardation factors of the compounds examined ranged from about 1.7 to 9.0. While significant, these retardation factors are relatively low; retardation factors which are orders of magnitude higher have been observed for some compounds. Anderson and Pankow (1986) predicted that the retardation factors for several very hydrophobic polychlorinated biphenyl (PCB) isomers in a certain silty aquitard are extremely high, ranging from 270,000 to 1,400,000; compounds with such high retardation factors, will be essentially immobile if no transporting organic matter or particles are moving with the groundwater. At the same site, the retardation factors for the smaller and less hydrophobic 1,2,4-trichlorobenzene and 1,2,4,5-tetrachlorobenzene were estimated to be 120 and 600, respectively. For the even less hydrophobic compound PCE, the retardation factor in the same material would be expected to be about an order of magnitude less than for the chlorinated benzenes. Thus, depending on the compound, varying degrees of hydrophobicity can cause many orders of magnitude difference in mobility.

As noted above, sorption for a given compound can vary between sites. At the sandy site of the Stanford-Waterloo experiment, the retardation factor for PCE averaged around 4.5 (Roberts *et al.*, 1986). The retardation factor for PCE in sand and gravels near the River Aare is about 5 (Schwarzenbach *et al.*, 1983). In the sand and gravel aquifer at the Otis Air Force Base on Cape Cod in Massachusetts, Barber *et al.* (1988) has found that PCE exhibits a retardation factor of ~1 (no retardation). As with PCE, literature values for the retardation factor for TCE at sandy sites are generally less than 10, often between 1 and 2.5 (Mackay, 1990; Mehran *et al.*, 1987; Wilson *et al.*, 1981).

The Stanford-Waterloo injection experiment demonstrated some of the complexities of interpreting the effects of sorption on transport in the field. Based on a simplistic model of sorption in a homogeneous system, "**ideal**" breakthrough curves are symmetrical. However, the breakthrough curves observed in the Stanford-Waterloo experiment were not all symmetrical (Roberts *et al.*, 1986). "**Tailing**" breakthrough curves such as those in Figure 8.3 indicate "**non-ideal**" behavior. Asymmetrical breakthrough curves with long tails are commonly observed at field sites and also in laboratory experiments. We note that ideal behavior in a homogeneous material is characterized by a constant retardation factor for a given compound. However, the retardation factor for each of the compounds in the Stanford-Waterloo experiment was observed to *increase* during the course of the experiment (Figure 8.4). Suggested reasons for the observed non-ideal behavior include both pore-scale and field-scale rate-limited processes. In order to understand such non-ideal behavior, it is important to understand the concepts and assumptions implicit in the assumption of ideal behavior.

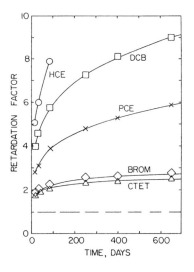

Figure 8.4   Plume retardation factors over time estimated from field synoptic sampling results in Stanford-Waterloo injection experiment. HCE = hexachloroethane; DCB = dichlorobenzene; PCE = tetrachloroethylene; BROM = bromoform; CTET = carbon tetrachloride. (Reprinted with permission from Roberts *et al.*, 1986.)

8.3 SORPTION MECHANISMS: EFFECTS OF SORBATE AND SORBENT ON SOIL/WATER PARTITIONING

8.3.1 Definitions

A plot of sorbed concentration vs. solution concentration at a given temperature is a **sorption isotherm**. Isotherms for various organic compounds on several natural subsurface samples have been obtained (*e.g.*, Weber *et al.*, 1992; Ball and Roberts, 1991a).

For dilute solutions of chlorinated solvents sorbing to soils, sorption isotherms are often linear with a zero intercept (*e.g.*, Figure 8.5). For **linear sorption**, the partition coefficient, also known as the distribution coefficient, K_d expresses the ratio of the equilibrium sorbed and solution phase concentrations, and equals the slope of the isotherm, *i.e.*,

$$K_d = \frac{C_s}{C_w} \tag{8.1}$$

where C_s and C_w are the concentrations of the compound of interest in the solid phase (mass of sorbate/mass of solid) and water phase (mass of solute/volume of water), respectively. For the linear case, the dimensions of K_d are volume of water per mass of solid, typically mL/g.

For linear sorption in a saturated system, and when equilibrium between the solid and solution phases occurs rapidly (and reversibly) with respect to flow velocity, the retardation factor R is given by

$$R = \frac{v}{v_c} = 1 + \frac{\rho_b}{\theta_w} K_d \tag{8.2}$$

(Freeze and Cherry, 1979) where v and v_c are the average linear velocities of the water and the contaminant respectively, ρ_b is the bulk density of the solids, and θ_w is the water-filled porosity. R is independent of C_w when the isotherm is linear.

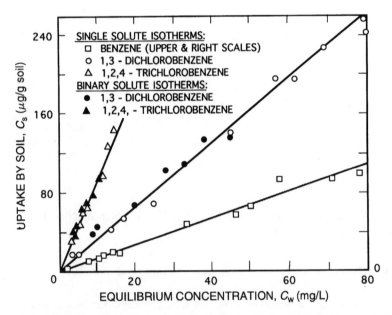

Figure 8.5 Examples of linear equilibrium isotherms for three hydrophobic compounds and a moderate to high f_{oc} soil. (Reprinted with permission from Chiou *et al.*, 1983.)

A **Freundlich** relationship, of the form

$$C_s = K_f C_w^{1/n} \tag{8.3}$$

is often used to fit non-linear isotherms, as shown in Figure 8.6 for a sample of sand from the Borden aquifer. The quantity $1/n$ describes the degree of deviation from linearity and K_f indicates the magnitude of sorption. Values of K_f and $1/n$ are usually obtained by fitting sorption data. Non-linear isotherms are considered to be most important at high concentrations when the sorption capacity of the solids is approached (*e.g.*, Murphy *et al.*, 1990; Grathwol, 1990). Non-linear isotherms can often be approximated as linear at low concentrations (Ball and Roberts, 1991a). However, extrapolation from low to high concentrations assuming linear behavior can produce significant errors (Figure 8.6).

The retardation factor corresponding to a Freundlich sorption isotherm is given by

$$R = 1 + \frac{\rho_b}{\theta_w} \frac{1}{n} K_f C_w^{[1/n-1]} \tag{8.4}$$

and is dependent on solution concentration. As seen in Figure 8.7, this type of behavior has been found for sorption of PCE to Borden sand. Non-linear isotherms suggest that competition between organic compounds should affect sorption. When $1/n < 1$ for each

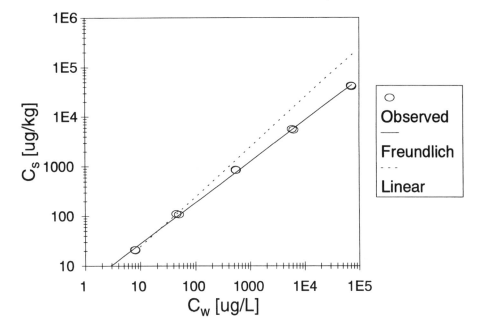

Figure 8.6   Example of non-linear equilibrium isotherm for tetrachloroethylene (PCE) in low f_{oc} Borden sand from the site of the Stanford-Waterloo injection experiment. The projection of K_d for approximately linear, low concentration range is shown. The projection emphasizes the importance of the non-linearity at high concentrations.

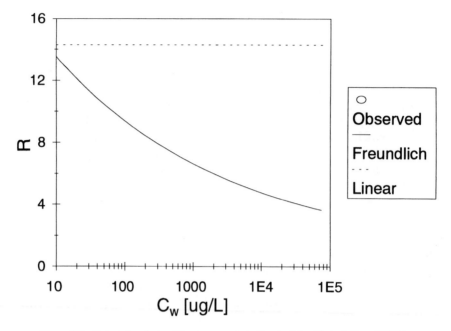

Figure 8.7 Retardation factor (*R*) versus concentration for tetrachloroethylene (PCE) in Borden sand corresponding to the isotherm shown in Figure 8.6. The value of *R* depends on the concentration for the non-linear isotherm. The projected linear retardation factor obtained from low concentration data is given as a dashed line.

of the competing compounds, sorption of a particular solute will generally be decreased when others are present at significant concentrations (McGinley *et al.*, 1993). Although Brusseau and Rao (1989) suggest that, in most cases, organic contaminant concentrations in groundwater are sufficiently low that they are within the range of the linear portion of the isotherm, sufficiently high concentrations may be present near chlorinated solvent sources that isotherm non-linearity may be important.

An understanding of the mechanisms underlying sorption of chlorinated solvents to aquifer materials is needed to allow reliable prediction of sorption in diverse subsurface environments. Unfortunately, the mechanism(s) for the sorption of nonionic organic compounds are not yet completely defined nor agreed upon in the literature. In this chapter, **"adsorption"** will be taken to refer to an interaction which occurs at the *surface* of a solid; **"absorption"** will refer to the uptake of the sorbate *within* the volume (or a fraction of the volume) of the sorbing phase. Based on various empirical observations and theoretical arguments, several researchers believe that sorption of nonionic organic compounds to soils is dominated by an absorption mechanism (Chiou *et al.*, 1983, 1988, 1990; Chiou and Shoup, 1985; Gschwend and Wu, 1985). Others (*e.g.*, Murphy *et al.*, 1990; MacIntyre and Smith, 1984; Minglegrin and Gerstl, 1983) are proponents of adsorption mechanisms. Actually, there seems to be evidence to conclude that there is a spectrum of cases in which one or both mechanisms contribute (see Karickhoff, 1984; Hassett and Banwart, 1989).

8.3.2 Sorption to Soil Organic Carbon

In the "**hydrophobic sorption model**", it is absorptive partitioning between the dissolved phase and the organic fraction of the soil that is thought to be the mechanism for sorption (Chiou *et al.*, 1983). (This model is analogous to the "like dissolves like" partitioning of a compound that can occur when a hydrophobic organic compound partitions into a non-polar phase such as octanol or oil.) In this model, nonionic organic compounds are viewed as being "dissolved" in the organic portion of the soil solids. Figure 8.8 shows that for sorption by soils with $f_{oc} > 0.001$, the K_d value of a given chlorinated aromatic compound increases with increasing f_{oc}. Also, at constant f_{oc}, for a group of different compounds a trend of increasing K_d with decreasing solubility (increasing hydrophobicity) is demonstrated. These two observations have been commonly made for sorption of nonionic organic pollutants from low concentration aqueous solutions, generally less than half of the water solubility

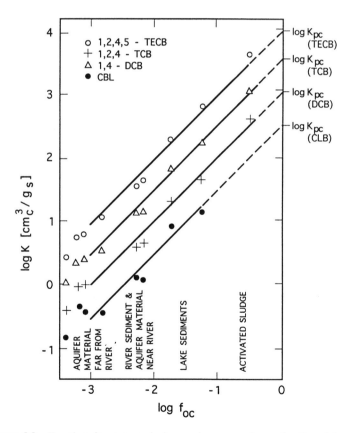

Figure 8.8 K_d values for some nonionic organic compounds as a function of the f_{oc} of the solid phase. (Reprinted with permission from Schwarzenbach and Westall, 1981.)

(Karickhoff, 1981; Karickhoff *et al.*, 1979; Chiou *et al.*, 1979, 1983; Schwarzenbach and Westall, 1981).

As discussed above, when sufficient solid organic carbon is present, K_d is generally directly proportional to f_{oc} (Schwarzenbach and Westall, 1981). In such cases, it is common to calculate the sorption coefficient normalized to the organic carbon content as $K_{oc} = K_d / f_{oc}$. For a given compound, K_{oc} values have been found to be approximately constant (within a one order of magnitude range) for sorption to a wide variety of sediments and soils (Karickhoff, 1981; Schwarzenbach and Westall, 1981). These and related studies suggest that sorption from dilute solutions is primarily a function of the solute's solubility or hydrophobicity, with the sorptive nature of the organic carbon (gram for gram) in the solid materials being remarkably constant from location to location (Chiou *et al.*, 1983). In the studies listed above and in others (*e.g.*, Gerstl, 1990), K_{oc} values have been correlated with compound-specific properties such as **solubility** S (mg/L) and K_{ow} that can be found in the literature (*e.g.*, see Montgomery and Welkom, 1990; Hansch and Leo, 1979). The resulting correlation equations can be used for estimating K_{oc} for compounds based either upon S or K_{ow}, with estimation of K_d then possible given the f_{oc} of the solids.

The form of the correlation equations available for estimating K_{oc} from K_{ow} is

$$\log K_{oc} = a \log K_{ow} + b \quad ; \tag{8.5}$$

the correlation equation based on solubility is

$$\log K_{oc} = c \log S + d \quad , \tag{8.6}$$

where a, and b, as well as c and d are empirical, compound-class-dependent parameters that are derived by regression of the available data. Some of the most commonly-used regression coefficients from the literature were obtained by Karickhoff (1981, 1984), Schwarzenbach and Westall (1981), and Chiou *et al.* (1983). The coefficients discussed in those studies were derived using data for a variety of compounds and sediment/soil samples.

Values of K_{ow} and S vary over several orders of magnitude for organic compounds of typical interest. This variation causes a similar range of variation in the corresponding K_d values for a soil material of interest. The K_{ow} values for very hydrophobic chemicals, such as some PCBs, are greater than about 10^4. Moderately hydrophobic compounds, such as the di- and trichlorobenzenes, have K_{ow} values in the 10^3-10^4 range. K_{ow} values for TCE, CTET and other chlorinated solvent compounds are in the 10-10^3 range.

Correlation equations like Eqs.(8.5) and (8.6) provide a quick and inexpensive method for qualitatively predicting sorption. However, one does need to remember that there are always limitations involved in using empirically-based equations in describing naturally-variable environmental systems, and that these equations apply best for sorption to soils and sediments when f_{oc} is larger than $\sim$0.001 (Schwarzenbach and Westall, 1981). We also note that when using either Eq.(8.5) or Eq.(8.6), it is best to choose a form of the regression equation that is based on data for compounds that are as similar as possible to the compound(s) of interest (*e.g.*, of the same compound class); some researchers have suggested that within a homologous series of compounds, a K_{oc} estimate will be within a factor of 2 of the measured value (Schwarzenbach and Westall, 1981; Karickhoff, 1981).

Recommended values for a and b for Eq.(8.5) are given in Table 8.1 for halogenated nonaromatic compounds (which includes almost all of the chlorinated solvents) and also for halogenated aromatic compounds (e.g., p-dichlorobenzene); recommended values for c and d for Eq.(8.6) are given in Table 8.2. As a result of the many sorption studies that have been carried out involving common groundwater pollutants, desired K_{oc} values may often be found directly in the literature (Montgomery and Welkom, 1990), though we note again that K_{oc} values measured for a given compound in different soils can vary by as much as an order of magnitude.

In addition to using Eqs.(8.5) and (8.6), K_{oc} values can also be estimated based on the value of the "molecular connectivity index", a parameter which is calculated from the molecular structure of a compound. An equation incorporating this index was found to adequately predict K_{oc} values for a test group of diverse compounds (Sabljic, 1987). However, Sabljic (1987) has shown that this index alone is no better at predicting the K_{oc} values of a large test group of compounds than are Eqs.(8.5) or (8.6). Other correlation equations have been developed which include corrections for molecular structure. Again, however, these are not necessarily more accurate than those based on measured K_{ow} or S values (Gerstl, 1990).

TABLE 8.1   Coefficients for Log K_{oc}-Log K_{ow} Correlation.

Compound class	a	b	r^2	Reference
nonaromatic, halogenated compounds	0.827	-0.039	0.698	Gerstl (1990)
aromatic halogenated compounds	0.722	0.417	0.855	Gerstl (1990)
TCE, PCE, DCB, and benzene on low f_{oc} solids	0.69	0.22	0.99	Piwoni and Banerjee (1989)

TABLE 8.2   Coefficients for Log K_{oc}-Log S Correlation.

Compound class	c	d	r^2	Reference
nonaromatic, halogenated compounds	−0.346	1.28	0.452	Gerstl (1990)
aromatic halogenated compounds	−0.475	1.318	0.839	Gerstl (1990)

The Stanford-Waterloo natural-gradient field tracer experiment (Mackay *et al.*, 1986a) provided benchmark, quantitative bulk field measurements of R for several halogenated compounds for a low-carbon sandy aquifer. These values can be compared to values predicted based on f_{oc} as measured for the Borden aquifer, although the f_{oc} value of the aquifer (0.0002) is much lower than the generally accepted threshold value for sorption dominance by organic carbon. Listed in Table 8.3 are the field-measured R values along with the values predicted using three regression equations from the literature. The relative degrees of retardation of the compounds in the aquifer agree with the predicted sequence. However, the predicted R values are typically lower than the field values (Ball and Roberts, 1991a; Ptacek and Gillham, 1992; Roberts *et al.*, 1986; Curtis *et al.*, 1986). Generally, the predicted K_d values are a factor of two-to-five times lower than would be needed to obtain agreement between the measured and predicted R values. This example emphasizes the "order of magnitude" accuracy of the correlation-based estimates of K_d.

Ball and Roberts (1991b) found that full sorption equilibrium was reached only after very long contact times, much longer than the contact times used for standard K_d measurements. Therefore, there is a possibility that some of the K_d values in the literature do not reflect equilibrium conditions (Ball and Roberts, 1991c). As a result, existing correlation equations may have a built-in bias to **underestimate sorption**. Another limitation may be related to the type and amount of organic carbon in the soil. We note that most of the available correlation equations were derived from observations of sorption in surficial soils, sediments, and sludges, with f_{oc} values greater than 0.001. Typical sand

TABLE 8.3 Measured (Field) and Calculated Retardation Coefficients for Three Chlorinated Hydrocarbons in Borden Sand.

Compound (a)	Log K_{ow}	Measured	(c)	(d)	(e)	(f)
			\multicolumn{4}{c}{Calculated (b)}			
CTET	2.73-2.83 (g)	1.8-2.5	1.31-1.37	1.01	1.18-1.22	1.24-1.48
PCE	2.53-3.78 (h)	2.7-5.9	1.22-2.79	1.01-1.02	1.12-2.34	1.23-1.40
DCB	3.38-3.55 (g)	3.9-9.0	1.92-2.21	1.02	1.12-1.15	1.20-2.86

(a) CTET = carbon tetrachloride, PCE = tetrachloroethylene, DCB = 1,2-dichlorobenzene;

(b) linear retardation (Eq.(8.2)) with $\rho_b = 1.81$ g/cm^3, $\theta_w = 0.33$, $f_{oc} = 0.0002$, and K_{oc} is from cited correlations or source;

(c) equation of Schwarzenbach and Westall (1981);

(d) equation of Chiou *et al.* (1983) and assuming that $f_{oc} = 0.5 \times$ OM (OM = organic matter);

(e) using equation of Gerstl (1990) for halogenated hydrocarbons;

(f) calculated from K_{oc} values as cited in Montgomery and Welkom (1990);

(g) Montgomery and Welkom (1990); and

(h) as cited by Ball and Roberts (1992).

and gravel aquifers, like the examples in Table 8.4, have very low f_{oc} values. Low f_{oc} values pose two problems for use of the correlation estimation methods. Firstly, low f_{oc} values themselves are difficult to measure accurately (Ball and Roberts, 1991c). Secondly, sorption may not be dominated by organic matter in systems of very low f_{oc}. The literature on sorption in low f_{oc} materials is not as complete as that for high f_{oc} soils. Murphy *et al.* (1990) found that the typical correlation equations do not accurately predict K_d values when f_{oc} is low. When K_{oc} is back-calculated as K_d/f_{oc}, MacIntyre *et al.* (1991) and Mackay *et al.* (1986b) have found poor correlation between K_{oc} and K_{ow} values in low f_{oc} sandy materials, suggesting that sorption may not be dominated by organic carbon in these media. Therefore, although mineral surfaces have been shown to be unimportant in sorption of nonionic organic compounds in high f_{oc} soils, it has been suggested that sorption to minerals may play a significant role in low f_{oc} systems.

TABLE 8.4   Organic Carbon Content (f_{oc}) of Typical Sand Aquifers (after Mackay, 1990).

Site location	Organic carbon content	Material
Gloucester, Ontario	0.001–0.006	interstratified silts, sands, gravels
Borden, Ontario	0.0002	medium to fine sand
Moffett Naval Air Station, California	0.0011	coarse gravel
Otis Air Force Base, Massachusetts	0.0001–0.0075	sand and gravel

8.3.3 Sorption Directly to Mineral Surfaces

It has been shown that organic compounds can **sorb directly to mineral surfaces** (Perlinger and Eisenreich, 1991; Perlinger *et al.*, 1993). For nonionic compounds, such sorption is perhaps most pronounced in materials with substantial **swelling clay content**, and in materials of **low f_{oc} value** (Karickhoff, 1984). The literature on the sorption of chlorinated solvent compounds to natural, clay-rich soils and sediments is limited. In a review of the pertinent literature, Karickhoff (1984) suggested that at ratios of swelling clay fraction to organic matter fraction of greater than approximately 25 to 60, adsorption to mineral surfaces will dominate the sorption. In several studies, measured K_d values for chlorinated hydrocarbons in a low f_{oc} clay-rich material were found to be approximately an order of magnitude greater than would have been predicted based just on the f_{oc} value (Barone *et al.*, 1992; Myrand *et al.*, 1992; Allen-King *et al.*, 1995; Johnson *et al.*, 1989); sorption to clay mineral surfaces was identified as a possible explanation for the enhanced sorption. When Allen-King *et al.* (1995) reduced the f_{oc} value of their clay by baking, the measured K_d values were correspondingly reduced. Recent research has suggested that in some instances, the organic surface coatings on the clay (rather than direct mineral surface adsorption) may be responsible for enhancing the sorption beyond what would be expected based on the f_{oc} value alone (Murphy *et al.*, 1990; Smith *et al.*, 1990b).

In low f_{oc} materials, such as the aquifer materials listed in Table 8.4, there is evidence to suggest that minerals other than clays may affect sorption (Piwoni and Banerjee, 1989; Stauffer and MacIntyre, 1986). In sand from the Borden aquifer (Ball and Roberts, 1991a; Mackay *et al.*, 1986b; Curtis *et al.*, 1986) and in sand from the sand and gravel aquifer at Otis Air Force Base on Cape Cod in Massachusetts (Barber *et al.*, 1992), measured sorption has been found to be greater than expected based just on the measured value of f_{oc}. We also note that Ball and Roberts (1991a) found that for very long contact times, PCE and 1,2,4,5-tetrachlorobenzene sorption coefficients were about an order of magnitude greater than one would expect from $K_{oc}f_{oc}$ calculations, and that the sorption isotherms were non-linear over a wide concentration range. They hypothesized that slow intraparticle diffusion was responsible for the long equilibration period. They found that the presence of freshly-broken surfaces in a pulverized sample did not significantly change the equilibrium K_d values compared to a natural sample, a result which they interpreted to mean that surface coatings (not necessarily organic) were likely important in this low f_{oc} material.

8.4 METHODS FOR MEASURING SORPTION

8.4.1 General

The sorption of organic compounds to subsurface materials has been measured using both small- and large-scale methods. In the laboratory, the commonly used small-scale methods are **batch experiments** and **column experiments**. A **field column method** has also recently been developed (Gillham *et al.*, 1990). Large-scale methods include **natural-gradient** and **forced-gradient** field tests.

In studies involving volatile compounds such as the halogenated solvents, care must be taken during all steps of the measurement process to prevent losses. Materials such as glass and stainless steel should be chosen so as to minimize sorption losses to the measurement equipment (Lion *et al.*, 1990). Control experiments should be carried out to evaluate the importance of any volatilization and sorption losses. It should be noted that Teflon may sorb some compounds enough to affect the results (Ball, 1989).

8.4.2 Small-Scale Methods

8.4.2.1 Batch methods

Batch methods can be used to measure a K_d value for a discrete sample under conditions which maximize the contact between the solids and the solution. Typical short term batch methods are described by Ptacek and Gillham (1992), Lion *et al.* (1990), and Curtis *et al.* (1986). In these methods, a subsample of the solids is placed in a vial, the vial is filled with an aqueous solution containing the compound(s) of interest, and the vial is mixed for a set period of time. The equilibration should take place at a temperature similar to those in the subsurface (K_d values are temperature dependent). After equilibration, centrifugation is used to separate the phases. The aqueous phase and/or the solid phase are sampled and analyzed. For sampling and analysis of the aqueous phase alone, mass balance is used to determine the concentration on the solids. Vials are usually replicated and prepared over a range of initial concentrations to allow the generation of an isotherm. If the equilibration temperature differs from the subsurface temperature of interest, temperature corrections on the measured partition coefficient can be made (Curtis *et al.*, 1986).

Short term batch methods typically call for a 24 to 48 hr contact time (*e.g.*, Brusseau and Rao, 1989). It has been noted that the rate of uptake from the solution is very rapid initially, but decreases significantly after the first few hours of contact. Equilibrium is assumed following the contact period. However, as noted in the previous section, results collected over the past few years with Borden sand cast doubt over the assumption that equilibration is always reached during a 24 to 48 hr contact time. For example, the low concentration batch K_d values found by Ball and Roberts (1991a) for very long contact periods (several months) were more than half an order of magnitude greater than Ptacek and Gillham's (1992) 24-hr batch values. On the other hand, long-term sorption studies conducted with different compounds and sand from another site suggest that equilibrium was attained within 24 hr (MacIntyre *et al.*, 1991). It would seem that the assumption of equilibrium after ~24 hr may not generally be appropriate. Methods for conducting batch experiments may improve for the measurement of equilibrium sorption coefficients.

In batch methods, the formation of suspended microparticles has been shown to affect the determination of a sorption coefficient. The interference of microparticles can be avoided for volatile compounds by measuring concentrations in the headspace instead of the aqueous phase (Garbarini and Lion, 1985), or by varying the solids/water ratio when a significant effect is suspected (Gschwend and Wu, 1985).

8.4.2.2 Column methods

In column methods, the contact between the aqueous and solid phases is more like the natural field conditions than it is in the batch experiments. Laboratory column methods have been described by Ptacek and Gillham (1992), MacIntyre *et al.* (1991) and Brusseau *et al.* (1991a, 1991b), among others. The methods generally include packing aquifer material into a column, establishing a steady flow of water through the column, injecting a small volume of an aqueous solution containing the compounds of interest as well as a non-reactive tracer, then collecting samples of the effluent water over time.

An *in situ* field column method has been developed by Gillham *et al.* (1990) and used by Ptacek and Gillham (1992) for measuring retardation of chlorinated solvents in the sandy Borden aquifer. In this method, a natural column of aquifer material is isolated from the surrounding material by a split spoon core barrel, which then serves as the container for the column. Prior to installation, the core barrel is fitted with two screened zones for injecting and withdrawing solutions. The natural geochemistry and stratigraphy of the system are preserved in this method.

For all column methods, data analysis is achieved by fitting a transport model to the breakthrough curves. The retardation factor and the distribution coefficient are obtained from the curve fitting exercise. However, these values may not be as accurate as those obtained by batch methods because non-equilibrium and transport effects often complicate the interpretation of column results.

8.4.3 Large-Scale Methods

Few large-scale natural-gradient tests such as the Stanford-Waterloo injection experiment have been conducted due to the labor and cost associated with such undertakings. Nevertheless, these tests are the best-documented cases of how transport in a natural system is affected by sorption. As such, this type of field experiment provides a benchmark against which other methods for measuring partitioning can be compared. Forced-gradient tests can be conducted over shorter periods of time than natural-gradient tests, and may therefore prove to be very useful for measuring large-scale effects of sorption on transport in situations where accurate field information is essential.

In a forced-gradient test, a solution containing a tracer is injected in one well while pumping occurs at another well. Because of the gradient induced by pumping, the travel time between the two wells is less than it would be under natural conditions. Samples of the effluent water from the pumping well and from piezometers along the flowpath are collected. The forced-gradient test conducted by Mackay et al. (1994) involved injecting dissolved chlorinated solvents together with conservative tracers at a site directly adjacent to the site of the Stanford-Waterloo field experiment. Alternatively, at a contaminated site, clean water can be injected, thus desorbing contaminants from the system (Whiffin and Bahr, 1985; Bahr, 1989; Mackay and Thorbjarnson, 1990; Mackay et al., 1994). For either method, the results are analyzed by fitting breakthrough curves with a numerical transport model. If the data are sufficiently detailed, insight can be gained on the spatial variability of the hydraulic conductivity, as well as the contaminant sorption capacity and kinetics.

8.5 NON-IDEAL SORPTION BEHAVIOR IN A SATURATED SYSTEM

8.5.1 Non-Ideal Breakthrough Curves

Breakthrough curves generated from column and field experiments are defined as ideal if they fit the advection-dispersion equation with a retardation term that assumes linear, reversible, instantaneous (i.e., equilibrium) sorption. A non-sorbing and a sorbing tracer (tritium and calcium respectively) were found to demonstrate ideal behavior in the laboratory column experiment represented in Figure 8.9.a. When normalized by the retardation factor, the breakthrough curves for the two tracers are coincident (Figure 8.9.b). In the same experiment, diuron, a nonionic organic pesticide compound, was found to exhibit non-ideal behavior. The breakthrough curve for diuron shows both early breakthrough as well as tailing compared to the ideal tracers in Figure 8.9.b. Similar non-ideal breakthrough curves were observed at the field scale by Bahr (1989) with the compound tetrahydrofuran for samples taken in a piezometer along the flowpath between the injection and purge wells of a forced-gradient field test. We also note that asymmetry and tailing were observed in the breakthrough curves of PCE and CTET in the Stanford-Waterloo experiment (see also Section 8.2 and Figure 8.3). Non-ideal breakthrough curves, such as those shown in Figures 8.3 and 8.9 have frequently been observed for nonionic organic compounds in column experiments (Ptacek and Gillham, 1992; Lee et al., 1988, 1991;

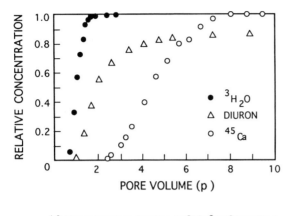

Figure 8.9.a Breakthrough curves from a saturated column experiment. ^{45}Ca and ^{3}H$_2$O demonstrate ideal behavior of retarded and conservative tracers, respectively.

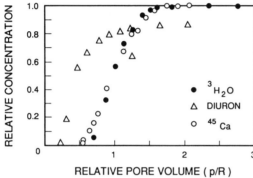

Figure 8.9.b Diuron does not behave "ideally". (Reprinted with permission from Nkedi-Kizza *et al.*, 1989.)

Brusseau *et al.*, 1989b, 1991a,; Nkedi-Kizza *et al.*, 1989; Bouchard *et al.*, 1988) and in the field (Mackay *et al.*, 1994; Mackay and Thorbjarnson, 1990; Bahr, 1989; Roberts *et al.*, 1986).

As has been noted above, non-ideal behavior yields **early breakthrough** and **tailing** relative to ideal behavior. Travel time for contaminant movement from a source to a designated location such as a drinking-water well would be overpredicted by models assuming ideal behavior. Thus, the well would become contaminated more quickly than expected. In remedial applications, the long tails (extended section of low concentration at long times) of breakthrough curves relative to the ideal case mean that the amount of pumping required to remediate a site using the pump-and-treat method will be significantly greater than predicted based on ideal behavior (Mackay and Cherry, 1989).

Non-ideal behavior has been attributed to both **pore-scale effects** and **field-scale effects**. The reader is referred to Brusseau and Rao (1989) for an in-depth discussion of pore-scale contributions to non-ideal sorption. The references cited below are primarily those which have appeared subsequent to the review by Brusseau and Rao (1989), or which are of particular relevance. Recent research has suggested that **field-scale heterogeneity** may be more important than pore-scale effects in producing non-ideal behavior in the field.

8.5.2 Pore-Scale Mechanisms Causing Non-Ideal Behavior

Non-ideal behavior due to pore-scale effects may be due to **isotherm non-linearity**, **non-singularity** (*i.e.* hysteresis), and/or to **non-equilibrium sorption**. In general, the last of these is considered to be the most important. Isotherm non-linearity will result in either early breakthrough or tailing, depending upon the value of n in the Freundlich isotherm (Eq.(8.3)). However, the simultaneous occurrence of both early breakthrough *and* tailing as commonly observed, cannot be accounted for by isotherm non-linearity. Similarly, hysteresis in an adsorption/desorption isotherm can cause tailing, but not early breakthrough. Therefore, the typically-observed non-ideal behavior is not generally attributed to either isotherm non-linearity or hysteresis.

In recent field studies, apparently anomalous, long-term persistence of volatile chlorinated hydrocarbons has been attributed to kinetically slow desorption (Pignatello *et al.*, 1990, 1993; Pavlostathis and Jaglal, 1991). Non-equilibrium sorption is caused by the combined effects of the flow characteristics, the nature of the sorbate, and the nature of the sorbent (Valocchi, 1985). It has been observed that the nature of the sorbent has a dominant effect on the degree of non-equilibrium observed. For the small chlorinated solvent molecules, the properties of the sorbate will exert only a secondary effect (Brusseau and Rao, 1991).

Non-equilibrium sorption has been attributed to physical and/or chemical mechanisms. Physical non-equilibrium is conceptualized as **rate-limited sorption** due to a resistance to mass transfer between two regions in the porous medium. For example, the mass transfer resistance may be conceptualized as mass transfer by diffusion from "**mobile water**" in interconnected pores into regions of "**immobile water**", such as dead-end pores. Chemical non-equilibrium has been characterized by two types of reaction sites, "**fast sites**" and "**slow sites**". Typically, the fast sites are considered to equilibrate instantaneously; the slow sites are assumed to be rate-limited, and are often characterized using a first order mass transfer rate. Nkedi-Kizza *et al.* (1984) have shown that under certain conditions, physical and chemical non-equilibrium conceptual models are mathematically equivalent.

Transport models incorporating non-equilibrium effects require more parameters than models assuming ideal sorption. The additional parameters account for: 1) the rate of the rate-limited step; 2) the volume ratio of the immobile and mobile zones; and/or 3) the distribution of sorption capacity between different types of sorption sites. Determination of the non-equilibrium parameters is generally achieved by fitting models to experimentally-determined breakthrough curves (Brusseau *et al.*, 1989b). However, because of the number of fitting parameters, there is a danger that non-unique solutions may be obtained by this method. The parameters are not easily measured independently, although methods have been developed to approach this goal (Karickhoff, 1980; Brusseau *et al.*, 1990; Ball and Roberts, 1991a,b). Because of the mathematical similarity between physical and chemical non-equilibrium models, a good fit with one of the models does not generally confirm the validity of the assumed mechanism.

It has been argued that results such as those presented in Figure 8.9 do not support the mobile/immobile water concept as a cause of non-equilibrium effects (Nkedi-Kizza *et al.*, 1989; Brusseau and Rao, 1989). Simply stated, although immobile domains of water (*e.g.*, dead-end pores) should affect non-sorbing tracers as well as sorbing tracers, effects on non-sorbing tracers are not typically observed. In such cases, the immobile/mobile water concept may still fit the observations if the immobile water is a small percentage of the total, and the immobile zone contains a large percentage of the sorption sites. Proof of such a mechanism would be difficult to obtain.

Two similar cases of a physical cause of non-equilibrium invoke slow sites accessed either by slow diffusion into organic matter, or intraparticle diffusion into mineral or soil grains. Intraorganic matter diffusion has been shown to be consistent with experimental results in several studies (Ptacek and Gillham, 1992; Brusseau *et al.*, 1991a, 1990, 1989a, 1989b; Lee *et al.*, 1988, 1991; Nkedi-Kizza *et al.* 1989; Bouchard *et al.*, 1988). The major arguments supporting this mechanism as a rate-limiting step in non-equilibrium sorption are: 1) asymmetrical breakthrough curves for sorbing organic compounds in the presence of symmetrical curves for ideal tracers; and 2) symmetrical breakthrough curves for sorbing organic compounds and diminished retardation after the soil is treated to reduce the organic matter content. Intraparticle diffusion in mineral grains is thought by some researchers to control the rate of sorption in Borden sand (Ball and Roberts, 1991a, 1991b; Curtis and Roberts, 1986). When organic matter is distributed through a soil particle, intraorganic matter diffusion becomes intraparticle diffusion (Wu and Gschwend, 1986). For such diffusion-limited sorption, the sorption rate constant will be inversely proportional to K_d. Both intraorganic matter and intraparticle diffusion are consistent with the two-stage sorption behavior frequently observed in batch measurements. Finally, we note that although non-ideal behavior has been observed frequently with sorbing organic compounds, there are some cases, generally with very low organic carbon materials, in which non-equilibrium effects were negligible (MacIntyre *et al.*, 1991).

8.5.3 Contribution of Spatial Variability in the Field to Non-Ideal Sorption Behavior

Figure 8.3 shows a typical asymmetric field breakthrough curve for PCE with a tail of slowly-declining concentration. In a remedial application, the concentration at which pumping can safely be discontinued (assuming no remaining source area containing liquid solvent) would usually be very far down on the tail because drinking water standards are often much lower than groundwater contamination levels. The amount of pumping required will be much greater than would be predicted based upon ideal transport.

In the previous section, we considered how non-ideal sorption at the pore-scale affects lab-scale test results. In some cases, non-ideal behavior at the field scale has been ascribed to pore-scale processes (Bahr, 1989; Goltz and Roberts, 1988). Alternatively, **spatial variability** in the hydraulic conductivity K and in K_d can result in apparently non-ideal, field-scale asymmetry in breakthrough curves. Heterogeneity in a layered system can be thought of as a special case of physical non-equilibrium. In this scenario, layers of low hydraulic conductivity provide zones of slow uptake and release of solute due to mass transfer resistance between layers. Sorption within layers and non-equilibrium effects within layers can also contribute to apparent non-ideal behavior in the field. K_d has been observed to vary significantly in space, even in what most would consider a relatively homogeneous sandy aquifer (Mackay *et al.*, 1986b and 1994).

Recent theoretical research (Burr, 1992) suggests that moderate heterogeneity, such as that present in the relatively uniform sand at the Borden site, may be a dominant factor in creating apparently non-ideal field-scale transport of a sorbing solute, and that pore-scale effects may be secondary. In this research, the increasing trend of R with time in the natural-gradient field test (Figure 8.4) can be obtained by assuming spatially-variable and negatively-correlated K and K_d values.

8.6 EFFECTS ON SORPTION CAUSED BY PROPERTIES OF THE AQUEOUS PHASE

8.6.1 General

Solution effects on sorption act primarily through effects on solubility. In general, mechanisms which increase solubility also decrease sorption of organic compounds, and *vice versa*. Effects are generally most significant for very hydrophobic compounds since the effect on the solubility of such compounds can be large. Usually, natural geochemical variability has no significant effect on the sorption of organic compounds. Effects can be observed when the concentrations of dissolved organic compounds are large, or in the presence of surfactants or co-solvents.

System parameters which can affect sorption can be classified into two groups: 1) **geochemical parameters** (temperature, pH, and ionic strength); and 2) **dissolved or suspended/colloidal material parameters** (*e.g.*, anthropogenic organic compounds such as the ones already under transport at the site, co-solvents, surfactants, natural humic organic matter, and colloidal particles).

8.6.2 Effects of Natural Aqueous Geochemistry

Variability in the inorganic geochemistry of groundwater does not generally have much effect on the sorption of nonionic organic compounds. The solubility of a given compound may either increase or decrease with increasing temperature within the narrow, environmentally-relevant range; the behavior is compound specific. As a result, depending upon the compound, sorption will decrease or increase with temperature, respectively. For some chlorinated compounds (CTET, BROM, PCE, and DCB) K_d has often been found to vary by less than 10% over the range of 9 °C to 23 °C (Curtis *et al.*, 1986; Ptacek and Gillham, 1992). In one of those studies, the greatest observed variation was 33% for DCB. Thus, K_d variation due to temperature is probably small compared to other uncertainties.

For the halogenated solvent compounds, the pH does not have much effect on sorption. For example, no significant effect on TCE sorption on a silty clay material was observed between pH 3 to 13 (Pavlostathis and Jaglal, 1991). For ionizable compounds like pentachlorophenol (PCP) and other organic acids and bases, however, sorption can be strongly influenced by pH (Lee *et al.*, 1990, 1991; Jafvert *et al.*, 1990). The degree of influence which pH has on sorption depends on the magnitude of the differences in affinities of the ionized and neutral species for the solid phase, as well as the ability to enter into ionic interactions such as ion pair formation and ion exchange (Johnson and Westall, 1990).

Increased ionic strength decreases solubility of hydrophobic organic compounds, and increases sorption, due to a "salting out" effect. The effect is not large (Karickhoff *et al.*, 1979). Pavlostathis and Jaglal (1991) observed little effect on TCE sorption over a range of ionic strengths under 0.1 *M* (*e.g.* up to 5.9 g/L NaCl). When the ionic strength exceeded 0.1 *M*, the degree of sorption was increased. Sorption of nonionic organic compounds from a high ionic strength solution approximately equivalent to seawater (NaCl $\approx$ 0.5 *M*) is predicted to be only ~20% greater than from distilled water (Karickhoff, 1984).

In summary, variability in typical geochemical parameters over normal ranges results in little or no effect on the sorption of nonionic organic compounds. For ionizable compounds, however, significant pH effects may occur.

8.6.3 Effects of Co-Solvents, Dissolved Organic Matter, Suspended Colloids, and Surfactants

8.6.3.1 Co-solvents

When an organic solvent that is at least somewhat miscible with water is mixed with water, the properties of the water are changed. Methanol and acetone are solvents that are "completely miscible" with water, *i.e.*, miscible with water over all proportions. As the fraction organic **co-solvent** increases, the solubility of a third organic compound will increase and the sorption of that compound to soils will decrease. A shallow, negatively-sloped log-linear relationship has been observed between sorption coefficient and fraction organic co-solvent in solution (Nkedi-Kizza *et al.*, 1985; Woodburn *et al.*, 1986). The degree of reduction in sorption depends on the identity of the co-solvent, and is apparently relatively independent of the specific properties of the sorbing solids. Co-solvents have been shown to significantly increase mobility only at relatively high co-solvent concentrations, greater than about 5% of the solution (Nkedi-Kizza *et al.*, 1987). This result suggests that except for close to source zones contaminated with mixed wastes including large quantities of co-solvents, co-solvent effects on plume mobility will usually not be significant. In addition to completely miscible co-solvents, there are examples of co-solvents which are not completely miscible with water. The effects of such partially-miscible co-solvents on organic contaminant mobility are similar on a mass fraction basis to those of the completely miscible solvents (Rao *et al.*, 1990).

8.6.3.2 Dissolved organic matter (DOM) and suspended colloidal material

Sorption to **dissolved macromolecular organic matter** as well as to **suspended colloidal matter** will increase the mobility of an organic compound in the subsurface. This effect is referred to as **facilitated transport**. Laboratory studies have shown that partitioning of organic compounds from water to natural dissolved organic matter ("DOM", *e.g.*, "humic acid" and "fulvic acid") is generally rapid, linear, reversible, and non-competitive (Chiou *et al.*, 1986). The magnitude of the effect of DOM on the transport of a compound of interest depends on: 1) the distribution coefficient for the compound of interest to the DOM; and 2) the concentration of the DOM (Magee *et al.*, 1991).

Laboratory studies such as those by Chin *et al.* (1990), Spurlock and Biggar (1990), and Abdul *et al.* (1990) suggest that the mobility of organic compounds can be significantly enhanced by DOM-facilitated transport, but only for very hydrophobic compounds with log K_{ow} values greater than 4 to 5 (Chin *et al.*, 1990) and only when DOM concentrations are very high (*e.g.*, 100 mg/L). Since the chlorinated solvents have relatively low K_{ow} values, the effect of DOM on chlorinated solvent transport will be negligible.

There is some evidence to show that natural DOM travels at greater velocity than bulk water, probably due to exclusion from small pores (Enfield *et al.*, 1989). Enhanced mobility due to DOM may be made more significant in this special circumstance, but the chlorinated solvents will remain largely unaffected.

Recently, some research has been done on the effects on contaminant mobility that can be caused by non-filterable, colloidal inorganic microparticles (*e.g.*, clays and iron and manganese hydrous oxides) (Ryan and Gschwend, 1990). The conclusions of that work are similar to the findings for DOM, *i.e.*, the mobility of some compounds can be enhanced due to sorption to mobile colloidal particles (Ryan and Gschwend, 1990). However, as with the effects of DOM, the effects of colloidal particles on chlorinated solvent transport will be negligible.

8.6.3.3 Surfactants

Surfactants are a broad class of compounds representing a wide variety of properties and uses, *e.g.*, as detergents and emulsifiers. The effects of surfactants on solubility and sorption cause this group of compounds to be of interest in groundwater remediation research. In particular, at concentrations of surfactant above the "**critical micelle concentration**" (CMC) for the surfactant of interest, aggregates (*i.e.*, **micelles**) of the surfactant molecules form. Hydrophobic organic compounds will readily **partition** into the micelles. Thus, above the CMC, the apparent solubility of a hydrophobic organic compound can be increased significantly (Kile and Chiou, 1989). Laboratory research has recently shown that flushing of contaminated porous media with surfactant solutions can facilitate the removal of organic compounds, particularly for very hydrophobic contaminants (Abdul and Gibson, 1991). The enhancement of mobility by surfactant addition is currently a very active research area (*e.g.*, Abdul *et al.*, 1992).

At low concentrations, below the CMC, surfactants are dispersed throughout an aqueous solution and are also concentrated at the air/water and water/solid interfaces. The effect of the surfactant on organic compound behavior depends not only on the concentration, but also on the type of surfactant: anionic, nonionic, or cationic. The solubilities of organic compounds have been shown to be increased by the presence of low concentrations of nonionic surfactants (Kile and Chiou, 1989). (The increase in solubility is small compared to the effect observed above the CMC.) The effect is believed to be due to association of the organic compound with surfactant monomers. Aronstein *et al.*

(1991) demonstrated in laboratory studies that the enhanced desorption of a hydrophobic organic compound caused by the addition of a nonionic surfactant also enhanced the biodegradability of the compound. No enhanced desorption was observed with low concentrations of anionic surfactant.

In contrast with anionic and non-ionic surfactants, since cationic surfactants can sorb strongly to natural, negatively-charged solids (*e.g.*, clays), they can **enhance contaminant sorption** by creating an organic coating on the solid phase (Boyd *et al.*, 1988). Indeed, cationic surfactant-coated clay tested in laboratory studies was found to be more sorptive of organic compounds than the uncoated clay (Boyd *et al.*, 1988). Laboratory research indicates that the mobility of dissolved organic compounds in an aquifer may be decreased significantly when the subsurface is treated with a cationic surfactant (Burris and Antworth, 1992). (There was no apparent decrease in the hydraulic conductivity.) Holsen *et al.* (1991) obtained a similar result with anionic surfactant-coated clays at low pH. Research on the application of surfactants to *limit* plume mobility is in progress.

8.7 SORPTION TO UNSATURATED SOIL

Sorption in unsaturated porous media depends on the degree of unsaturation of the material. At field capacity and wetter, the sorption will be essentially the same as if the medium was saturated. However, in relatively dry soils, mechanisms apparently exist which can increase the sorption coefficient above that for wet soils. One can differentiate soils according to three water content regimes (Ong and Lion, 1991a): extremely dry (*i.e.*, oven dry), an intermediate dry range, and moderately dry to wet (approximately field capacity and greater). The specific water contents for these regimes depend on the properties of the porous medium, particularly the specific surface area.

In the moderately-dry to wet range, the mechanisms for sorption of hydrophobic organic compounds to the solid phase are the same as those discussed for saturated materials: all of the solid grains are covered with water. Partitioning between the aqueous and gaseous phases is governed by Henry's Law (Ong and Lion, 1991a; Call, 1957 as cited in Ong and Lion, 1991b; Spencer and Cliath, 1970), and the K_d value for water/solid partitioning is the same as it is when none of the void space is filled with air. Assuming linear and instantaneous partitioning, retardation can be described according to the relationships presented in Chapter 6.

In the laboratory, sorption of gas phase hydrophobic organic compounds to oven dry materials has been shown to occur **directly to unhydrated mineral surfaces** (Chiou and Shoup, 1985). Sorption of TCE to solids under these circumstances can be four orders of magnitude stronger than in the corresponding saturated system (Peterson *et al.*, 1988). This enhanced sorption is only of importance when there is less than one molecular layer of water on the mineral surfaces (Spencer and Cliath, 1970; Ong and Lion, 1991a, 1991b), a condition which exists only under extraordinarily dry conditions (Chiou and Shoup, 1985; Rhue *et al.*, 1989).

Ong and Lion (1991b) found that apparent K_d values for TCE for air dried soils at 68% relative humidity were about three times greater than K_d values at field capacity for five different mineral solids. In this intermediate water content range, although there are one to five monolayers of water on the mineral surfaces, there is not enough water for significant dissolution into the water layer to occur. Sorption in this range of water content can be attributed to two possible mechanisms: 1) direct adsorption on unhydrated surfaces which may be present due to uneven coverage of the surfaces by water; and/or 2) accumulation of the compound at the air/water interface. The second phenomenon is well known in the surface chemistry literature. At this low water content range, the air-water interface is very large relative to the volume of water. Thus, accumulation at the interface may contribute significantly to sorption under these conditions.

At field capacity and greater, it has been shown that Henry's Law accurately describes partitioning between the gas and soil water phases (Ong and Lion, 1991a; and, Call, 1957, as cited by Ong and Lion 1991b). The critical water content for adherence to Henry's Law is equivalent to five molecular layers, but the weight percent varies depending on the surface area of the medium of interest. Ong and Lion (1991a) found that the critical water content varied for five materials tested from less than 5% for kaolinite and iron oxide, up to 15-25% for alumina, humics-coated alumina, and montmorillinite. Shearer *et al.* (1973) observed no changes in the partitioning process above a 4% water content in Gila silt loams (desert soils, ~18% clay, 0.6% organic matter).

Although additional research is needed to determine the significance of enhanced sorption to dry soils, the laboratory results discussed above suggest that such enhanced sorption will only be important under very dry conditions. Ong and Lion (1991a) and Smith *et al.* (1990a) speculate that soil in arid and semi-arid regions, and surface soils in temperate regions during the summer season may be dry enough to warrant consideration of the effects of this enhanced sorption of hydrophobic organic compounds.

8.8 CONCLUSIONS

Sorption can reduce the mobility of dissolved chlorinated solvents in groundwater. Sorption can also reduce the rate of biotransformation. The degree of sorption depends primarily on the identity of the compound of interest, the solids of interest, and the properties of the aqueous solution. The degree of sorption, as indicated by the distribution coefficient K_d is related to the hydrophobicity of the compound of interest. Somewhat hydrophobic chemicals such as TCE and CTET are sorbed to a much lower degree than are highly-hydrophobic compounds such as PCBs. When $f_{oc} > 0.001$, K_d values can be predicted based on tabulated K_{oc} values and the f_{oc} value of the solids of interest. Since the resulting K_d is an empirically-based estimate, it is important to use these predictions with the appropriate degree of caution.

If f_{oc} is measured accurately and is low ($< 0.1\%$), K_d is typically underestimated by predictions of the above type. The relatively higher K_d values found in low f_{oc} materials may be due to several causes, including direct interactions with mineral surfaces (*e.g.*, swelling clays) and a greater affinity of the sorbate for the sorbent organic carbon when f_{oc} is low.

Equilibrium linear or non-linear isotherms can be measured directly by batch methods with relatively small samples. Isotherm non-linearity can be significant in some materials when solvent concentrations are relatively high. Column experiments give an indication of the nature of non-equilibrium effects, and sorption coefficients can be deduced from the results of such experiments. The non-equilibrium effects serve to complicate the interpretation of sorption from the results. However, column experiments are typically run with flow velocities much greater than one would find in nature.

Large-scale methods provide the most accurate representation of retardation at the field-scale. Natural-gradient tests are viewed as research tools, and provide quantitative information about actual behavior in the field. Forced-gradient tests may be a practical method for determination of retardation, and they can provide information about non-ideal behavior which can facilitate the design of a pump-and-treat extraction system.

Non-ideal behavior, characterized by early breakthrough and prolonged tailing relative to ideal behavior, has important implications for the manner in which contaminated sites are treated. Early breakthrough suggests that the arrival time of a contaminant at a point of interest, such as a drinking water well, will be earlier than predicted based on the ideal model. Tailing has important implications for the operation of pump-and-treat systems. Because the concentrations in a tail are usually significant relative to drinking water standards, pumping may need to be continued for much longer than one would predict based on an ideal desorption model.

Non-ideal behavior has been observed in laboratory and field studies. It has been attributed to both pore-scale non-equilibrium sorption and to heterogeneities at the field scale. Recent research has suggested that pore-scale effects may be secondary to field-scale heterogeneities in causing non-ideal behavior at some sites.

Solution effects on sorption typically act through their effects on solubility. Factors which increase solubility tend to decrease sorption. Variations in pH, temperature, and ionic strength usually have only small effects on the extent of sorption. However, the presence of high concentrations of co-solvents and surfactants can reduce sorption and thus enhance mobility.

Except under very arid conditions, sorption in the unsaturated zone is controlled by the same mechanisms as in the saturated zone, with gas/water equilibrium following Henry's Law. Under very dry conditions, additional sorption mechanisms have been observed to enhance sorption to the solids by up to three-to-four orders of magnitude with respect to the same sorbent at field capacity or wetter. The water saturation at which sorption is enhanced varies with the texture and surface area of the materials.

ACKNOWLEDGEMENTS

Funding support for this research was provided in part by the University Consortium Solvents-in-Groundwater Research Program. Sponsors of the Program between 1988 and 1994 have included: The Boeing Company, Ciba-Geigy Corporation, Dow Chemical Canada/USA, Eastman Kodak Co., General Electric Co., Laidlaw Environmental Systems Ltd., Mitre Corporation, The Natural Sciences and Engineering Research Council of Canada, and the Ontario University Research Incentive Fund.

8.9 REFERENCES

Abdul, A. S., T. L. Gibson, and D. N. Rai (1990) "Use of humic acid solution to remove organic contaminants from hydrogeologic systems", *Environ. Sci. Technol.*, **24**, 328-333.

Abdul, A. S. and T. L. Gibson (1991) "Laboratory studies of surfactant-enhanced washing of polychlorinated biphenyl from sandy material", *Environ. Sci. Technol.*, **25**, 665-671.

Abdul, A. S., T. L. Gibson, C. C. Ang, J. C. Smith, and R. E. Sobczynski (1992). "*In situ* surfactant washing of polychlorinated biphenyls and oils from a contaminated site", *Ground Water*, **3**, 219-231.

Allen-King, R. M., L. M. McKay, and M. R. Trudell (1995) "Organic-carbon dominated trichloro-ethene sorption in a clay-rich glacial deposit", in preparation.

Anderson, M. R. and J. F. Pankow (1986) "A case study of a chemical spill: Polychlorinated biphenyls (PCBs) 3. PCB sorption and retardation in soil underlying the site", *Water Resources Research*, **22**, 1051-1057.

Aronstein, B. N., Y. M. Calvillo, and M. Alexander (1991) "Effect of surfactants at low concentrations on the desorption and biodegradation of sorbed aromatic compounds in soil", *Environ. Sci. Technol.*, **25**, 1728-1731.

Bahr, J. (1989) "Analysis of nonequilibrium desorption of volatile organics during a field test of aquifer decontamination", *J. Contaminant Hydrology*, **4**, 205-222.

Ball, W. P. (1989) Ph.D. Thesis, Stanford University, Stanford, California.

Ball, W. P. and P. V. Roberts (1991a) "Long-term sorption of halogenated organic chemicals by aquifer material. 1. Equilibrium", *Environ. Sci. Technol.*, **25**, 1223-1236.

Ball, W. P. and P. V. Roberts (1991b) "Long-term sorption of halogenated organic chemicals by aquifer material. 2. Intraparticle diffusion", *Environ. Sci. Technol.*, **25**, 1237-1249.

Ball, W. P. and P. V. Roberts (1991c) "Diffusive rate limitations in the sorption of organic chemicals. In: *Organic Substances and Sediments in Water, Vol 2., Processes and Analytical*, R. A. Baker (Ed.) Lewis Publishers, Boca Raton, Florida, pp. 273-310.

Ball, W. P. and P. V. Roberts (1992) "Comment on 'Long-term sorption of halogenated organic chemicals by aquifer material. 1. Equilibrium' ", *Environ. Sci. Technol.*, **26**, 2301-2302.

Barber, L. B., E. M. Thurman, M. P. Schroeder, and D. R. LeBlanc (1988) "Long-term fate of organic micropollutants in sewage-contaminated groundwater", *Environ. Sci. Technol.*, **22**, 205-211.

Barber, L. B., E. M. Thurman, and D. D. Runnells (1992) "Geochemical heterogeneity in a sand and gravel aquifer: Effect of sediment mineralogy and particle size on the sorption of chlorobenzenes", *J. Contaminant Hydrology*, **9**, 35-54.

Barone, F. S., R. K. Rowe, and R. M. Quigley (1992) "A laboratory estimation of diffusion and adsorption coefficients for several volatile organics in a natural clayey soil", *J. Contaminant Hydrology*, **10**, 225-250.

Bouchard, D. C., A. L. Wood, M. L. Campbell, P. Nkedi-Kizza, and P. S. C. Rao (1988) "Sorption nonequilibrium during solute transport", *J. Contaminant Hydrology*, **2**, 209-223.

Boyd, S. A., M. M. Mortland, and C. T. Chiou (1988) "Sorption characteristics of organic compounds on hexadecyltrimethylammonium-smectite", *Soil Sci. Soc. Am. J.*, **52**, 652-657.

Brusseau, M. L. and P. S. C. Rao (1989) "Sorption nonideality during organic contaminant transport in porous media", *CRC Crit. Rev. Environ. Control*, **16**, 33-93.

Brusseau, M. L. and P. S. C. Rao (1991) "Influence of sorbate structure on nonequilibrium sorption of organic compounds", *Environ. Sci. Technol.*, **25**, 1501-1506.

Brusseau, M. L., R. E. Jessup, and P. S. C. Rao (1989a) "Rate-limited sorption and nonequilibrium transport of organic chemicals in low organic carbon aquifer materials", *Water Resources Research*, **25**, 1137-1145.

Brusseau, M. L., P. S. C. Rao, R. E. Jessup, and J. M. Davidson (1989b) "Flow interruption: a method for investigating sorption nonequilibrium", *J. Contaminant Hydrology*, **4**, 223-240.

Brusseau, M. L., R. E. Jessup, and P. S. C. Rao (1990) "Sorption kinetics of organic chemicals: evaluation of gas-purge and miscible displacement techniques", *Environ. Sci. Technol.*, **24**, 727-735.

Brusseau, M. L., R. E. Jessup, and P. S. C. Rao (1991a) "Nonequilibrium sorption of organic chemicals: elucidation of rate-limiting processes", *Environ. Sci. Technol.*, **26**, 134-142.

Brusseau, M. L., A. L. Wood, and P. S. C. Rao (1991b) "Influence of organic cosolvents on the sorption kinetics of hydrophobic organic chemicals", *Environ. Sci. Technol.*, **25**, 903-910.

Burr, D. (1992) M.Sc. Thesis, University of Waterloo, Waterloo, Ontario, Canada.

Burris, D. R. and C. P. Antworth (1992) "*In situ* modification of an aquifer material in flow-through systems by a cationic surfactant to enhance retardation of organic contaminants", *J. Contaminant Hydrology*, **10**, 325-337.

Chin, Y.-P., W. J. Weber, Jr., and B. J. Eadle (1990) "Estimating the effects of dispersed organic polymers on the sorption of contaminants by natural solids. 2. Sorption in the presence of humic and other natural macromolecules", *Environ. Sci. Technol.*, **24**, 837-842.

Chiou, C. T. (1989) "Theoretical considerations of the partitioning uptake of nonionic organic compounds by soil organic matter", In: *Reactions and Movement of Organic Chemicals in Soils*, B. L. Sawhney and K. Brown (Eds.), Soil Sci. Soc. America Special Publication No. 22, pp. 1-29.

Chiou, C. T. D. E. Kile, and R. L. Malcolm (1988) "Sorption of vapors of some organic liquids on soil humic acid and its relation to partitioning of organic compounds in soil organic matter", *Environ. Sci. Technol.*, **22**, 298-303.

Chiou, C. T. and T. D. Shoup (1985) "Soil sorption of organic vapors and effects of humidity on sorptive mechanisms and capacity", *Environ. Sci. Technol.*, **16**, 1196-1200.

Chiou, C. T., L. J. Peters, and V. H. Freed (1979) "A physical concept of soil-water equilibria for nonionic organic compounds", *Science*, **206**, 831-832.

Chiou, C. T., P. E. Porter, and D. W. Schmedding (1983) "Partition equilibria of nonionic organic compounds between soil organic matter and water", *Environ. Sci. Technol.*, **17**, 227-231.

Chiou, C. T., R. L. Malcom, T. I. Brinton, and D. E. Kile (1986) "Water solubility enhancement of some organic pollutants and pesticides by dissolved humic and fulvic acids", *Environ. Sci. Technol.*, **20**, 502-508.

Chiou, C. T., J. F. Lee, and S. A. Boyd (1990) "The surface area of soil organic matter", *Environ. Sci. Technol.*, **24**, 1164-1166.

Curtis, G. P., P. V. Roberts, and M. Reinhard (1986) "A natural gradient experiment on solute transport in a sand aquifer. 4. Sorption of organic solutes and its influence on mobility", *Water Resources Research*, **22**, 2059-2067.

Enfield, C. G., G. Bengtsson, and R. Lindqvist (1989) "Influence of macromolecules on chemical transport", *Environ. Sci. Technol.*, **23**, 1278-1286.

Freeze, R. A. and J. A. Cherry (1979) *Groundwater*, Prentice Hall, Englewood Cliffs, New Jersey.

Garbarini, D. R. and L. W. Lion (1985) "Evaluation of sorptive partitioning of nonionic pollutants in closed systems by headspace analysis", *Environ. Sci. Technol.*, **19**, 1122-1128.

Gerstl, Z. (1990) "Estimation of organic chemical sorption by soils", *J. Contaminant Hydrology*, **6**, 357-375.

Gillham, R. W., M. J. L. Robin, and C. J. Ptacek (1990) "A device for *in situ* determination of geochemical transport parameters. 1. Retardation", *Ground Water*, **28**, 666-672.

Goltz, M. N. and P. V. Roberts (1988) "Simulations of physical nonequilibrium solute transport models: application to a large-scale field experiment", *J. Contaminant Hydrology*, **3**, 37-63.

Grathwol, P. (1990) "Influence of organic matter from soils and sediments from various origins on the sorption of some chlorinated aliphatic hydrocarbons: Implications on K_{oc} correlations", *Environ. Sci. Technol.*, **24**, 1687-1693.

Gschwend, P. M. and S. Wu (1985) "On the constancy of sediment-water partition coefficients of hydrophobic organic pollutants", *Environ. Sci. Technol.*, **19**, 90-96.

Hansch, C. and A. Leo (1979) *Substituent Constants for Correlation Analysis in Chemistry and Biology*, John Wiley, New York, New York.

Hassett, J. J. and W. L. Banwart (1989) "The sorption of nonpolar organics by soils and sediments", In *Reactions and Movement of Organic Chemicals in Soils*, B. L. Sawhney and K. Brown (Eds.) Soil Sci. Soc. America Special Publication No. 22., pp. 21-43.

Holsen, T. M., E. R. Taylor, Y-C. Seo, and P. R. Anderson (1991) "Removal of sparingly soluble organic chemicals from aqueous solutions with surfactant-coated ferrihydrite", *Environ. Sci. Technol.*, **25**, 1585-1589.

Jafvert, C. T., J. C. Westall, E. Grieder, and R. P. Schwarzenbach (1990) "Distribution of hydrophobic ionogenic compounds between octanol and water: Organic acids", *Environ. Sci. Technol.*, **24**, 1795-1803.

Johnson, C. A. and J. C. Westall (1990) "Effect of pH and KCl concentration on the octanol-water distribution of methylanilines". *Environ. Sci. Technol.*, **24**, 1869-1875.

Johnson, R. L., J. A. Cherry, and J. F. Pankow (1989) "Diffusive contaminant transport in natural clay: a field example and implications for clay-lined waste disposal sites", *Environ. Sci. Technol.*, **23**, 340-349.

Karickhoff, S. W., D. S. Brown, and T. A. Scott (1979) "Sorption of hydrophobic pollutants on natural sediments", *Water Research*, **13**, 241-248.

Karickhoff, S. W. (1980) "Sorption kinetics of hydrophobic pollutants in natural sediments". In: *Contaminants and Sediments, Volume 2*, R. A. Baker (Ed.), Ann Arbor Science, Ann Arbor, Michigan, 193-205.

Karickhoff, S. W. (1981) "Semi-empirical estimation of sorption of hydrophobic pollutants on natural sediments and soils", *Chemosphere*, **10**, 833-846.

Karickhoff, S. W. (1984) "Organic pollutant sorption in aquatic systems", *J. Hydraulic Eng.*, **110**, 707-735.

Kile, D. E. and C. T. Chiou (1989) "Water solubility enhancements of DDT and trichlorobenzene by some surfactants below and above the critical micelle concentration", *Environ. Sci. Technol.*, **23**, 832-836.

Lee, L. S., P. S. C. Rao, M. L. Brusseau, and R. A. Ogwada (1988) "Nonequilibrium sorption of organic contaminants during flow through columns of aquifer materials", *Environ. Toxicol. Chem.*, **7**, 779-793.

Lee, L. S., P. S. C. Rao, P. Nkedi-Kizza, and J. J. Delfino (1990) "Influence of solvent and sorbent characteristics on distribution of pentachlorophenol in octanol-water and soil-water systems", *Environ. Sci. Technol.*, **24**, 654-661.

Lee, L. S., P. S. C. Rao, and M. L. Brusseau (1991) "Nonequilibrium sorption and transport of neutral and ionized chlorophenols", *Environ. Sci. Technol.*, **25**, 722-729.

Lion, L. W., T. B. Stauffer, and W. G. MacIntyre (1990) "Sorption of hydrophobic compounds on aquifer materials: analysis methods and the effect of organic carbon", *J. Contaminant Hydrology*, **5**, 215-234.

MacIntyre, W. G., T. B. Stauffer, and C. P. Antworth (1991) "A comparison of sorption coefficients determined by batch, column and box methods on a low organic carbon aquifer material", *Ground Water*, **29**, 908-913.

MacIntyre, W. G. and C. L. Smith (1984) "Comment on 'Partition equilibria of nonionic organic compounds between soil organic matter and water' ", *Environ. Sci. Technol.*, **18**, 295.

Mackay, D. M., D. L. Freyberg, and P. V. Roberts (1986a) "A natural gradient experiment on solute transport in a sand aquifer. 1. Approach and overview of plume movement", *Water Resources Research*, **22**, 2017-2029.

Mackay, D. M., W. P. Ball, and M. G. Durant (1986b) "Variability of aquifer sorption properties in a field experiment on groundwater transport of organic solutes: methods and preliminary results", *J. Contaminant Hydrology*, **1**, 119-132.

Mackay, D. M. (1990) "Characterization of the distribution and behavior of contaminants in the subsurface", In: *Ground Water and Soil Contamination Remediation: Toward Compatible Science, Policy, and Public Perception*, National Academy Press, Washington, D.C., pp. 70-90.

Mackay, D. M. and K. W. Thorbjarnson (1990) *Flushing of Organic Contaminants from a Ground Water Plume at the Rocky Mountain Arsenal: Field and Laboratory Studies.* UCLA School of Public Health, Environmental Science and Engineering Program Technical Report No. 90-69, Volume I (report) and Volume II (appendices).

Mackay, D. M., G. C. Bianchi-Mosquera, A. Kopania, H. Kianjah and K. Thorbjarnson (1994) "A forced-gradient experiment on solute transport in the Borden aquifer. 1. Experimental methods and moment analyses of results", *Water Resources Research*, **30**, 369-383.

Mackay, D. M. and J. A. Cherry (1989) "Groundwater contamination: Pump-and-treat remediation", *Environ. Sci. Technol.*, **23**, 630-636.

Magee, B. R., L. W. Lion, and A. T. Lemley (1991) "Transport of dissolved organic macromolecules and their effect on the transport of phenanthrene in porous media", *Environ. Sci. Technol.*, **25**, 323-331.

McGinley, L. E. Katz, and W. J. Weber, Jr. (1993) "A distributed reactivity model for sorption by soils and sediments. 2. Multicomponent systems and competitive effects", *Environ. Sci. Technol.*, **27**, 1524-1531.

Mehran, M. M., R. L. Olsen, and B. M. Rector (1987) "Distribution coefficient of trichloroethylene in soil-water systems", *Ground Water*, **25**, 275-282.

Mihelcic, J. R. and R. G. Luthy (1991) "Sorption and microbial degradation of naphthalene in soil-water suspensions under denitrification conditions", *Environ. Sci. Technol.*, **25**, 169-177.

Minglegrin, U. and Z. Gerstl (1983) "Reevaluation of partitioning as a mechanism of nonionic chemicals adsorption in soils", *J. Environ. Qual.*, **12**, 1-11.

Montgomery, J. H. and L. M. Welkom (1990) *Groundwater Chemicals Desk Reference* Lewis Publishers, Boca Raton, Florida.

Murphy, E. M., J. M. Zachara, and S. S. Smith (1990) "Influence of mineral-bound humic substances on the sorption of hydrophobic organic compounds", *Environ. Sci. Technol.*, **24**, 1507-1516.

Myrand, D., R. W. Gillham, E. A. Sudicky, S. F. O'Hannesin, and R. L. Johnson (1992) "Diffusion of volatile organic compounds in natural clay deposits", *J. Contaminant Hydrology*, **10**, 159-177.

Nkedi-Kizza, P., J. W. Biggar, H. M. Selim, M. Th. van Genuchten, P. J. Wierenga, J. M. Davidson, and D. R. Nielson (1984) "On the equivalence of two conceptual models for describing ion exchange during transport through an aggregated oxisol", *Water Resources Research*, **20**, 1123-1130.

Nkedi-Kizza, P., P. S. C. Rao, and A. G. Hornsby (1985) "Influence of cosolvents on sorption of hydrophobic organic chemicals by soils", *Environ. Sci. Technol.*, **19**, 975-979.

Nkedi-Kizza, P., P. S. C. Rao, and A. G. Hornsby (1987) "Influence of organic cosolvents on leaching of hydrophobic organic chemicals through soils", *Environ. Sci. Technol.*, **21**, 1107-1111.

Nkedi-Kizza, P., M. L. Brusseau, P. S. C. Rao, and A. G. Hornsby (1989) "Nonequilibrium sorption during displacement of hydrophobic organic chemicals and ^{45}Ca through soil columns with aqueous and mixed solvents", *Environ. Sci. Technol.*, **23**, 814-820.

Ogram, A. V., R. E. Jessup, L. T. Ou, and P. S. C. Rao (1985) "Effects of sorption on biological degradation rates of 2,4-dichlorophenoxyacetic acid in soils", *Appl. Environ. Microbiol.*, **49**, 582-587.

Ong, S. K. and L. W. Lion (1991b) "Mechanisms for trichloroethylene vapor sorption onto soil minerals", *J. Environ. Qual.*, **20**, 180-188.

Ong, S. K. and L. W. Lion (1991a) "Effects of soil properties and moisture on the sorption of trichloroethylene vapor", *Water Research*, **25**, 29-36.

Pavlostathis, S. G. and K. Jaglal (1991) "Desorptive behavior of trichloroethylene in contaminated soil", *Environ. Sci. Technol.*, **25**, 274-279.

Perlinger, J. A. and S. J. Eisenreich (1991) "Sorption of alkylbenzenes to mineral oxides". In: *Organic Substances and Sediments in Water, Vol 2., Processes and Analytical*, R. A. Baker (Ed.), Lewis Publishers. Boca Raton, Florida, pp. 49-78.

Perlinger, J. A., S. J. Eisenreich, and P. D. Capel (1993) "Application of headspce analysis to the study of sorption of hydrophobic organic chemicals to α-Al_2O_3", *Environ. Sci. Technol.*, **27**, 928-937.

Peterson, M. S., L. W. Lion, and C. A. Shoemaker (1988) "Influence of vapor-phase sorption and diffusion on the fate of trichloroethylene in an unsaturated aquifer system", *Environ. Sci. Technol.*, **22**, 571-578.

Pignatello, J. J., F. J. Ferrandino, and L. Q. Huang (1993) "Elution of aged and freshly added herbicides from a soil", *Environ. Sci. Technol.*, **27**, 1563-1571.

Pignatello, J. J., C. R. Frink, P. A. Marin, and E. X. Droste (1990) "Field-observed ethylene dibromide in an aquifer after two decades", *J. Contaminant Hydrology*, **5**, 195-214.

Piwoni, M. D. and P. Banerjee (1989) "Sorption of volatile organic solvents from aqueous solution onto subsurface solids", *J. Contaminant Hydrology*, **4**, 163-179.

Ptacek, C. J. and R. W. Gillham (1992) "Laboratory and field measurements of nonequilibrium transport in the Borden Aquifer", *J. Contaminant Hydrology*, **10**, 119-158.

Rao, P. S. C., L. S. Lee, and R. Pinal (1990) "Cosolvency and sorption of hydrophobic organic chemicals", *Environ. Sci. Technol.*, **24**, 647-654.

Rhue, R. D., P. S. C. Rao, K. D. Pennell, and W. H. Reve (1989) "Competitive adsorption of alkylbenzene and water vapors on predominantly mineral surfaces", *Chemosphere*, **18**, 1971-1986.

Roberts, P. V., M. N. Goltz, and D. M. Mackay (1986) "A natural gradient experiment on solute transport in a sand aquifer. 3. Retardation estimates and mass balances for organic solutes", *Water Resources Research*, **22**, 2046-2058.

Ryan, P. A. and P. Gschwend (1990) "Colloidal mobilization in two Atlantic Coastal Plain aquifers: Field Studies", *Water Resources Research*, **26**, 307-322.

Sabljic, A. (1987) "On the prediction of soil sorption coefficients of organic pollutants from molecular structure: Application of a molecular topology model", *Environ. Sci. Technol.*, **21**, 358-366.

Schwarzenbach, R. P., W. Giger, W. Hoehn, and J. K. Schneider (1983) "Behavior of organic compounds during infiltration of river water to groundwater. Field Studies", *Environ. Sci. Technol.*, **17**, 472-479.

Schwarzenbach, R. P. and J. Westall (1981) "Transport of nonpolar organic compounds from surface water to groundwater. Laboratory sorption studies", *Environ. Sci. Technol.*, **15**, 1360-1366.

Shearer, R. C., J. Letey, W. J. Farmer, and A. Klute (1973) "Lindane diffusion in soil", *Soil Sci. Soc. Amer. Proc.*, **37**, 189-193.

Smith, J. A., C. T. Chiou, J. A. Krammer, and D. E. Kile (1990a) "Effect of soil moisture on the sorption of trichloroethene vapor to vadose-zone soil at Picatinny Arsenal, New Jersey", *Environ. Sci. Technol.*, **24**, 676-683.

Smith, J. A., P. R. Jaffe, and C. T. Chiou (1990b) "Effect of ten Quaternary ammonium cations on tetrachloromethane sorption to clay from water", *Environ. Sci. Technol.*, **24**, 1167-1172.

Spencer, W. F. and M. M. Cliath (1970) "Desorption of lindane from soil as related to vapor density", *Soil Sci. Soc. Amer. Proc.*, **34**, 574-578.

Spurlock, F. C. and J. W. Biggar (1990) "Effect of naturally occurring soluble organic matter on the adsorption and movement of simazine [2-chloro-4,6-bis(ethylamino)-s-triazine] in Hanford sandy loam", *Environ. Sci. Technol.*, **24**, 736-741.

Stauffer, T. B. and W. G. MacIntyre (1986) "Sorption of low-polarity organic compounds on oxide minerals and aquifer material", *Environ. Toxicol. Chem.*, **5**, 949-955.

Steen, W. C., D. F. Paris, and G. L. Baughman (1980) "Effects of sediment sorption on microbial degradation of toxic substances", In: *Contaminants and Sediments, Vol 1.*, R. A. Baker (Ed.), Ann Arbor Science, Ann Arbor, Michigan, pp. 477-482.

Valocchi, A. J. (1985) "Validity of the local equilibrium assumption for modeling sorbing solute transport through homogeneous soils", *Water Resources Research*, **21**, 808-820.

Weber, W. J., Jr., P. M. McGiney, and L. E. Katz (1992) "A distributed reactivity model for sorption by soils and sediments. 1. Conceptual basis and equilibrium assessments", *Environ. Sci. Technol.*, **26**, 1955-1962.

Whiffin, R. B. and J. M. Bahr (1985) "Assessment of purge well effectiveness for aquifer decontamination", In: *Proceedings: Fourth National Symposium on Aquifer Restoration and Ground Water Monitoring*, May 23-25, 1984, NWWA, Worthington, Ohio, 75-81.

Wilson, J. T., C. G. Enfield, W. J. Dunlop, R. L. Cosby, D. A. Foster, and L. B. Baskin (1981) "Transport and fate of selected organic pollutants in a sandy soil", *J. Environ. Qual.*, **10**, 501-506.

Woodburn, K. B., P. S. C. Rao, M. Fukui, and P. Nkedi-Kizza (1986) "Solvophobic approach for predicting sorption of hydrophobic organic chemicals on synthetic sorbents and soils", *J. Contaminant Hydrology*, **1**, 227-241.

Wu, S. and P. M. Gschwend (1986) "Sorption kinetics of hydrophobic organic compounds to natural sediments and soils", *Environ. Sci. Technol.*, **20**, 717-725.

9

Chemical and Microbiological Transformations and Degradation of Chlorinated Solvent Compounds

Barbara J. Butler and James F. Barker

Waterloo Centre for Groundwater Research
University of Waterloo,
Waterloo, Ontario, Canada, N2L 3G1

ABSTRACT

Chemical and microbial transformations of common haloaliphatic solvent compounds provide considerable potential for natural attenuation and remediation in the subsurface. Aerobically, abiotic hydrolysis rates are generally of little consequence, though there are significant exceptions (*e.g.*, 1,1,1-TCA). Anaerobically, on the other hand, reductive dechlorination can occur under strongly reducing conditions, especially in the presence of elemental iron. When sulfide is present, abiotic substitution of sulfide for aliphatic halogens (especially bromine) can occur. Generally, then, it can be said that reducing conditions hold the most potential for providing for abiotic transformations of solvent aliphatics.

In nature, subsurface microbes are likely involved in most transformations, either indirectly by creating chemical conditions that are favorable for abiotic reactions, or directly by conducting the transformations themselves. In general, compounds that are more highly halogenated are more prone to being transformed by reductive dehalogenation. Compounds with few halogens, such as vinyl chloride, may be more easily degraded under aerobic conditions. Nevertheless, the complete anaerobic degradation of both trichloroethylene (TCE) and tetrachloroethylene (PCE) to ethylene has been observed. Co-metabolic utilization by aerobic, methane oxidizers also provides some potential for aerobic bioremediation of many chlorinated solvent compounds. Close to DNAPL sources, inhibition of biotransformations due to high contaminant concentrations is likely to be a problem.

9.1 INTRODUCTION

The behavior of the chlorinated solvent compounds in the field is the net result of various processes operating in concert. These processes include advection, dispersion, sorption, chemical transformation, biotransformation, and perhaps vaporization. Many halocarbons do not usually react abiotically in groundwater environments. As a result, biotransformation reactions are important for their natural removal from contaminated systems. Indeed, in some situations, biotransformation of the original "parent" chlorinated solvent compounds has been implicated as the mechanism by which other "daughter" compounds come to pollute groundwaters (Parsons *et al.*, 1984; Cline and Viste, 1985; Lesage *et al.*, 1990; Major *et al.*, 1991). In the field, these occurrences may sometimes serve a useful predictive purpose, because prudent selection of the parameters analyzed in groundwater samples and sediment cores can allow one to characterize a contaminated site not only in hydrogeological and geochemical terms but also in microbiological terms. Together, this information may be used to predict behavior of the contaminant plume and may also aid in selection of the most feasible remediation strategy.

This chapter will generally be restricted to a discussion of the haloaliphatic chlorinated solvents. We will begin with a discussion of the chemical reactions of halocarbons, emphasizing the common chlorinated solvents. A short overview of the microbial ecology of subsurface systems and the general processes of biotransformation and biodegradation will follow. The remainder of the chapter will concern biotransformations of haloaliphatic compounds.

9.2 CHEMICAL REACTIONS

9.2.1 Overview

Many halocarbons have the potential for **chemical (abiotic) transformations** and **microbial transformations**. The realization of this potential depends upon the halocarbon and the groundwater environment. This section reviews the most likely chemical transformations in groundwaters. Many of the same reaction pathways are catalyzed by microbes. In many, if not most cases, the microbial reaction rate will be faster than the abiotic rate (*e.g.*, Jafvert and Wolfe, 1987). In addition, other microbial mechanisms may produce transformations of a contaminant when no abiotic reactions are likely.

Schwarzenbach *et al.* (1985) offer strong evidence of abiotic substitution reactions occurring in actual groundwater systems. Laboratory evidence for abiotic reductive dehalogenation is compelling (Gillham and O'Hannesin, 1992; Barbash and Reinhard, 1989; Reinhard *et al.*, 1990). Controlled field experiments support these findings (Acton, 1990), but conclusive field evidence is often elusive. The most significant transformation reactions have been reviewed by Baxter (1989) and Vogel *et al.* (1987). The nomenclature of Vogel *et al.* (1987) is followed below. Four reaction types have been recognized:

1. **Substitution** reactions include hydrolysis, for which water serves as the nucleophile, and substitution, for which other nucleophiles such as sulfide attack the halocarbon. In either case, the nucleophile (OH^- or S^-) replaces the halogen (X^-).
2. **Dehydrohalogenation** involves the elimination of HX and the formation of a C=C double bond in place of a C-C single bond (*i.e.*, an alkene forms at the expense of an alkane).
3. **Oxidation** is a common reaction for organics, given the rather reduced state of carbon in organic compounds. Since the presence of a halogen substituent in an organic compound makes for a more oxidized compound than would be the case in the absence of the halogen, the potential for oxidation (as by oxygen) decreases as the extent of halogenation increases. Various oxidation reactions are possible. Epoxidation may be the most significant, and it involves the addition of oxygen across the C=C bond of an alkene like TCE. The halogenated epoxide is usually reactive, producing halogenated aldehydes and acyl halides. Subsequent transformation products (*e.g.*, halogenated acids and alcohols, CO_2, and carbon monoxide) are usually short-lived in aqueous environments. No abiotic oxidations of typical halocarbon solvents have been reported, although microbial oxidations are found.
4. **Reduction** reactions are probably dominated by hydrogenolysis and dihalo-elimination. The former involves the breaking of a carbon-halogen bond with hydrogen then replacing the halogen. The latter involves the reductive removal of two

halogens, typically producing a C=C double bond from a C-C single bond (*i.e.*, producing an alkene from an alkane). Reductions are commonly microbially-mediated, but abiotic reductions have been observed.

9.2.2 Substitution Reactions

9.2.2.1 Hydrolysis and dehydrohalogenation

Hydrolysis and dehydrohalogenation are probably the most thoroughly studied abiotic transformations of the halocarbons (see Table 9.1). Early work by Dilling *et al.* (1975), the review and compilation by Mabey and Mill (1978), the predictive methodology of Lyman *et al.* (1982), the review of Vogel *et al.* (1987), and the recent experiments by Jeffers *et al.* (1989) summarize the most significant information. Hydrolysis reactions are usually first order (*i.e.*, dependent on the concentration of halocarbon), but are usually composed of a **neutral reaction** and a **base-catalyzed reaction** that are individually first order. The latter is pH dependent and, when it is important, the overall hydrolysis rate also depends on the concentration of the hydroxide ion. In some cases, the base-catalyzed reaction is faster than the neutral reaction even at neutral pH (*e.g.*, as with pentachloroethane and 1,1,2,2-tetrachloroethane in Table 2 of Jeffers *et al.*, 1989). Our discussions here will focus on *relative* hydrolysis rates, with the total hydrolysis rate at pH = 7 serving as the basis for comparison; the actual hydrolysis reaction mechanisms will not be considered.

TABLE 9.1   Abiotic Hydrolysis (Substitution and Dehydrohalogenation) Half-Lives at 10 to 25 °C of Halocarbons (Best Values).

Compound	Half-life in years (*ref*)	Compound	Half-life in years (*ref*)
Methanes		Ethanes	
Chloromethane	no data	Chloroethane	0.12 (*4*)
Dichloromethane	704 (*1*)	1,1-Dichloroethane	61 (*3*)
Trichloromethane	3500 (*1*), 1800 (*3*)	1,2-Dichloroethane	72 (*3*)
Tetrachloromethane	41 (*3*)	1,1,1-Trichloroethane	1.1(*3*), 1.7 (*5*), 2.5 (*6*)
Bromomethane	0.10 (*1*)	1,1,2-Trichloroethane	140 (*3*), 170 (*5*)
Dibromomethane	180 (*1*)	1,1,1,2-Tetrachloroethane	47(*3*), 380 (*5*)
Tribromomethane	690 (*1*)	1,1,2,2-Tetrachloroethane	0.3 (*8*), 0.4 (*3*), 0.8 (*5*)
Bromochloromethane	44 (*1*)	Pentachloroethane	0.01 (*3, 5*)
Bromodichloromethane	140 (*1*)	Hexachloroethane	1.8×10^9 (*3*)
Dibromochloromethane	270 (*1*)	Bromoethane	0.08 (*1*)
		1,2-Dibromoethane	2.5 (*7*)
Ethylenes			
1,1-Dichloroethylene	1.2×10^8 (*3*)		
Trichloroethylene	0.9 (*2*), 1.3×10^6 (*3*)		
Tetrachloroethylene	0.7 (*2*), 1.3×10^6 (*3*)		
1,2-Dichloroethylene	2.1×10^{10} (*3*)		

References: (*1*) Mabey and Mill (1978); (*2*) Dilling *et al.* (1975); (*3*) Jeffers *et al.* (1989); (*4*) Vogel *et al.* (1987); (*5*) Mabey *et al.* (1983); (*6*) Vogel and McCarty (1986); (*7*) Weintraub *et al.* (1986); (*8*) Cooper *et al.* (1987).

A considerable amount of laboratory data for **homogeneous substitution reactions** (*i.e.*, in aqueous solution, without solid surface catalysts) has been produced at elevated temperatures of 40 to 200 °C; the slow rate of reaction at environmental temperatures (0 to 30 °C) does not permit reasonable experiment times at ambient temperatures. The **rate constant** k at an environmental temperature (T_2) is usually extrapolated from the measured rate at an elevated temperature (T_1) using the Arrhenius equation,

$$\ln \frac{k_2}{k_1} = \frac{E_a}{R} \frac{(T_2 - T_1)}{T_1 T_2} \tag{9.1}$$

where temperature (T) is in degrees Kelvin (°C + 273.15), E_a is the activation energy (typically about 80 to 120 kJ/mol),and R is the gas constant, 8.314 J/mol-K. For typical activation energies, the reaction rate will decrease dramatically with decreasing temperature, about 3 to 4 fold for each 10 °C decrease. Before proceeding, we should also note that the reaction mechanisms and products observed at elevated temperatures may not always be representative of what occurs at ambient groundwater temperatures.

Hydrolysis will produce an alcohol from an alkane or alkene:

$$R\text{-}X + H_2O \rightarrow R\text{-}OH + H\text{-}X \tag{9.2}$$

where R is the part of the organic molecule unaffected by the reaction, -X is a halogen substituent, and -OH is the alcohol functional group. Non-alcohol products have also been found (Vogel *et al.*, 1987; Jeffers *et al.*, 1989). In some cases, these other products are further transformation products, but in many cases they are products of one or more competing dehydrohalogenation reactions. 1,2-dichloroethane has been found to yield some ethylene glycol (Jeffers *et al.*, 1989), as has 1,2-dibromoethane (Vogel *et al.*, 1987); ethylene glycol represents a classic replacement of both halogen atoms in these molecules by OH.

Chloroethane has been found to yield chloroethylene, also known as vinyl chloride (Jeffers *et al.*, 1989), and 1,2-dibromoethane has been found to yield bromoethylene (see Table 3 of Vogel *et al.*, 1987), indicating that dehydrohalogenation can occur according to

$$CH_2X\text{-}CH_2X \rightarrow CH_2 = CH_2X + HX, \quad X = Cl \text{ or } Br. \tag{9.3}$$

Vogel *et al.* (1987, see their Table 3) indicate that such dehydrohalogenation reactions are common. Jeffers *et al.* (1989) found that pentachloroethane yielded tetrachloroethylene (PCE). Roberts and Gschwend (1991) found the same reaction to be rapid, and noted that the reaction of hexachloroethane to PCE could proceed, in large part, via pentachloroethane.

Considerable discrepancies often arise when comparing older reviews and recent experimental studies. For example, compared to the study of Dilling *et al.* (1975), Jeffers *et al.* (1989) reported a much shorter ambient **half-life** ($t_{1/2}$) for carbon tetrachloride (41 *vs.* 7000 years), and the opposite for TCE and PCE. Due to the experimental difficulties encountered by Dilling *et al.* (1975), the more recent data of Jeffers *et al.* (1989) are usually accepted as correct. Where significant conflicts exist, the data from Dilling *et al.* (1975) do not appear in Table 9.1. The reader is cautioned to treat all half-lives as approximate.

Bromomethanes and bromochloromethanes react significantly faster than the corresponding chloromethanes. The chloromethanes show an increasing half-life as chlorination increases from 1 to 3 chlorines, but carbon tetrachloride has the shortest half-life of the chloromethanes; Jeffers *et al.* (1989) suggest some combination of steric and energetic effects may be responsible for these non-uniform trends in reactivity.

Like the halomethanes, the haloethanes show a large range in reaction rates, with the bromo- and dibromoethanes reacting significantly faster than their chlorinated analogs. The reaction rate is faster when the chlorines are on the same carbon, although the trend with increasing overall chlorination is inconsistent. The very reactive ($t_{1/2} < 3$ years) haloethanes include chloroethane, bromoethane, 1,2-dibromoethane, 1,1,1-trichloroethane, 1,1,2,2-tetrachloroethane and pentachloroethane. Chloroethane, the dichloroethanes, and 1,1,1-trichloroethane were found to produce alcohols (Jeffers *et al.*, 1989). However, Bouwer and McCarty (1983a) do report the abiotic production of acetic acid from 1,1,1-trichloroethane. 1,1,2-trichloroethane, tetrachloroethanes, and pentachloroethane were found to dehydrohalogenate to 1,2-dichloroethylene, TCE and PCE, respectively. For the chloroethanes, alcohols are probably the result of neutral hydrolysis, while dehydrohalogenation appears to be linked to alkaline hydrolysis and becomes more important as the degree of chlorination increases (Jeffers *et al.* 1989).

The chloroethylenes do not undergo significant hydrolysis reactions. Unfortunately, no studies for vinyl chloride (chloroethylene) were found. Although this compound may not be common as an *original* cause of contamination, its presence has been reported in many dissolved chlorinated solvent plumes. Since its drinking water standard is among the lowest for the halocarbons (see Table 1.13), the chemistry of formation and degradation of vinyl chloride is of considerable interest.

9.2.2.2 Nucleophilic substitution by reduced sulfur

Schwarzenbach *et al.* (1985) provided both field and laboratory evidence that the HS^- or H_2S that can be present under anaerobic conditions can act as stronger nucleophiles than water. Substitution reactions of the type

$$R\text{-}X + HS^- \rightarrow R\text{-}S\text{-}H + X^- \tag{9.4}$$

are therefore possible. Apparently, only haloalkanes are affected. In most groundwaters, reduced sulfur is a product of microbial sulfate reduction, and so the indirect, if not also the direct role of microbes is certain. Possible products include dialkyl sulfides, mercaptans, thiols and dithiols. Roberts *et al.* (1992) reported that dihalomethanes reacting with HS^- produce mainly poly(thiomethylene) ($HS\text{-}(CH_2\text{-}S)_n\text{-}H$) along with a minor amount of dithiomethane ($CH_2(SH)_2$).

Schwarzenbach *et al.* (1985), Barbash and Reinhard (1989), and others have demonstrated that reaction (9.4) can occur abiotically, but that its reaction rate can be enhanced by microbial catalysts. Abiotic half-lives at 25 °C for 1,2-dichloroethane and 1,2-dibromoethane were observed to be about 6 years and 40 to 70 days respectively (Barbash and Reinhard, 1989). Kriegman-King and Reinhard (1992) demonstrated that minerals increased the rate of abiotic transformation of carbon tetrachloride to CS_2 in the presence of HS^-; the transformation mechanism was not clear. Both Haag and Mill (1988) and Roberts *et al.* (1992) note that polysulfides, which are expected when elemental sulfur is present under reduced conditions at pH 7 and higher, react much faster with haloalkanes than HS^-. Hydrolysis and sulfide substitution reactions can occur concurrently, as has been evidenced by the presence of both alcohols from hydrolysis and sulfur-bearing hydrocarbons from sulfide substitution.

9.2.3 Reduction Reactions

As noted above, two important reductive dechlorination reactions are **hydrogenolysis** and **dihaloelimination**. The former involves the simple replacement of a halogen by a hydrogen, and the latter involves the removal of two halogens with the formation of an additional C=C double bond.

Abiotic reductive dechlorination reactions have been reported in a number of circumstances, These include:

1. Hexachloroethane and carbon tetrachloride were transformed to TCE and chloroform, respectively, in the presence of reductants such as HS^-, L-cysteine, and Fe^{2+}, in the presence of zeolite, biotite, vermiculite, pyrite, and marcasite, and in the presence of the Fe-, Mn-, organic matter-rich fraction of Borden aquifer material (Reinhard *et al.*, 1990);

2. Wang and Tan (1990) reported the reduction of TCE, bromoform, and carbon tetrachloride to ethane, methane, and methane, respectively, during a Pt-catalyzed reaction between elemental magnesium and water, producing H_2; and

3. A number of biochemical systems were found to have this effect, including vitamin B_{12} (Co), coenzyme F_{430} and hematin (Fe) (Gantzer and Wackett, 1991); and

4. Systems involving Fe^0 have been used to reductively dehalogenate carbon tetrachloride, chloroform, TCE, and PCE, with half-lives of 2 to 4000 minutes (O'Hannesin and Gillham, 1992).

A useful approach for evaluating the possibility of reductive dehalogenation was presented by Vogel *et al.* (1987, see their Figure 6). Testing for a favorable **free energy change** for the overall redox reaction can be easily carried out visually for various combinations of oxidations and reductions. Higher halogenation produces higher relative reduction potentials and the potential for release of more free energy during reduction. Both hexachloroethane and 1,2-dibromoethane have higher electrochemical reduction potentials than oxygen, and so are theoretically reducible under typical aerobic conditions. Essentially all reductive dehalogenation reactions are energetically favored when coupled with typical inorganic (*e.g.*, H_2 to H^+, and Fe^{2+} to $Fe(OH)_3$) and biological (ferredoxin$_{red}$ to ferredoxin$_{ox}$, NADH to NAD^+) redox couples.

Following the method of Vogel *et al.* (1987), we have calculated the free energy change per mol of electrons transferred for a single dechlorination step (hydrogenolysis), *i.e.*, for the reaction

$$\tfrac{1}{2}RCl + \tfrac{1}{2}H^+ + e^- \rightarrow \tfrac{1}{2}RH + \tfrac{1}{2}Cl^- \qquad (9.5)$$

The free energy yields were calculated at 25 °C, for water with a pH of 7.0, and at a Cl^- concentration of 10^{-3} *M*. The results are presented in Figure 9.1. In all cases, there is a favorable free energy yield, indicating that the dechlorination reaction is, in general, thermodynamically favored under the assumed conditions.

The free energy yields for selected chlorinated halocarbons undergoing a single dechlorination reduction were also calculated when coupled to each of the following oxidations: Fe^0 to Fe^{2+}, Mn^0 to Mn^{2+}, S^{2-} to S^0, and CH_4 (methane) to HCO_3^-. The overall free energy yields per mol of electron transferred were calculated at 25 °C for water at a pH of 7.0, with Cl^-, Fe^{2+}, Mn^{2+}, S^{2-}, CH_4, and HCO_3^-, each present at 10^{-3} *M*. Figure 9.2 gives the free energy yields for the sequential dechlorination of tetrachloroethylene (PCE) to ethylene (EE), and for tetrachloroethane (TCEA) to trichloroethane (TCA), and carbon tetrachloride (CT) to chloroform (CF). As seen in Figure 9.2, in all cases, there is a free energy gain, indicating that each of these overall reactions is thermodynamically favored for the specified conditions. Note that Fe^0 oxidation produces the most free energy. This is consistent with the success that has been observed with using Fe^0 oxidation to abiotically dechlorinate some solvents (Gillham and O'Hannesin, 1992). In the sequence of PCE to ethylene, it is interesting to note that thermodynamically, the least favored reaction is *trans*-1,2-dichloroethylene (12tDCE) to vinyl chloride (VC). This would suggest that *trans*-1,2-dichloroethylene might be a more commonly-found product than vinyl chloride.

The above analysis indicates that most chlorinated solvents are susceptible to reduction reactions. However, this potential is rarely met except under very reducing conditions, and usually not without mediation by bacteria. Pignatello (1986) reported that aerobic degradation of 1,2-dibromoethane occurred only with microbial mediation. Jafvert and Wolfe (1987) found that hexachloroethane, 1,1,2,2-tetrachloroethane, 1,2-diiodoethane, 1,2-dibromoethane, but not 1,2-dichloroethane were rapidly degraded (within days) in anoxic sediment microcosms. The reactions were faster in biologically active systems, but were significant in inhibited systems. This indicates that the reactions are possible abiotically, but that microbial activity can enhance the reaction rates. Products from hexachloroethane included PCE; ethylene was generated from dibromo- and diiodoethane. Criddle *et al.* (1986) also reported loss of hexachloroethane from anaerobic microcosms made from Borden sand. Reexamining their data reveals that sterile controls showed about the same rate of mass loss as did non-sterile microcosms, implicating an abiotic reaction (dihaloelimination). Similar abiotic reduction reactions in homogeneous and heterogeneous systems consisting of minerals and Borden aquifer material have recently been observed and may be closely coupled to microbially-produced reductants such as ferrous iron and sulfides, and perhaps mediated by humic acids *in situ* (Reinhard *et al.*, 1990). Acton (1990) noticed a slight increase in TCE along with significant losses of PCE after about 21 days in anaerobic Borden sand microcosms, and in anaerobic field columns. This could be a result of hydrogenolysis of PCE to TCE, again perhaps abiotically since it proceeded in sterile controls and also in a field column treated with formaldehyde.

a. Sequence: HCA to EA

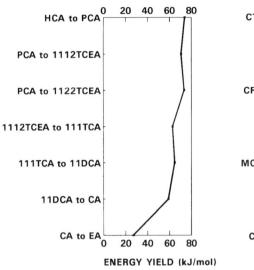

b. Sequence: CT to M

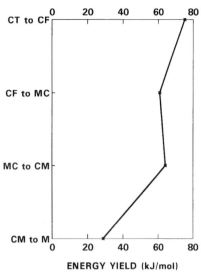

c. Sequence: PCE to EE

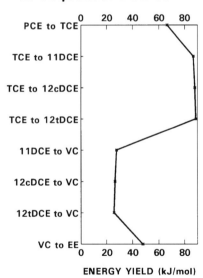

Figure 9.1   Free energy yield per mol e^- for single dechlorinations of chloroethanes, chloromethanes, and chloroethylenes, where aqueous species are 10^{-3} M, pH = 7 following the method of Vogel *et al.* (1987). *a. Sequence for hexachloroethane* (HCA) *to ethane* (EA); PCA = pentachloroethane; 1112TCEA = 1,1,1,2-tetrachloroethane; 1122TCEA = 1,1,2,2-tetrachloroethane; 111TCA = 1,1,1-trichloroethane; 11DCA = 1,1,-dichloroethane; CA = chloroethane; EA = ethane. *b. Sequence for carbon tetrachloride* (CT) *to methane* (M); CF = chloroform; MC = methylene chloride; CM = chloromethane; M = methane. *c. Sequence for tetrachloroethylene* (PCE) *to ethylene* (EE); TCE = trichloroethylene; 11DCE = 1,1-dichloroethylene; 12cDCE = *cis*-1,2-dichloroethylene; 12tDCE = *trans*-1,2-dichloroethylene; VC = vinyl chloride; EE = ethylene.

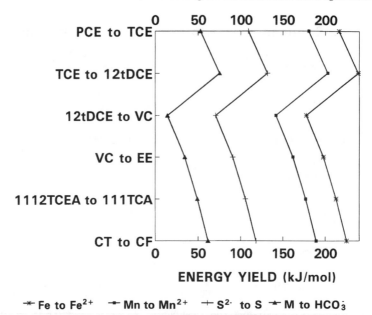

Figure 9.2   Free energy yield per mol e^- for sequential dechlorination of tetrachloroethylene (PCE) and for dechlorination of TCEA and CT. Aqueous species are 10^{-3} M and pH $= 7$. DCE and TCEA are 12tDCE and 1112TCEA respectively, but there is little difference for other isomers.

9.2.4 Implications for Field Studies and for Remediation

Only the nucleophilic substitution by reduced sulfur and reductive dehalogenation have been demonstrated to be significant abiotic transformations in groundwaters. Attributing changes in either the presence or absence of halocarbons or the concentrations of halocarbons to abiotic processes is usually difficult. Bouwer and McCarty (1983a) indicate that 1,1,2-trichloroethane can be degraded by three pathways under extremely anaerobic (**methanogenic**) conditions. One pathway involves an initial abiotic dehydrohalogenation to 1,1-dichloroethylene. Thus, the presence of the latter compound in contaminated groundwater could suggest that this abiotic reaction is significant. However, Jeffers *et al.* (1989) did not detect this product from the hydrolysis of 1,1,1-trichloroethane, though it could have been present as a low yield product, or it could be favored only under very anaerobic conditions. Cline and Viste (1985) do report 1,1-dichloroethylene in groundwaters apparently contaminated by 1,1,1-trichloroethane. This could support the abiotic reaction model, although other sources of 1,1-dichloroethylene are possible. Another pathway leads biologically from trichloroethane through 1,1-dichloroethane to chloroethane which can then undergo abiotic hydrolysis to ethanol. 1,1-dichloroethane was also reported by Cline and Viste (1985) where 1,1-dichloroethylene was found, suggesting that the pathway leading through ethanol could also be operative at this field site. However, ethanol was not determined in that study.

One can argue that chlorinated compounds which have short (perhaps < 1 year) hydrolysis half lives (see Table 9.1) should not be found at significant concentrations in dissolved plumes distant from a source. This hypothesis should be tested against field data. It implies that compounds such as chloroethane, 1,1,2,2-tetrachloroethane and pentachloroethane should not be persistent contaminants. Cline and Viste (1985) indicate that 1,1,2,2-tetrachloroethane was found at the water table on the site of a solvent recovery operation in Wisconsin, but was neither found at depth, nor downgradient; other halocarbons were found, some still at relatively high concentrations. Chloroethane was found only at depth downgradient, and appears to be a possible product of trichloroethane transformation (see above).

In a controlled field experiment in the Borden aquifer, a number of dissolved haloaliphatic compounds at concentrations of 20 to 35 μg/L were injected into the groundwater. Hexachloroethane suffered about 70% mass removal within 85 d, and essentially complete removal within 330 d (Roberts *et al.*, 1986). Subsequent laboratory and field studies (Criddle *et al.*, 1986; Reinhard *et al.*, 1990; Acton, 1990) suggest that an abiotic, reductive dechlorination reaction was likely responsible. Although the Borden aquifer segment used in this experiment was generally aerobic, zones of low and/or undetected oxygen (<1 mg/L) were commonly encountered. Such zones, as well as anaerobic microsites, could have been active in this transformation. Higher-than-injected PCE levels were noted in the early part of the field experiment when hexachloroethane was suffering the most significant mass loss, perhaps supporting the transformation of hexachloroethane to PCE. Laboratory experiments (*e.g.*, Acton, 1990) have found that PCE is persistent.

Where dissolved plumes are evaluated for evidence of the fate of halocarbons, two aspects of the water chemistry should be investigated. One is the redox condition. Reductive dechlorination is restricted to anaerobic systems, and so reactions of this type can only be invoked for anaerobic waters. Redox potential is not reliably determined in groundwaters, but an interpretation of the concentrations of redox-sensitive parameters such as oxygen, nitrate/ammonia, sulfate/sulfite, methane, Fe(III)/Fe(II) etc. along with the pH can provide an estimate of the redox level. The other aspect that should be considered in plume evaluation is the possible presence of non-halogenated breakdown products such as alcohols and acids. To substantiate that hydrolysis is occurring in a given circumstance, the presence of these products should be established. Unfortunately, these products are, in general, more easily biodegraded than their halogenated precursors, and so can be difficult to detect even as they are being generated. Most field investigations to date have not sought these products and this type of evidence for hydrolysis of halocarbons has not yet been gathered.

Because the environmental conditions that promote dehalogenation reactions (low redox level, HS^-, Fe^{2+}, etc.) are the result of microbial processes, clear delineation between chemical and biological processes will be difficult in the field. Perhaps such a distinction is only worthwhile when *in situ* remediation is considered. For example, if the remediation is microbially based, the need to maintain a microbial reaction may require considerable manipulation of the subsurface environment, perhaps involving injection of reductants, nutrients, primary substrates, etc. This may be difficult. For remediation by abiotic means, adding elemental iron as in a permeable zone through which the ground-water flows appears to produce useful abiotic reductive dechlorination (O'Hannesin and Gillham, 1992).

9.3 MICROBIOLOGY OF THE SUBSURFACE

9.3.1 General

This section discusses concepts critical to understanding how natural microbial popula-tions exist and function, how they react when challenged with pollutants such as chlori-nated solvents, and how we may exploit knowledge of their biodegradative potential to help predict the behavior of contaminant plumes. An exhaustive review of the microbial ecology of the subsurface and the biodegradative potential of subsurface microorganisms is beyond the scope of this work; articles covering these areas are available (Poindexter, 1981; Large, 1983: McCarty et al., 1984; Alexander, 1985; Grady, 1985; Zeikus et al., 1985; Ghiorse and Wilson, 1988; Morgan and Watkinson, 1989).

9.3.2 Ecological Considerations

Early studies have shown a sharp decline in the **microbial populations** in soils with increasing depth (e.g., Waksman, 1916). These findings coupled with the low levels of available nutrients in groundwaters have led many to assume that microbial activity in the subsurface is extremely limited and unimportant. However, our growing understanding of the terrestrial subsurface, both as an important source of potable water and as a waste repository (intended or unintended), have led to a re-consideration of it as a habitat for a variety of microorganisms (McNabb and Dunlap, 1975). Indeed, it has become evident that although microbial populations do decline with depth in the unsaturated zone, they frequently increase again when the saturated zone is reached. Indigenous microorganisms can be widely distributed in groundwaters, often in numbers comparable to some soils and surface waters (Wilson et al., 1983; Hirsch and Rades-Rohkohl, 1983; Ghiorse and Balkwill, 1985; Balkwill et al., 1989; Jones et al., 1989; and others).

   To allow survival, activity, and growth of its population, a microbial habitat must provide **nutrients** for the synthesis of cellular constituents and the generation of energy. Thus, sources of carbon, nitrogen, phosphorus, sulfur and low levels of various elements (Fe, Mg, Mn, etc.) must be available. Heterotrophic organisms require organic carbon sources; autotrophic organisms can use carbon dioxide as a sole source of carbon. A group of aerobic, C_1-utilizing bacteria, including the methanotrophs, occupy an intermediate position. They are "specialized heterotrophs", and are able to use reduced, one-carbon compounds as sole sources of carbon and energy.

   Suitable **electron donors** (such as organic compounds) together with **electron ac-ceptors** (such as O_2, nitrate, ferric iron, sulfate, CO_2, or certain types of simple organic compounds) are required for the generation of energy. N, P, and S sources may be organic or inorganic, with some microorganisms able to use either while others are more restricted. Physical and chemical factors such as the E_H (redox potential), pH, and temperature will also profoundly influence the size, type, and activity of the microbial population. In shallow aquifers at least, the pH and temperature are commonly in ranges conducive to microbial activity (Ghiorse and Wilson, 1988). However, key nutrients may be depleted in the subsurface environment because they are removed at the surface by soil microbiota during infiltration of water into the ground.

Even pristine groundwaters contain some dissolved organic carbon (DOC), leached from sedimentary rocks and/or freshly transported to the subsurface in recharge water (McNabb and Dunlap, 1975). DOC concentrations ranging from 0.1 to 10 mg/L are common, although DOC levels can reach several tens of mg/L (Freeze and Cherry, 1979). The specific chemical composition of naturally-occurring organic matter is largely unknown; much of it may resemble humus, and biodegrade slowly. Typical levels of DOC are sufficient for the growth of oligotrophic microorganisms, that is, organisms adapted to exploit habitats with low nutrient fluxes (Poindexter, 1981). McNabb and Dunlap (1975) suggest that the quality, not the quantity, of available carbon in the subsurface may limit microbial activity.

The release of organic contaminants into the subsurface at concentrations well in excess of the normal level of organic matter may significantly alter the makeup of the microbial population. Bacteria suited to higher nutrient levels (copiotrophs), facultative oligotrophs that are able to adapt to higher nutrient concentrations, or allochthonous ("foreign") bacteria imported into the subsurface (*e.g.*, along with the spilled pollutant), may become dominant in an environment that is no longer oligotrophic. The original oligotrophs may not be able to compete for the available nutrients. Obligately oligotrophic microorganisms are **inhibited** by excess carbon, perhaps because of the accumulation of **toxic metabolites** such as hydrogen peroxide, or because of inhibition of certain **enzymes** (Kuznetsov *et al.*, 1979).

Contaminant compounds, if present in high enough concentration in the environment, may impair or destroy microbial activity. Phelps *et al.* (1988) could not detect microbial biomass in areas of a subsurface profile contaminated with very high levels (> 500 mg/L) of TCE, although active, TCE-degrading microorganisms were present in surrounding, less contaminated areas. Belay and Daniels (1987) reported that halogenated hydrocarbons, particularly brominated compounds, were toxic to the methanogens; sensitivity varied, depending on the bacterium and the compound tested, but dibromoethane, the most toxic compound tested, completely inhibited all test bacteria at a concentration of 1.3 mg/L. Despite the potential toxicity of many contaminants, evidence suggests that the metabolic potential for contaminant degradation is often present in the subsurface environment. Ventullo and Larson (1985) found that bacterial populations in pristine and contaminated groundwaters had the potential to metabolize several xenobiotic organic substrates, although at reduced rates compared with surface water systems.

An increase in substrate carbon as a result of a spill may cause a previously carbon-limited microbial population to become limited by another nutrient such as N or P. Oxygen-containing groundwaters may become anoxic as the available oxygen is used to oxidize the added organic matter. As a result, the activity of strictly aerobic microorganisms will cease. Facultative anaerobes may continue activity, although metabolic pathways may change. *Escherichia coli*, for example, mineralizes glucose to carbon dioxide and water aerobically, but in the absence of oxygen it can ferment glucose to produce organic acids, ethanol, carbon dioxide, and hydrogen. Strict anaerobes will be active in anoxic groundwaters when the redox potential is sufficiently low. However, these bacteria may be extremely sensitive to oxygen (Hungate, 1969), and could be scarce in recently-anaerobic groundwaters. Some species can survive adverse conditions as resistant endospores and will renew growth when environmental conditions are more conducive to their activity. Sulfate-reducing bacteria are quite oxygen tolerant and seem relatively widespread, even in aerobic environments. They remain inactive until the redox potential falls to -100 mV or less (Postgate, 1984). Jones *et al.* (1989) found viable methanogens and sulfate-reducing bacteria throughout the depth profile of Atlantic Coastal Plains sediments although the sediments were not predominantly anaerobic. It should be noted, however, that anaerobic microsites are easily established even in environments that are essentially aerobic (Mayfield and Aldworth, 1974).

9.3.3 General Biotransformation Processes

An understanding of biologically-mediated transformations is critical to the prediction of organic contaminant behavior in the subsurface. Parsons *et al.* (1984) emphasize this conclusion in a description of the problems associated with PCE-contaminated water: one may need to search for the point source of a contaminant that is different from the main contaminant that is being found in the water, while concurrently preparing to remove a **daughter contaminant** which groundwater microbiota may produce in the future through metabolism of the main contaminant. The biotransformation potential of a given groundwater environment is dependent upon the enzymatic systems operating there. Considerable differences in this potential exist even within anaerobic environments, because different microbial types function under the various redox conditions, and not all microorganisms can do all things. For example, in laboratory studies, the anaerobic degradation of monochlorophenols and monochlorobenzoates was more often successful in methanogenic enrichments than in denitrifying or sulfate-reducing enrichments (Genthner *et al.*, 1989). Extremely reducing, methanogenic conditions favor many important biotransformations including those of halogenated one- and two-carbon hydrocarbons and of halogenated aromatic hydrocarbons (Kobayashi and Rittmann, 1982; Wilson and Wilson, 1985). Given the complete range of redox conditions in groundwaters, a wide range of biotransformations is theoretically possible; however, because a specific flow system may have a small redox range and the diversity of its microbial population is finite, the actual biotransformation potential may be quite limited.

Biotransformation pathways can be complex and obscure, especially in field situations. Natural microbial communities can be highly **interdependent**, and the biotransformation of a given compound may require the concerted activity of a number of community members. The efficient function of a methanogenic community, for example, requires the obligate interaction of fermentative, acetogenic, and methanogenic bacteria

(Large, 1983). With respect to the degradation of xenobiotic compounds, the biodegradative capacity of a community is often greater than that of any single component of that community. A single microbial species possesses a limited amount of genetic information, and relatively limited adaptive potential, although it may adapt through mutation. The adaptive potential of a **community** is much greater because the genetic capability of each community member is in effect at the disposal of the whole community. A community has a better chance of possessing the means to detoxify a toxic contaminant. Members of a microbial community may acquire new metabolic capabilities from others in the community by **gene transfer**. For example, the transfer of genes for 3-chlorobenzoate catabolism has been documented in a natural surface water environment (Fulthorpe and Wyndham, 1989).

The study of microbial communities should aid the understanding of contaminant biotransformations in the natural environment more than the study of pure cultures. Unfortunately, such study is exceedingly difficult. Consequently, much of our knowledge is based on pure culture work. Another problem with an oligotrophic environment such as the subsurface is that those types of nutrient concentrations do not support the production of sufficient biomass to be studied with many of our present biochemical and physiological research tools (Poindexter, 1981).

Organic contaminants may serve as **primary substrates** for a microbial population, or may be **cometabolized**. Cometabolism is "the transformation of a non-growth substrate in the obligate presence of a growth substrate or another transformable compound" (Dalton and Stirling, 1982). In primary metabolism the organic substrate is used as a source of carbon and energy, and may be mineralized, or fermented to other organic products. A phenomenon sometimes observed when multiple primary substrates are present is diauxic growth, a result of catabolite repression. When multiple substrates are available, bacteria may use only the most readily-metabolized substrate, and production of the enzymes needed for the degradation of the other substrate(s) will be repressed until the best substrate has been exhausted; the poorer substrates may then persist. Schmidt and Alexander (1985) reported that a *Pseudomonas* strain metabolized glucose and aniline diauxically (glucose preferred) at 300 μg/L each, although the compounds were metabolized simultaneously when present at 3 μg/L each. Biodegradation of a given primary substrate (typically at mg/L concentrations) may also be affected by other "secondary substrates" at μg/L levels. The outcome will depend on the primary contaminant substrate of interest, the concentration of the second substrate, and the nature of the microorganisms in the environment (Schmidt and Alexander, 1985). *Pseudomonas* sp. (strain LP), for example, simultaneously metabolizes methylene chloride and acetate, but degrades methylene chloride preferentially over acetate, whether as the primary or as the secondary substrate, providing the methylene chloride concentration is below an inhibitory level of 10 mg/L (LaPat-Polasko *et al.*, 1984).

Many biotransformations of xenobiotic compounds result from cometabolic reactions. Because of a lack of specificity with respect to substrate binding, some enzymes will act on compounds that are analogs of their natural substrates and will transform them (Slater and Bull, 1982). The microorganism gratuitously metabolizes the compound in question, but derives no benefit from doing so. Three important points follow from this concept of cometabolism. Firstly, in cometabolism, the energy and carbon requirements of the microorganisms must be met by other, primary substrates. Secondly, because no benefit is derived from the cometabolized substrate, growth of the microbial population will not be correlated with transformation of that compound. In contrast, utilization of a primary substrate is correlated with population growth. Thirdly, unless they serve as substrates for some further enzyme-catalyzed step, perhaps conducted by another member of the microbial community, products of cometabolic reactions may accumulate in the environment. Such a product may also be of environmental concern, and may be more problematic than its parent: as discussed above, vinyl chloride accumulates from the transformation of more highly chlorinated ethylenes under methanogenic conditions, and is of greater toxicological concern than the parent compounds. Product compounds are commonly less hydrophobic than substrates, and tend to migrate more rapidly in groundwaters because they undergo less sorptive retardation (see also Figure 2.6 in Chapter 2). Cometabolism and secondary substrate utilization may be significant removal processes in groundwaters, because low (μg/L) levels of certain compounds are considered hazardous. Removal of more than 99% of certain chlorobenzenes and other aromatics was observed when these were added at concentrations of less than 15 μg/L to a bioreactor where acetate at 1 mg/L served as the primary substrate (McCarty *et al.*, 1984).

In the natural environment, degradation of an organic compound may lower the concentration of the compound to a **threshold level** below which degradation will not occur (Alexander, 1985). McCarty *et al.* (1984) discuss the parameter S_{min}, which is the minimum bulk concentration of rate-limiting substrate able to sustain a biofilm in steady state. The concept applies equally to single cells. Thus, a substrate concentration exists below which an organism cannot obtain sufficient energy to function. S_{min} values of 0.1 to 1.0 mg/L are typical for aerobic utilization of organic compounds such as acetate under steady-state conditions in biofilms (McCarty *et al.*, 1984), and may be even lower for oligotrophs. However, S_{min} values may be higher for anaerobic systems than for aerobic systems (McCarty *et al.*, 1981). *In situ*, microorganisms use a range of organic substrates, so the overall S_{min} value may be a sum for a number of compounds. The threshold concept also applies to the transformation of compounds that are not primary substrates, because enzyme induction and activity, as well as growth, are subject to a minimum inducer/substrate concentration. However, if the microbial population is using an unrestricted primary substrate, the threshold level for the xenobiotic compound may be below the detection levels of current analytical techniques (Alexander, 1985).

It has sometimes been assumed that biotransformation rates are proportional to concentration. **Extrapolations** are therefore commonly made from high laboratory concentrations to low environmental concentrations, though such extrapolations are not always valid. Boethling and Alexander (1979) found that degradation of diethylamine was proportional to concentration over the range from 10 mg/L to 10 μg/L. Alexander (1985) reported that in stream water, 80% or more of added 2,4-D was removed at initial concentrations of 200 μg/L and 22,000 μg/L. However, for the same time period, less than 10% was removed for an initial concentration of 2 μg/L. Kinetic models describing the rate of substrate transformation as a function of initial substrate concentration and bacterial cell density have been developed (Simkins and Alexander, 1984; Alexander, 1985).

The biotransformation of organic contaminants in the subsurface is a multifaceted process. Wang *et al.* (1984) reported an interesting situation where isopropyl N-phenylcarbamate (IPC) was mineralized in lake water when present at 400 μg/L, but was cometabolized to organic products at 1000 μg/L. At the lower level, it was suggested that IPC served as a primary substrate for oligotrophic growth, but that the higher level inhibited oligotrophic activity and copiotrophs unable to function at the low substrate level then cometabolized the compound. The example illustrates the dynamic nature of biotransformations in the natural environment. Substrate utilization patterns, the active segment of the microbial population, and the makeup of the microbial population can shift depending upon conditions. Similarly, halogenated hydrocarbons may be recalcitrant, degraded as a primary substrate, or cometabolized, depending upon the halocarbon involved, the site-specific microbial populations, and the environmental conditions. Biotransformation at the dilute, **leading edge** of a contaminant plume may be conducted by the natural oligotrophic population, while activity within the more concentrated **plume core** may involve a very different, adapted microbial population.

Retardation of contaminants by sorption may also be critical in facilitating biotransformation of plume fronts. Where contaminants are readily biotransformed, as was the case in a study of a contaminant plume derived from creosote waste, biotransformation rates may be, in effect, instantaneous within the context of slow groundwater flow (Wilson *et al.*, 1985). The length of the adaptation period may be influenced by the time required for the destruction of inhibitors (the compound of interest itself, or some other), the concentration of the compound, presence of other substrates, rarity of the microorganism capable of the transformation, time required for small populations to become large enough to effect a detectable compound loss, competition for inorganic nutrients, the physicochemical conditions at the site, or the time required for the creation of a new genotype (Wyndham, 1986; Wiggins *et al.*, 1987; Wiggins and Alexander, 1988). It should also be recognized that adaptation may fail to occur.

9.4 BIOTRANSFORMATION OF HALOALIPHATIC COMPOUNDS

9.4.1 General

Because few of the enzyme systems involved in halocarbon degradation have been thoroughly investigated, the **pathways** of halocarbon biotransformation are not documented completely. Although all of the abiotic reactions affecting halocarbons discussed above might also be catalyzed by microorganisms, the current literature suggests that only a few reaction types are common. Leisinger (1983) indicated that biotransformations of halocarbons were of three general types: nucleophilic substitution, oxidation, and reductive dehalogenation.

9.4.2 Aerobic Biotransformations

The aerobic utilization of haloalkanes such as dichloromethane (Brunner *et al.*, 1980; Stucki *et al.*, 1981; LaPat-Polasko *et al.*, 1984) and 1,2-dichloroethane (Stucki *et al.*, 1983; Janssen *et al.*, 1985) as primary growth substrates has been reported. Cometabolic reactions seem to be more commonplace, and such biotransformations of many haloalkanes and haloalkenes have been reported under a variety of environmental conditions.

With respect to haloalkanes as primary growth substrates, Stucki *et al.* (1981) reported that a dichloromethane-utilizing *Hyphomicrobium* species produced formaldehyde by first catalyzing the nucleophilic displacement of both chloride atoms. *Xanthobacter autotrophicus* GJ10 possesses two hydrolytic dehalogenases. One of these is plasmid-borne, and is specific for short-chain haloalkanes; the second is specific for halogenated carboxylic acids (Janssen *et al.*, 1985; Tardif *et al.*, 1991). A pathway was proposed for the growth substrate 1,2-dichloroethane which involved dehalogenation to 2-chloroethanol, then oxidation by a nonspecific methanol dehydrogenase to 2-chloroacetaldehyde. The chloroacetaldehyde was dehydrogenated to 2-chloroacetate, and the latter was dehalogenated by the haloalkanoic dehydrogenase to acetate which can be metabolized through normal catabolic pathways (Janssen *et al.*, 1985). Some halocarbons actually act as "**suicide substrates**", that is, they are metabolized to intermediates that impair cell function. For example, the toxicant bromoacetaldehyde is produced from 1,2-dibromoethane (Janssen *et al.*, 1987).

Aerobic cometabolism of some haloalkenes may occur via a number of catabolic oxygenases. Examples include biotransformation by nonspecific activity of methane monooxygenase (MMO), by propane monooxygenase, by oxygenases normally involved in the catabolism of aromatic compounds, by ammonia monooxygenase, and by alkene monooxygenases. One important feature of aerobic, cometabolic transformation of the chloroethylenes is that vinyl chloride does not appear as a product (Fogel *et al.*, 1986) as it does anaerobically (see below).

Wilson and Wilson (1985) observed degradation of TCE to CO_2 in an unsaturated soil column exposed to 0.6% natural gas in air, and suggested that the degradation resulted from the action of methanotrophic microorganisms. Experiments with a methane-utilizing mixed culture (Fogel *et al.*, 1986) and a pure methanotroph culture (Little *et al.*, 1988) demonstrated halocarbon degradation to CO_2 and other products. The range of substrates included dichloroethylenes and vinyl chloride, as well as TCE. PCE was recalcitrant. Further studies with methane-enriched soils indicated that some chloroalkanes were also removed (Henson *et al.*, 1988). Enrichment cultures derived from methane-stimulated soil degraded dichloromethane, chloroform and 1,2-dichloroethane as well as TCE, *cis*-1,2-dichloroethylene, and *trans*-1,2-dichloroethylene, but not PCE, carbon tetrachloride, or 1,1,1-trichloroethane (Henson *et al.*, 1989); the latter *was* apparently removed from the methane-enriched soil (Henson *et al.*, 1988).

In methanotrophic growth, MMO catalyzes the oxidation of methane to methanol, but the enzyme has a broad substrate specificity (Large, 1983) and can oxidize and dechlorinate halogenated methanes (Haber *et al.*, 1983). Mixed function oxidase systems catalyze the epoxidation of chlorinated alkenes (Miller and Guengerich, 1982), and methanotrophs are known to epoxidate ethylene (Hou *et al.*, 1979). Thus, MMO-catalyzed degradation of chloroalkenes is believed to occur via epoxidation and subsequent hydrolysis (Fogel *et al.*, 1986; Little *et al.*, 1988). For example, Little *et al.* (1988) suggested that TCE epoxide forms and then spontaneously breaks down to dichloroacetate, glyoxylate, and the C_1 compounds carbon monoxide and formate. Glyoxylate and dichloroacetate were detectable products of TCE degradation in pure methanotroph cultures (Little *et al.*, 1988). Most methanotrophs are unable to utilize multi-carbon compounds, thus accumulation of these products is not unexpected. Carbon monoxide and formate could be oxidized further. It is noteworthy that in mixed methane-utilizing cultures and soil column systems, a larger fraction of the TCE carbon appears as CO_2 and less as water soluble organic carbon than in pure methanotroph cultures. Compounds such as glyoxylate are readily metabolized by heterotrophs in the mixed systems (Little *et al.*, 1988).

The aerobic degradation of TCE to CO_2, chloride, and other nonvolatile products has been reported for a number of aromatic-degrading bacteria (Nelson *et al.*, 1987; Nelson *et al.*, 1988; Harker and Kim, 1990). Activity of the required enzyme is induced by a compound such as toluene, and the enzyme fortuitously oxidizes TCE. TCE itself cannot induce enzyme synthesis. TCE degradation is inhibited by the natural enzyme substrate, and vice versa, as the two compounds compete for the same catalyst (Folsom *et al.*, 1990). The toluene dioxygenase of *Pseudomonas putida* F1 also degrades 1,1-, *cis*-1,2- and *trans*-1,2-dichloroethylene, but not PCE, vinyl chloride, or ethylene (Wackett and Gibson, 1988). *P. cepacia* G4 and *P. mendocina* possess toluene monooxygenase activities which also transform TCE (Nelson *et al.*, 1987; Shields *et al.*, 1989; Winter *et al.*, 1989). An *Alcaligenes eutrophus* strain possesses both a chromosomal phenol-dependent pathway and a plasmid-encoded 2,4-dichlorophenoxyacetic acid pathway to degrade TCE (Harker and Kim, 1990). The routes of TCE degradation by these aromatic-degraders have not been completely delineated, but are assumed to be similar to that for MMO, *i.e.*, the formation of unstable oxoderivatives which decompose to nonchlorinated compounds. Radiolabelled glyoxylate and formate were detected in a *P. putida* F1 culture incubated with ^{14}C-TCE (Wackett and Householder, 1989).

Degradation of TCE by aromatic-degraders has been described mostly for pure, laboratory cultures. The exceptions to this are the initial work of Nelson *et al.* (1986) who reported one positive result out of 43 samples, and a paper discussing pilot studies in both surface bioreactors and *in situ* remediation (Nelson and Kinsella, 1990). However Nelson *et al.* (1988) believe that microorganisms possessing the required oxygenase activities are not uncommon in the natural environment. They suggest that TCE recalcitrance reflects a lack of the appropriate inducing conditions. TCE may be aerobically biodegraded *in situ* if an appropriate growth substrate is also present.

Under aerobic conditions, the autotrophic, nitrifying bacterium *Nitrosomonas europaea* can biotransform a number of di- and trihalogenated alkanes, vinyl chloride, the three dichloroethylene isomers, cis-bromoethylene, and TCE (Vannelli *et al.*, 1990); it cannot degrade carbon tetrachloride, PCE, or *trans*-dibromoethylene. The cometabolic reactions are catalyzed by ammonia monooxygenase. This activity may be useful in bioremediation schemes because the bacteria grow on ammonia and carbon dioxide, and do not require an organic carbon source.

It should be noted that halogenated hydrocarbons may produce deleterious effects in the bacteria responsible for their biotransformation. Such effects have been reported in aromatic-degraders (Wackett and Householder, 1989), methanotrophs (Alvarez-Cohen and McCarty, 1991; Henry and Grbić-Galić, 1991; Oldenhuis *et al.*, 1991), in a *Xanthobacter* strain that cometabolizes chloroalkenes via monooxygenase (Ensign *et al.*,

1992), and in *Nitrosomonas* (Rasche *et al.*, 1991). Usually, toxicity appears to result from a nonspecific covalent binding of reactive degradation intermediates to cellular proteins, including the enzyme responsible for the cometabolic reaction. Recovery of laboratory cultures is possible under conditions allowing *de novo* synthesis of the affected biomolecules (Wackett and Householder, 1989; Oldenhuis *et al.*, 1991; Rasche *et al.*, 1991).

9.4.3 Anaerobic Biotransformations

9.4.3.1 General

Many chlorinated aliphatic compounds are reductively dechlorinated under anaerobic conditions. This appears to be the sole route of PCE biodegradation, and TCE is also resistant to biodegradation in aerobic environments, except under the special circumstances reviewed above. Tri- and tetrahalogenated methanes and ethanes are generally recalcitrant under aerobic conditions, but are transformed anaerobically. The following paragraphs discuss the biotransformation of haloalkanes and haloalkenes under the various anaerobic redox environments defined earlier. It must be emphasized, as will become evident in the discussion below, that the dehalogenation activity of mixed cultures under given redox conditions (*e.g.*, nitrate-reducing conditions) does not imply that the microorganisms utilizing that electron acceptor (*e.g.*, those reducing nitrate) are the ones responsible for the observed dehalogenation. A **fermentative microorganism**, for example, might be active over the entire redox spectrum and could conceivably be a source of dehalogenating activity under aerobic, nitrate-reducing, sulfate-reducing or methanogenic conditions. Pure culture studies are generally required to attribute dehalogenation unequivocally to a certain type of microorganism utilizing a certain electron acceptor.

9.4.3.2 Haloalkanes

The transformation of carbon tetrachloride and brominated trihalomethanes has been observed under denitrifying conditions in batch culture (Bouwer and McCarty, 1983b). Reductive dechlorination of carbon tetrachloride to chloroform was detected, but carbon tetrachloride was also mineralized to CO_2 and some carbon was assimilated by the biomass. In anoxic biofilm columns under denitrifying, sulfate-reducing, or methanogenic conditions, reductive dehalogenation was the predominant mechanism of removal of a number of halogenated aliphatic compounds, but $^{14}CO_2$ production from labelled carbon tetrachloride and 1,2-dibromoethane was also noted (Bouwer and Wright, 1988). Egli *et al.* (1988) suggested that acetogens in the mixed, denitrifying cultures could have produced the observed CO_2. *Acetobacterium woodii* catalyzes reductive dechlorination, and transforms carbon tetrachloride to CO_2, although the CO_2-producing reactions have not been elucidated (Egli *et al.*, 1988). Criddle *et al.* (1990a) have in fact isolated a denitrifying *Pseudomonas* sp. that transforms carbon tetrachloride, forming CO_2 and an unidentified water-soluble fraction as major products. These authors note, however, that denitrifying microorganisms able to transform carbon tetrachloride seem rare, supporting the suggestion of Egli's group.

The denitrifying pseudomonad of Criddle *et al.* (1990a) possesses a unique carbon tetrachloride transformation pattern, as little or no chloroform is produced. Competing pathways for carbon tetrachloride transformation seem more usual, not only in mixed culture systems (Bouwer and Wright, 1988, for example), but also within single strains of bacteria. The two major biotic pathways are hydrogenolysis (which produces chloroform (and dichloromethane under sufficiently reducing conditions)), and hydrolysis (which produces CO_2) (Egli *et al.*, 1988; Criddle *et al.*, 1990a, 1990b; Criddle and McCarty, 1991). Criddle and McCarty (1991) have demonstrated these processes in an electrolytic model system, concluding that they may occur simultaneously, and that the latter biotransformation could involve the hydrolytic reduction of carbon tetrachloride to formate or carbon monoxide, followed by oxidation to carbon dioxide. A similar reduction then subsequent oxidation, might also explain the production of acetic acid from 1,1,1-trichloroethane by a fermentative *Clostridium* sp. (see below). In either instance, an additional electron donor would be required for microbial metabolism because no extra electrons are released by the proposed transformation sequence (Criddle and McCarty, 1991).

Escherichia coli has been found to reductively dechlorinate carbon tetrachloride (Criddle *et al.*, 1990b). In that study, the product distribution and the rate of biotransformation were both found to be electron acceptor-dependent. The most rapid biotransformation occurred under fermentative conditions, where most labelled carbon from ^{14}C-carbon tetrachloride was recovered as chloroform or as cell-bound ^{14}C; almost no CO_2 was formed. Under fumarate-respiring conditions, a larger portion of the label was associated with CO_2 and the nonvolatile but soluble fraction; chloroform was still produced. Relatively little activity was observed when oxygen or nitrate were provided as the electron acceptors (Criddle *et al.*, 1990b).

A fermentative *Clostridium* sp. isolated from a methanogenic bioreactor known to degrade PCE, TCE, 1,1,1-trichloroethane, and chloroethane was shown to reductively dechlorinate 1,1,1-trichloroethane to 1,1-dichloroethane; other products, including acetic acid were also produced (Galli and McCarty, 1989a). It was proposed that 1,1,1-trichloroethane may compete with natural electron acceptors (*e.g.*, amino acids) present in the growth medium (Galli and McCarty, 1989b). Comparison of the transformation capabilities of the *Clostridium* sp. and the parent methanogenic mixed culture (Vogel and McCarty, 1987) clearly showed that multiple strains were responsible for the activity observed in the mixture. The *Clostridium* accumulated 1,1-dichloroethane from 1,1,1-trichloroethane, whereas the mixed culture carried the biotransformation further, producing chloroethane and CO_2. The mixed culture also degraded PCE and TCE (Vogel and McCarty, 1987), but the *Clostridium* did not (Galli and McCarty, 1989a).

Reductive dechlorination of halomethanes and haloethanes under sulfate-reducing conditions has been observed (*e.g.*, Bouwer and Wright, 1988). Egli *et al.* (1987) showed that *Desulfobacterium autotrophicum* reduces carbon tetrachloride to chloroform and dichloromethane, and 1,1,1-trichloroethane to 1,1-dichloroethane.

Ethane, ethylene and acetylene production from bromoethane, dibromo- or dichloroethane, and 1,2-dibromoethylene, respectively, have been observed in pure cultures of a number of methanogens (Belay and Daniels, 1987). Combinations of dehydrohalogenation and reductive dehalogenation reactions were suggested as the pathways. Mikesell and

Boyd (1990) suggested that the methanogen *Methanosarcina* sp. DCM may dechlorinate chloromethanes to CO_2 and other products via methyltransferase, a corrinoid enzyme that normally binds methanol. CO_2 formation from the chloromethane was presumed to occur via the same pathway by which CO_2 is formed from methanol disproportionation.

In vitro, reductive dehalogenation of chloromethanes by both corrinoids and the methanogen-specific cofactor F_{430} has been demonstrated with titanium (III) citrate or dithiothreitol as the electron donor (Krone *et al.*, 1989a,b; Holliger *et al.*, 1992a). In *Methanobacterium thermoautotrophicum*, it is the factor F_{430}-associated enzyme methyl-coenzyme M reductase, not the corrinoid enzymes, that is able to catalyze reductive dechlorination of 1,2-dichloroethane (Holliger *et al.*, 1992b). Corrinoid enzymes may still be important, however, since not all dechlorinating anaerobes possess F_{430}. Dechlorination catalyzed by cell extracts of *Methanosarcina barkeri* seems to involve both corrinoids and factor F_{430} (Holliger *et al.*, 1992a). Egli *et al.* (1988) suggest that the dechlorinating ability of acetogens, too, may be correlated with possession of corrinoid enzymes of the acetyl CoA pathway.

9.4.3.3 Haloalkenes

The anaerobic biotransformation of chloroethylenes has been demonstrated in methanogenic, fixed film bioreactors (Bouwer and McCarty, 1983a; Vogel and McCarty, 1985), in anaerobic soils (Kloepfer *et al.*, 1985), in muck from an aquifer recharge basin (Parsons *et al.*, 1984), in anaerobic sewage sludge (Fathepure and Boyd, 1988a), in subsurface materials (Wilson *et al.*, 1986; Barrio-Lage *et al.*, 1987; Suflita *et al.*, 1988; Major *et al.*, 1991), in mixed methanogenic enrichment cultures (Baek and Jaffe, 1989; Freedman and Gossett, 1989), in sulfate-reducing enrichments (Bagley and Gossett, 1990), in groundwater-derived enrichments (Kastner, 1991), in pure cultures of methanogens (Fathepure *et al.*, 1987; Fathepure and Boyd, 1988b), and in the sulfidogenic, dehalogenating bacterium strain DCB-1 (Fathepure *et al.*, 1987).

Under highly-reducing conditions, the chloroethylenes are transformed mainly through successive reductive dechlorinations from PCE to TCE to *cis*-1,2-dichloroethylene to vinyl chloride (Parsons *et al.*, 1984; Parsons and Lage, 1985; Barrio-Lage *et al.*, 1986; Vogel and McCarty, 1985). The compound *cis*-1,2-dichloroethylene is the predominant dichlorinated species (Parsons and Lage, 1985; Barrio-Lage *et al.*, 1986; Scholz-Muramatsu *et al.*, 1990; Major *et al.*, 1991) although Freedman and Gossett (1989) detected predominantly the trans isomer in their enrichments. 1,1-dichloroethylene is the least significant isomer, and may be the product of sulfide-mediated abiotic dechlorination (Kastner, 1991). The non-chlorinated products CO_2 (Vogel and McCarty, 1985) and ethylene (Freedman and Gossett, 1989) have also been detected in mixed enrichment culture studies. Subsidiary pathways also operate in mixed cultures. Barrio-Lage *et al.* (1986) detected chloroethane production in microcosms spiked with *cis*-1,2-dichloroethylene. Chloroethane was a product of TCE degradation in the mixed cultures studied by Baek and Jaffe (1989). Their evidence suggested that fermentative bacteria were important in the hydrogenation of the C=C double bond. More chloroethane was evolved when a mixture of two cultures (one enriched for fermentative bacteria and the second for methanogenic bacteria) was used as the inoculum than when the inoculum was taken only from the methanogenic enrichment.

Reductive dechlorination under methanogenic conditions is dependent upon the availability of an electron donor such as acetate, methanol, or H_2, and frequently parallels methane production (Fathepure *et al.*, 1987; Freedman and Gossett, 1989). The ratio of dechlorination to methane production varies with the compound being attacked. Strains of *Methanosarcina* dechlorinated about 0.71 μmole of chloroform per millimol of methane produced, but only about 0.05 μmole of PCE per mmole methane (Fathepure *et al.*, 1987; Fathepure and Boyd, 1988b; Mikesell and Boyd, 1990). Since highly chlorinated compounds are most readily dechlorinated (Vogel *et al.*, 1987), the rate-limiting step in the conversion of PCE to ethylene by a methanogenic enrichment is the final step from vinyl chloride to ethylene (Freedman and Gossett, 1989).

In some studies of dechlorination under methanogenic conditions, methanol has appeared to be more effective than acetate as a source of the reducing equivalents (Barrio-Lage *et al.*, 1987; Fathepure *et al.*, 1987; Freedman and Gossett, 1989), though it is not clear why this is so. It could be significant that methanol metabolism by methanogens involves additional steps not required to metabolize other methanogenic substrates, *e.g.*, the step catalyzed by methyltransferase I, the corrinoid enzyme invoked by Mikesell and Boyd (1990) in their scheme for dechlorination reactions (see above). Consistent with this view, Fathepure *et al.* (1987) suggest the higher dechlorination rate by a *Methanosarcina* sp. growing on methanol may be related to the reducing power generated. Methanol metabolism produces six reducing equivalents, versus two reducing equivalents from acetate. Acetate-cleaving methanogens are nevertheless clearly capable of reductive dechlorination (Fathepure and Boyd, 1988a).

The inhibitor 2-bromoethanesulfonate (BES) blocks the final step in methanogenesis (see Zeikus *et al.*, 1985), and affects PCE and TCE degradation as well as methane production in mixed, methanogenic cultures (Fathepure and Boyd, 1988a; Freedman and Gossett, 1989). This suggests that methanogens play a key role in observed reductive dechlorinations. In contrast, Scholz-Muramatsu *et al.* (1990) found that if methanogenesis was inhibited with BES in a mixed culture fed with benzoate and PCE, dechlorination of PCE to *cis*-1,2-dichloroethylene continued as benzoate was fermented. They suggested that during benzoate fermentation, a portion of the benzoate was reduced to cyclohexyl-carboxylate while the rest was oxidized to acetate, with PCE accepting the electrons from the oxidation. Thus, both benzoate itself and PCE served as electron acceptors.

Gossett and his group have adapted their methane-producing enrichments to high PCE levels (up to 55 mg/L aqueous concentration, DiStefano *et al.*, 1991). Under these conditions, methanogenesis ceased, apparently inhibited by the PCE level, but virtually complete conversion of PCE to ethylene occurred with little vinyl chloride accumulation. An electron balance showed that methanol consumed by the cultures was accounted for by dechlorination (31%) and acetate production (69%). Evidence of a shift in the makeup of the microbial population from methanol-utilizing methanogens to predominantly methanol-utilizing acetogens was obtained, suggesting that the latter were responsible for dechlorination. However, because the microbial population was mixed and interactive, direct proof is lacking and other explanations are possible (DiStefano *et al.*, 1991).

PCE dechlorination stoichiometrically related to sulfide production has been observed in sulfide-reducing enrichment cultures (Bagley and Gossett, 1990). Such cultures exhibited virtually no methane production in the presence of BES, but PCE-dechlorinating ability was equal to that of equivalent cultures devoid of BES. This evidence suggests that reductive dechlorination may have been brought about by sulfate-reducing bacteria (Bagley and Gossett, 1990). The authors noted that the sulfate-reducing enrichments were not nearly as effective in PCE transformation as their methanogenic enrichments (Freedman and Gossett, 1989) operated under similar conditions.

Based on the above discussions, we can conclude that reductive dehalogenation of halogenated, aliphatic hydrocarbons has been observed under anaerobic conditions. These transformations are carried out by certain fermentative, acetogenic, nitrate-reducing, sulfate-reducing and methanogenic bacteria. The reactions appear to be cometabolic in nature, although assimilation of some carbon has been observed (Bouwer and McCarty, 1983a,b), and the strain DCB-1 may gain energy from the dehalogenation (Dolfing and Tiedje, 1987)).

The accumulated data suggest that the reductive dehalogenation is fortuitously catalyzed by certain types of enzymes, with the halogenated compounds acting as alternate electron acceptors in place of the natural acceptor molecules (Egli et al., 1987; 1988; Freedman and Gossett, 1989; Galli and McCarty, 1989b; Mikesell and Boyd, 1990; Scholz-Muramatsu et al., 1990; Criddle et al., 1990a; Holliger et al., 1992a,b). Whether enzyme proficiency is type-specific and/or species-specific remains to be determined. This is an area of current research interest. Cofactors such as cytochromes, NADH, or the unusual methanogenic coenzymes (e.g., F_{430}), could mediate electron transfer, and it is not known whether intracellular or extracellular electron transfer reactions are responsible for reductive dehalogenations. An alternate view might be that reductive dechlorination is driven by any of the enzymes in question, simply as a result of nonspecific diversion of reducing power generated during normal catalytic activity from the normal substrate-product reaction to the chlorinated compound. Then, reductive dechlorination would be governed by the amount of enzyme protein(s) and cofactor(s) available and the ease with which the chlorinated compound is dechlorinated under the given redox environment. The fact that microorganisms have strain-specific capabilities to reductively dechlorinate only certain compounds suggests that the first view may prove to be correct, i.e., some enzymes are more adept at the process than others. Fathepure and Boyd (1988a) observed that two species of *Methanosarcina* differed in their ability to dechlorinate PCE, and some types of anaerobic bacteria may not transform halocarbons at all (Fathepure et al., 1987; Egli et al., 1988). Because of the importance of phenomena such as interspecies hydrogen transfer and cross-feeding in anaerobic consortia, however, other community members are likely to indirectly influence reductive dechlorination.

9.4.4 Laboratory Studies

Most of the studies discussed in the previous sections were performed in the laboratory under ideal reaction conditions. Flow was incorporated as a parameter in some studies;

others were conducted under static conditions. The progression from pure, laboratory cultures to enrichment cultures to microcosms using materials taken from the field is one of increasing complexity, but also one of increasing reality in terms of what occurs in the natural environment. The more "real" the laboratory study, the more difficulty encountered in pinpointing the operative chemical or biological mechanism(s) and influential factors. Thus, although pure chemical/culture work is invaluable for defining mechanisms and pathways, and also for testing hypotheses, we must continue to grapple with more complex systems if we are to understand the abiotic/biotic transformation potentials of natural environments.

Laboratory studies, particularly with pure cultures, are frequently conducted at temperatures optimal for activity of the microorganisms, often above 20 °C. However, most groundwater systems in high latitudes are considerably cooler. Laboratory experiments at lower temperatures are therefore more realistic, because not only are reaction rates affected by temperature, but different bacterial strains are adapted to distinct temperature ranges.

Information on the rates and products of biotransformations and the microbial population dynamics of natural aquifer communities under *in situ* conditions are needed. However, many studies of reductive dechlorination have been conducted using microbial enrichments derived from wastewater treatment systems, not from contaminated groundwaters. Comparison of sewage sludges from different sources have shown considerable variation in their degradation capacity (Fathepure and Boyd, 1988a). Whether subsurface environments will demonstrate the same heterogeneity with respect to biodegradative capability is not known, but since microbial numbers may be smaller in the subsurface than in sewage sludges, one might expect that the probability of a certain microorganism's presence will be lower in the subsurface than in sewage sludge. Few data are available to support or rebut this contention, but Kastner's (1991) study of reductive dechlorination, which was conducted with groundwater-derived enrichment cultures, suggests results from wastewater/sludge enrichments may not be directly applicable to all groundwater environments. Kastner (1991) demonstrated that reductive dechlorination of PCE and TCE could be driven by the transition of aerobic, contaminated groundwater-derived enrichments to anaerobic conditions (E_H equal to between -150 and -210 mV). *cis*-1,2-dichloroethylene was the major product, but no further dechlorination occurred and no methane was detected. Repeated anaerobic subculture of the dechlorinating cultures resulted in a gradual loss of dechlorinating capacity. Only aerobic subcultures stably maintained dechlorination activity, indicating that the aerobic-anaerobic shift was necessary for biotransformation. Enrichments derived from pristine sites had no ability to reductively dechlorinate under similar conditions. The observed *cis*-1,2-dichloroethylene accumulation is comparable to what is observed in contaminated aquifers in Germany, where *cis*-1,2-dichloroethylene is often the main contaminant, and only traces of vinyl chloride and methane are observed (Kastner, 1991).

Table 9.2 summarizes the conditions under which biotransformation of a given compound has been documented in laboratory studies. Key references are cited. Some were chosen in part because they mention earlier work. The comments in Table 9.2 provide additional information. In studies classed as "anaerobic" for example, a distinction

TABLE 9.2 Summary of Laboratory Observations on Biotransformations.

Compound	Condition	Biotransformation	Reference	Comments
chloromethane	aerobic	no	Janssen et al. (1985)	pure culture
	methane-oxidizing	yes	Dalton & Stirling (1982)	
	aromatic-oxidizing			
	NH_3-oxidizing	yes	Rasche et al. (1991)	
	anaerobic			
	NO_3^--reducing			
	SO_4^{2-}-reducing			
	CO_2-reducing			
dichloromethane	aerobic	yes	LaPat-Polasko et al. (1984)	
	methane-oxidizing	yes	Henson et al. (1988); Stirling & Dalton (1982)	
	aromatic-oxidizing			
	NH_3-oxidizing	yes	Vannelli et al. (1990)	
	anaerobic			
	NO_3^--reducing	yes	Bouwer & McCarty (1983); Brunner et al. (1980)	
	SO_4^{2-}-reducing			
	CO_2-reducing	yes	Gossett & Freedman (1989)	
bromomethane	aerobic			
	methane-oxidizing	yes	Dalton & Stirling (1982)	
	aromatic-oxidizing			
	NH_3-oxidizing	yes	Rasche et al. (1990a)	
	anaerobic			
	NO_3^--reducing			
	SO_4^{2-}-reducing			
	CO_2-reducing			
dibromo-methane	aerobic			
	methane-oxidizing			
	aromatic-oxidizing			
	NH_3-oxidizing	yes	Vannelli et al. (1990)	
	anaerobic			
	NO_3^--reducing			
	SO_4^{2-}-reducing			
	CO_2-reducing			

TABLE 9.2 *continued*

Compound	Condition	Biotransformation	Reference	Comments
dibromochloro-methane	abiotic	yes	Bouwer & McCarty (1983a)	
	aerobic	no/no	Bouwer et al. (1981); Tabak et al. (1981)	
	methane-oxidizing			
	aromatic-oxidizing			
	anaerobic			
	NO_3^--reducing	yes	Bouwer & McCarty (1983b)	
	SO_4^{2-}-reducing	yes	Bouwer & McCarty (1983a)	
	CO_2-reducing	yes	Bouwer & McCarty (1983a)	
bromodichloro-methane	abiotic	yes	Bouwer & McCarty (1983a)	
	aerobic	yes/no	Tabak et al. (1981)/Bouwer et al. (1981)	
	methane-oxidizing			
	aromatic-oxidizing			
	anaerobic			
	NO_3^--reducing	yes	Bouwer & McCarty (1983b); Bouwer & Wright (1988)	
	SO_4^{2-}-reducing	yes	Bouwer & Wright (1988)	
	CO_2-reducing	yes	Bouwer & McCarty (1983a); Bouwer & Wright (1988)	
tribromomethane (bromoform)	abiotic	yes	Bouwer & McCarty (1983a)	
	aerobic	yes	Tabak et al. (1981)	
	methane-oxidizing			
	aromatic-oxidizing			
	anaerobic			
	NO_3^--reducing	yes	Bouwer & McCarty (1983b); Bouwer & Wright (1988)	
	SO_4^{2-}-reducing	yes	Bouwer & Wright (1988)	
	CO_2-reducing	yes	Bouwer & McCarty (1983a); Bouwer & Wright (1988)	
trichloromethane (chloroform)	aerobic	yes/no	Tabak et al. (1981)/Bouwer et al. (1981)	
	methane-oxidizing	yes	Henson et al. (1988)	
	aromatic-oxidizing			
	NH_3-oxidizing	yes	Vannelli et al. (1990)	
	anaerobic	yes	Galli & McCarty (1989a)	fermentative
	NO_3^--reducing	no	Bouwer & McCarty (1983a); Bouwer & Wright (1988)	
	SO_4^{2-}-reducing	no	Bouwer & Wright (1988)	
	CO_2-reducing	yes	Bouwer & McCarty (1983a); Mikesell & Boyd (1990)	
carbon tetrachloride	abiotic	yes	Reinhard et al. (1990)	
	aerobic	yes	Tabak et al. (1981)	

293

TABLE 9.2 *continued*

Compound	Condition	Biotransformation	Reference	Comments
	methane-oxidizing	no	Henson et al. (1989)	
	aromatic-oxidizing			
	NH_3-oxidizing	no	Vannelli et al. (1990)	
	anaerobic	yes	Criddle et al. (1990b); Egli et al. (1988)	fermentative-/autotroph
	NO_3^--reducing	yes/no	Criddle et al. (1990a)/Egli et al. (1988)	
	SO_4^{2-}-reducing	yes & no/yes	Egli et al. (1988)/Bouwer & Wright (1988)	2 species/-
	CO_2-reducing	yes	Bouwer & McCarty (1983a); Bouwer & Wright (1988)	
chloroethane	aerobic	no	Janssen et al. (1985)	pure culture
	methane-oxidizing			
	aromatic-oxidizing			
	NH_3-oxidizing	yes	Rasche et al. (1990b)	
	anaerobic			
	NO_3^--reducing			
	SO_4^{2-}-reducing			
	CO_2-reducing			
bromoethane	aerobic	yes	Janssen et al. (1985)	
	methane-oxidizing			
	aromatic-oxidizing			
	NH_3-oxidizing	yes	Vannelli et al. (1990)	
	anaerobic			
	NO_3^--reducing			
	SO_4^{2-}-reducing			
	CO_2-reducing	yes	Belay & Daniels (1987)	
1,1-dichloro-ethane	aerobic	yes	Tabak et al. (1981)	
	methane-oxidizing	yes	Henson et al. (1989)	
	aromatic-oxidizing			
	NH_3-oxidizing	yes	Rasche et al. (1991)	
	anaerobic			
	NO_3^--reducing			
	SO_4^{2-}-reducing			
	CO_2-reducing	yes	Vogel & McCarty (1987)	
1,2-dichloro-ethane	aerobic	yes	Janssen et al. (1985)	
	methane-oxidizing	yes	Henson et al. (1988)	

TABLE 9.2 *continued*

Compound	Condition	Biotransformation	Reference	Comments
	aromatic-oxidizing			
	NH$_3$-oxidizing	yes	Rasche et al. (1991)	
	anaerobic			
	NO$_3^-$-reducing			
	SO$_4^{2-}$-reducing	yes	Bouwer & McCarty (1983a); Egli et al. (1987)	
	CO$_2$-reducing			
1,2-dibromoethane	aerobic	yes	Pignatello (1986)	
	methane-oxidizing			
	aromatic-oxidizing			
	NH$_3$-oxidizing	yes	Vannelli et al. (1990)	
	anaerobic			
	NO$_3^-$-reducing	no	Bouwer & McCarty (1983b)	
	SO$_4^{2-}$-reducing			
	CO$_2$-reducing	yes	Belay & Daniels (1987); Bouwer & Wright (1988)	
1,1,1-trichloro-ethane	abiotic	yes	Vogel & McCarty (1987)	pure culture
	aerobic	no	Janssen et al. (1985)	soil/enrichment
	methane-oxidizing	yes/no	Henson et al. (1988)/Henson et al. (1989)	
	aromatic-oxidizing			
	NH$_3$-oxidizing	yes	Vannelli et al. (1990)	
	anaerobic			
	NO$_3^-$-reducing	maybe/no	Bouwer & Wright (1988)/Bouwer & McCarty (1983b)	
	SO$_4^{2-}$-reducing	maybe/yes	Bouwer & Wright (1988)/Egli et al. (1987)	
	CO$_2$-reducing	yes	Vogel & McCarty (1987); Bouwer & Wright (1988)	
1,1,2-trichloro-ethane	aerobic	no/yes	Janssen et al. (1985)/Castro & Belser (1990)	pure culture
	methane-oxidizing	yes	Henson et al. (1989)	
	aromatic-oxidizing			
	NH$_3$-oxidizing	yes	Vannelli et al. (1990)	
	anaerobic			
	NO$_3^-$-reducing			
	SO$_4^{2-}$-reducing			
	CO$_2$-reducing			
1,1,2,2-tetra-chloroethane	aerobic	no	Janssen et al. (1985)	pure culture
	methane-oxidizing			
	aromatic-oxidizing			

295

TABLE 9.2 *continued*

Compound	Condition	Biotransformation	Reference	Comments
	NH_3-oxidizing	yes	Rasche et al. (1991)	
	anaerobic			
	NO_3^--reducing			
	SO_4^{2-}-reducing			
	CO_2-reducing	yes	Bouwer & McCarty (1983a)	
hexachloroethane	abiotic	yes	Reinhard et al. (1990)	
	aerobic	yes	Tabak et al. (1981)	
	methane-oxidizing			
	aromatic-oxidizing			
	anaerobic			
	NO_3^--reducing	yes	Bouwer & Wright (1988)	
	SO_4^{2-}-reducing	yes	Bouwer & Wright (1988)	
	CO_2-reducing	yes	Bouwer & Wright (1988)	
vinyl chloride	aerobic	yes	Davis & Carpenter (1990)	
	methane-oxidizing	yes	Fogel et al. (1986)	
	propane-oxidizing	yes	Wackett et al. (1989)	
	aromatic-oxidizing	no	Wackett & Gibson (1988)	
	NH_3-oxidizing	yes	Vannelli et al. (1990)	
	anaerobic			
	NO_3^--reducing			
	SO_4^{2-}-reducing			
	CO_2-reducing	yes	Vogel & McCarty (1985)	
1,1-DCE (gem-)	aerobic	yes	Tabak et al. (1981)	
	methane-oxidizing	yes	Fogel et al. (1986)	
	propane-oxidizing	yes	Wackett et al. (1989)	
	aromatic-oxidizing	yes	Wackett & Gibson (1988)	
	NH_3-oxidizing	yes	Vannelli et al. (1990)	
	anaerobic	yes	Barrio-Lage et al. (1986)	muck microcosm
	NO_3^--reducing			
	SO_4^{2-}-reducing			
	CO_2-reducing	yes	Wilson et al. (1986)	
cis-1,2-DCE	aerobic	yes	Tabak et al. (1981)	
	methane-oxidizing	yes	Fogel et al. (1986)	

TABLE 9.2 *continued*

Compound	Condition	Biotransformation	Reference	Comments
	propane-oxidizing	yes	Wackett et al. (1989)	
	aromatic-oxidizing	yes	Wackett & Gibson (1988)	
	NH$_3$-oxidizing	yes	Vannelli et al. (1990)	
	anaerobic	yes	Barrio-Lage et al. (1986)	muck microcosm
	NO$_3^-$-reducing			
	SO$_4^{2-}$-reducing			
	CO$_2$-reducing	yes	Wilson et al. (1986)	
trans-1,2-DCE	aerobic	yes	Tabak et al. (1981)	
	methane-oxidizing	yes	Fogel et al. (1986)	
	propane-oxidizing	yes	Wackett et al. (1989)	
	aromatic-oxidizing	yes	Wackett & Gibson (1988)	
	NH$_3$-oxidizing	yes	Vannelli et al. (1990)	
	anaerobic	yes	Barrio-Lage et al. (1986)	muck microcosm
	NO$_3^-$-reducing			
	SO$_4^{2-}$-reducing			
	CO$_2$-reducing	yes	Wilson et al. (1986)	
TCE	aerobic	yes/no	Tabak et al. (1981)/Bouwer et al. (1981)	
	methane-oxidizing	yes	Wilson & Wilson (1985); Little et al. (1988)	
	propane-oxidizing	yes	Wackett et al. (1989)	
	aromatic-oxidizing	yes	Wackett & Gibson (1988); Harker & Kim (1990)	
	NH$_3$-oxidizing	yes	Vannelli et al. (1990)	
	anaerobic	yes	Barrio-Lage et al. (1986)	muck microcosm
	NO$_3^-$-reducing			
	SO$_4^{2-}$-reducing	yes	Bagley & Gossett (1990)	
	CO$_2$-reducing	yes	Wilson et al. (1986); Freedman & Gossett (1989)	
PCE	aerobic	yes/no	Tabak et al. (1981)/ Bouwer et al. (1981)	
	methane-oxidizing	no	Fogel et al. (1986)	
	propane-oxidizing	no	Wackett et al. (1989)	
	aromatic-oxidizing	no	Wackett & Gibson (1988)	
	NH$_3$-oxidizing	no	Vannelli et al. (1990)	
	anaerobic	yes	Scholz-Muramatsu et al. (1990)	fermentative
	NO$_3^-$-reducing	no	Bouwer & Wright (1988)	
	SO$_4^{2-}$-reducing	yes	Bagley & Gossett (1990)	
	CO$_2$-reducing	yes	Fathepure & Boyd (1988b); Freedman & Gossett (1989)	

is drawn between a case wherein the redox state was undefined (*e.g.,* Barrio-Lage *et al.,* 1986), and one wherein the microbial activity was fermentative (*e.g.,* Galli and McCarty, 1989a). The broad, aerobic biodegradative capacity recorded by Tabak *et al.* (1981) may be somewhat optimistic, based on the results of others, while the inability of the *Xanthobacter* isolate of Janssen *et al.* (1985) to aerobically degrade certain chloromethanes and chloroethanes does not mean isolates with broader substrate ranges will not be found in the future. If its significance was observed under conditions conducive to biotransformation, abiotic transformation is also noted in Table 9.2.

A comparison of biotransformation rates of various halogenated hydrocarbons via the different pathways discussed above would be most useful. However, because of the wide range in experimental conditions and methods of reporting results, meaningful comparisons are difficult. Table 9.3 summarizes some reported rates for PCE and TCE. Most are derived from pure culture studies, and are likely to differ significantly from field rates. However, unlike field-derived rate data, they do relate biotransformation to the amount of microbial biomass present. In general, the rates of PCE transformation by the anaerobic species are slower than the rates of TCE transformation by the aerobic cultures. Strain DCB-1, the fastest dechlorinator of the anaerobes listed, was isolated from an anaerobic consortium (Dolfing and Tiedje, 1987) which degraded PCE even

TABLE 9.3   Biotransformation of Chloroethenes.

Culture, condition	Degradation rate (μmol/d-mg protein)	Reference
	PCE degradation	
strain DCB-1, anaerobic	0.00234	Fathepure *et al.* (1987)
Methanosarcina sp., anaerobic	8.4×10^{-4}	Fathepure *et al.* (1987)
M. mazei, anaerobic	4.8×10^{-4}	Fathepure *et al.* (1987)
	TCE degradation	
mixed methanotrophs, aerobic, + CH_4	0.06	Fogel *et al.* (1986)
Methylosinus trichosporium aerobic, + CH_4	> 52[†]	Tsien *et al.* (1989)
Pseudomonas putida F1 aerobic, toluene induced	2.6[†]	Wackett and Gibson (1988)
P. cepacia G4 aerobic, phenol induced	6.8	Folsom *et al.* (1990)
Alcaligenes eutrophus AE0106, aerobic, phenol induced	0.3	Harker and Kim (1990)
Nitrosomonas europaea, aerobic, + NH_3	0.99[‡]	Vannelli *et al.* (1990)

[†]converted from g cells dry weight to mg protein by assuming a cell is 55% protein (dry weight)

[‡]converted from g cells wet weight to mg protein by assuming that 1 g cells wet weight is equivalent to 0.29 g cells dry weight, and using the above conversion to protein

[††]Conversion factors are from Ingraham *et al.* (1983), p. 3.

faster than the monoculture of DCB-1 (Fathepure *et al.*, 1987). Of the TCE-transforming cultures, the mixed methanotrophic culture of Fogel *et al.* (1986) was grown at 20 °C, while the other heterotrophic aerobic rates were assayed at 26 to 30 °C. The latter range is probably better for the microbes. One cannot directly compare the unknown methanotrophic strain(s) of the mixed culture with the *M. trichosporium* strain studied by Tsien *et al.* (1989), but it is likely that part of the vast difference in their reported TCE transformation rates is attributable to the optimization of culture conditions by Tsien *et al.* (1989). In addition, not all biomass in a methanotrophic mixture will be active in TCE transformation. An expectation of a 100-fold improvement in biotransformation rates through optimization of conditions for microbial activity in the field is unrealistic. Smaller improvements should be feasible, however.

A series of dynamic column studies of biofilm-mediated degradation (McCarty *et al.*, 1981; Bouwer and McCarty, 1983a; Bouwer and McCarty, 1983b; McCarty *et al.*, 1984; Vogel and McCarty, 1985; Vogel and McCarty, 1987; Bouwer and Wright, 1988) has produced valuable information on transformation pathways and also on how to approach the modelling of transformation processes (*e.g.*, see Bouwer and Wright, 1988). These studies have usually employed low concentrations of halocarbons (less than 100 μg/L) that are similar to levels in contaminated groundwaters. However, the primary substrate concentrations (from 1 up to 250 mg/L) and thus the amount of biomass may be higher than normally encountered in the subsurface. The modelling aspect allows predictions about real situations to be made. For example, Bouwer and Wright (1988) found that shorter retention times increased the adaptation period and decreased the extent of compound removed. They suggested that in the field, biotransformations of pollutants may be less favorable in the vicinity of injection and extraction wells where local ground-water velocities are relatively high. These authors also believe that laboratory-derived k/K_s ratios (maximum specific substrate utilization rate/half-velocity constant) may be useful in estimating pollutant half-lives in groundwater. Estimated half-lives were shortest under aerobic and methanogenic conditions, and significantly longer under denitrifying and sulfate-reducing conditions (Bouwer and Wright, 1988). Extrapolations from their model run indicated that biotransformation could be significant even at the very low microbial concentrations typical of subsurface environments.

9.4.5 Field Studies

The major advantage of **field studies** is that there the observed behavior is real and demonstrable. On the other hand, field studies of actual contamination are often impaired by a poor definition of input history. Moreover, the control and precision of laboratory experiments cannot be duplicated, even in extensively monitored field experiments. A recently described *in situ* microcosm testing device which is usable in fairly permeable subsurface materials offers an intriguing intermediate study approach (Gillham *et al.*, 1990).

In terms of expanding our knowledge base, the ideal field study is probably one that is highly controlled, and supported by supplementary laboratory studies using micro-cosms and perhaps enrichment cultures as well. The design of field experiments is often based on laboratory studies. Once field experiments such as those involving injections of contaminants and tracers are initiated, they can be monitored, but often not substantially altered. The collected field data are used to construct hypotheses concerning what is happening in the subsurface. Supplementary laboratory studies allow such hypotheses to be tested. Plausible explanations of unforseen field occurrences may be more readily obtained using the relatively simple, easily manipulated environment of a laboratory microcosm. Hopefully, consistent information is obtained from the field and laboratory studies.

The study at the **Moffett Field Naval Air Station** is an example where an integrated field-and-laboratory-study approach was taken (Semprini *et al.*, 1987; Roberts *et al.*, 1989; Roberts *et al.*, 1990; Lanzarone and McCarty, 1990; Semprini *et al.*, 1990). Similarly, controlled studies have been conducted at the **Borden Landfill** (Base Borden, Ontario) study site, which is probably the most-studied aquifer in the world (*e.g.*, see *J. Hydrol.* 1983, Vol. 63, No. 1/2 and *Water Resources Research*, 1986, Vol. 22, No. 13).

The site studied by Major *et al.* (1991) is not the result of a controlled spill, but through fortuitous circumstances it provides a good study area for PCE. For example, PCE's less chlorinated daughter compounds were never stored on-site. Also, the plume is well isolated and occupies a relatively small area. Extensive analyses conducted on groundwater from the site, including a search for possible biotransformation products and substrates for microbial activity, have allowed hypotheses regarding on-site biotransformations to be made. Studies of laboratory microcosms have confirmed the hypotheses and have suggested directions for future experimental investigation regarding the *in situ* fate of the contaminants. Comparisons of this site, where biologically-mediated reductive dechlorination is occurring, with other ostensibly similar sites where the halocarbons are recalcitrant, should prove enlightening.

9.4.6 Bioremediation

Where subsurface environments do not favor the rapid, natural biotransformation of halocarbon contaminants, there is an increasing interest in creating more favorable conditions, *i.e.*, in conducting *in situ* **bioremediation** of dissolved chlorinated solvents. The discussion of haloaliphatic biotransformation presented in the preceding sections makes it clear that difficulties will be encountered in real-world bioremediation of sites contaminated by these compounds. For example, an attempted aerobic bioremediation process will not completely degrade highly-chlorinated species such as PCE; an anaerobic process can degrade PCE, but it will also allow the accumulation of less chlorinated daughter products such as vinyl chloride. Complete degradation of a mixture of hexachlorobenzene, PCE and chloroform to water-soluble metabolic products and CO_2 has been obtained in a laboratory-scale, two-stage anaerobic-aerobic biofilm reactor (Fathepure and Vogel, 1991). Thus, the sequential application of both aerobic and anaerobic conditions in an aquifer might be ideal, but large scale manipulation of the redox potential in a contaminated aquifer is not easily carried out. Alternatively, if we consider a simplified scenario of a zone contaminated with a chloroethylene mixture, one approach might be to initially encourage anaerobic conditions in the aquifer (especially near the source zone), favoring reductive dechlorination. This is a "go-with-the-flow" approach: assuming that there is enough metabolizable carbon, N, P, etc. (as is the case in many landfill leachates), and given enough time, anaerobic conditions will evolve naturally (*e.g.*, see Lesage *et al.*, 1990). Eventually, accumulation of less chlorinated daughter products and perhaps methane should become apparent downgradient, and significant dilution of the plume with uncontaminated, oxygenated water may begin to occur. Aerobic metabolism by methanotrophs could then be encouraged in this aerobic zone, perhaps by pumping O_2 or H_2O_2 into the plume to degrade the less-chlorinated compounds. Alternatively, a downgradient pump-and-treat system could bring the less chlorinated contaminants to the surface for treatment in aerobic bioreactors.

Exploitation of aromatic-degrading bacteria to **cometabolize** TCE and other compounds remains a remediation possibility, but a major difficulty is that induction of the desired oxygenases requires the provision of toluene or phenol. In some instances, these aromatics may comprise part of the contaminant plume, but it is difficult to conceive of regulatory agencies approving purposeful spills of one priority pollutant to clean up a second. Less harmful means of induction must be found if these microorganisms are to be commonly used *in situ*. A TCE-degrading mutant strain not requiring induction has been developed (Shields and Reagin, 1992). Pump-and-treat systems employing bioreactors of pre-induced, aromatic-degrading bacteria can also be envisioned. Folsom and Chapman (1991) recently demonstrated TCE degradation by phenol-fed *P. cepacia* G4 in a recirculating bioreactor; they reported an average degradation rate of 0.7 g TCE per day per gram of cell protein.

A limited amount of research has been directed toward **genetically-engineered**, TCE-degrading bacteria (Winter *et al.*, 1989; Zylstra *et al.*, 1989). The genes for toluene dioxygenase of *P. putida* have been successfully cloned into *Escherichia coli* (Zylstra *et al.*, 1989). Interestingly, TCE degradation rates were more sustained in *E. coli* than in *P. putida*, suggesting that *E. coli* suffered less metabolic damage. Recombination of the toluene dioxygenase activity with a more TCE-tolerant host strain may be a fruitful strategy for optimizing TCE biodegradation (Zylstra *et al.*, 1989).

In situ remediation schemes which stimulate **methane-oxidizing microbial populations** are probably the most feasible of the currently available approaches. Methane occurs naturally and is not a "priority pollutant", so that its controlled introduction into the subsurface should be relatively acceptable. Additionally, because of the remarkably broad substrate specificity of MMO, a wide range of pollutants might be affected by this approach. Cometabolic attack on haloalkanes, haloalkenes, ethers, cyclic hydrocarbons, and aromatic hydrocarbons has been demonstrated.

A comprehensive investigation of the feasibility of stimulating native methane-oxidizing populations to degrade chlorinated compounds *in situ* has been conducted (Roberts *et al.*, 1989; Roberts *et al.*, 1990; Semprini *et al.*, 1990). Methane and oxygen were introduced into a shallow, confined, sand and gravel aquifer contaminated with TCE, dichloroethylene and vinyl chloride. Alternative pulsing of oxygen and methane kept clogging of the injection well under control. The temporary cessations of methane feed inherent in the pulse system actually improved halocarbon transformation; since methane and the halocarbons compete for the same enzyme, methane pulsing may have reduced the periods of methane inhibition of halocarbon degradation without starving the population of primary substrate for extended periods. It was found that in the field, the microbial population actively transformed halocarbons for only a short time after the methane feed was stopped. In the small, biostimulated zone of the aquifer, a steady state was achieved after about 2 weeks. The extents of transformation were approximately 95% for vinyl chloride, 85% for *trans*-1,2-dichloroethylene, 40% for *cis*-1,2-dichloroethylene, and 20% for TCE (Roberts *et al.*, 1989).

When water that is contaminated with a chlorinated solvent is pumped to the surface, common treatments have included **air stripping** and/or **adsorption** of the contaminants on charcoal or activated carbon. An attractive alternative treatment method is to process the pumped water in **bioreactors**, thereby avoiding either the release of the pollutants to the atmosphere or the need to dispose of contaminated adsorbent materials.

Microbial consortia that are fed methane, propane, and other organic substrates have been used to remove TCE and dichloroethylenes from water in laboratory-scale bioreactors. In one study, both propane and a propane-methane mixture were found to be superior to methane alone as primary substrate, possibly because the consortium was able to use propane more efficiently than methane, or because propane does not compete as effectively as methane for the TCE-transforming enzymes (Phelps *et al.*, 1990). Using a methane-fed bioreactor with a 50 min residence time, Strandberg *et al.* (1989) observed removal of more than 50% of the TCE and more than 90% of the *cis*-1,2-dichloroethylene from a synthetic groundwater containing 1 mg/L of each compound. Additional degradation of the TCE was obtained with liquid recycle in the bioreactor, but an upper limit for TCE degradation of 90 to 95% was encountered. Although a satisfactory explanation has not been advanced, other groups have apparently also observed this result (Strandberg *et al.*, 1989). Enrichments capable of dealing with relatively high halocarbon levels can be developed. The bioreactors of Phelps *et al.* (1990) were fed 20 mg/L TCE, and earlier work with batch cultures produced consortia capable of degrading more than 99% of TCE added at 50 mg/L (Fliermans *et al.*, 1988). Interestingly, the early batch cultures were not methanotrophic enrichments. Although the TCE-degrading consortia were stimulated by methane, they could not use it as a sole carbon and energy source (Fliermans *et al.*, 1988).

It has been found that TCE degradation is not unduly inhibited by the presence of dichloroethylene (Strandberg *et al.*, 1989), and priority pollutants were not detected among the bioreactor products (Strandberg *et al.*, 1989; Phelps *et al.*, 1990). These are advantages that may not be obtainable in anaerobic bioremediation schemes because all studies of anaerobic chloroethylene dehalogenation to date have clearly shown sequential transformation, not parallel transformation. The less chlorinated compounds (*e.g.*, vinyl chloride) accumulate while more highly chlorinated compounds are dechlorinated, and significant dechlorination of these daughter products does not begin until the parent has disappeared (*e.g.*, see Major *et al.*, 1991). Unfortunately, the daughter products are also contaminants of concern. However, laboratory and field observations of partial vinyl chloride dechlorination to ethylene and ethane (Freedman and Gossett, 1989; Major *et al.*, 1991; de Bruin *et al.*, 1992) and the virtually complete transformation of high levels of PCE to ethylene in laboratory enrichments (DiStefano *et al.*, 1991) provide optimism that useful *in situ* anaerobic bioremediation schemes will be forthcoming.

9.5 CONCLUSIONS

Many halogenated compounds are susceptible to abiotic transformations in the groundwater environment. The hydrolysis of bromomethane and several haloethanes including bromoethane, chloroethane and 1,1,1-trichloroethane and 1,1,2,2-tetrachloroethane, should limit the occurrence of such compounds in groundwaters. Some reactions produce chloroethylenes, so hydrolysis alone may not completely detoxify contaminated groundwaters. Nucleophilic substitution of sulfur for both bromide and chloride also produces mixed benefits, with mercaptans and vinyl chloride among the reported products.

Reductive reactions are perhaps the most significant reactions in groundwaters, with both abiotic and biologically-mediated pathways. It may not be possible, and perhaps not useful, to distinguish the abiotic versus biotic nature of these reactions, since biological reactions are almost always required to produce the strongly reducing conditions under which reduction reactions are favored. Only in anaerobic plumes should we expect significant abiotic transformation of halocarbons. Persistence under aerobic conditions is anticipated. Many chlorinated solvents enter the subsurface without easily metabolized substrates and these may produce persistent halocarbon plumes in aerobic groundwater. The coupling of reductive dechlorination with Fe^0 oxidation appears to be an exciting *in situ* remedial possibility in such cases.

Microbial transformation of haloaliphatic compounds is not rare, and although in many instances our knowledge of such processes is not derived from groundwater environments, we now have unequivocal evidence that biotransformation reactions critically influence the subsurface behavior of halogenated compounds. Although our understanding of the various biotransformations that have been observed is sometimes incomplete, available evidence suggests that it is possible to manipulate the environment of the microbial population(s) in ways that will encourage (or discourage) these microbially-mediated reactions. Such manipulation can be used to help control the behavior of contaminant plumes. *In situ*, a major problem will be controlling the hydrogeologically complex subsurface environment so that the desired conditions are established and effectively maintained throughout the contaminated area (see Chapter 2).

ACKNOWLEDGEMENTS

Funding support for this research was provided in part by the University Consortium Solvents-in-Groundwater Research Program. Sponsors of the Program between 1988 and 1994 have included: The Boeing Company, Ciba-Geigy Corporation, Dow Chemical Canada/USA, Eastman Kodak Co., General Electric Co., Laidlaw Environmental Systems Ltd., Mitre Corporation, The Natural Sciences and Engineering Research Council of Canada, and the Ontario University Research Incentive Fund.

304 Chemical / Microbiological Transformations and Degradation   Chap. 9

9.6 REFERENCES

Acton, D. W. (1990) "Enhanced in situ biodegradation of aromatic and chlorinated aliphatic hydrocarbons in anaerobic, leachate-impacted groundwaters. M.Sc. Thesis, University of Waterloo, Waterloo, Ontario.

Alexander, M. (1985) "Biodegradation of organic chemicals", *Environ. Sci. Technol.* **18**, 106-111.

Alvarez-Cohen, L. and P. L. McCarty (1991) "Product toxicity and cometabolic competitive inhibition modeling of chloroform and trichloroethylene transformation by methanotrophic resting cells", *Appl. Environ. Microbiol.* **57**, 1031-1037.

Baek, N. H. and P. R. Jaffe (1989) "The degradation of trichloroethylene in mixed methanogenic cultures", *J. Environ. Qual.* **18**, 515-518.

Bagley, D. M. and J. M. Gossett (1990) "Tetrachloroethene transformation to trichloroethene and *cis*-dichloroethene by sulfate-reducing enrichment cultures", *Appl. Environ. Microbiol.* **56**, 2511-2516.

Balkwill, D. L., J. F. Fredrickson, and J. M. Thomas (1989) "Vertical and horizontal variations in the physiological diversity of the aerobic chemoheterotrophic bacterial microflora in deep southeast coastal plain subsurface sediments", *Appl. Environ. Microbiol.* **55**, 1058-1065.

Barbash, J. E. and M. Reinhard (1989) "Abiotic dehalogenation of 1,2-dichloroethane and 1,2-dibromoethane in aqueous solution containing hydrogen sulfide", *Environ. Sci. Technol.* **23**, 1349-1357.

Barrio-Lage, G. A., F. Z. Parsons, R. S. Nassar, and P. A. Lorenzo (1986) "Sequential dehalogenation of chlorinated ethenes", *Environ. Sci. Technol.* **20**, 96-99.

Barrio-Lage, G. A., F. Z. Parsons, R. S. Nassar, and P. A. Lorenzo (1987) "Biotransformation of trichloroethene in a variety of subsurface materials", *Environ. Toxicol. Chem.* **6**, 571-578.

Baxter, R. M. (1989) "Reductive dehalogenation of environmental contaminants: a critical review", *Water Poll. Research J. Canada* **24**, 299-322.

Belay, N. and L. Daniels (1987) "Production of ethane, ethylene, and acetylene from halogenated hydrocarbons by methanogenic bacteria", *Appl. Environ. Microbiol.* **53**, 1604-1610.

Boethling, R. S. and M. Alexander (1979) "Effect of concentration of organic chemicals on their biodegradation by natural communities", *Appl. Environ. Microbiol.* **37**, 1211-1216.

Bouwer, E. J., B. E. Rittmann, and P. L. McCarty (1981) "Anaerobic degradation of halogenated 1- and 2-carbon organic compounds", *Environ. Sci. Technol.* **15**, 596-599.

Bouwer, E. J. and P. L. McCarty (1983a) "Transformation of 1-and 2-carbon halogenated aliphatic organic compounds under methanogenic conditions", *Appl. Environ. Microbiol.* **45**, 1286-1294.

Bouwer, E. J. and P. L. McCarty (1983b) "Transformations of halogenated organic compounds under denitrification conditions", *Appl. Environ. Microbiol.* **45**, 1295-1299.

Bouwer, E. J. and J. P. Wright (1988) "Transformation of trace halogenated aliphatics in anoxic biofilm columns", *J. Contam. Hydrol.* **2**, 155-169.

Brunner, W., D. Staub, and T. Leisinger (1980) "Bacterial degradation of dichloromethane", *Appl. Environ. Microbiol.* **40**, 950-958.

Castro, C. E. and N. O. Belser (1990) "Biodehalogenation: oxidative and reductive metabolism of 1,1,2-trichloroethane by *Pseudomonas putida*–biogeneration of vinyl chloride", *Environ. Toxicol. Chem.* **9**, 707-714.

Cline, P. V. and D. R. Viste (1985) "Migration and degradation patterns of volatile organic compounds", *Waste Management & Research* **3**, 351-360.

Cooper, W. J., M. Mehran, D. J. Riusech, and J. A. Joens (1987) "Abiotic transformation of halogenated organics. 1. Elimination reaction of 1,1,2,2-tetrachloroethane and formation of 1,1,2-trichloroethane", *Environ. Sci. Technol.* **21**, 1112-1114.

Criddle, C. S. and P. L. McCarty (1991) "Electrolytic model system for reductive dehalogenation in aqueous environments", *Environ. Sci. Technol.* **25**, 973-978.

Criddle, C. S., P. L. McCarty, M. C. Elliott, and J. F. Barker (1986) "Reduction of hexachloroethane to tetrachloroethylene in groundwater", *J. Contam. Hydrol.* **1**, 133-142.

Criddle, C. S., J. T. DeWitt, D. Grbić-Galić, and P. L. McCarty (1990a) "Transformation of carbon tetrachloride by *Pseudomonas* sp. strain KC under denitrification conditions", *Appl. Environ. Microbiol.* **56**, 3240-3246.

Criddle, C. S., J. T. DeWitt, and P. L. McCarty (1990b) "Reductive dehalogenation of carbon tetrachloride by *Escherichia coli* K-12", *Appl. Environ. Microbiol.* **56**, 3247-3254.

Dalton, H. and D. I. Stirling (1982) "Co-metabolism", *Phil. Trans. R. Soc. Lond. B* **297**, 481-496.

Davis, J. W. and C. L. Carpenter (1990) "Aerobic biodegradation of vinyl chloride in groundwater samples", *Appl. Environ. Microbiol.* **56**, 3878-3880.

De Bruin, W. P., M. J. J. Kotterman, M. A. Posthumus, G. Schraa, and A. J. B. Zehnder (1992) "Complete biological reductive transformation of tetrachloroethene to ethane", *Appl. Environ. Microbiol.* **58**, 1996-2000.

Dilling, W. L., N. B. Tefertiller, and G. J. Kallos (1975) "Evaporation rates and reactivities of methylene chloride, chloroform, 1,1,1-trichloroethane, trichloroethylene, tetrachloroethylene, and other chlorinated compounds in dilute aqueous solutions", *Environ. Sci. Technol.* **9**, 833-838.

DiStefano, T. D., J. M. Gossett, and S. H. Zinder (1991) "Reductive dechlorination of high concentrations of tetrachloroethene to ethene by an anaerobic enrichment culture in the absence of methanogenesis", *Appl. Environ. Microbiol.* **57**, 2287-2292.

Dolfing, J. and J. M. Tiedje (1987) "Growth yield increase linked to reductive dechlorination in a defined 3-chlorobenzoate degrading methanogenic coculture", *Arch. Microbiol.* **149**, 102-105.

Egli, C., R. Scholtz, A. M. Cook, and T. Leisinger (1987) "Anaerobic dechlorination of tetrachloromethane and 1,2-dichloroethane to degradable products by pure cultures of *Desulfobacterium* sp. and *Methanobacterium* sp.", *FEMS Microbiol. Lett.* **43**, 257-261.

Egli, C., T. Tschan, R. Scholtz, A. M. Cook, and T. Leisinger (1988) "Transformation of tetrachloromethane to dichloromethane and carbon dioxide by *Acetobacterium woodii*", *Appl. Environ. Microbiol.* **54**, 2819-2824.

Ensign, S. A., M. R. Hyman, and D.J. Arp (1992) "Cometabolic degradation of chlorinated alkenes by alkene monooxygenase in a propylene-grown *Xanthobacter* strain", *Appl. Environ. Microbiol.* **58**, 3038-3046.

Fathepure, B. Z. and S.A. Boyd (1988a) "Reductive dechlorination of perchloroethylene and the role of methanogens", *FEMS Microbiol. Lett.* **49**, 149-156.

Fathepure, B. Z. and S.A. Boyd (1988b) "Dependence of tetrachloroethylene dechlorination on methanogenic substrate consumption by *Methanosarcina* sp. strain DCM", *Appl. Environ. Microbiol.* **54**, 2976-2980.

Fathepure, B. Z. and T. M. Vogel (1991) "Complete degradation of polychlorinated hydrocarbons by a two-stage biofilm reactor", *Appl. Environ. Microbiol.* **57**, 3418-3422.

Fathepure, B. Z., J. P. Nengu, and S. A. Boyd (1987) "Anaerobic bacteria that dechlorinate per-chloroethene", *Appl. Environ. Microbiol.* **53**, 2671-2674.

Fliermans, C. B., T. J. Phelps, D. Ringelberg, A. T. Mikell, and D. C. White (1988) "Mineralization of trichloroethylene by heterotrophic enrichment cultures", *Appl. Environ. Microbiol.* **54**, 1709-1714.

Fogel, M. M., A. R. Taddeo, and S. Fogel (1986) "Biodegradation of chlorinated ethenes by a methane-utilizing mixed culture", *Appl. Environ. Microbiol.* **51**, 720-724.

Folsom, B. R., P. J. Chapman, and P. H. Pritchard (1990) "Phenol and trichloroethylene degradation by *Pseudomonas cepacia* G4: kinetics and interactions between substrates", *Appl. Environ. Microbiol.* **56**, 1279-1285.

Folsom, B. R. and P. J. Chapman (1991) "Performance characterization of a model bioreactor for the biodegradation of trichloroethylene by *Pseudomonas cepacia* G4", *Appl. Environ. Microbiol.* **57**, 1602-1608.

Freedman, D. L. and J. M. Gossett (1989) "Biological reductive dechlorination of tetrachloroethyl-ene and trichloroethylene to ethylene under methanogenic conditions", *Appl. Environ. Microbiol.* **55**, 2144-2151.

Freeze, R. A. and J. A. Cherry (1979) *Groundwater*, Prentice-Hall, Englewood Cliffs, NJ.

Fulthorpe, R. A. and R. C. Wyndham (1989) "Survival and activity of a 3-chlorobenzoate-catabolic genotype in a natural system", *Appl. Environ. Microbiol.* **55**, 1584-1590.

Galli, R. and P. L. McCarty (1989a) "Biotransformation of 1,1,1-trichloroethane, trichloromethane and tetrachloromethane by a *Clostridium* sp.", *Appl. Environ. Microbiol.* **55**, 837-844.

Galli, R. and P. L. McCarty (1989b) "Kinetics of biotransformation of 1,1,1-trichloroethane by *Clostridium* sp. strain TCAIIB", *Appl. Environ. Microbiol.* **55**, 845-851.

Gantzer, C. J. and L. P. Wackett (1991) "Reductive dechlorination catalyzed by bacterial transition-metal coenzymes", *Environ. Sci. Technol.* **25**, 715-722.

Genthner, B. R. S., W. A. Price, and P. H. Pritchard (1989), "Anaerobic degradation of chloroaro-matic compounds under a variety of enrichment conditions", *Appl. Environ. Microbiol.* **55**, 1466-1471.

Ghiorse, W. C. and D. L. Balkwill (1985) "Microbiological characterization of subsurface envi-ronments", In: *Ground Water Quality*, C. H. Ward, W. Giger, and P. L. McCarty (Eds.) Wiley, New York, pp. 387-398.

Ghiorse, W. C. and J. T. Wilson (1988) "Microbial ecology of the terrestrial subsurface", *Adv. Appl. Microbiol.* **33**, 107-172.

Gillham, R. W. and S. F. O'Hannesin (1992) "Metal-catalyzed abiotic degradation of halogenated organic compounds", presented at the 1992 International Assoc. Hydrogeologists Conf. "Modern Trends in Hydrogeology", Hamilton, Ontario, Canada, May 10-13. Available as paper Q-23 from Waterloo Centre for Groundwater Research, Univ. of Waterloo, Waterloo, Ontario N2L 3G1.

Gillham, R. W., R. C. Starr, and D. J. Miller (1990) "A device for in situ determination of geochemical transport parameters. 2. Biochemical reactions", *Ground Water* **28**, 858-862.

Gossett, J. M. and D. L. Freedman (1989) "Biotransformation of dichloromethane in methanogenic systems", Third Int. Meeting, NATO/CCMS Pilot Study on Demonstration of Remedial Action Technologies for Contaminated Land and Groundwater, Nov 6-9, 1989, Montreal.

Grady, C. P. (1985) "Biodegradation: Its measurement and microbiological basis", *Biotechnol. Bioeng.* **27**, 660-674.

Haag, W. R. and T. Mill (1988) "Some reactions of naturally occurring nucleophiles with haloalkanes in water", *Environ. Toxicol. Chem.* **7**, 917-924.

Haber, C. L., L. N. Allen, S. Zhao, and R. S. Hanson (1983) "Methylotrophic bacteria: biochemical diversity and genetics", *Science* **211**, 1147-1153.

Harker, A. R. and Y. Kim (1990) "Trichloroethylene degradation by two independent aromatic degrading pathways in *Alcaligenes eutrophus* JMP134", *Appl. Environ. Microbiol.* **56**, 1179-1181.

Henry, S. M. and D. Grbić-Galić (1991) "Influence of endogenous and exogenous electron donors and trichloroethylene oxidation toxicity on trichloroethylene oxidation by methanotrophic cultures from a groundwater aquifer", *Appl. Environ. Microbiol.* **57**, 236-244.

Henson, J. M., M. V. Yates, and J. W. Cochran (1989) "Metabolism of chlorinated methanes, ethanes, and ethylenes by a mixed bacterial culture growing on methane", *J. Ind. Microbiol.* **4**, 29-35.

Henson, J. M., M. V. Yates, J. W. Cochran, and D. L. Shackleford (1988) "Microbial removal of halogenated methanes, ethanes, and ethylenes in an aerobic soil exposed to methane", *FEMS Microbiol. Ecol.* **53**, 193-201.

Hirsch, P. and E. Rades-Rohkohl (1983) "Microbial diversity in a groundwater aquifer in Northern Germany", *Dev. Ind. Microbiol.* **24**, 183-200.

Holliger, C., G. Schraa, E. Stupperich, A. J. M. Stams, and A. J. B. Zehnder (1992a) "Evidence for the involvement of corrinoids and factor F430 in the reductive dechlorination of 1,2-dichloroethane by *Methanosarcina barkeri*", *J. Bacteriol.* **174**, 4427-4434.

Holliger, C., S. W. M. Kengen, G. Schraa, A. J. M. Stams, and A. J. B. Zehnder (1992b) "Methyl-coenzyme M reductase of *Methanobacterium thermoautotrophicum* H catalyzes the reductive dechlorination of 1,2-dichloroethane to ethylene and chloroethane", *J. Bacteriol.* **174**, 4435-4443.

Hou, C.T., R. N. Patel, A. I. Laskin, and N. Barnabe (1979) "Microbial oxidation of gaseous hydrocarbons: Epoxidation of C$_2$ to C$_4$ n-alkenes by methylotrophic bacteria", *Appl. Environ. Microbiol.* **38**, 127-134.

Hungate, R. E. (1969) "A roll tube method for cultivation of strict anaerobes", *Methods Microbiol.* **3B**, 117-132.

Ingraham, J. L., O. Maaloe, and F. C. Neidhardt (1983) *Growth of the Bacterial Cell*, Sinauer Associates Inc., Sunderland, MA.

Jafvert, C. T. and N. L. Wolfe (1987) "Degradation of selected halogenated ethanes in anoxic sediment-water systems", *Environ. Toxicol. Chem.* **6**, 827-837.

Janssen, D. B., A. Scheper, L. Dijkhuizen, and B. Witholt (1985) "Degradation of halogenated aliphatic compounds by *Xanthobacter autotrophicus* GJ10", *Appl. Environ. Microbiol.* **49**, 673-677.

Janssen, D. B., D. Jager, and B. Witholt (1987) "Degradation of n-haloalkanes and α, ω-dihalo-alkanes by wild-type and mutants of *Acinetobacter* sp. strain GJ70", *Appl. Environ. Microbiol.* **53**, 561-566.

Jeffers, P. M., L. M. Ward, L. M. Woytowitch, and N. L. Wolfe (1989) "Homogeneous hydrolysis rate constants for selected chlorinated methanes, ethanes, ethenes, and propanes", *Environ. Sci. Technol.* **23**, 965-969.

Jones, R. E., R. E. Beeman, and J. M. Suflita (1989) "Anaerobic metabolic processes in the deep terrestrial subsurface", *Geomicrobiol. J.* **7**, 117-131.

Kastner, M. (1991) "Reductive dechlorination of tri- and tetrachloroethylenes depends on transition from aerobic to anaerobic conditions", *Appl. Environ. Microbiol.* **57**, 2039-2046.

Kleopfer, R. D., D. M. Eastley, B. B. Haas, T. G. Deihl, D. E. Jackson, and C. J. Wurrey (1985) "Anaerobic degradation of trichloroethylene in soil", *Environ. Sci. Technol.* **19**, 277-280.

Kobayashi, H. and B. E. Rittmann (1982) "Microbial removal of hazardous organic compounds", *Environ. Sci. Technol.* **16**, 170A-181A.

Kriegman-King, M. R. and M. Reinhard (1992) "Transformation of carbon tetrachloride in the presence of sulfide, biotite, and vermiculite", *Environ. Sci. Technol.* **26**, 2198-2206.

Krone, U. E., K. Laufer, R. K. Thauer, and H. P. C. Hogenkamp (1989a) "Coenzyme F_{430} as a possible catalyst for the reductive dehalogenation of chlorinated C_1 hydrocarbons in methanogenic bacteria", *Biochemistry* **28**, 10061-10065.

Krone, U. E., R. K. Thauer, and H. P. C. Hogenkamp (1989b) "Reductive dehalogenation of chlorinated C_1-hydrocarbons mediated by corrinoids", *Biochemistry* **28**, 4908-4914.

Kuznetsov, S. I., G. A. Dubinina, and N. A. Lapteva (1979) "Biology of oligotrophic bacteria", *Annu. Rev. Microbiol.* **33**, 377-387.

Lanzarone, N. A. and P. L. McCarty (1990) "Column studies on methanotrophic degradation of trichloroethene and 1,2-dichloroethane", *Ground Water* **28**, 910-919.

LaPat-Polasko L. T., P. L. McCarty, and A. J. B. Zehnder (1984) "Secondary substrate utilization of methylene chloride by an isolated strain of *Pseudomonas* sp.", *Appl. Environ. Microbiol.* **47**, 825-830.

Large, P. J. (1983) *Methylotrophy and Methanogenesis*, American Society for Microbiology, Washington, D.C.

Leisinger, T. (1983) "Microorganisms and xenobiotic compounds", *Experientia* **39**, 1183-1191.

Lesage, S., R. E. Jackson, M. W. Priddle, and P. G. Riemann (1990) "Occurrence and fate of organic solvent residues in anoxic groundwater at the Gloucester Landfill, Canada", *Environ. Sci. Technol.* **24**, 559-566.

Little, C. D., A. V. Palumbo, S. E. Herbes, M. E. Lidstrom, R. L. Tyndall, and P. J. Gilmer (1988) "Trichloroethylene biodegradation by a methane-oxidizing bacterium", *Appl. Environ. Microbiol.* **54**, 951-956.

Lyman, W. J., W. F. Ruhl, and D. H. Rosenblatt (1982) *Handbook of Chemical Property Estimation Methods*, McGraw-Hill, New York, New York.

Mabey, W. and T. Mill (1978) "Critical review of hydrolysis of organic compounds in water under environmental conditions", *Phys. Chem. Ref. Data* **7**, 383-415.

Major, D. W., E. W. Hodgins, and B. J. Butler (1991) "Field and laboratory evidence of *in situ* biotransformation of tetrachloroethene to ethene at a chemical transfer facility in North Toronto". In: *On-site Bioreclamation Processes for Xenobiotic and Hydrocarbon Treatment*, R. E. Hinchee and R. F. Olfenbuttel (Eds.), Butterworth-Heinemann, Boston, pp. 147-171.

Mayfield, C. I. and R. L. Aldworth (1974) "Acetylene reduction in artificial soil aggregates amended with cellulose, wheat straw, and xylan", *Can. J. Microbiol.* **20**, 1503-1507.

McCarty, P. L., M. Reinhard, and B. E. Rittmann (1981) "Trace organics in groundwater", *Environ. Sci. Technol.* **15**, 40-51.

McCarty, P. L., B. E. Rittmann, and E. J. Bouwer (1984) "Microbiological processes affecting chemical transformations in groundwater". In: *Ground Water Pollution Microbiology*, G. Bitton and C. P. Gerba (Eds.), Wiley and Sons, Toronto, pp. 89-115.

McNabb, J. F. and W. J. Dunlap (1975) "Subsurface biological activity in relation to ground-water pollution", *Ground Water* **13**, 33-44.

Mikesell, M. D. and S. A. Boyd (1990) "Dechlorination of chloroform by *Methanosarcina* strains", *Appl. Environ. Microbiol.* **56**, 1198-1201.

Miller, R. E. and F. P. Guengerich (1982) "Oxidation of trichloroethylene by liver cytochrome P-450: evidence for chlorine migration in a transition state not involving trichloroethylene oxide", *Biochemistry* **21**, 1090-1097.

Morgan, P. and R. J. Watkinson (1989) "Microbiological methods for the cleanup of soil and ground water contaminated with halogenated organic compounds", *FEMS Microbiol. Rev.* **63**, 277-300.

Nelson, M. J. K. and J. V. Kinsella (1990) "In situ degradation of trichloroethylene", Abstract of a paper presented at the First International Symposium on Microbiology of the Deep Subsurface, Orlando, Fla., Jan. 15-19, 1990.

Nelson, M. J. K., S. O. Montgomery, E. J. O'Neill, and P. H. Pritchard (1986) "Aerobic metabolism of trichloroethylene by a bacterial isolate", *Appl. Environ. Microbiol.* **52**, 383-384.

Nelson, M. J. K., S. O. Montgomery, W. R. Mahaffey, and P. H. Pritchard (1987) "Biodegradation of trichloroethylene and involvement of an aromatic biodegradative pathway", *Appl. Environ. Microbiol.* **53**, 949-954.

Nelson, M. J. K., S. O. Montgomery, and P. H. Pritchard (1988) "Trichloroethylene metabolism by microorganisms that degrade aromatic compounds", *Appl. Environ. Microbiol.* **54**, 604-606.

O'Hannesin, S. F. and R. W. Gillham (1992) "A permeable reaction wall for in situ degradation of halogenated organic compounds", presented at the 1992, 45th Can. Geotech. Soc. Conf., Toronto, Ontario, Oct. 25-28, 1992. Available as paper Q-25 from Waterloo Centre for Ground-water Research, Univ. of Waterloo, Waterloo, Ontario N2L 3G1.

Oldenhuis, R., J. Y. Oedzes, J. J. van der Waarde, and D. B. Janssen (1991) "Kinetics of chlorinated hydrocarbon degradation by *Methylosinus trichosporium* OB3b and toxicity of trichloroethylene", *Appl. Environ. Microbiol.* **57**, 7-14.

Parsons, F. and G. B. Lage (1985) "Chlorinated organics in simulated groundwater environments", *J. Am. Water Works Assoc.* **77**, 52-59.

Parsons, F., P. R. Wood, and J. DeMarco (1984) "Transformations of tetrachloroethene and trichloroethene in microcosms and groundwater", *J. Am. Water Works Assoc.* **76**, 56-59.

Phelps, T. J., D. Ringelberg, D. Hedrick, J. Davis, C. B. Fliermans, and D. C. White (1988) "Microbial biomass and activities associated with subsurface environments contaminated with chlorinated hydrocarbons", *Geomicrobiol. J.* **6**, 157-170.

Phelps, T. J., J. J. Niedzielski, R. M. Schram, S. E. Herbes, and D. C. White (1990) "Biodegradation of trichloroethylene in continuous-recycle expanded-bed bioreactors", *Appl. Environ. Microbiol.* **56**, 1702-1709.

Pignatello, J. J. (1986) "Ethylene dibromide mineralization in soils under aerobic conditions", *Appl. Environ. Microbiol.* **51**, 588-592.

Poindexter, J. S. (1981) "Oligotrophy. Fast and famine existence", *Adv. Microb. Ecol.* **5**, 63-89.

Postgate, J. R. (1984) *The Sulphate-Reducing Bacteria*, 2nd edition, Cambridge University Press, Cambridge, U.K.

Rasche, M. E., M. R. Hyman, and D. J. Arp (1990a) "Biodegradation of halogenated hydrocarbon fumigants by denitrifying bacteria", *Appl. Environ. Microbiol.* **56**, 2568-2571.

Rasche, M. E., R. E. Hicks, M. R. Hyman, and D. J. Arp. (1990b) "Oxidation of monohalogenated ethanes and n-chlorinated alkanes by whole cells of *Nitrosomonas europaea*", *J. Bacteriol.* **172**, 5368-5373.

Rasche, M. E., M. R. Hyman, and D. J. Arp (1991) "Factors limiting aliphatic chlorocarbon degradation by *Nitrosomonas europaea*: Cometabolic inactivation of ammonia monooxygenase and substrate specificity", *Appl. Environ. Microbiol.* **57**, 2986-2994.

Reinhard, M., G. P. Curtis, and M. R. Kriegman (1990) "Abiotic reductive dechlorination of carbon tetrachloride and hexachloroethane by environmental reductants", Project Summary, EPA/600/S2-90/040. Sept. 1990.

Roberts, A. L. and P. M. Gschwend (1991) "Mechanism of pentachloroethane dehydrochlorination to tetrachloroethylene", *Environ. Sci. Technol.* **25**, 76-86.

Roberts, A. L., P. N. Sanborn, and P. M. Gschwend (1992) "Nucleophilic substitution reactions of dihalomethanes with hydrogen sulfide species", *Environ. Sci. Technol.* **26**, 2263-2274.

Roberts, P. V., M. N. Goltz, and D. M. Mackay (1986) "A natural gradient experiment on solute transport in a sand aquifer. III. Retardation estimates and mass balances for organic solutes", *Water Resources Research* **22**, 2047-2058.

Roberts, P. V., L. Semprini, G. D. Hopkins, D. Grbić-Galić, P. L. McCarty, and M. Reinhard (1989) "In-situ aquifer restoration of chlorinated aliphatics by methanotrophic bacteria", Technical Report No. 310, June 1989, Department of Civil Engineering, Stanford University, Stanford, California.

Roberts, P. V., G. D. Hopkins, D. M. Mackay, and L. Semprini (1990) "A field evaluation of in-situ biodegradation of chlorinated ethenes: Part 1. Methodology and field site characterization", *Ground Water* **28**, 591-604.

Schmidt, S. K. and M. Alexander (1985) "Effect of dissolved organic carbon and second substrates on the biodegradation of organic compounds at low concentrations", *Appl. Environ. Microbiol.* **49**, 822-827.

Scholz-Muramatsu, H., R. Szewzyk, U. Szewzyk, and S. Gaiser (1990) "Tetrachloroethylene as electron acceptor for the anaerobic degradation of benzoate", *FEMS Microbiol. Lett.* **66**, 81-86.

Schwarzenbach, R. P., W. Giger, C. Schaffner, and O. Wanner (1985) "Groundwater contamination by volatile halogenated alkanes: abiotic formation of volatile sulfur compounds under anaerobic conditions", *Environ. Sci. Technol.* **19**, 322-327.

Semprini, L., P. V. Roberts, G. D. Hopkins, and D. M. Mackay (1987) "A field evaluation of in-situ biodegradation methodologies for the restoration of aquifers contaminated with chlorinated aliphatic compounds: results of a preliminary investigation", Dept. of Civil Engineering, Stanford Univ. Technical Report No. 302.

Semprini, L., P. V. Roberts, G. D. Hopkins, and P. L. McCarty (1990) "A field evaluation of in-situ biodegradation of chlorinated ethenes: Part 2. The results of biostimulation and biotransformation experiments", *Ground Water* **28**, 715-727.

Shields, M. S. and M. J. Reagin (1992), "Selection of a *Pseudomonas cepacia* strain constitutive for the degradation of trichloroethylene", *Appl. Environ. Microbiol.* **58**, 3977-3983.

Shields, M. S., S. O. Montgomery, P. J. Chapman, S. M. Cuskey, and P. H. Pritchard (1989) "Novel pathway of toluene catabolism in the trichloroethylene-degrading bacterium G4", *Appl. Environ. Microbiol.* **55**, 1624-1629.

Simkins, S. and M. Alexander (1984) "Models for mineralization kinetics with the variables of substrate concentration and population density", *Appl. Environ. Microbiol.* **47**, 1299-1306.

Slater, J. H. and A. T. Bull (1982) "Environmental microbiology: biodegradation", *Phil. Trans. Roy. Soc. Lond. B*, **297**, 575-597.

Strandberg, G. W., T. L. Donaldson, and L. L. Farr (1989) "Degradation of trichloroethylene and trans-1,2-dichloroethylene by a methanotrophic consortium in a fixed-film, packed-bed bioreactor", *Environ. Sci. Technol.* **23**, 1422-1425.

Stucki, G., R. Galli, H.-R. Ebersold, and T. Leisinger (1981) "Dehalogenation of dichloromethane by cell extracts of *Hyphomicrobium* DMS", *Arch. Microbiol.* **130**, 366-371.

Stucki, G., U. Krebser, and T. Leisinger (1983) "Bacterial growth on 1,2-dichloroethane", *Experientia* **39**, 1271-1273.

Suflita, J. M., S. A. Gibson, and R. E. Beeman (1988) "Anaerobic biotransformations of pollutant chemicals in aquifers", *J. Ind. Microbiol.* **3**, 179-194.

Tabak, H. H., S. A. Quave, C. I. Mashni, and E. F. Barth (1981) "Biodegradability studies with organic priority pollutant compounds", *J. Water Poll. Control Fed.* **53**, 1503-1518.

Tardif, G., C. W. Greer, D. Labbe, and P. C. K. Lau (1991) "Involvement of a large plasmid in the degradation of 1,2-dichloroethane by *Xanthobacter autotrophicus*", *Appl. Environ. Microbiol.* **57**, 1853-1857.

Tsien, H.-C., G. A. Brusseau, R. S. Hanson, and L. P. Wackett (1989) "Biodegradation of trichloroethylene by *Methylosinus trichosporium* OB3b", *Appl. Environ. Microbiol.* **55**, 3155-3161.

Vannelli, T., M. Logan, D. M. Arciero, and A. B. Hooper (1990) "Degradation of halogenated aliphatic compounds by the ammonia-oxidizing bacterium *Nitrosomonas europaea*", *Appl. Environ. Microbiol.* **56**, 1169-1171.

Ventullo, R. M. and R. J. Larson (1985) "Metabolic diversity and activity of heterotrophic bacteria in ground water", *Environ. Toxicol. Chem.* **4**, 759-771.

Vogel, T. M. and P. L. McCarty (1985) "Biotransformation of tetrachloroethylene to trichloroethylene, dichloroethylene, vinyl chloride, and carbon dioxide under methanogenic conditions", *Appl. Environ. Microbiol.* **49**, 1080-1083.

Vogel, T. M. and P. L. McCarty (1987) "Abiotic and biotic transformations of 1,1,1-trichloroethane under methanogenic conditions", *Environ. Sci. Technol.* **21**, 1208-1213.

Vogel, T. M., C. S. Criddle, and P. L. McCarty (1987) "Transformation of halogenated aliphatic compounds", *Environ. Sci. Technol.* **21**, 722-736.

Wackett, L. P. and D. T. Gibson (1988) "Degradation of trichloroethylene by toluene dioxygenase in whole-cell studies with *Pseudomonas putida* F1", *Appl. Environ. Microbiol.* **54**, 1703-1707.

Wackett, L. P. and S. R. Householder (1989) "Toxicity of trichloroethylene to *Pseudomonas putida* F1 is mediated by toluene dioxygenase", *Appl. Environ. Microbiol.* **55**, 2723-2725.

Waksman, S. A. (1916) "Bacterial numbers in soil at different depths, and in different seasons of the year", *Soil Sci.* **1**, 363-380.

Wang, T. C. and C. K. Tan (1990) "Reduction of halogenated hydrocarbons with magnesium hydrolysis process", *Bull. Environ. Contam. Toxicol.* **45**, 149-156.

Wang, Y.-S., R. V. Subba-Rao, and M. Alexander (1984) "Effect of substrate concentration and organic and inorganic compounds on the occurrence and rate of mineralization and cometabolism", *Appl. Environ. Microbiol.* **47**, 1195-1200.

Weintraub, R. A., G. W. Jex, and H. A. Moye (1986) "Chemical and microbial degradation of 1,2-dibromoethane (EDB) in Florida ground water, soil, and sludge". In: *Evaluation of Pesticides in Ground Water* W. Y. Garner, R. C. Honeycutt, and H. A. Nigg (Eds.), American Chemical Society, Washington, D.C., pp. 294-310.

Wiggins, B. A., S. H. Jones, and M. Alexander (1987) "Explanations for the acclimation period preceding the mineralization of organic chemicals in aquatic environments", *Appl. Environ. Microbiol.* **53**, 791-796.

Wiggins, B. A. and M. Alexander (1988) "Role of chemical concentration and second carbon sources in acclimation of microbial communities for biodegradation", *Appl. Environ. Microbiol.* **54**, 2803-2807.

Wilson, B. H., G. B. Smith, and J. F. Rees (1986) "Biotransformations of selected alkylbenzenes and halogenated aliphatic hydrocarbons in methanogenic aquifer material: a microcosm study", *Environ. Sci. Technol.* **20**, 997-1002.

Wilson, J. T. and B. H. Wilson (1985) "Biotransformation of trichloroethylene in soil", *Appl. Environ. Microbiol.* **49**, 242-243.

Wilson, J. T., J. F. McNabb, D. L. Balkwill, and W. C. Ghiorse (1983) "Enumeration of bacteria indigenous to a shallow water-table aquifer", *Ground Water* **21**, 134-142.

Wilson, J. T., J. F. McNabb, J. W. Cochran, T. H. Wang, M. B. Tomson, and P. B. Bedient (1985) "Influence of microbial adaptation on the fate of organic pollutants in ground water", *Environ. Toxicol. Chem.* **4**, 721-726.

Winter, R. B., K.-M. Yen, and B. D. Ensley (1989) "Efficient degradation of trichloroethylene by a recombinant *Escherichia coli*", *Biotechnology* **7**, 282-285.

Wyndham, R. C. (1986) "Evolved aniline catabolism in *Acinetobacter calcoaceticus* during continuous culture of river water", *Appl. Environ. Microbiol.* **51**, 781-789.

Zeikus, J. G., R. Kerby, and J. A. Krzycki (1985) "Single-carbon chemistry of acetogenic and methanogenic bacteria", *Science* **227**, 1167-1173.

Zylstra, G. J., L. P. Wackett, and D. T. Gibson (1989) "Trichloroethylene degradation by *Escherichia coli* containing the cloned *Pseudomonas putida* F1 toluene dioxygenase genes", *Appl. Environ. Microbiol.* **55**, 3162-3166.

10
The Effects of Chlorinated Solvents on the Permeability of Clays

Tammy A. Middleton[1] **and John A. Cherry**[2]

[1]Golder Associates Ltd.
180 Columbia St. W.
Waterloo, Ontario
Canada, N2L 3L3

[2]Waterloo Centre for Groundwater Research
University of Waterloo
Waterloo, Ontario
Canada N2L 3G1

ABSTRACT

There is disagreement in the scientific community as to whether liquid chlorinated solvents and other organic non-aqueous phase liquids (NAPLs) can cause clay soils to shrink and crack, thereby greatly increasing their permeability. However, a careful consideration of factors such as water miscibility of the organic liquids of interest as well as the details of the laboratory experiments that have been carried out allows a resolution of many of the contradictions that exist in the literature. It can be shown that in hydrated (*i.e.*, wet) clay soils, chlorinated solvents and other organic NAPLs apparently do not cause permeability increases. This is likely due to the exclusion of the organic liquid from the clay double layers. When NAPL solvents are forced through clay samples, the permeability increases that have been observed can be attributed to the mechanical formation of fractures due to large fluid gradients and low lateral confining stresses on the samples. Exposure to aqueous solutions of these organic compounds does not influence permeability because solutions at or below the solubility limit are too dilute to affect clay double layers. It can be concluded that chlorinated solvents in NAPL form are unlikely to cause shrinking, cracking, or permeability increases in natural or engineered clay barriers under field conditions. However, further study is required on the chemical and physical effects of such liquids on smectitic clay slurries.

10.1 INTRODUCTION

In preceding chapters of this book, the movement and fate of chlorinated solvents in aquifers and aquitards have been described. Various conceptual model situations have been discussed, including cases where accumulations of free-phase solvent rest on low-permeability strata, or penetrate into fractures in low-permeability matrix materials. In many field situations, low-permeability strata or matrix materials contain clay minerals. In the early 1980s, laboratory research suggested that some types of industrial organic chemicals, including chlorinated solvents, could chemically interact with clay-rich materials in such a way that **shrinkage and cracking** would take place in these materials (Green *et al.*, 1981; Brown *et al.*, 1984). It was concluded that such cracks would lead to large **permeability increases** in these clays. Sponsored in part by the U.S.EPA, these results had much influence, even though they were preliminary and controversial in nature. Thus, many groundwater scientists and engineers came to believe that accumulations of chlorinated solvent chemicals on clay strata and in fractured, clayey deposits could cause increases of permeability in these materials, resulting in deeper movement of the chemicals. These results have prompted further laboratory studies of this topic.

The published results of the initial and subsequent studies of the effects of organic chemicals on clays reveal several important inconsistencies, and as a result, some of the various conclusions are contradictory. This chapter provides a review of the published literature in this area. Areas of contradiction and controversy are identified and, where possible, explanations for the inconsistencies are provided. The study of clay/organic chemical interactions spans many disciplines, including colloid and surface science, geotechnical engineering, clay mineralogy, organic chemistry, and hydrogeology; the interdisciplinary nature of this topic has contributed to the lack of agreement in the literature. Although few of the studies used chlorinated solvents, many of them used other organic chemicals that provide results directly relevant to solvent-clay interactions. With rare exceptions, the literature is based on laboratory studies. The extension of the results from the laboratory experiments to field situations will need to be carried out carefully because field conditions such as soil fabric, confining stress, fluid gradient, and time scales of exposure cannot easily be replicated in the laboratory.

This chapter first presents some necessary background information on the chemical mechanisms controlling the swelling and shrinkage of clay minerals, the differences between "dry" and "water-wet" clays, and the properties of organic chemicals. This is followed by a review of laboratory and field investigations. The term "permeability" is used here to denote the *intrinsic permeability*. This is distinct from the "hydraulic conductivity" which is the proportionality constant in Darcy's Law between groundwater velocity and hydraulic head (Freeze and Cherry, 1979). Since the hydraulic conductivity value is partially dependent on the effects of the density and viscosity of the permeating fluid, a change in this value does not necessarily imply a change in the actual transmissive properties of the porous medium. For this reason it preferable to use the intrinsic permeability value, which depends only on the porous medium.

10.2 MECHANISMS CONTROLLING THE SWELLING OF CLAYS

10.2.1 General

It is well known that brines and other liquids with high electrolyte concentrations can increase the permeability of clay soils by chemically causing shrinking and cracking to occur (Acar and Seals, 1984; Mitchell and Madsen, 1987; and others). Chemical interactions can also occur between organic chemicals and clay minerals. There are two types of processes to be considered here: 1) **interlayer processes** (*i.e.*, intraparticle processes) that occur in "swelling clays"; and 2) **interparticle processes** (*i.e.*, between particle processes) that can occur in all clay minerals. Both types of processes can cause **shrinkage** of the bulk clay soil and, as a result, enlargement of pore spaces or the opening of tension cracks.

10.2.2 Interlayer Mechanisms

The "swelling clays" (*e.g.*, the smectites and some vermiculites) undergo **intracrystalline expansion or contraction** in the crystal c-axis direction which can result in significant volume changes of the clay mass. The basal spacing, which is the degree of intracrystalline expansion of clays, can be affected by organic liquids. The basal spacings of swelling clays depend in part on the number and type of molecules adsorbed between the structural layers of the clays. The intrusion of organic molecules into the interlayer spaces of swelling clays can potentially result in either an increase or a decrease in the basal spacing. Van Olphen (1977) and Theng (1974) provide reviews of this process.

10.2.3 Interparticle Mechanisms

Interparticle swelling, also referred to as **double layer swelling**, affects all types of clay. This process is described by the Gouy-Chapman theory of the diffuse double layer ("double layer theory"). Van Olphen (1977) and Mitchell (1976) provide reviews of this theory. In short, the surfaces of clay minerals carry a net negative charge. Cations accumulate at the clay surfaces due to electrostatic attraction, but there is also a tendency for the cations to diffuse away from the surfaces into areas of lower cation concentration. Anions are electrostatically repelled from the negatively charged surfaces. The negatively-charged clay surface together with the adjoining, equilibrium, aqueous distribution of cations and anions is the **diffuse double layer**. When two negatively-charged clay particles approach one other, there is an electrostatic repulsion. The repulsion is roughly proportional to the inverse of the separation distance between the particles (Van Olphen, 1977). These repulsive forces influence the arrangement of individual clay particles, and therefore the permeability of bulk clays.

Some aspects of the behavior of clay particles in soils have been inferred from the study of clay particles in colloidal suspensions. The study of clay colloids shows that as the thickness of the double layers increases, the repulsive forces between clay particles also increases, and the clays tend to form a dispersed fabric with evenly spaced particles and small pore sizes. As the thickness of the double layer decreases, the repulsive forces between clay particles decrease, and the particles tend to form a flocculated fabric containing **aggregates of particles** with large pores in and between the aggregates (Van Olphen, 1977). A soil with a flocculated fabric has a greater permeability than a soil with a dispersed fabric.

One of the factors that determines the thickness of the double layer is the **dielectric constant** of the pore liquid. The dielectric constant of a liquid is an inverse measure of the permeability of the liquid to electrical forces (Brownlow, 1979). A more polar liquid will have a higher dielectric constant and will result in a thicker double layer. Water, the usual pore liquid in the subsurface, has a high dielectric constant (see Table 10.1). Some common **light non-aqueous phase liquids (LNAPLs)** such as benzene, xylene and toluene, and **dense non-aqueous phase liquids (DNAPLs)** such as chlorinated solvents like trichloroethylene (TCE), perchloroethylene (PCE), and carbon tetrachloride have very low dielectric constants.

If an organic liquid of low dielectric constant enters the pore spaces of a clay soil and the organic molecules replace the water molecules in the double layers, then theory predicts that there will be a shrinkage of the double layer surrounding each clay particle, and a tendency for the particles to move more closely together. When there are no significant effective stresses on the soil and clay aggregates in the soil, then cracks or macropores may open around the aggregates with the result that there will be an increase in permeability. In contrast, a significant effective stress acting on the soil can prevent the opening of cracks and macropores by causing soil consolidation when double layer shrinkage weakens soil strength. This can result in bulk soil shrinkage and a reduced permeability. Effective stress is considered in more detail below.

TABLE 10.1   Properties of Some Common Nonionic Organic Compounds at 20-25 °C.

Compound	Chemical formula	Water solubility (mg/L)	Density (g/cm^3)	Dielectric constant
Water	H_2O	—	1.00	80.4
Acetone	C_3H_6O	completely miscible	0.79	21.5
Ethanol	C_2H_5OH	completely miscible	0.79	25.0
Methanol	CH_3OH	completely miscible	0.79	33.6
Dioxane	$C_4H_8O_2$	completely miscible	1.03	2.2
Benzene	C_6H_6	1791	0.88	2.3
m-Xylene	C_8H_{10}	146	0.88	2.3
Toluene	C_7H_{10}	421	0.87	2.4
Cyclohexane	C_6H_{12}	55	0.78	2.0
Heptane	C_7H_{16}	3	0.68	1.9
Nitrobenzene	$C_6H_5N_2$	1900	1.20	35.7
Carbon tetrachloride	CCl_4	805	1.59	2.2
Tetrachloroethylene	C_2Cl_4	150	1.62	2.2
Trichloroethylene	C_2HCl_3	1100	1.46	3.3

Values taken from Howard (1990), Mitchell and Madsen (1987) and Abdul *et al.* (1990)

10.3 WATER-WET *VS.* DRY CLAYS, AND THE ISSUE OF WETTABILITY

It is important to differentiate between studies of organic liquid interactions involving dehydrated clays, and those involving water-wet clays. The term "**water-wet**" is used here to denote clay soils that have water as a pore liquid (as in nearly all field situations); the soil pore space need not be 100% occupied by water. A hydrated clay mineral has a different crystal structure and different behavior than does the corresponding "**dry**" clay. This is particularly true for the swelling clays. Clays in their natural state are always hydrated to some extent because polar water molecules are strongly attracted to the cations adsorbed on the surfaces of clays; the complete dehydration of a clay mineral requires temperatures in excess of 100 °C (Mitchell, 1976). Thus, although studies of dry clays in contact with organic liquids provide fundamental information on relevant chemical and physical interactions, this information is often not directly applicable to field situations.

In clay soils, polar water molecules are attracted to negatively-charged clay surfaces more strongly than are non-polar organic molecules. Thus, in a water-wet clay, an organic liquid phase will generally be the **non-wetting liquid**, and water will be the wetting fluid. (Water wetting is also generally observed for other types of geologic media besides clays.) However, in a dry clay, an organic liquid phase will be the **wetting fluid** and air will be the non-wetting fluid.

The ability of a low-water-solubility organic liquid to "wet," *i.e.*, directly contact a clay mineral is a fundamental control on the interactions between the clay and the organic liquid. When an organic liquid phase penetrates a water-saturated (*i.e.*, a water-wet) clay, **interfacial tension** (*i.e.*, surface tension) will restrict the flow of the organic phase to the largest pores in the clay. Although water will be displaced from the centers of the pores, a film of water will remain to surround the clay, separating the clay from the intruded organic liquid. This phenomenon was observed by Mossop (1980) in the Athabasca tar sands where oil is the non-wetting liquid. In clays, under these types of circumstances, there is a film of water between the organic liquid and the clay surfaces, and the organic liquid is prevented from contacting or entering the clay double layers, other than in dissolved form (Middleton, 1990).

10.4 RELEVANT PROPERTIES OF ORGANIC CHEMICALS

There are three broad categories of organic liquids: organic acids, organic bases, and nonionic (*i.e.*, uncharged) organic compounds (Anderson *et al.*, 1985a). In this chapter, we are concerned only with neutral compounds, the class which includes the chlorinated solvents. Neutral organic compounds have sometimes been further subdivided into **"water-miscible"** and **"water-immiscible"** sub-classes. However, it is very important to note that no organic liquid is totally immiscible with water: every organic liquid possesses a finite solubility in water, and so if a small enough amount of any liquid is brought into contact with water, all of that amount will dissolve and there would be no organic liquid phase. We can conclude that the adjective "water-immiscible" is oversimplified and should be avoided; **"low-water-solubility"** is preferable, and will be used here. There is no problem with the adjective "water-miscible," as we realize that it means a compound that is completely soluble in water.

Low-water-solubility organic liquids, including the chlorinated solvents, are non-polar and have low dielectric constants. Water-miscible organic liquids (such as low molecular weight alcohols and acetone) are generally polar molecules and have moderate to high dielectric constants. Exceptions to these classifications do occur. For example, although dioxane is generally considered to be non-polar, as a relatively low molecular weight cyclic ether, it is miscible with water over all proportions.

10.5 LABORATORY INVESTIGATIONS OF CLAY/ORGANIC INTERACTIONS

10.5.1 X-Ray Diffraction Studies of Intracrystalline Swelling

A variety of approaches have been employed to study the effects of organic liquids on clay permeability. X-ray diffraction studies and laboratory permeability tests have been the most successful. **Intracrystalline swelling** of the smectitic clay minerals can be measured directly by X-ray diffraction (XRD). The degree of crystal expansion is commonly described by the basal "*d*-spacing" of the clay crystal. Various researchers have used XRD techniques to measure the effects of organic liquids on the expansion of swelling clays. Griffin *et al.* (1984) conducted the only published study of the effect of low-water-solubility organic chemicals on the intracrystalline swelling of hydrated swelling clays. In that study, undiluted organic chemicals were added to aged, water-clay slurries. Exposure of the hydrated smectite to carbon tetrachloride resulted in no change in the *d*-spacing. When clay gels were exposed to acetone, which is totally miscible with water, increased intracrystalline swelling was observed, while exposure to alcohols resulted in a decrease in the *d*-spacing.

Barshad (1952) immersed dehydrated smectite and vermiculite clays in pure organic liquids, then analyzed the clay-organic mixtures by XRD. Tests were performed with pure organic liquids including low-water-solubility compounds (hydrocarbons and ethers) as well as high solubility compounds (low molecular weight alcohols and ketones). Mixtures of organic liquids were also tested. No tests were conducted with chlorinated solvents. The results showed that the degree of crystal expansion is strongly influenced by both the morphology of the organic molecule and the dielectric constant of the organic liquid. Increasing the dielectric constant of a mixture of fluids by varying the composition of the mixture resulted in an increase in the basal *d*-spacing. However, there was no simple relationship between basal *d*-spacing and dielectric constant which held for all organic fluids. Barshad's (1952) work with low-water-solubility organic compounds has limited applicability to water-wet clays, where it is unlikely that a low-polarity organic molecule will displace highly polar water molecules from clay interlayer spaces.

Barshad (1952), Brindley *et al.* (1969), Brown *et al.* (1984), and Brown and Thomas (1987) provide details of XRD studies of clays exposed to water-miscible organic fluids. XRD studies performed using various concentrations (0 to 100%) of water-miscible organic liquids are more relevant in determining the behavior of water-wet clays. Tests have shown that variations in the organic content of an aqueous solution produce variations in clay *d*-spacing, but no simple relationship between the dielectric constant of the organic liquid and the degree of intracrystalline swelling has been observed. At low concentrations of alcohols or acetone, the basal *d*-spacing of clays have been observed to increase over that obtained with pure water. At some "critical" compound- and clay-dependent concentration, an abrupt decrease in basal spacing occurs, to a value that is less than that obtained with pure water. Reported critical concentrations for alcohols and acetone range from about 20% to 50% by volume (7% to about 50% by mole fraction). There is no agreement between researchers on the exact values of the critical concentrations, or on a corresponding "critical dielectric constant" of the organic liquid/water mixture. The concentration and the morphology of water-miscible organic chemicals are apparently strong influences on intracrystalline swelling, and concentrated solutions of some water-miscible organics can cause shrinkage of hydrated swelling clays.

10.5.2 Laboratory Permeability Tests

10.5.2.1 General

Most of the data on the effect of organic liquids on the permeability of clays comes from **laboratory permeability tests**, and much of the controversy about the effects of organic liquids on clays derives from these studies. Most of the reported permeability tests have been conducted on compacted clay samples; few tests on natural undisturbed clay (*i.e.*, non-compacted or non-remolded clay) have been performed. Laboratory permeability tests conducted to measure the effects of exposure to organic chemicals on the bulk permeability of clay soils can indicate changes to bulk permeability such as those caused by changes in clay fabric, but they cannot identify the mechanisms of the underlying chemical interactions. Interpreting the results of these tests is often complicated by influences from factors such as the permeameter type, the imposed hydraulic gradient, the confining stress placed on the specimen, and the nature of the test fluid (fully or only partly water miscible). We attribute many of the apparent inconsistencies in the reported effects of clay-organic chemical interactions to the influence of one or more of these factors.

10.5.2.2 The influence of permeameter type on laboratory determination of permeability

One of the major influences on the outcomes of laboratory permeability tests is the specific design of the permeameter equipment. Daniel *et al.* (1985), Boynton and Daniel (1985), Bowders *et al.* (1986), and Mitchell and Madsen (1987) have reviewed the various types of permeameters appropriate for testing fine grained soils, and their effect on measured permeability.

Laboratory permeameters are of two general types: **rigid-wall cells** (see Figure 10.1), and **flexible-wall cells** (see Figure 10.2). Rigid-wall permeameters have various designs: materials can be tested inside the original compaction mold or sampling tube, trimmed into a rigid-wall chamber, or tested inside a consolidation cell. Rigid-wall permeameters are less expensive and are simple to use. The principal weakness of these devices is the potential for **"side-wall leakage"**. Because the hydraulic gradient used is commonly as high as 50 to 1000, test results are often suspected of having been influenced by side-wall leakage. Another limitation of the rigid-wall permeameter is the inability to monitor or control **stress** on the sample. When clay/permeant reactions result in shrinkage of the specimen, a rigid-wall device allows the formation of fractures or macropores. The specimen may also pull away from the walls of the permeameter, causing a large increase in permeability. Under such conditions, the results of the tests cannot be applied directly to field situations of interest because it is unlikely that the conditions that permitted the fracture formation in the laboratory specimen would be representative of the stress conditions existing at the field scale.

Some rigid-wall permeameters allow application of vertical confining stresses and the measurement of sample volume changes in the vertical direction. Vertical stresses in a permeameter simulate the **overburden load** at depth in a field situation, and to some extent prevent fracture formation and side-wall leakage. Stiff or stony soil samples are nevertheless susceptible to side-wall leakage even under vertical confining stress, though these permeameters perform well on softer soils (Daniel *et al.*, 1985).

Flexible-wall permeability tests can be conducted in a modified triaxial cell. The specimen is contained within a flexible (usually latex) membrane. Pressurized fluid surrounding the membrane applies a confining stress on the soil, and holds the membrane against the side of the sample, thereby preventing side-wall leakage while allowing sam-

PRESSURE   VENT

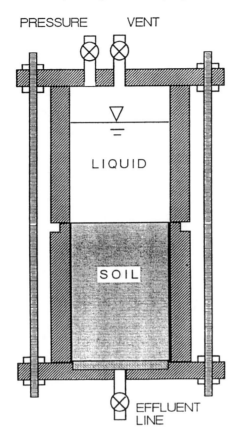

Figure 10.1 Schematic diagram of a
typical rigid-wall permeameter.

ple deformation. Stress conditions on the sample are controlled and monitored. Disadvantages of this approach include the cost and complexity of the equipment, the potential for incompatibility between the permeant fluids (*e.g.*, a chlorinated solvent of interest) and the flexible membrane, and the need for a lateral confining pressure larger than the influent fluid pressure. The last feature may result in excessive effective stress at the effluent end of the specimen.

   In a flexible-wall permeameter, the applied confining stress should cause consolidation of the specimen when chemical interactions between soil and permeant induce a reduction in interparticle repulsion forces. Fractures and macropores are therefore less likely to form than in a rigid-wall cell. Instead, sample consolidation may occur, and permeability values will not increase to the same degree as in an unconfined rigid-wall test. In fact, the measured permeability may decrease. We note then that a close monitoring of specimen volume changes during organic fluid permeation may help identify changes in the specimen. At the same time, sample consolidation and concomitant decreases in permeability observed in flexible-wall permeameter tests may not be representative of field situations, particularly when the effective confining stresses in the laboratory are larger than the *in situ* field stresses.

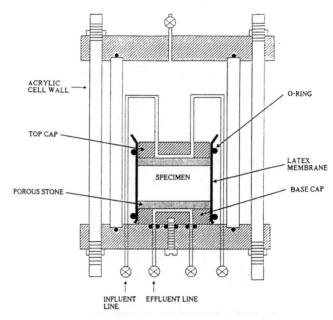

Figure 10.2   Schematic diagram of a typical flexible-wall permeameter.

10.5.2.3 Hydraulic gradients used in permeability tests

Natural groundwater gradients in clayey strata are generally less than 1. Gradients across compacted clay liners beneath landfills are unlikely to exceed 20 (Dunn and Mitchell, 1984). However, in almost all laboratory permeability tests, limited testing times and small specimen sizes necessitate the use of **large hydraulic gradients**, much higher than those found in the field, *e.g.*, gradients of 50 to 1000.

In both rigid-wall and flexible-wall tests of compacted clay, with water as the permeant, increased gradients commonly result in slightly lower measured permeability values (Foreman and Daniel, 1986; Dunn and Mitchell, 1984). High gradients can cause particle migration within a specimen due to seepage forces (Dunn and Mitchell, 1984) or, in the case of flexible-wall tests, specimen consolidation by increased maximum effective stress. In permeability tests using water-wet clay and NAPLs, the relationship between hydraulic gradient and measured permeability is more complex, particularly for tests using rigid-wall permeameters. There is evidence that an increased NAPL gradient can cause increases in measured permeability under some conditions (Quigley and Fernandez, 1989; Middleton, 1990). Consideration of the physical flow of a NAPL provides a possible explanation. Forces of interfacial tension will prevent entry of a NAPL into the influent end of a clay specimen until the entry pressure for the NAPL phase is exceeded. The magnitude of the entry pressure will depend, in part, on the size of the voids (pores, fissures, etc.) in the clay specimen. With the NAPL as the non-wetting fluid in the system, the NAPL will enter the largest available voids in the clay, typically the largest pores and fractures. If a sufficient entry pressure is achieved, "breakthrough" of the NAPL occurs soon thereafter, and the NAPL begins to exit from the effluent end of the clay specimen. At this point, the NAPL is present in one or several small connected flow channels within the specimen, but the relative saturation of the organic fluid expressed on a bulk sample basis is typically very small. In almost all reported tests, a large value of NAPL hydraulic gradient[†] was necessary to achieve breakthrough of the immiscible-phase fluid through clay specimens. The evidence suggests that large values of NAPL hydraulic gradient create physical forces which open **flow channels** in clay under low confining stress (as with rigid-wall permeameters). Perhaps the physical mechanism relates to the difference in fluid pressure between the clay pore water and the intruding NAPL fluid, causing a change in the effective stress on the NAPL flow channels within the specimens (see below).

10.5.2.4 Permeability tests on "dry" clays/organic mixtures

Permeability tests have been conducted with dry clay soils compacted or mixed with various organic fluids. For these dry soil tests, the issue of water miscibility is not relevant. Therefore, both polar and non-polar organic chemicals are discussed together here. Permeability tests on dry clay/organic fluid mixtures are expected to show the extreme effects of organic fluids on clay fabric. Michaels and Lin (1954) and Mesri and Olson (1971) performed rigid-wall permeability tests and consolidation tests, respectively, using dry clays mixed with pure organic fluids including alcohols, benzene, and carbon tetrachloride. They found that the hydraulic conductivity decreased as the polarity (and dielectric constant) of the test fluid increased. Using rigid-wall permeability tests, Fernandez (1984, 1989), Fernandez and Quigley (1985), and Schramm *et al.* (1986) obtained similar results. These results are consistent with **double layer theory**: fluids of low dielectric constant cause double layer contraction, causing a **flocculated soil fabric** with large **inter-aggregate pore spaces**, and greater permeability.

10.5.2.5 Permeability tests of water-wet clays and NAPLs

In nearly all field situations, soils are at least partly **saturated with water** before they become contaminated with organic chemicals. Thus, permeability tests with water-wet materials are more relevant to actual field sites than are tests with soils that are totally water-dry. In many investigations of the permeability of water-wet clays to organic fluids, low-water-solubility organic fluids were not considered to be distinct from organic fluids that are totally water miscible. Since **wettability** has a significant effect on clay-organic fluid interactions, laboratory studies using organic liquids that are totally water miscible should not be expected to provide a reliable indication of the permeability behavior of organic liquids that are not.

Most of the published permeability results using low-water-solubility organic liquids have been obtained using LNAPLs (Table 10.1) and compacted clay specimens.

[†]The NAPL hydraulic gradient on the clay specimen is directly related to the NAPL "head drop" across the clay specimen, which is equal to the difference between the fluid pressures of NAPL at the influent and effluent ends of the specimen.

Tests using LNAPLs are relevant to our study of chlorinated solvents because many of the LNAPLs and the chlorinated solvents have similar dielectric constants and solubilities, and so are expected to interact with the double layers of clay minerals in similar manners. Early research sponsored in part by the U.S. EPA showed large increases of the hydraulic conductivities of water-wet compacted clays when permeated with low-water-solubility organic liquids in rigid-wall permeameters (Brown *et al.*, 1984; Brown *et al.*, 1986; Anderson *et al.*, 1985a). Hydraulic conductivity increases of up to three orders of magnitude over the values obtained with water were measured during passage of only ~ 0.25 pore volumes of flow of the organic liquids through the columns. These results were obtained for tests performed using both swelling and non-swelling clays, with xylene and heptane, and using gradients of 31 to 361 (Figure 10.3). Brown *et al.* (1986) also obtained increases in hydraulic conductivity in similar tests using various low-water-solubility commercial petroleum products. As confirmation of the observed permeability changes caused by xylene and heptane, Anderson *et al.* (1985a) reported that the macroscopic structure of clay specimens changed from a massive structure to a blocky structure.

   In rigid-wall tests of non-swelling compacted clays using heptane and TCE, Daniel and Broderick (1985) obtained results that were similar to those discussed above. In clays compacted with Standard Proctor effort, the hydraulic conductivity values increased before even 0.2 pore volumes of the test fluids had passed through the permeameter.

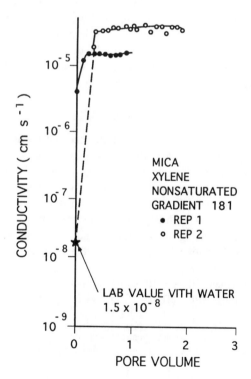

MICA
XYLENE
NONSATURATED
GRADIENT 181
   • REP 1
   ○ REP 2

LAB VALUE VITH WATER
1.5 x 10^{-8}

Figure 10.3 The hydraulic conductivity of water-wet, compacted illitic clay permeated with concentrated xylene, as measured in a rigid-wall permeameter. (Reprinted with permission from Brown *et al.*, 1986.)

The imposed gradient ranged from 100 to 300. However, an increase in the degree of compaction of the clay prior to permeation resulted in no breakthrough of the organic fluids: the entry pressure of the organic fluids could not then be achieved with their testing apparatus.

Brown *et al.* (1986) tested the effect of varying the hydraulic gradient in rigid-wall tests. Tests were conducted using water, a fully water-miscible liquid (acetone), and a low-water-solubility liquid (xylene) as permeants through water-wet clay. They concluded that no relationship could be found between the gradient and hydraulic conductivity. Measured hydraulic conductivity values for each organic fluid varied over two orders of magnitude with no apparent pattern. Each measurement was performed on a different sample of compacted clay. However, the possibility that variability between samples obscured a gradient *vs.* hydraulic conductivity relationship was not examined.

Green *et al.* (1981) also used rigid-wall permeameters and smectite and kaolinite clays in tests with benzene, *m*-xylene, TCE, and carbon tetrachloride. In the majority of their tests, the measured hydraulic conductivity values obtained with the organic fluids were less than that obtained with water. However, they reported that although decreases in hydraulic conductivity were common, some tests with carbon tetrachloride, benzene and xylene exhibited a "breakthrough phenomenon" which consisted of a rapidly-occurring, large increase in permeability. The hydraulic gradients used in these tests were not reported. Green *et al.* concluded that the low dielectric constant, low-water-solubility liquids which they studied have the potential to cause bulk sample shrinkage and consequently increases in hydraulic conductivity in clays.

Anderson *et al.* (1985b) used a double-ring (rigid-wall) permeameter to test a soil-bentonite-water slurry with pure xylene under a hydraulic gradient of 36. Large increases in measured hydraulic conductivity were recorded immediately after the introduction of the xylene. Increases occurred in both the side wall area and in the central portion of the specimens, indicating that the increases were not caused solely by side-wall leakage.

Abdul *et al.* (1990) used rigid-wall permeameters to permeate vacuum-compacted clay slurries with nine low-water-solubility organic liquids, including TCE, PCE, benzene, and xylene. A smectitic clay was tested with all nine organic liquids, and a kaolin clay was tested with all liquids except the two chlorinated solvents. Tests were performed with relatively low permeant fluid heads of about 1 meter, on samples about 5 to 6 centimeters in length. In the smectitic clay, both chlorinated solvents caused almost immediate large hydraulic conductivity increases and visible cracking. All of the other concentrated organic liquids caused visible cracking and large hydraulic conductivity increases in both the smectitic clay and the kaolin. Abdul *et al.* did not correlate the observed results with any specific properties of the liquids, nor discuss mechanisms of clay/organic liquid interactions. However, all of the organic liquids used in the study have dielectric constants much lower than that of water. These are the only reported tests that have been conducted using relatively low gradients in which low-water-solubility liquids penetrated and caused permeability increases in clays. In contrast to other studies which used physically compacted clays, the clay specimens in this study were prepared as a slurry and vacuum compacted. This mode of compaction may have had an influence on the test results.

Evans *et al.* (1985) obtained similar results in testing a vacuum-compacted bentonite-sand-water slurry. The test medium was permeated with carbon tetrachloride in a flexible-wall permeameter, using a hydraulic gradient of approximately 100 and an average effective stress of 207 kPa. The hydraulic conductivity of the test medium increased by two orders of magnitude approximately three days after introduction of the solvent. Data on sample consolidation during the test were not presented.

Comparing the results from different types of permeameters, Bowders (1985) and Foreman and Daniel (1986) found that water-wet clays permeated with low-water-solubility fluids (heptane and TCE) showed significant hydraulic conductivity increases in rigid-wall tests. In contrast, no entry of the organics was achieved in flexible-wall cells. They attributed these results to bulk soil shrinkage and the opening of flow channels which could occur in the rigid-wall cell but not in the flexible-wall cell. Foreman and Daniel (1986) performed additional tests and determined that some, but not all, of the hydraulic conductivity increase in rigid-wall tests could be attributed to side wall flow. They also determined that a finite "gradient" (*i.e.*, entry pressure) existed below which the low-water-solubility organic fluids would not penetrate the clay specimens in rigid-wall cells. Other studies using flexible-wall cells to test compacted, water-wet clays with low-water-solubility permeants have also either obtained large hydraulic conductivity decreases, or have been unable to achieve a sufficient entry pressure to allow penetration of the organic fluid through the clay (Acar *et al.*, 1985; Uppot and Stephenson, 1989). Bowders (1985) also reported one case where large hydraulic conductivity values were measured in a flexible-wall cell when the permeant was able to "short circuit" the specimen by leaking along the clay/Teflon interface associated with the Teflon film placed between the soil sample and the latex membrane to prevent degradation of the membrane by organic fluids; the Teflon film may have formed a semi-rigid cylinder and allowed side-wall flow.

Fernandez (1984; 1989) and Quigley and Fernandez (1989) tested compacted clays in a rigid-wall permeameter and measured hydraulic conductivity values for several low-water-solubility organic liquids (cyclohexane, benzene, and xylene). The results were similar to or less than the value obtained with water. Channel flow and early breakthrough of the pure organic liquid were observed in some tests. They concluded that **unflawed**, water-wet clays do not exhibit increased hydraulic conductivity when permeated by such liquids: interfacial tension effects create high breakthrough pressures and flow can only occur by displacement of water from pre-existing macropores. However, the introduction of a totally-water-miscible liquid such as acetone, or the addition of a surfactant to the water/clay/organic fluid system, each resulted in decreased breakthrough pressures and increases in measured hydraulic conductivity. The same authors reported flow-rate dependent hydraulic conductivity measurements during permeation of compacted clay with cyclohexane (a low-water-solubility liquid) in a rigid-wall, constant flow permeameter. The measured permeability increased with increasing gradient (Fernandez, 1989; Quigley and Fernandez, 1989). They concluded that the cyclohexane was forced along microfissures or channels which expanded or contracted in proportion to the gradient of the immiscible fluid.

In tests similar to those discussed above, Middleton (1990) found that permeation of compacted illitic clay with PCE in rigid-wall permeameters did not result in chemically-induced permeability increases. The flow of the solvent was restricted to microfractures and channels in the clay. Tests of unconfined compacted clay showed that permeability values varied with the flow rate of the solvent through the sample. Tests were conducted by establishing a constant flow of NAPL through the clay specimens. The measured permeability increased as the flow rate increased, and decreased again as the flow rate decreased. This behavior was attributed to **physical deformation** of the clay by large solvent fluid pressures, whereby forces created by two-phase flow within the deformable clay acted to increase the volume of flow channels as the pressure of the non-wetting fluid increased. This is an explanation for why gradient-dependent permeability values are observed only when a low-water-solubility liquid penetrates a water-wet clay, and not in the case of the permeation of water itself.

Middleton *et al.* (1992) reported tests on cores of naturally fractured, illitic clay that were permeated with PCE. The tests were performed in a flexible-wall permeameter under low effective stresses and low gradients. Under constant effective stresses, the permeability to the chlorinated solvent was less than or equal to the permeability to water, and no significant volume changes of the samples were measured during permeation with the solvent (Figure 10.4). These are the only reported tests on an undisturbed clay with natural fractures.

The results of laboratory permeability tests of clays with NAPLs can be summarized as follows. In tests where a sufficient entry pressure was achieved to allow penetration of a NAPL into the clay, all flexible-wall tests and some unconfined rigid-wall tests have shown either no increase, or a decrease in measured permeability relative to that

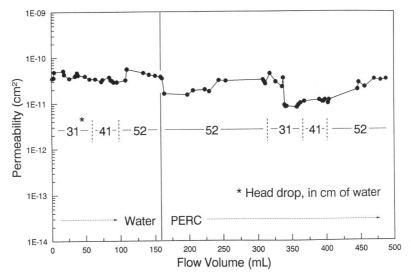

Figure 10.4 Permeability *vs.* cumulative flow for sequential permeation of water and tetrachloroethylene (PER) in illitic clay under a low gradient (~ 10) and low effective stress (4.1 kPa). (Reprinted with permission from Middleton *et al.*, 1992.)

of water. Early breakthrough of the pure organic fluids occurred in all cases. The pure organic fluid, because it was restricted by interfacial tension to macro-pore channels in the specimen, occupied only a small portion of the total pore volume of the specimen. In some unconfined rigid-wall tests, penetration of NAPL into the specimens resulted in rapid breakthrough of the pure organics and large (up to three orders of magnitude or more) increases in measured permeability. Some but not all of the NAPL flow was due to side wall flow. These large permeability increases may be due to the formation of fractures caused by physical (not chemical) phenomena that are attributable to the high NAPL fluid pressures used in the tests. The exceptions to the above are the results of Abdul *et al.* (1985) when chlorinated solvents caused large permeability increases in swelling clays in both rigid-wall and flexible-wall tests. The mode of clay compaction may have had an important influence on these results.

10.5.2.6 Permeability tests using aqueous solutions of NAPL chemicals

Research on the permeation of water-wet clays with aqueous solutions of low-water-solubility organic chemicals (usually at their solubility limit) have been in good agreement. No changes in hydraulic conductivity were observed in any flexible-wall or rigid-wall tests (Daniel *et al.*, 1988; Bowders, 1985; Acar *et al.*, 1985; Evans *et al.*, 1985; Abdul *et al.*, 1990). This is consistent with double layer theory inasmuch as dilute solutions of organic chemicals do not have dielectric constants significantly lower than that of water.

10.5.2.7 Permeability tests of clays and water-miscible organic fluids

There is general agreement among researchers that concentrated, water-miscible, neutral organic chemicals such as low molecular weight alcohols and acetone can increase the permeability of water-wet clays. This applies to both swelling and non-swelling clays. Increases in permeability have been explained in terms of the ability of these liquids to **fully mix with water**, permeate the clay, and decrease the dielectric constant of the pore fluid, thereby causing changes to the clay fabric and pore sizes as predicted by double layer theory. Fernandez and Quigley (1985), Acar *et al.* (1985), and Foreman and Daniel (1986) have provided some of the more recent work with water-miscible organic liquids.

The application of sufficient effective stress to clay specimens permeated with water-miscible organic fluids generally results in chemically-induced **consolidation** of the clay, and either no increase, or even a decrease in the measured permeability. Figure 10.5, taken from Acar *et al.* (1985), illustrates that the final measured hydraulic conductivity in tests with a water-miscible organic fluid decreases as the average effective confining stress on the specimen is increased. This indicates that chemically-induced permeability increases can be prevented by the application of sufficient effective stress on the clay. Therefore, if chemically-induced desiccation of a clayey stratum or liner occurs at depth where the overburden load is sufficient, whether the overburden is waste material in a landfill or natural deposits, the permeability would not increase.

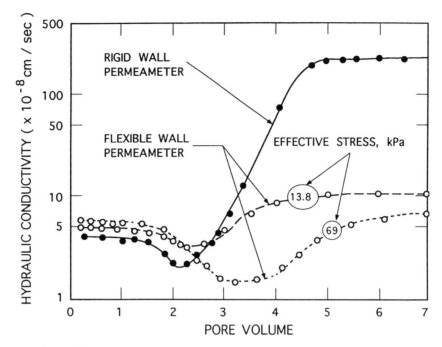

Figure 10.5   The effect of effective stress and permeameter type on the measured hydraulic conductivity of water-wet compacted kaolinite permeated with concentrated acetone. (Adapted with permission from Acar *et al.*, 1985.)

Water-miscible organic fluids can contact clay soils at concentrations in water that range from 0% to 100%. Because water has a dielectric constant that is large relative to organic compounds, the dielectric constant of an aqueous solution will decrease as the fractional organic content increases (Brown and Thomas, 1987). As illustrated in Figure 10.6, recent work indicates that the concentrations of the water-miscible organics must be above about 50-80% in order for laboratory-measured permeability values to increase over the permeability to water (Fernandez and Quigley, 1988; Brown *et al.*, 1984; Bowders, 1985). In terms of double-layer theory, contraction of clay double layers may not occur until a "critical" dielectric constant of the pore fluid is reached. The critical dielectric constant may vary depending on the clay minerals and soil fabric. For swelling clays, water-miscible organics could also cause changes in intracrystalline swelling, which may also affect the critical concentration of the organic necessary to cause clay permeability increases.

As with low-water-solubility compounds, tests using very dilute (less than 5%) solutions of water-miscible organic compounds show no increases in hydraulic conductivity or permeability (Acar *et al.*, 1985; Daniel *et al.*, 1988; Bowders, 1985). This is as expected since the dielectric constant of water is not changed much by the addition of small amounts of water-miscible organic chemicals.

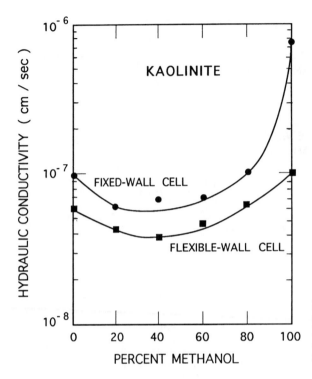

Figure 10.6 The measured hydraulic conductivity of water-wet, compacted kaolinite permeated with aqueous solutions of methanol. (Reprinted with permission from Bowders, 1985.)

10.5.2.8 The influence of clay mineral type on permeability to organic fluids

Little information is available on the influence of clay mineral type on the permeability of soils to organic fluids. Experimental results suggest that smectite clays, as swelling clays, may undergo larger increases in permeability than illite or kaolinite clays on exposure to water-miscible organic liquids (Anderson *et al.*, 1982; Foreman and Daniel, 1986; Acar and D'Hollosy, 1987). This may be caused by the chemical structure of the clay, or by physical properties such as plasticity.

10.6 FIELD STUDIES

Despite a broad interest in chemical interactions between low-water-solubility organic chemicals and clays, there have been few reported field investigations of this topic, probably because of the difficulty in directly observing the effects of organic chemicals on clays. At most sites, there is only limited potential for direct examination of clays exposed to organic chemicals. This is especially true for sites contaminated with chlorinated solvents due to the required depth of excavation and the risk of causing further movement of the solvents while obtaining soil samples.

Field experiments of DNAPL/clay interactions are being conducted by the University of Waterloo at a site near Sarnia, in southwestern Ontario. The site is located in an extensive illitic clay deposit of glacial origin. Free-phase TCE was placed at the bottom of boreholes below the water table, in both shallow weathered clay and in deeper unweathered clay. Soil core samples which had been in direct contact with the solvent in shallow boreholes for two years currently show no visible cracking or fabric changes in the clay. TCE in contact with the unweathered clay in one borehole for 11 months and in another nearby borehole for 6.5 years moved downward in the clay by molecular diffusion, but showed no evidence of transport through fractures or by advection in the porous medium (Poulsen *et al.*, 1993). There was no evidence to suggest that exposure to the solvent had caused increased permeability of the clay in any of the boreholes. In the laboratory, samples of the same illitic clay immersed in TCE or PCE and stored for one year show no visible fractures or changes to the clay fabric, even under examination using a scanning electron microscope. Also, after one year, the solvent showed no wetting of the clay surfaces (Middleton, 1990).

At a site in Smithville, Ontario, dense oils containing chlorinated solvents and chlorobenzenes were found to have moved through a natural clay deposit and entered an underlying fractured limestone aquifer. Initially, it was suspected that chemical inter-actions between the oils and the clay had facilitated their movement through the clay. However, it was later concluded that the oils had moved downward through pre-existing fractures in the clay deposit. At a site at Wilsonville, Illinois, organic chemicals includ-ing chlorinated solvents, pesticides, and aromatic compounds have migrated through a clayey glacial till at rates 100 to 1000 times greater than had been predicted (Griffin *et al.*, 1984; Herzog *et al.*, 1989). However, the primary reason for the rapid migration was discovered to be the presence of pre-existing fractures in the till. Nevertheless, the investigators concluded that organic-clay interactions may have caused permeabilities larger than those attributable to the natural fractures.

10.7 CONCLUSIONS

In laboratory experiments on water-wet clays, water-miscible organic chemicals have a different effect on clay permeability than low-water-solubility organic chemicals. Water-miscible organics above a critical concentration can increase the permeability of clay soils, apparently due to the ability of these fluids to fully penetrate into the clay and shrink clay double layers by reduction of the solution dielectric constant. Critical concentrations for low molecular weight alcohols and acetone are on the order of 50% to 80% organic content by volume in water. In the case of swelling clays, intracrystalline swelling or shrinkage may also affect permeability.

Permeation of clays by aqueous solutions of chlorinated solvents and other low-water-solubility liquids at concentrations at or below their solubility limits (usually less than 2% by volume) does not influence the permeability of clays. This agrees with double layer theory because low concentrations of these organic chemicals do not decrease the dielectric constant of the aqueous solution to any significant extent.

Low-water-solubility organic liquids, including the chlorinated solvents, appar-ently do not chemically increase the permeability of water-wet clay soils through dou-ble layer effects or changes to intracrystalline swelling. These liquids require a certain breakthrough pressure to overcome interfacial tension effects and penetrate into water-wet clays. When penetration occurs, flow of the immiscible liquid is restricted to (pre-existing) macro-pores or fractures in the clay. In laboratory permeability tests under very low confining stresses, mechanical fracturing of clay soils under large organic fluid gradients can result in increased permeability. Although the chemical or physical mechanisms causing the permeability increases may not be well understood, we do know that the mode of compaction and therefore the strength of the clay specimens may be an important influence on such test results.

Based on the results of the laboratory studies, conclusions can be drawn regarding field situations. Exposure to chlorinated solvents and other low-water-solubility liquids is unlikely to cause shrinking, cracking, or permeability increases in natural clay strata or compacted clay barriers. This is because interfacial tension prevents these liquids from entering the clay porous medium, and because the solubilities of these chemicals are too low to affect the dielectric constant of the fluid. In situations where the solubility of chlorinated solvent in groundwater is increased by the presence of co-solvents or surfactants, chemically-induced shrinkage of clayey materials may occur. However, if this takes place at depth below ground surface, confining stresses due to the overburden load would likely prevent an increase in the permeability. Care should therefore be taken when using surfactants or alcohols for in-situ remediation to ensure that enhanced solubility effects do not cause permeability increases.

Particular concern for permeability increases caused by organic chemicals pertains to borehole seals and engineered barriers such as landfill liners and cutoff walls. Borehole seals and engineered barriers commonly contain chemically-sensitive clays such as smectites (*e.g.*, bentonite) that may shrink considerably when exposed to high concentrations of water-miscible organic chemicals under low confining stress conditions. However, we discovered no documented cases where such permeability increases have occurred at field sites.

The conclusions presented here differ substantially from those of Barbee (1994) in his recent review of the environmental fate of chlorinated hydrocarbons. He concludes that chlorinated hydrocarbon liquids are able to rapidly penetrate low permeability clays and significantly increase clay hydraulic conductivity. However, Barbee (1994) based his conclusions on an incomplete review of laboratory studies. Further, he did not distinguish between studies using low-water-solubility and water-miscible organic liquids: one of his primary references was the laboratory study using acetone and ethanol that was conducted by Brown and Thomas (1987).

This discussion has shown that by grouping the results of laboratory research according to solubility of the organic fluid, "dry" or "water-wet" clays, type of permeameter, and other factors, many apparent contradictions in the literature can be resolved. Nevertheless, further research is needed. The influence of specific clay mineral types on clay/organic interactions should be determined with a focus on the chemical and physical interactions between swelling clays and low water solubility organic liquids. The influence of the mode of compaction of clay specimens and the effective stress conditions on permeability test results should be determined in order to more confidently apply laboratory test results to field problems.

ACKNOWLEDGEMENTS

Funding support for this research was provided in part by the University Consortium Solvents-in-Groundwater Research Program. Sponsors of the Program between 1988 and 1994 have included: The Boeing Company, Ciba-Geigy Corporation, Dow Chemical Canada/USA, Eastman Kodak Co., General Electric Co., Laidlaw Environmental Systems Ltd., Mitre Corporation, The Natural Sciences and Engineering Research Council of Canada, and the Ontario University Research Incentive Fund.

10.8 REFERENCES

Abdul, A. S., T. L. Gibson, and D. N. Rai (1990) "Laboratory studies of the flow of some organic solvents and their aqueous solutions through bentonite and kaolin clays", *Ground Water*, **28**, 524-533.

Acar, Y. B. and E. D'Hollosy (1987) "Assessment of pore fluid effects using flexible wall and consolidation permeameters". In: *Geotechnical Practice for Waste Disposal*, 1987, R. D. Woods (Ed.), Geotechnical Special Publication No. 13. American Society of Civil Engineers, 231-245.

Acar, Y. B., A. Hamidon, S. P. Field, and L. Scott (1985) "The effect of organic fluids on the hydraulic conductivity of compacted kaolinite". In: *Hydraulic Barriers in Soil and Rock*, American Society for Testing and Materials, Special Technical Publication 874, A. I. Johnson, R. K. Frobel, N.J. Cavalli, and C.B. Pettersson (Eds.), American Society for Testing and Materials, Philadelphia, 171-187.

Acar, Y. B. and R. K. Seals (1984) "Clay barrier technology for shallow land waste disposal facilities", *Hazardous Waste*, **1**, 167-181.

Anderson, D. C., K. W. Brown, and J. W. Green (1982) "Effect of organic fluids on the permeability of clay soil liners". In: *Land Disposal of Hazardous Waste, Proceedings of the Eighth Annual Research Symposium,* Ft. Mitchell, Kentucky, EPA-600/9-82-002, 179-190.

Anderson, D. C., K. W. Brown, and J. C. Thomas (1985a) "Conductivity of compacted clay soils to water and organic liquids", *Waste Management and Research*, **3**, 339-349.

Anderson, D. C., W. Crawley, and J. D. Zabcik (1985b) "Effects of various liquids on clay soil: bentonite slurry mixtures". In: *Hydraulic Barriers in Soil and Rock*, American Society for Testing and Materials, Special Technical Publication 874, A. Johnson, R. K. Frobel, N. J. Cavalli, and C. B. Pettersson (Eds.), American Society for Testing and Materials, Philadelphia, 93-103.

Barbee, G. C. (1994) "Fate of chlorinated aliphatic hydrocarbons in the vadose zone and ground water", *Ground Water Monitoring and Remediation*, **9**, No. 1 (Winter), 129-140.

Barshad, I. (1952) "Factors affecting the interlayer expansion of vermiculite and montmorillonite with organic substances", *Soil Sci. Soc. Amer. Proc.*, **16**, 176-182.

Bowders, J. J. (1985) *The Influence of Various Concentrations of Organic Liquids on the Hydraulic Conductivity of Compacted Clay*, Geotechnical Engineering Dissertation GT85-2, The University of Texas at Austin, Austin, Texas.

Bowders, J. J., D. E. Daniel, G. P. Broderick, and H. M. Liljestrand (1986) "Methods for testing the compatibility of clay liners with landfill leachate". In: *Proceedings: Hazardous and Industrial Solid Waste Testing: Fourth Symposium*, American Society for Testing and Materials, Philadelphia, Special Technical Publication 886, 233-250.

Boynton, S. S. and D. E. Daniel (1985) "Hydraulic conductivity testing of compacted clay", *J. Geotech. Eng.*, **3**, 465-478.

Brindley, G. W., K. Wiewiora, and A. Wiewiora (1969) "Intracrystalline swelling of montmorillonite in some water-organic mixtures. Clay organic studies XVIII", *Amer. Mineralogist*, **54**, 1635-1644.

Brown, K. W. and J. C. Thomas (1987) "A mechanism by which organic liquids increase the hydraulic conductivity of compacted clay materials", *Soil Sci. Soc. Amer. J.*, **51**, 1451-1459.

Brown, K. W., J. C. Thomas, and J. W. Green (1984) "Permeability of compacted soils to solvents, mixtures, and petroleum products". In: *Land Disposal of Hazardous Waste, Proceedings of the Tenth Annual Research Symposium*, Ft. Mitchell, KY. EPA-600/9-007, 124-137.

Brown, K. W., J. C. Thomas, J. W. Green (1986) "Field cell verification of the effects of concentrated organic solvents on the conductivity of compacted soils", *Hazardous Waste and Hazardous Materials*, **3**, 1-19.

Brownlow, A. H. (1979) *Geochemistry*, Prentice-Hall, Englewood Cliffs, N.J.

Daniel, D. E. and G. P. Broderick (1985) "Stabilization of compacted clay liners against attack by concentrated organic chemicals", Unpublished report to Chemical Manufacturers Association, Washington, D.C.

Daniel, D. E., D. C. Anderson, and S. S. Boynton (1985) "Fixed-wall versus flexible-wall permeameters", In: *Hydraulic Barriers in Soil and Rock*, A. Johnson, R. K. Frobel, N. J. Cavalli and C. B. Pettersson (Eds.), Special Technical Publication 874, American Society for Testing and Materials, Philadelphia, pp. 107-126.

Daniel, D. E., H. M. Liljestrand, G. P. Broderick, and J. J. Bowders (1988) "Interaction of earthen liner materials with industrial waste leachate", *Hazardous Waste and Hazardous Materials*, **5**, 93-108.

Dunn, R. J. and J. K. Mitchell (1984) "Fluid conductivity testing of fine-grained soils", *J. Geotech. Eng.*, American Society of Civil Engineers, **110**, 1648-1665.

Evans, J. C., H.-Y. Fang, and J. J. Kugelman (1985) "Organic fluid effects on the permeability of soil-bentonite slurry walls". In: *Proceedings: National Conference on Hazardous Wastes and Environmental Emergencies*, May 14-16, Cincinnati, OH, 267-271.

Fernandez, F. (1984) *The Effect of Organic Hydrocarbon Liquids on the Hydraulic Conductivity of Natural Soils*, M.E.Sc. Thesis, University of Western Ontario, London, Ontario.

Fernandez, F. (1989) *The Effects of Waste Leachates on the Hydraulic Conductivity of Natural Clays*, Ph.D. Thesis, University of Western Ontario, London, Ontario.

Fernandez, F. and R. M. Quigley (1985) "Hydraulic conductivity of natural clays permeated with simple liquid hydrocarbons", *Canadian Geotech. J.*, **22**, 205-214.

Fernandez, F. and R. M. Quigley (1988) "Viscosity and dielectric constant controls on the hydraulic conductivity of clayey soils permeated with water-soluble organics", *Canadian Geotech. J.*, **25**, 582-589.

Foreman, D. E. and D. E. Daniel (1986) "Permeation of compacted clay with organic chemicals", *J. Geotech. Eng.*, American Society of Civil Engineers, **112**, 669-681.

Freeze, R. A. and J. A. Cherry (1979) *Groundwater*, Prentice-Hall, Englewood Cliffs, NJ.

Green, W. J., G. F. Lee, and R. A. Jones (1981), "Clay-soils permeability and hazardous waste storage", *J. Water Pollut. Control Fed.*, **53**, 1347-1354.

Griffin, R. A., R. E. Hughes, L. R. Follmer, C. J. Stohr, W. J. Morse, T. M. Johnson, J. K. Bartz, J. D. Steele, K. Cartwright, M. M. Killey, and P. B. Dumontelle (1984) "Migration of industrial chemicals and soil-waste interactions at Wilsonville, Illinois". In: *Land Disposal of Hazardous Waste, Proceedings of the Tenth Annual Research Symposium*, Ft. Mitchell, KY. EPA-600/9-84-007, 61-77.

Herzog, B. L., R. A. Griffin, C. J. Stohr, L. R. Follmer, W. J. Morse, and W. J. Su (1989) "Investigation of failure mechanisms and migration of organic chemicals at Wilsonville, Illinois", *Ground Water Monitoring Review,* **9**, No. 2 (Spring), 82-89.

Howard, P. H. (1990) *Handbook of Environmental Fate and Exposure Data for Organic Chemicals, Volume II, Solvents*, Lewis Publishers, Boca Raton, FL.

Mesri, G. and R. E. Olson (1971) "Mechanisms controlling the permeability of clays", *Clays and Clay Minerals*, **19**, 151-158.

Michaels, A. S. and C. S. Lin (1954) "Permeability of kaolinite", *Ind. Eng. Chem.*, **46**, 1239-1246.

Middleton, T. A. (1990) *The Effect of Chlorinated Solvents on the Permeability of Fractured Clay.* M.Sc. Thesis, University of Waterloo, Waterloo, Ontario.

Middleton, T. A., J. A. Cherry, and R. N. Quigley (1992) "The effect of tetrachloroethylene on the permeability of a fractured clay under constant stress conditions". In: *Proceedings* [published 1992] *of the Conference on Subsurface Contamination By Immiscible Fluids*, K. U. Weyer (Ed.), International Association of Hydrogeologists, Calgary, Alberta, April 18-20, 1990. Order from A. A. Balkema, Old Post Road, Brookfield, Vermont, 05036.

Mitchell, J. K. (1976) *Fundamentals of Soil Behavior*, John Wiley and Sons, New York, NY.

Mitchell, J. K. and F. T. Madsen (1987) "Chemical effects on clay hydraulic conductivity". In: *Proceedings of the Specialty Conference on Geotechnical Practice for Waste Disposal*, 1987, R. D. Woods (Ed.) American Society of Civil Engineers, Geotechnical Special Publication, No. 13, 87-116.

Mossop, G. D. (1980) "Geology of the Athabasca oil sands", *Science*, **207**, 145-152.

Poulsen, M. M., R. L. Johnson, B. L. Parker, and J. A. Cherry (1993) "Diffusion of trichloroethylene in a natural clay: A field experiment". In: *Contaminated Soil '93*, F. Arendt, G. J. Annokkee, R. Bosman, and W. J. van den Brink (Eds.), Kluwer Academic Publishers, Netherlands, 547-548.

Quigley, R. M., and F. Fernandez (1989) "Clay/organic interactions and their effect on the hydraulic conductivity of barrier clays". In: *Contaminant Transport in Groundwater*, H. E. Kobus and W. Kinzelbach (Eds.), Balkema, Rotterdam, 117-124.

Schramm, M., A. W. Warrick, and W. H. Fuller (1986) "Permeability of soils to four organic liquids and water", *Hazardous Waste and Hazardous Materials*, **3**, 21-27.

Theng, B. K. G. (1974) *The Chemistry of Clay-Organic Reactions*, Adam Hilger, Bristol, England.

Uppot, J. O. and R. W. Stephenson (1989) "Permeability of clays under organic permeants", *J. Geotech. Eng.*, **115**, 115-131.

Van Olphen, H. (1977) *An Introduction to Clay Colloid Chemistry*, John Wiley and Sons, New York.

11

Physics Governing the Migration of Dense Non-Aqueous Phase Liquids (DNAPLs) in Fractured Media

Bernard H. Kueper[1] and David B. McWhorter[2]

[1]Department of Civil Engineering
Queen's University, Kingston, Ontario, Canada K7L 3N6

[2]Department of Agricultural and Chemical Engineering
Colorado State University, Fort Collins, CO, USA

ABSTRACT

DNAPL will enter a water-saturated fracture if the capillary pressure at the leading edge of the DNAPL body exceeds the fracture entry pressure, as determined by the properties of the fluid and of the medium. Once in a fracture network, DNAPL migration can be rapid, and will be governed by geological structure. Pooled DNAPL can be mobilized by groundwater pumping, which can be desirable in a waterflooding operation, but undesirable if mobilization occurs towards previously uncontaminated areas. Unlike LNAPL, the height of DNAPL accumulated in a borehole gives little indication of conditions in the formation.

11.1 INTRODUCTION

At many sites throughout North America and other parts of the world where a **dense non-aqueous phase liquid (DNAPL)** is known to be present in the subsurface, a **fractured** aquitard or bedrock underlies a relatively shallow overburden. Because the bulk retention capacity of most types of porous media is relatively low, even small volumes of DNAPL

337

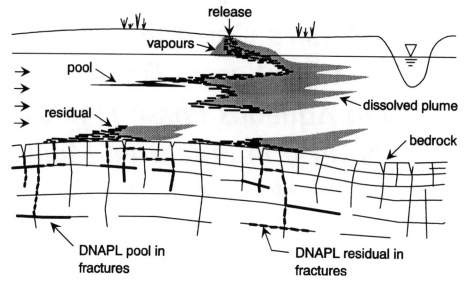

Figure 11.1   DNAPL accumulation above fractured bedrock.

will in general have the potential to migrate down to the base of these overburden deposits. DNAPL will then be exposed to fractures and the issue arises as to whether or not the DNAPL has the potential to enter the fractures that are present. Such a scenario is illustrated in Figure 11.1 where DNAPL has come to rest as **pools** in local bedrock depressions. Also of interest is the case where DNAPL has been placed in a lagoon excavated directly into fractured rock, or where DNAPL has been placed in a lined waste impoundment where the liner of interest is constructed of a material such as clay which may contain fractures.

This chapter will focus on the issue of DNAPL migration through fractured media below the water table. It has been our experience that at the majority of sites where DNAPL migration through fractures is an issue, the problem of concern has been DNAPL entry into water filled fractures. As in the case of porous media, fractures in clay or rock exhibit **capillary properties**. The concepts of interfacial tension, wettability, capillary pressure, and relative permeability discussed in Chapter 3 are therefore all relevant to the case of DNAPL migration through fractured media. The reader is encouraged to review those concepts since they will not be repeated here. This chapter will in general be restricted to a discussion of DNAPL as an immiscible phase, and will not address the issue of DNAPL dissolution or matrix diffusion. These topics are treated separately in Chapters 7 and 12, respectively.

11.2 DNAPL ENTRY INTO FRACTURES

In many cases, the volume of DNAPL released at ground surface will be sufficient to bring about migration through overburden deposits such that the DNAPL comes to rest above a fractured aquitard (or fractured bedrock) in the form of one or more pools. In order for DNAPL to enter a fracture underlying a pool, the capillary pressure at the base of the pool must overcome the **entry pressure** of the fracture. Assuming that the DNAPL is non-wetting with respect to water and that the system is at hydrostatic equilibrium, the **capillary pressure** at the base of the pool is given by

$$P_c = (\rho_{nw} - \rho_w)gh \quad , \tag{11.1}$$

where P_c is the capillary pressure, ρ_{nw} is the non-wetting phase (DNAPL) density, ρ_w is the wetting phase (water) density, g is the gravitational constant, and h is the height of the pool. Eq.(11.1) assumes that the top of the pool exists at a capillary pressure of zero. The entry pressure of a rough-walled fracture is approximated by (Kueper and McWhorter, 1991)

$$P_e = \frac{2\sigma\cos\theta}{e} \quad , \tag{11.2}$$

where P_e is the entry pressure of interest, σ is the interfacial tension between DNAPL and water, θ is the contact angle on the fracture walls, and e is the largest fracture aperture. If it is assumed that water in the fracture is in hydraulic equilibrium with water in the porous medium overlying the fracture, Eqs.(11.1) and (11.2) can be equated to yield the **minimum pool height H** giving rise to entry into a fracture:

$$H = \frac{2\sigma\cos\theta}{(\rho_{nw} - \rho_w)ge} \quad . \tag{11.3}$$

As discussed in Kueper and McWhorter (1991), this expression can be adjusted for cases where the top of the pool does not necessarily exist at zero capillary pressure.

Eq.(11.3) shows that the minimum pool height required for entry into a fracture is directly proportional to the DNAPL-water interfacial tension, and inversely proportional to the difference in fluid densities and the fracture aperture. It is also important to note that the critical pool height given by Eq.(11.3) is independent of depth below the water table. This is consistent with the fact that capillary pressures dictate the behavior of two-phase systems, with absolute pressures having very little influence in near-surface environments.

Figure 11.2 presents a plot of minimum pool height vs. fracture aperture invaded for a variety of interfacial tensions and DNAPL densities. Cases A and B represent tetrachloroethylene (*i.e.*, perchloroethylene, or PCE), a common chlorinated solvent having a high density (1620 kg/m³). Case A is assigned an interfacial tension of 0.045 N/m, which is typical of industrial grade PCE which has not been exposed to impurities. Case B, on the other hand, represents PCE having an interfacial tension of only 0.009 N/m as a result of exposure to a surfactant or detergent. The Case A curve shows that pool heights on the order of 0.2-1.0 m have the potential to invade fracture apertures on the order of 10-100 μm (microns), while the Case B curve shows that much smaller apertures are invaded for the same pool height as a result of the lower interfacial tension. Cases C and D in Figure 11.2 are assigned a DNAPL density of 1100 kg/m³, and a DNAPL-water interfacial tension of 0.045 N/m and 0.009 N/m, respectively. It is clear that much greater pool heights are required for a low density DNAPL

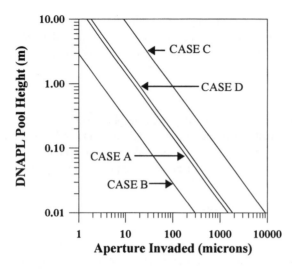

Figure 11.2 Pool height *vs.* fracture aperture invaded.

to initiate entry into fractures, particularly when the interfacial tension has not been lowered.

Once a DNAPL has entered a fracture or fracture network, **progressively smaller aperture fractures will be invaded** if the DNAPL is allowed to extend itself vertically while remaining a continuous phase. In other words, the capillary pressure at the base of the DNAPL accumulation is a function of not only the pool height in the overburden overlying the fractures in question, but also the height of DNAPL accumulated in fractures beneath this pool. Consider, for example, the scenario illustrated in Figure 11.3. Shown is a 0.25 m high accumulation of trichloroethylene (TCE) in a local bedrock depression. The TCE-water interfacial tension is assumed to be 0.04 N/m. The capillary pressure at point A is 1,127.7 Pa, implying that fractures as small as 70 μm will be invaded (fracture entry pressure given by $2\sigma/e$). In Figure 11.3, the aperture at point A is greater than this and DNAPL has entered the fracture network. If the DNAPL were to stop moving and reach a static distribution as shown, the capillary pressure at points B and C would be 5,638.5 Pa and 10,149.2 Pa, respectively. This would require that the fracture apertures at points B and C be no larger than 14.2 μm and 7.9 μm, respectively. Since such a rapid reduction in fracture aperture with depth is not likely in a rock environment, it is probable that the pool will not come to rest as shown, but rather will continue to drain into the fracture network until it is completely depleted.

In some cases, DNAPL may be pooled above a fractured aquitard as illustrated in Figure 11.4 such that the capillary pressure at the base of the DNAPL pool is insufficient to bring about entry into fractures. Figure 11.4 shows a pumping well situated in a lower aquifer beneath the fractured aquitard. If **aggressive pumping** is carried out in this well, water pressures in the aquitard will be lowered from below, resulting in an increase in capillary pressure at the base of the DNAPL pool. This **will promote the entry of DNAPL into fractures**, thereby worsening the extent of contamination at the site. If the height of the DNAPL pooled above the fractures is very near to the critical pool

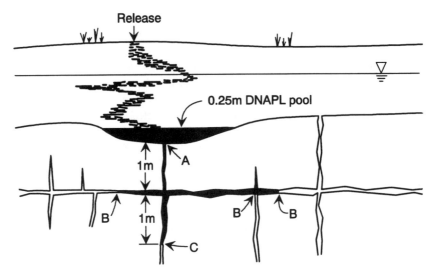

Figure 11.3 Pool of TCE in bedrock depression. TCE can enter progressively smaller aperture fractures with depth as a result of an increase in capillary pressure brought about by vertical accumulation.

height, even a slight lowering of water pressure from below may bring about entry into the previously uninvaded fractures.

At many sites where overburden covers fractured bedrock or a fractured aquitard, soil samples can be obtained and analyzed to determine if an actual DNAPL phase is present. If a soil sample obtained from immediately above a fractured medium is found to contain residual or pooled DNAPL, this can be used as an indication of whether or not the DNAPL had the potential to invade a given size fracture. DNAPL found in a

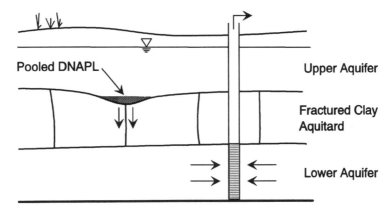

Figure 11.4 DNAPL pooled above a fractured aquitard. Pumping from below aquitard will promote the downward re-mobilization of DNAPL.

silt as either residual or pools, for example, must have existed at either a high capillary pressure or a low interfacial tension to be able to invade such a fine grained material. These same conditions promote DNAPL entry into small fractures.

Figure 11.5 presents a plot of aperture invaded *vs.* DNAPL saturation in porous media of varying permeability immediately above a fracture. To construct this plot it was necessary to establish the relationship between capillary pressure and saturation for the porous medium and the fluid pair of interest. A Brooks and Corey (1964) capillary pressure relationship and a DNAPL-water interfacial tension of 0.045 N/m has been assumed here. The Brooks-Corey parameters are based on PCE-water capillary pressure curves measured on samples of sand obtained from the Borden aquifer near Alliston, Ontario (Kueper and McWhorter, 1991). The relationship between capillary pressure and permeability is assumed to follow a modified form of the Leverett function (Leverett, 1941) as established by Kueper and Frind (1991). The figure clearly shows that DNAPL present in progressively lower permeability porous media has the potential to enter progressively smaller aperture fractures.

In the above examples it has been assumed that the water beneath a DNAPL pool is in hydrostatic equilibrium with water above the pool. Figure 11.6 presents a scenario where this is not the case. Shown is a lined lagoon containing both DNAPL and water. Because the liner is comprised of a low permeability material such as clay, the water table in the formation outside of the liner is not at the same elevation as the water inside the

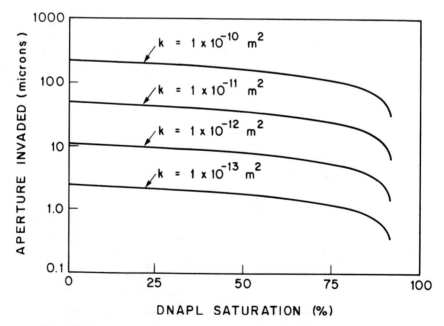

Figure 11.5 Fracture aperture invaded *vs.* DNAPL saturation in porous medium overlying fractures. (Reprinted with permission from Kueper and McWhorter, 1991).

lagoon. In this case, the height of the water table outside the liner has a direct influence on the critical pool height of DNAPL that can be supported inside the lagoon prior to penetration of fractures. DNAPL will invade the fractures when the following condition is satisfied (Kueper *et al.*, 1992):

$$A + B\frac{\rho_{nw}}{\rho_w} - C \geq \frac{2\sigma\cos\theta}{e\rho_w g} \quad , \tag{11.4}$$

where A is the thickness of the water layer inside the lagoon, B is the thickness of the DNAPL layer, and C is the height of the water table above the base of the lagoon. It is clear that maintaining a high water table outside of the liner is a step that can be taken to minimize the risk of DNAPL entry into fractures.

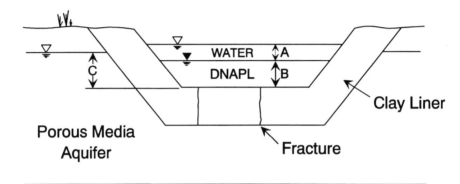

Figure 11.6   DNAPL accumulation in a lined waste disposal pond. (Reprinted with permission from Kueper *et al.* (1992).)

11.3 RATES OF DNAPL MIGRATION THROUGH FRACTURES

Once having entered a fracture, DNAPL will preferentially migrate through the larger aperture pathways of a fracture plane since these offer the **least capillary resistance** to movement. The overall saturation of DNAPL achieved in the fracture during this migration will be a function of the maximum capillary pressure generated. Recent laboratory measurements by Reitsma and Kueper (1994) have demonstrated that rough-walled fractures exhibit capillary behavior analogous to porous media. Figure 11.7 presents a capillary pressure-saturation curve measured in a single fracture in limestone. The fracture was subjected to a normal stress of 12.5 kPa. The hydraulic aperture of the fracture at this loading was measured to be 112 μm, which is substantially less than the 189 μm aperture corresponding to initial invasion of the non-wetting fluid (fracture entry pressure). The drainage curve shown in the figure was found to be well represented by a Brooks-Corey type of porous media capillary pressure curve. This is not surprising given the analogy between the pores and pore throats in a porous medium and the variable aperture regions in a rough-walled fracture. The figure clearly shows that higher non-wetting saturations are attained in the fracture plane at higher capillary pressures. It is

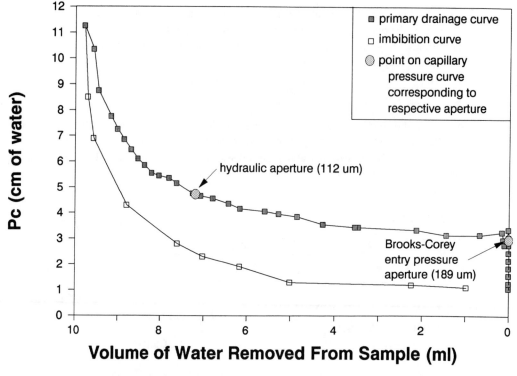

Figure 11.7 Capillary pressure-saturation curve for a limestone fracture. (Reprinted with permission from Reitsma and Kueper (1994)).

important to note, however, that the fracture exhibits a virtually non-existent residual non-wetting phase saturation upon wetting.

To investigate the **rates** at which DNAPL can traverse a fractured aquitard, numerical simulations were carried out in the solution domain illustrated in Figure 11.8 using the DNAPL fracture migration model developed by Kueper and McWhorter (1991). The figure shows DNAPL pooled at the base of overburden deposits which overlie a 5 m thick fractured aquitard. The DNAPL of interest is assigned a viscosity of 0.00057 Pa-s and an interfacial tension with water of 0.045 N/m. Figure 11.9 presents a plot of the time taken for DNAPL to first reach the lower aquifer as a function of fracture aperture. The DNAPL pool height is set at 0.5 m. Two cases are shown, one for a DNAPL density of 1200 kg/m^3 and one for a density of 1460 kg/m^3. It is clear that the first arrival times are very sensitive to fracture aperture, consistent with the fact that fracture transmissivity is proportional to the cube of the aperture (de Marsily, 1986). For the higher density case (properties of TCE), very short first arrival times are exhibited for fracture apertures larger than 50 μm. The lower curve approaches an asymptote at an aperture of 39.9 μm, which is the smallest aperture that can be invaded by the 0.5 m high pool. For the lower density case the first arrival times are longer and the asymptotic aperture is higher since the 0.5 m pool height generates a smaller capillary pressure, and since the gravity driving

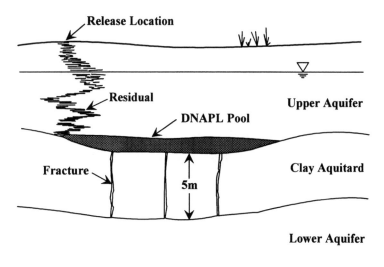

Figure 11.8   DNAPL pooled above fractured aquitard. Solution domain for results presented in Figure 11.9.

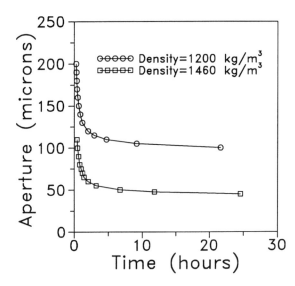

Figure 11.9   Time taken for first arrival of DNAPL at lower aquifer versus fracture aperture.

force is reduced. It follows that larger pool heights and lower viscosities will in general bring about quicker first arrival times.

To examine the rate at which DNAPL can migrate along horizontal to sub-horizontal fractures, numerical simulations were carried out in the solution domain illustrated in Figure 11.10. Shown is a pool of DNAPL which has accumulated in a bedrock depression. A set of parallel, slightly dipping fractures is shown to extend a large horizontal distance from the pool. The DNAPL pool height is set at 0.25 m, and the DNAPL is assigned the

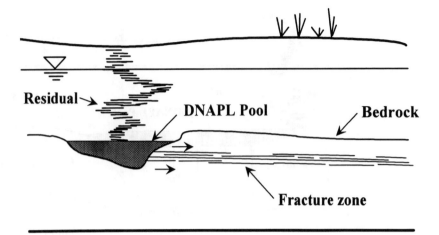

Figure 11.10 DNAPL pool feeding horizontal fractures in bedrock. Solution domain for results presented in Figure 11.11.

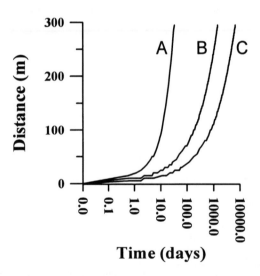

Figure 11.11 Distance *vs.* time for leading edge of DNAPL migration in a set of fractures.

properties of TCE with an interfacial tension of 0.030 N/m. Figure 11.11 presents a plot of distance vs. time for the leading edge of the DNAPL front for three cases. Case A, which represents a set of parallel 100 μm fractures dipping at 2 degrees, shows very high rates of migration. Case B, which represents the same set of fractures with a horizontal orientation, shows comparatively slower rates because of the reduced gravity driving force. Case C represents a set of 75 μm fractures with a horizontal orientation; the rates of migration are substantially slower than the other cases because of the reduced intrinsic permeability of the fractures, and because of a reduced relative permeability to the TCE as a result of a higher fracture entry pressure. The rates of migration for all three cases would be higher for a greater pool height at the inflow because of an increase in capillary pressure.

11.4 RESIDUAL AND POOLED DNAPL

Once the source of the DNAPL to a fracture has been depleted, the DNAPL will **re-distribute** itself in the form of residual and pools. Although quantitative studies are scarce, residual DNAPL is expected to form in fractures due to by-passing and snap-off mechanisms analogous to residual formation in porous media. The underlying premise here is that the rough-walled nature of fractures will provide enough variability in topology to allow these processes to take place. However, since the topology of a rough-walled fracture is not as irregular as in a porous medium, it may be reasoned that residual in the form of small, disconnected blobs and ganglia of organic liquid will not be abundant. This is consistent with the small residual contents in simulated fractures constructed from glass plates by Schwille (1988), and the extremely low residual non-wetting phase saturation exhibited by the capillary pressure curve measured by Reitsma and Kueper (1994).

Pools are distinct from residual in that they are formed when a migrating DNAPL body can no longer overcome capillary resistance at the leading edge. Figure 11.12 illustrates a pool of DNAPL which has formed in an inclined fracture as a result of a narrowing of the fracture at the leading edge of the pool. By carrying out a one-dimensional force balance and assuming that groundwater flow in the fracture is at steady-state, the pool will remain **stationary** when

$$\frac{\Delta\rho}{\rho_w} L \sin\alpha + h(0) - h(L) \leq \frac{P_e(L) - P_c(0)}{\rho_w g} \quad , \tag{11.5}$$

where L is the pool length, $\Delta\rho$ is the difference in density between DNAPL and water, α is the dip of the fracture, $h(0)$ is the hydraulic head at the trailing edge of the pool, $h(L)$ is the hydraulic head at the leading edge of the pool, $P_e(L)$ is the entry pressure of the fracture at the leading edge of the pool, and $P_c(0)$ is the capillary pressure at the trailing edge of the pool.

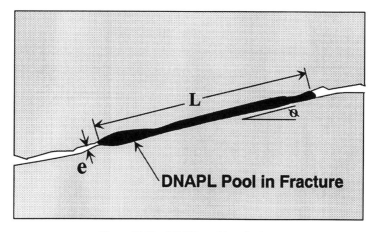

Figure 11.12   DNAPL pool in a fracture.

The first term in Eq.(11.5) represents the influence of gravity acting down-dip. Applied to a horizontal fracture, this term is zero. The second term represents the influence of the groundwater gradient across the pool, and reduces to zero for a hydrostatic wetting phase distribution. The term on the right-hand side represents the capillary resistance of the fracture. Eq.(11.5) can be re-arranged to solve for L, the maximum stable pool length for a given set of flow conditions. It is clear that upward hydraulic gradients result in a longer stable pool length, and that longer pools can be sustained in more shallow dipping fractures. It can also be seen that an in-situ lowering of interfacial tension will reduce the capillary resistance of a fracture, resulting in possible pool mobilization.

In the case where **groundwater pumping** is initiated in the vicinity of pooled DNAPL, the increase in hydraulic gradient across the pool will lead to the possibility that the pool will be **displaced** further along the fracture. Such a scenario can arise if a pump-and-treat system is operated in the vicinity of pooled DNAPL. Figure 11.13 illustrates a hypothetical site where DNAPL pools exist in fractures. A series of pumping wells need to be placed to bring about hydraulic interception of the dissolved phase plume which is evolving, but it is not known how far downstream of the DNAPL pools the wells must be placed if mobilization of the DNAPL in the fractures is to be avoided. Eq.(11.5) demonstrates that any increase in hydraulic gradient will mobilize DNAPL if pools exist at their maximum stable length. For pool lengths below the maximum stable length, a certain incremental increase in hydraulic gradient can be tolerated.

In practice it is generally not possible to determine whether or not pools exist at or near their maximum stable length. A conservative approach would therefore be to

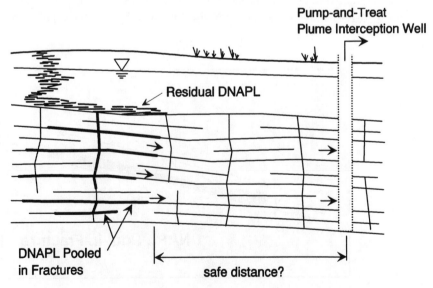

Figure 11.13 Pool mobilization due to operation of pump-and-treat recovery wells.

locate plume interception wells far downgradient from suspected pool locations so that the impact of pumping on the pools themselves will be minimal. An alternative approach would be to place plume interception wells directly within the region of pooled DNAPL. In this case any pool mobilization would be back towards the already-contaminated region. The latter approach has the added advantage of minimizing the extent of aquifer that will be impacted by dissolved contamination during the operation of the pump-and-treat system. Care must be taken, however, to ensure that capture zones extend far enough downstream to encompass all pooled DNAPL.

11.5 DNAPL MIGRATION THROUGH FRACTURE NETWORKS

To date, there has been very little research carried out examining the migration of DNAPL through **fracture networks**. This is in part due to the fact that DNAPL migration through fractured media is in itself a relatively new area of interest, and in part because both laboratory and field experimentation are very difficult in fracture networks. In addition, the development of numerical models to simulate DNAPL migration through fracture networks is only recently underway. The work which has been performed to date examining DNAPL in single fractures, however, can be used to direct a general discussion.

Once initial entry into a fracture network has taken place, a DNAPL will preferentially migrate through the larger aperture fractures, entering intersecting fractures only if the local capillary pressure exceeds the entry pressure of the newly encountered fractures. The overall pattern of DNAPL migration will be governed by both fluid and media properties. Figure 11.14 shows a sequence of horizontally bedded sedimentary rocks with a waste lagoon containing DNAPL at ground surface. The rock units differ from each other in overall bulk permeability. The upper unit is highly fractured while the lower unit is less fractured and contains fractures with smaller apertures. Figure 11.14.a shows the possible DNAPL migration pathways when the DNAPL has a low interfacial tension. As can be seen, a large number of individual fractures are invaded because the fracture entry pressures are low. This results in little lateral spreading through the fracture system and large ultimate depths of migration.

Figure 11.14.b illustrates the migration pathways which can arise from a DNAPL having a high interfacial tension with water (*e.g.*, 0.045 N/m). In this case not as many individual fractures are invaded because fracture entry pressures are higher. The pool height in the lagoon and the density driving force can only generate capillary pressures sufficient to enter the largest aperture fractures. In addition, substantial lateral flow takes place above the less permeable rock unit since high capillary pressures are required for penetration. Even if the lower permeability rock unit becomes penetrated, lateral flow will continue above it since the relative permeability to DNAPL will be higher in the overlying, more fractured unit. As shown in the figure, large amounts of lateral spreading can occur through major bedding partings. Because DNAPL-water interfacial tension largely dictates what the ultimate lateral and vertical extent of DNAPL migration will be in a fracture network, care should be taken to have this value measured whenever a sample of the DNAPL of interest can be obtained.

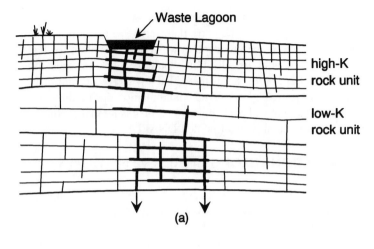

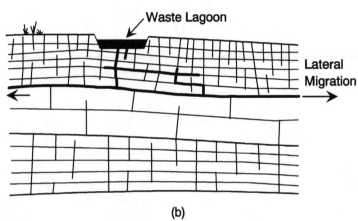

Figure 11.14   a. DNAPL migration pathways for a low interfacial tension system; b. DNAPL migration pathways for a high interfacial tension system.

In addition to the properties of the DNAPL itself, it should be clear that **fracture connectivity**, **spacing**, and **orientation** also have pronounced effects on DNAPL migration pathways through fracture networks. As in porous media, DNAPL migration will be largely structure controlled. DNAPL will migrate through those pathways which offer the least capillary resistance. These pathways will not necessarily be the same as those involved in the flow of the groundwater. Moreover, since hydraulic gradients in most natural groundwater systems are typically very low, they will have little influence on the directions of DNAPL migration through the fractures. A comprehensive monitoring program in fractured media should therefore focus on having boreholes placed according to structure, not necessarily according to the direction of groundwater flow.

11.6 HEIGHT OF DNAPL IN A WELL

In the event that DNAPL is observed in a borehole in a fractured medium, it can obviously be concluded that the site is a DNAPL site. Beyond this, however, it is difficult to infer exactly what the conditions are in the surrounding formation. Figure 11.15 presents a series of schematics where boreholes have intersected a DNAPL pool in fractured media. In Case A, the presence of DNAPL in the wellbore corresponds to the presence of DNAPL in the formation at the same general elevation. If the top of the pool in the formation exists at a capillary pressure of zero, the elevation of the water-DNAPL interface in the wellbore will equal the elevation of the top of the pool in the formation. What is not known, however, is the distance to which the pool extends below the borehole.

In Case B, the identical height of DNAPL exists in the borehole as in Case A, but no DNAPL is present in the formation at this elevation. In this case, DNAPL has entered at an upper elevation and accumulated at the base of the borehole. The DNAPL does not exit the borehole because the height of accumulation is insufficient to generate a capillary pressure in excess of the local fracture entry pressures. Case C illustrates a case of borehole short-circuiting where the capillary pressure has exceeded the fracture entry pressures, resulting in penetration of fractures at lower elevation.

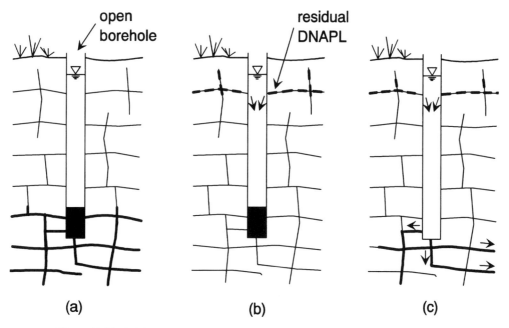

Figure 11.15   Height of DNAPL in a well: a. DNAPL in well corresponds to DNAPL in formation; b. DNAPL in well has entered from an upper elevation and does not correspond to DNAPL in formation at lower elevation; c. borehole short-circuiting.

11.7 CONCLUSIONS

Although research pertaining to multiphase flow in fractured media is still in its infancy, much has been learned by drawing analogies with the flow of immiscible fluids in porous media. In particular, the concepts of wettability, capillarity, and relative permeability apply as well to fractured media as they do to porous media. The underlying reason for this is the close analogy which exists between the distribution of apertures in a fracture plane or network, and the distribution of pores and pore throats in a porous medium.

Laboratory and numerical experimentation to date has focused primarily on the flow of two immiscible fluids through a single fracture. While advances in the numerical modeling of multiphase flow through fracture networks will certainly be made in the near future, controlled physical experimentation in actual fracture networks will not likely be commonplace because of the inherent difficulty in artificially creating such networks in the laboratory, and because intentional releases of DNAPL at actual field sites is usually prohibited. The study of DNAPL behavior at accidental spill sites generally does not serve as a fully adequate alternative because of uncertainty in the volumes, rates, times, location, condition, and composition of the liquid(s) released. Our overall understanding of DNAPL migration through fracture networks will therefore be based largely on theoretical analyses and inferences obtained at accidental spill sites.

ACKNOWLEDGEMENTS

Funding support for this research was provided in part by the University Consortium Solvents-in-Groundwater Research Program. Sponsors of the Program between 1988 and 1994 have included: The Boeing Company, Ciba-Geigy Corporation, Dow Chemical Canada/USA, Eastman Kodak Co., General Electric Co., Laidlaw Environmental Systems Ltd., Mitre Corporation, The Natural Sciences and Engineering Research Council of Canada, and the Ontario University Research Incentive Fund.

11.8 REFERENCES

Brooks, R. H. and A. T. Corey (1964) "Hydraulic properties of porous media", Hydrology Paper No. 3, Civ. Eng. Dept., Colorado State University, Fort Collins, CO, U.S.A.

de Marsily, G. (1986) *Quantitative Hydrogeology*, Academic Press, New York, NY.

Kueper, B. H. and E. O. Frind (1991) "Two-phase flow in heterogeneous porous media. 2. Model Application", *Water Resources Research*, **27**, 1058-1070.

Kueper, B. H. and D. B. McWhorter (1991) "The behavior of dense, non-aqueous phase liquids in fractured clay and rock", *Ground Water*, **29**, 716-728

Kueper, B. H., C. S. Haase, and H. King (1992) "Leakage of DNAPL from waste impoundments constructed in fractured rock and clay: Theory and case history", *Canadian Geotechnical Journal*, **29**, 234-244.

Leverett, M. C. (1941) "Capillary behavior in porous solids", *Trans. AIME, Petrol. Div.*, 142, 152-169.

Reitsma, S. and B. H. Kueper (1994) "Laboratory measurement of capillary pressure-saturation curves in natural rock fractures", *Water Resources Research*, In press.

Schwille, F. (1988) *Dense Chlorinated Solvents in Porous and Fractured Media: Model Experiments.* Translated by James F. Pankow, Lewis Publishers, Boca Raton, Florida.

12

The Effects of Molecular Diffusion on DNAPL Behavior in Fractured Porous Media

Beth L. Parker, John A. Cherry, and Robert W. Gillham

Waterloo Centre for Groundwater Research
University of Waterloo
Waterloo, Ontario, Canada N2L 3G1

ABSTRACT

In fractured media, diffusion of contaminant mass from highly conductive fractures into the relatively immobile pore water of the matrix between fractures affects the persistence of dense non-aqueous phase liquids (DNAPLs) in fractures. This diffusion causes a redistribution of the contaminant mass within source areas in fractured porous media such as unlithified clay-rich deposits and sedimentary rocks. A theoretical analysis using parameter values typical for chlorinated solvents and fractured geologic media indicate that the chemical mass storage capacity of the matrix for dissolved and sorbed chemical mass often greatly exceeds the DNAPL-phase storage capacity of the adjacent fractures. This condition allows complete disappearance of the DNAPL phase from fractures by dissolution and subsequent diffusion into the porous matrix. For idealized fracture systems, these diffusion rates are shown to be very rapid for the common chlorinated solvents (dichloromethane, trichloroethylene, and tetrachloroethylene), ranging from a few minutes to a few years for fracture and matrix properties typical of clay-rich deposits, and days to a few decades for sedimentary rock systems. Hence, the contaminant mass can undergo a complete change in state and position as DNAPL located in high permeability fractures dissolves and moves into the matrix. These conclusions have many implications regarding site monitoring and interpretations for DNAPLs in fractured source zones. For example, mass removal by in-situ methods is likely to be controlled by reverse diffusion and desorption from the low permeability matrix between fractures rather than by dissolution and mobilization of DNAPL from difficult-to-find DNAPL-laden fractures.

12.1 INTRODUCTION

The flow of **dense non-aqueous phase liquids (DNAPLs)** in fractured media is discussed in Chapter 11. A simplifying assumption made in that chapter so as to allow one to focus on the physics of the flow was that the material making up the fractured medium has insufficient **matrix porosity** to allow significant contaminant mass, either as the DNAPL phase itself, or dissolved in groundwater, to enter the matrix. For certain field situations this assumption is valid. However, for others, the porosity of the matrix material between the fractures can have important effects on the fate and behavior of DNAPLs in fracture networks. The focus of this chapter will therefore be on the entry of **dissolved** contaminants into the matrix porosity. Fractured geologic media in which the matrix porosity is most likely to have significant influence on DNAPL behavior include fractured clayey or silty deposits as well as sedimentary rocks in which the matrix porosity is appreciable. The latter include shales, siltstones, sandstones, limestones, and dolomites. Crystalline rocks such as granites and marble generally have insignificant matrix porosity.

Although fractures will be conceptualized in this chapter as smooth parallel plates, in reality they have rough surfaces with irregular apertures which are closed over parts of their areas (Figure 12.1.a). This conceptualization, though a severe simplification of reality, allows useful analyses of contaminant behavior in fractured porous media to be made. Also, while the DNAPL phase can enter into and move within a fracture network, we will assume that it cannot enter as a phase into matrix blocks between the fractures (Figure 12.1.b). Thus, for matrix blocks, we will be assuming that the **entry pressure** for the DNAPL is not exceeded under field conditions. This assumption is valid for many though not all situations in fractured porous media.

In addition to the matrix porosity, important properties of fractured porous media include the **fracture aperture**, the **fracture porosity**, the **sorption capacities** of the matrix material for the contaminants of interest, and the **effective diffusion coefficients** of those contaminants in the matrix. The matrix porosity (ϕ_m) (also referred to as the

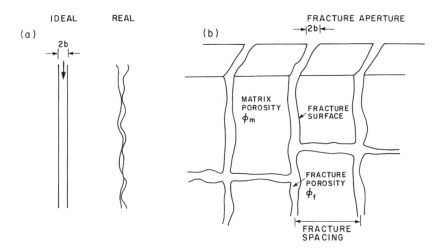

Figure 12.1   a. Idealized smooth parallel-plate fracture with uniform aperture *vs.* actual rough-walled, variable aperture fractures. b. Schematic diagram of fracture network within a geologic medium, and definition of terms.

"primary porosity") is the void space between the individual solid grains in the matrix blocks. The fracture porosity (ϕ_f) is the void space offered only by the fracture network. The parameter ϕ_f is a function of the mean fracture aperture and the mean fracture spacing. Few reliable measurements have been made for fracture porosity or fracture aperture because of the exceptional difficulties involved in making such determinations. The literature suggests that for fractured clayey or silty deposits in the groundwater zone, fracture porosity, expressed as the percent of void space provided by fractures per unit volume of bulk medium, generally ranges from 0.0001 to 0.1%; for fractured sedimentary rocks, with the exception of solution-channelled or karstic limestones or dolomites, the upper end of the range is 1%.

Estimated values for fracture porosities and apertures are normally derived from field measurements of bulk hydraulic conductivity carried out in boreholes or wells, combined with information on the frequency of fractures (distances between hydraulically-conductive fractures) derived from cores, borehole geophysical logs or outcrops. Figure 12.2.a, adapted from Hoek and Bray (1981), illustrates the dependence of the bulk hydraulic conductivity on the fracture spacing and the fracture aperture. The relations are for a set of parallel fractures with uniform spacing and smooth parallel-plate apertures. The bulk hydraulic conductivity increases directly with the number of fractures per unit length, and directly with the cube of the fracture aperture. Figure 12.2.b illustrates the dependence of the fracture porosity on fracture aperture and the fracture spacing.

As an example, a fracture porosity on the order of 0.1% would be relatively large, and if the fractures were aligned with the direction of groundwater flow, they would normally cause a very large bulk hydraulic conductivity (greater than 6×10^{-4} m/s). (Note that a 1.0 mm wide fracture spaced every meter of rock would represent a 0.1% fracture porosity case). In contrast, matrix porosities are commonly much larger than

1%: non-indurated clayey deposits typically have matrix porosities in the range of 20 to 70%; many sedimentary rocks have matrix porosity values of 5 to 15%.

Based on the above information, it can be concluded that the void space in the matrix of fractured porous media is commonly orders of magnitude larger than the void space provided by the fracture network. This observation has important implications for

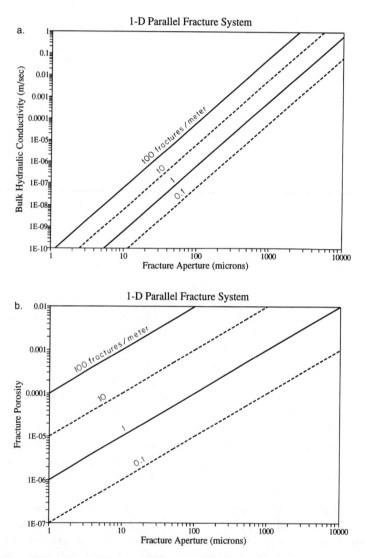

Figure 12.2   a. Bulk hydraulic conductivity (after Hoek and Bray, 1981), and b. fracture porosity as a function of fracture spacing and fracture aperture for a set of parallel fractures in one direction.

how DNAPLs behave in fractured porous media. In particular, the chemical mass storage capacity of the fractures themselves per unit volume of geologic medium will often be very small. Therefore, a small volume of DNAPL released into a fractured porous medium will often spread extensively throughout the fracture network and eventually occupy a large volume of bulk medium. In addition to the very small total void space due to fractures, the non-wetting phase liquid saturation within the fractures is likely to be less than 1.0. (As described in Chapter 11, this saturation value is a function of the fluid pressures and of the variations in fracture aperture along the fracture surface.) In nearly all cases, it is expected that the DNAPL of interest will be the non-wetting fluid, and therefore that a thin film of water (the wetting fluid) will exist between the DNAPL and the fracture walls (Figure 12.3.a). Because fracture apertures are typically quite small, a DNAPL in fractures will exhibit a large surface area in contact with the water.

Molecular diffusion is the process by which chemical molecules move due to random, "Brownian" motion. If a concentration gradient is present, this motion causes molecules to move from regions of high concentration to regions of low concentration. This process is described mathematically by Fick's First Law as

$$J_D = -\phi D_e \frac{\partial C_w}{\partial x} \quad , \tag{12.1}$$

where J_D is the diffusive flux, ϕ is the system porosity (in this case ϕ_m), D_e is the effective diffusion coefficient in the porous medium, C_w is the dissolved aqueous-phase concentration, and x is distance. Eq.(12.1) is one of several gradient-flux laws used in the physical sciences to describe processes that occur at the molecular scale. Other examples include Darcy's Law for fluid flow through a porous medium due to pressure gradients, Fourier's Law for conduction of heat due to temperature gradients, and Newton's Law of viscosity where the magnitude of fluid shear stress created by velocity gradients is directly proportional to the rate of deformation of the fluid particles.

It was Foster (1975) who first recognized the important effect of **diffusive loss** of dissolved chemical mass from fractures into rock matrices. Foster (1975) used this process to explain the distribution of tritium in fractured limestone (chalk). Following Foster (1975), there have been numerous studies of the diffusive loss of dissolved chemical mass from fractures to the matrix in fractured rock and in fractured clayey deposits. For the latter, these include field studies (Day, 1977; Goodall and Quigley, 1977; McKay *et al.*, 1993a, 1993b, and 1993c), laboratory studies (Grisak *et al.*, 1980; Sudicky *et al.*, 1985; and Starr *et al.*, 1985), and mathematical modeling studies (Grisak and Pickens, 1980 and 1981; Tang *et al.*, 1981; Sudicky and Frind, 1982; Germain and Frind; 1989; Sudicky and McLaren, 1992). These studies have established the dominant influences of fracture aperture, matrix porosity, and D_e for the contaminant on the movement of dissolved species in fracture networks.

Most chlorinated solvents have limited, but nevertheless significant, aqueous solubilities that allow the DNAPL phase to slowly dissolve across the contact area between a DNAPL and adjacent water. Parker *et al.* (1994) and Parker and McWhorter (1994) have discussed how chemical mass will dissolve into the adjacent water film in a fracture, that a chemical concentration gradient will then be established in the aqueous phase, and that

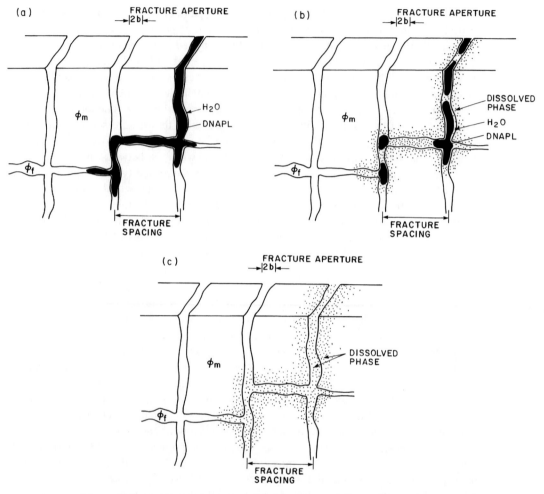

Figure 12.3 Conceptual model for the distribution of DNAPL in a saturated, fractured porous medium with DNAPL as the non-wetting fluid in the fractures. a. Early time: interconnected DNAPL phase. b. Intermediate time: disconnected DNAPL blobs. c. Late time: diffusion haloes in the matrix around fractures that once contained DNAPL.

contaminant mass will then move into the porous matrix by molecular diffusion. Using 1-D and 3-D models for idealized systems, they showed that in some fractured porous media, some DNAPLs (particularly the chlorinated solvents), can **disappear** from fractures in very short time periods, resulting in nearly all of the contaminant mass ultimately moving into the matrix as dissolved and sorbed contaminant.

The above process is described schematically in Figure 12.3, which illustrates the distribution of the contaminant mass in a fractured porous medium at early, intermediate, and late times. At early times, immobile DNAPL and water co-exist in the fractures; the DNAPL is the non-wetting fluid and is present in the largest aperture regions in the fractures, in accordance with capillary pressure considerations. The DNAPL is surrounded by a film of water (as the wetting fluid), and dissolution of the DNAPL phase into the aqueous phase occurs. The concentration of the chemical dissolved in the water film immediately adjacent to the DNAPL quickly becomes saturated with that chemical, and dissolved mass concurrently diffuses into the immobile pore water in the matrix. In Figure 12.3.b, a significant amount of the DNAPL has dissolved, thereby causing the remaining DNAPL to disconnect and redistribute within the larger fracture aperture regions so as to achieve minimal interfacial energy between the two fluids. Eventually (see Figure 12.3.c), the DNAPL dissolves completely, resulting in its disappearance as a separate phase. The chemical mass then exists as diffusion haloes around the fractures that once contained DNAPL. The time periods required for complete DNAPL phase disappearance are specific to the chemical and porous medium conditions. Subsequent flushing of the fractures with uncontaminated groundwater will cause diffusion out of the matrix and into the moving groundwater as the concentration gradients are reversed.

Based on the work of Parker *et al.* (1994) and Parker and McWhorter (1994), we now describe the processes and consequences of DNAPL-phase disappearance from fractures. This is followed by considerations of the effects of matrix diffusion on dissolved-phase plumes migrating through fractured porous media under the influence of advection and dispersion in the fracture network, and diffusion and sorption in the matrix. The implications for migration rates towards downgradient receptors and for current practices used in subsurface investigations and remediation are discussed.

12.2 DNAPL PERSISTENCE IN FRACTURES

12.2.1 Approach

Three sets of calculations are presented in this section to illustrate the relative importance of the diffusive disappearance of an organic liquid phase containing a single component from fractures within a porous medium. The first set of calculations simply compare the mass storage capacity for a DNAPL material within fractures to the mass storage capacity within the matrix blocks that are located between the fractures of a well-characterized fracture network in a particular natural deposit of clay till. The second and third sets of calculations illustrate how quickly mass transfer by diffusion into the porous matrix blocks occurs for typical porous geologic media. Methods to calculate the times for DNAPL-phase disappearance in the fractures due to dissolved-phase diffusion into the matrix are presented. Two idealized fracture cases are considered: a single, parallel-plate fracture adjacent to an infinite porous medium, and sets of parallel fractures in one and three dimensions with corresponding matrix blocks having finite dimensions (*i.e.*, finite distances between fractures).

For this study, four DNAPL chemicals and three fractured media types were selected to represent the range of values typical for real field sites and common DNAPL chemicals. These calculations are also used to illustrate the sensitivity effects of various parameters typical of these environments on the time for DNAPL phase disappearance. The four chemicals selected for these calculations include three chlorinated aliphatics (tetrachloroethylene (PCE), trichloroethylene (TCE), and dichloromethane (DCM)), and one chlorinated aromatic (1,2,4-trichlorobenzene (TCB)). These compounds are commonly used in industry as single-component liquids. Their aqueous solubilities span a wide range that encompasses nearly all of the DNAPL-type contaminants found in groundwater. Table 12.1 gives the relevant physical-chemical properties for the calculations carried out here. The relevant geologic media parameters include the matrix porosity, dry bulk density, fractional organic carbon content, and tortuosity. Parker *et al.* (1994) summarize measured values obtained from the literature for a variety of fractured geologic media. Based on these values, ranges in parameters were selected to be typical of a clay, a sandstone/shale, and a crystalline rock; Table 12.2 presents the values selected for the calculations.

TABLE 12.1   Chemical Properties of Selected Halogenated and Non-Halogenated Organic Compounds Used for Diffusive Mass Loss Calculations (20-25°C).

Compound	Molecular Formula	S_w^1 mg/L	K_{oc} mL/g	MW	ρ^1 g/cm^3	$D_o^{2,3}$ cm^2/s
DCM	CH$_2$Cl$_2$	20,000	11[6a]	85.0	1.33	12.4 × 10^{-6}
TCE	C$_2$HCl$_3$	1,420[4]	92[6a]	131.5	1.46	10.1 × 10^{-6}
PCE	C$_2$Cl$_4$	240[4]	380[6a]	166.0	1.63	9.4 × 10^{-6}
1,2,4-TCB	C$_6$H$_3$Cl$_3$	30[5]	3,200[6b]	181.5	1.46[5]	5.3 × 10^{-6}

Notes:

[1] Schwille (1988)

[2] Bonoli & Witherspoon (1968) for 20°C

[3] Wilke & Chang (1955) for 20°C

[4] Broholm *et al.* (1992) for 23–24°C

[5] Mercer & Cohen (1990)

[6] Schwarzenbach *et al.* (1993)

[a] $\log K_{om} = -0.70 \log S_w + 0.35$

[b] $\log K_{om} = -0.93 \log S_w - 0.17$

where $K_{oc} = 1.724 K_{om}$ (Fetter, 1993)

The scientific literature provides laboratory-measured values for the **free-solution diffusion coefficients** D_o of many organic chemicals and mixtures of chemicals. However, no such values could be found for the four compounds considered here. D_o values for the four compounds were therefore calculated using a correlation equation developed by Wilke and Chang (1955) for dilute solutions of single organic solutes in water. It is the **apparent tortuosity factor** τ which relates the free-solution diffusion coefficient for a chemical species to its **effective diffusion coefficient** D_e in a porous medium. The value of τ can range between zero and unity. Correlation equations for τ as a function of porosity (in this case ϕ_m) are found in the literature in the general form

$$\frac{D_e}{D_o} = \tau \simeq \phi^p \quad , \tag{12.2}$$

TABLE 12.2   Geologic Parameters for Three Types of Fractured Media Used for Comparison of TCE Mass Loss Rates Due to Diffusion and Sorption to Matrix Solids.

Parameter	Type of Geological Medium		
	Clay[1]	Shale/Sandstone[2]	Granite[3]
porosity: ϕ	0.35	0.10	0.006
bulk density: ρ_b (g/cm^3)	1.6	2.4	2.63
fraction organic carbon: f_{oc}	0.01	0.001	0
apparent tortuosity: τ	0.33	0.10	0.06
	Combined Parameters: TCE with Geologic Medium		
effective diffusion coefficient: D_e (cm^2/s)	3.3×10^{-6}	1.0×10^{-6}	6.0×10^{-7}
retardation factor: R	5.2	3.2	1

NOTES:

[1] Johnson *et al.* (1989)

[2] Feenstra *et al.* (1984); Barone *et al.* (1990)

[3] Skagius and Neretnieks (1986)

where the exponent p varies between 1.3 to 5.4, depending on the type of porous geologic medium (Dullien, 1992; Lerman, 1979; and Millington and Quirk, 1961). Low porosity values result in small τ values and low D_e values. Eq.(12.2) is useful because, in many cases, measured D_e values are rarely available.

The chemical mass in the matrix consists of the dissolved mass in the pore water plus the mass sorbed to the matrix solids. The ratio between the two is given by the **retardation factor** R

$$R = 1 + \frac{\rho_b}{\phi_m} K_d \quad , \tag{12.3}$$

where K_d (mL/g) is the distribution coefficient for the compound of interest between the solid and aqueous phases. The value of R will be a constant for a particular chemical/porous medium combination. For non-ionic organic compounds, the equilibrium distribution coefficient K_d (mL/g) for the compound of interest between the solid and aqueous phases is commonly predicted using the fraction of organic carbon f_{oc} in the porous matrix and the partition coefficient of the compound of interest to organic carbon K_{oc} (mL/g) together with the equation

$$K_d = K_{oc} f_{oc} \quad . \tag{12.4}$$

K_{oc} values can be predicted using a correlation equation such as

$$\log K_{oc} = -a \log S_w + b \quad , \tag{12.5}$$

where the appropriate correlation coefficients a and b and the aqueous solubility values S_w of interest can be obtained from the literature (Schwarzenbach *et al.*, 1993; Fetter, 1993; Broholm *et al.*, 1992; Schwille, 1988). Chapter 8 provides additional information regarding the assumptions and limitations involved in using correlation equations like

Eqs.(12.4) and (12.5). R values for the calculations discussed here were obtained using Eqs.(12.3)-(12.5).

12.2.2 Contaminant Mass Storage Capacities

With the above conceptual model in mind for the disappearance of a DNAPL phase in a fractured porous medium, chemical mass in the medium can exist as: 1) DNAPL phase in the fractures; and 2) dissolved and sorbed chemical mass in the matrix blocks between the fractures. The **relative storage capacities** of these two regions in a given fractured porous medium will determine the potential for complete DNAPL phase disappearance in that medium. The fracture and matrix storage capacities for a given DNAPL will depend on the DNAPL density, aqueous phase solubility, and the partition coefficient to the matrix solids. Since the maximum possible aqueous concentration is given by the solubility, then M_m, the maximum chemical mass storage capacity in the matrix per unit volume of fractured porous medium (dissolved plus sorbed), is given by

$$M_m = \phi_m S_w R \tag{12.6}$$

The chemical mass storage capacity in the fractures per unit volume of fractured medium M_f (as DNAPL), is given by

$$M_f = \phi_f \rho \tag{12.7}$$

where ϕ_f is the porosity due to the fractures, and ρ is the density of the DNAPL. When $M_m \geq M_f$, then the potential exists for all of the DNAPL mass in the fractures to dissolve and diffuse into the surrounding matrix material.

To illustrate the above principles for a static case, an example of relative contaminant mass storage capacities is now presented using the fracture characteristics of a surficial clay till deposit in southwestern Ontario, Canada. Field-measured values for fracture apertures and fracture spacings at the site were determined by McKay (1991) and McKay et al. (1993a). We will assume a representative fracture aperture of 15 μm (based on detailed hydraulic data, the fracture apertures were found to be log-normally distributed between 1 and 43 μm). We will also assume a mean fracture spacing of 0.06 m over the depth of visible fractures (6 m). These values yield a calculated fracture porosity of $10^{-3.6}$. This is in the upper range of values calculated by McKay et al. (1993a). Mass storage capacity calculations were performed for three common chlorinated solvents assuming matrix parameters measured for this clay till (Johnson et al., 1989). In a bulk volume of the fractured clay with dimensions of 10 m x 10 m and 6 m deep, the total fracture void volume equals 0.145 m³, and the matrix void volume equals 222 m³ ($\phi_m = 0.37$). Results for this example, given in Table 12.3, show that $M_m > M_f$ for all three solvents.

Using the same fracture network, calculations can also be performed for a typical sedimentary rock. We now let $\phi_m = 0.10$, and $f_{oc} = 0.001$. Although the matrix storage capacity is reduced for this case due to the lower values of ϕ_m and f_{oc}, we still have that $M_m > M_f$ for DCM and TCE (Table 12.3), again indicating the potential for the complete disappearance of these two DNAPL liquids from such fractures.

TABLE 12.3 Contaminant Mass Storage Capacities in Fractures and in the Matrix for Natural Fractured Systems. (The fracture network characteristics are based on concepts presented by McKay (1991).)

Geologic Medium	Chemical	DNAPL Mass in Fracture kg	Dissolved Mass in Matrix kg	Sorbed Mass in Matrix kg	Total Mass in Matrix kg
Type-Clay	DCM	193	4,440	1,064	5,504
	TCE	212	311	1,067	1,378
	PCE	235	53	528	582
Type-Sedimentary Rock	DCM	193	1,200	228	1,428
	TCE	212	84	229	313
	PCE	235	14	113	128

Notes: Clay properties after Johnson *et al.*, 1989:

$\phi = 0.37$ $\rho_b = 1.6$ g/cm^3 $f_{oc} = 0.01$.

Shale/Sandstone Properties after Feenstra *et al.* (1984) and Barone (1989):

$\phi = 0.10$ $\rho_b = 2.4$ g/cm^3 $f_{oc} = 0.001$

Chemical properties from Schwille (1988);

Aqueous solubility for TCE and PCE from Broholm *et al.* (1992).

12.2.3 Rates of DNAPL Loss from Single Fractures

An analytical solution for 1-D diffusion of chemical mass from a fracture surface into the pore water of the matrix was used to calculate DNAPL disappearance times for single-component liquids. Figure 12.4, which is the conceptual model corresponding to the analytical solution, involves a single, parallel-plate fracture containing stagnant DNAPL as a non-wetting liquid. The DNAPL is assumed to fill all of the fracture aperture except for a thin film of water (as the wetting phase) that is assumed to be present along the fracture walls.

The chemical mass flux (M/L^2-T) from the fracture surface into the porous matrix is described by the 1-D form of Fick's First Law, Eq.(12.1). The flux is proportional to ϕ_m, to D_e, as well as to the negative of the concentration gradient of the contaminant in the aqueous phase ($-\partial C_w / \partial x$). It is the concentration gradient that is the driving force for mass transfer. Combining Fick's First Law with the equation for conservation of mass yields Fick's Second Law,

$$\frac{D_e}{R} \frac{\partial^2 C_w}{\partial x^2} = \frac{\partial C_w}{\partial t} \quad , \tag{12.8}$$

where the retardation factor R accounts for partitioning to the solid matrix materials. The analytical solution for diffusive flux at the fracture surface ($x = 0$) at any time t is

$$J_D(0, t) = \phi S_w \sqrt{\frac{R D_e}{\pi t}} \quad , \tag{12.9}$$

where it is assumed that the porous medium is of infinite extent in the direction of diffusion, with constant ϕ_m, D_e, R, and that the concentration at the fracture surface boundary (*i.e.*, at $x = 0$) is constant and equal to the aqueous solubility of the chemical

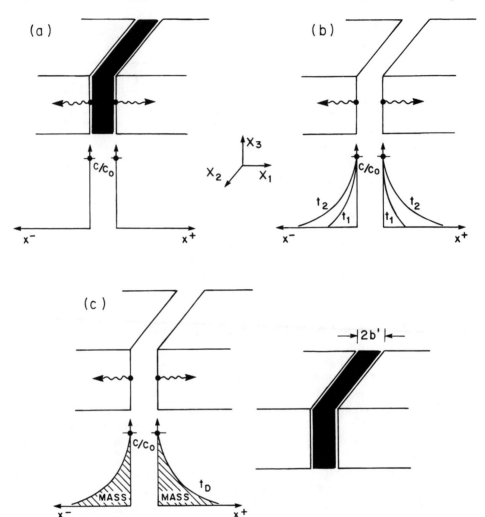

Figure 12.4   a. Physical model used for 1-D diffusion calculations for DNAPL-phase mass loss from a single, parallel-plate fracture with a constant aperture equal to $2b$. The initial conditions are illustrated with the concentration equal to the aqueous solubility limit at the fracture surface and zero concentration in the matrix. b. Schematic of future conditions and concentration profiles at various time periods $t_1 < t_2 < t_D$. c. Conversion of dissolved and sorbed mass in matrix into an equivalent thickness of DNAPL film in a smooth parallel-plate fracture.

$(C_w(0, t) = S_w)$. The initial aqueous phase concentration in the matrix pore water is assumed to be zero $(C_w(x, 0) = 0)$.

Figure 12.4.a illustrates the initial conditions with the concentration at the fracture surface established at the aqueous solubility, and zero concentration in the porous matrix. At $t > 0$, diffusion into the porous matrix results in concentration *vs.* distance profiles of the type shown in Figure 12.4.b. As chemical mass penetrates further and further into the matrix, the concentration gradient (and therefore the driving force for diffusion) decreases with time. According to Eq.(12.9), the mass flux at the fracture surface $J_D(0, t)$ is inversely proportional to the square root of time. Analytical solutions for a variety of other initial and boundary conditions can be obtained from the literature (see Crank, 1975, and Carslaw and Jaeger, 1959).

Eq.(12.9) can be integrated over the time period of interest to provide the total mass diffused into the matrix per unit area of fracture face (M_t). For the parallel-plate fracture case illustrated in Figure 12.4, the solution is

$$M_t = \phi S_w \frac{4}{\sqrt{\pi}} \sqrt{R D_e t} \tag{12.10}$$

Eq.(12.10) accounts for diffusion occurring in both the positive and negative directions (diffusion from both fracture surfaces). The time that elapses between the first arrival of the DNAPL in the fracture and the time required for complete disappearance of the DNAPL is the **disappearance time** t_D. An expression for t_D can be obtained directly from Eq.(12.10). In particular, when $t = t_D$, then M_t will correspond to all of the DNAPL originally in the fracture, *i.e.*, it will correspond to the product of the void volume of the fracture with the density of the DNAPL, all divided by the surface area in the fracture. At that point in time, M_t can then be expressed in terms of the parallel plate fracture aperture $2b$ yielding

$$t_D = \frac{\pi \rho^2}{16 S_w^2 \phi_m^2 D_e R}(2b)^2 \quad . \tag{12.11}$$

Figure 12.4.c thus illustrates the conversion of the mass diffused into the matrix at t_D into an **equivalent DNAPL thickness** ($2b'$) for a single parallel-plate fracture.

As indicated by Eq.(12.10), M_t is directly proportional to ϕ_m and S_w, and is proportional to the square root of R, D_e, and t. However, an examination of the sensitivity of M_t to the various characteristics of a porous medium/chemical combination is made difficult by the fact that a particular property can affect another parameter. For example, S_w affects R (see Eqs.(12.4) and (12.5)). Similarly, ϕ_m affects both τ and R (see Eqs.(12.2) and (12.3)). To de-couple the secondary effects of S_w and ϕ_m on R, we will first consider the mass loss to a porous medium when $R = 1$ (no sorption). This case is conservative in the sense that when $R > 1$, the rate of mass loss is faster and therefore t_D values will be smaller. Other more complicated cases will be considered later. The range of fracture apertures used in the calculations vary from 0.01 to 1000 μm, which is consistent with fracture apertures easily invaded with reasonable heights of continuous DNAPL phase (see Kueper and McWhorter (1991), and also Chapter 11).

Figures 12.5.a and 12.5.b show, for selected times, the equivalent fracture aperture $2b'$ from which various chlorinated solvents would disappear as a function of S_w in clay and sandstone/shale when $R = 1$. For example, in a clay (Figure 12.5.a), TCE, with a solubility of 1,400 mg/L, would disappear from a fracture with an aperture of 13 μm in 10 days. The maximum time considered in the figure is 50 years since this would correspond to the period during which solvents have been widely used (*i.e.*, since the 1940's).

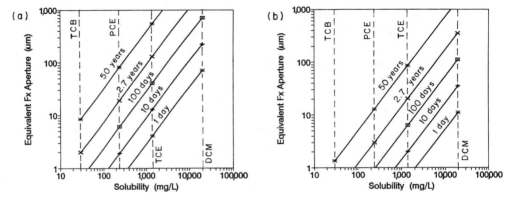

Figure 12.5   Amounts of DNAPL-phase loss expressed in terms of equivalent fracture aperture as a function of DNAPL solubility in water for selected times. No sorption ($R = 1$). a. Type clay. b. Type sandstone/shale. (Fx = fracture.)

DNAPL disappearance for the higher solubility compounds is rapid. For example, in the clay considered here, within 100 days, DCM in a 706 μm fracture and TCE in a 41 μm fracture would completely disappear by diffusion into the matrix. Smaller amounts of PCE and TCB would disappear in the same length of time due to their lower solubilities. Within 2.7 years in clay, all of the PCE in a 19 μm fracture and all the TCB in a 2 μm fracture would diffuse into the matrix. Within 50 years, DNAPL in fractures with apertures ranging from 9 μm (TCB) to 10 mm (DCM) would disappear completely into the clay matrix.

As noted above, the fracture apertures in the weathered, clay-rich deposits within 1 to 4 meters of ground surface at the site in southwestern Ontario mentioned above ranged between 1 and 43 μm (McKay *et al.*, 1993a). The same authors provide a summary of hydraulic apertures for other near-surface fractured, unlithified clay deposits, with values ranging from 1 to 100 μm. Thus, over the range of solubilities typical of single-component DNAPL chemicals, disappearance times presented in Figure 12.5.a are short (a few days to a few years) for fracture apertures typical of these deposits.

Figure 12.5.b presents results for a sedimentary rock (*e.g.*, a sandstone or a shale) with a matrix porosity of 10%. As seen in Eq.(12.11), the t_D value for a given fracture aperture is inversely proportional to ϕ_m^2. With a typical sandstone/shale porosity being approximately one-third that of a typical clay, and also because D_e is smaller for the sedimentary rock, t_D is a factor of 40 larger for the sandstone/shale than it is for the clay. Therefore, for a 13 μm fracture, TCE would disappear into the clay matrix in 10 days, but would require 400 days to disappear into the sandstone/shale matrix. Field-measured values for hydraulic fracture apertures in moderate-permeability sedimentary rocks range from 80-200 μm for a sandstone aquifer on Prince Edward Island (Francis and Gale, 1988) and 120-200 μm for a shale aquitard in southern Ontario (Novakowski and Cherry, 1988) to 120-588 μm for a dolomite aquifer in southern Ontario (Reichart, 1992; Feenstra, 1993). Considering these aperture values and Figure 12.5.b, complete disappearance of the common chlorinated solvents would require on the order of a few years or longer in these materials.

The disappearance times for TCE can also be calculated for a relatively non-porous rock matrix like granite (Figure 12.6). The geologic parameters used for these calculations are summarized in Table 12.2. Crystalline rocks such as granite are relatively non-porous with ϕ_m values that are usually one to three orders of magnitude lower than for sedimentary deposits (Skagius and Neretnieks, 1986); f_{oc} values are near zero. Figure 12.6 illustrates that long time periods are required for significant amounts of chlorinated solvents to be lost from fractures in crystalline rocks. After 27 years, only a 3 μm fracture-equivalent of TCE will be able to diffuse into the granite as compared to 116 μm and 940 μm for the sedimentary rock and clay, respectively. Considering that fracture apertures in rock aquifers can commonly exceed 100-300 μm, complete DNAPL disappearance in crystalline rocks will generally require several centuries.

The results of these initial $R = 1$ simulations clearly show that diffusion into the matrix of a fractured, porous geologic material can be a very significant process causing much or all of the initial DNAPL mass to disappear from the fractures. The results further show that the rate of disappearance is strongly dependent on S_w and ϕ_m. Considering typical materials, chlorinated solvent phase loss from fractures in clay can be very rapid. In sedimentary rock, it is much slower, but nevertheless significant. In crystalline rock, such loss is likely to be minor.

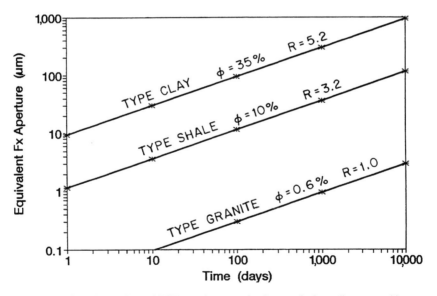

Figure 12.6 Comparison of TCE mass loss rates for three geologic media expressed in terms of equivalent DNAPL-phase fracture aperture and time for DNAPL disappearance: Type clay with $R = 5.2$, type sandstone/shale with $R = 3.2$, and type granite $R = 1$. Parameter values provided in Table 12.2. (Fx = fracture.)

As noted above, the solubility of a DNAPL has a direct effect on its mass loss from a fracture, and an indirect effect on its mass loss through its influence on the partitioning to the matrix solids. As shown in Eq.(12.5) and in Table 12.1, low solubility chemicals have larger K_{oc} values and thus higher preference for the organic carbon present in the matrix. The effects of **sorption** on chemical mass loss from a fracture is a result of its effect on the retardation factor R (see Eqs.(12.3) and (12.4)). For a particular chemical, the value of f_{oc} in the porous matrix determines the value of R, and hence the degree of sorption. Values of f_{oc} for clay-rich deposits typically range between 0.001–0.01 (*e.g.*, see Johnson *et al.*, 1989; Myrand *et al.*, 1992; Anderson and Pankow, 1986; Rowe and Barone, 1991; and Russell, 1993); lower f_{oc} values are likely for lithified sedimentary deposits such as shales and sandstones, with typical values expected to range from 0.0001 to 0.001.

The sorption effect on mass loss from fractures is demonstrated for four chlorinated solvents in Figures 12.7.a-12.7.d by varying f_{oc} for a clay. Because of the low absolute partitioning for DCM, varied partitioning has a small effect on t_D values for this compound (Figure 12.7.a). Increasing effects are observed for TCE, PCE, and TCB since within this group, K_{oc} increases (S_w decreases). We also note that sorption has a greater effect when there is more organic carbon in the porous matrix. For example, for TCB, after 2.7 years, a clay matrix with f_{oc} values of 0.0, 0.001, and 0.01 will result in the disappearance of 2 μm, 8 μm and 24 μm worth of this DNAPL.

In order that the effects of various chemical and porous media properties on disappearance times could be demonstrated, the calculations presented thus far have been for a single fracture in an infinite porous medium. However, in a real porous medium, distances between fractures are finite, causing diffusion to occur in all directions. We also note that the matrix material between fractures has geometries that are variable from site to site, and possibly from location to location at a particular site. Nevertheless, in some cases, the matrix volume can be represented by blocks or columns.

The **matrix block size** becomes relevant when chemical mass invades the matrix to the extent that the concentration gradients become reduced by the chemical mass that is diffusing into the block from the opposite side. Figure 12.8 shows orthogonal sets of parallel fractures in all three dimensions (x_1, x_2, and x_3) with generic diffusion profiles in the matrix for three time periods. At time t_1, the diffusion profiles essentially do not overlap, and the rate of mass loss from both fractures can be calculated using the semi-infinite column approach for the single fracture case presented above. However, once the profiles begin to overlap to any significant extent (t_2 and t_3), the rate of mass loss decreases due to decreased concentration gradients. The point in time when these competing diffusion profiles overlap to a significant extent in the matrix blocks depends on the distance between the fractures as well as on the sorption properties of the chemical and the porous medium. The analytical solutions for calculating disappearance times for cases with finite distances between fractures are presented below in Section 12.2.4.

As discussed in Section 12.2.2, the possibility of complete DNAPL-phase disappearance can be addressed by comparing the maximum (*i.e.*, solubiity-limited) chemical mass storage capacity in the matrix (M_m) to the DNAPL storage capacity in the fractures (M_f), without consideration of the diffusion time. The values of the critical (*i.e.*, minimum) distance between parallel fractures for DNAPL-phase disappearance are presented

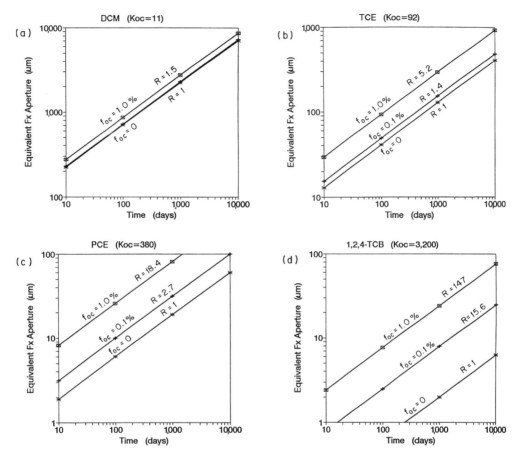

Figure 12.7 Effects of sorption ($R > 1$) on DNAPL phase disappearance times in a clay deposit for four chlorinated organic chemicals with different K_{oc} values and a range of fractional organic carbon contents ($f_{oc} = 0.00$ to 0.01): a. methylene chloride (DCM). b. trichloroethylene (TCE). c. perchloroethylene (PCE). d. 1,2,4-trichlorobenzene (TCB). (Fx = fracture.)

in Figures 12.9.a through 12.9.d for $f_{oc} = 0.001$ as a function of ϕ_m and fracture aperture. The results for the four chemicals in a 100 μm fracture in a 10% porosity matrix (representative of a porous sedimentary rock) show critical distances of < 0.01, 0.1, 0.7 and 5 m for DCM, TCE, PCE and TCB, respectively. These results can be useful when interpreting conditions at actual field sites, *e.g.*, when evaluating the possible presence of DNAPL-phase chemicals in fractures whose apertures have been estimated based on bulk hydraulic conductivities and fracture spacing.

12.2.4 Rates of DNAPL Loss from 3-D Fracture Networks

An analytical solution for the 3-D diffusion of chemical mass from a fracture into pore water in matrix blocks represented as rectangular, parallelepipeds can be used to calculate

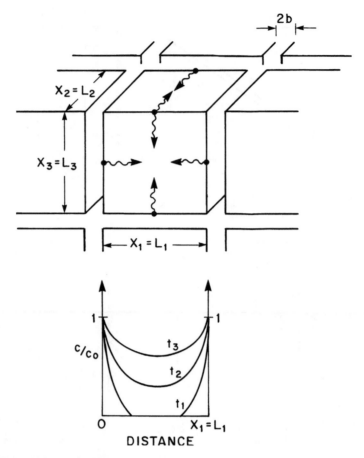

Figure 12.8   Schematic diagram of orthogonal sets of parallel fractures in three dimensions with finite dimension matrix cubes. Generic concentration *vs.* distance profiles for three time periods illustrating the effect of competing diffusion profiles at time steps t_2 and t_3.

disappearance times for single-component DNAPLs. Figure 12.8 shows the conceptual model for the most general case wherein a matrix block that is bounded by fractures on all sides has finite lengths in each principal direction ($x_1 = L_1$, $x_2 = L_2$, $x_3 = L_3$). In this 3-D case, Fick's Second Law for a sorbing solute is

$$\frac{D_e}{R}\left(\frac{\partial^2 C_w}{\partial x_1^2} + \frac{\partial^2 C_w}{\partial x_2^2} + \frac{\partial^2 C_w}{\partial x_3^2}\right) = \frac{\partial C_w}{\partial t} \quad . \tag{12.12}$$

Constant values for D_e, R, and ϕ_m will be assumed. Parker and McWhorter (1994) present the details regarding the development of the analytical solution to Eq.(12.12) for the following initial and boundary conditions: 1) the concentration at the fracture surfaces is constant at the aqueous phase solubility S_w (*i.e.*, $C_w = S_w$ at $x_i = 0$, and $x_i = L_i$ or

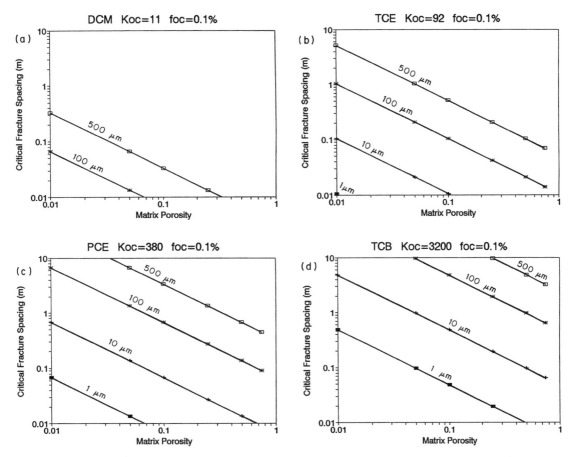

Figure 12.9 The critical fracture spacing required for complete DNAPL phase disappearance in an equivalent fracture aperture calculated as a function of the matrix storage capacity with $f_{oc} = 0.001$ for four compounds: a. methylene chloride (DCM). b. trichloroethylene (TCE). c. perchloroethylene (PCE). d. 1,2,4-trichlorobenzene (TCB). The critical fracture spacing is the minimum spacing that allows complete disappearance and results in an aqueous concentration in the fracture and in the matrix equal to the aqueous solubility limit.

$i = 1, 2,$ and 3 throughout the time period of interest); and 2) initially, the concentration in the matrix pore water is zero (*i.e.*, $C_w(x_1, x_2, x_3) = 0$).

The solution for calculating the total mass diffused at any selected time (M_t) is

$$M_t = S_w R \phi_m L_1 L_2 L_3 (1 - P_1 P_2 P_3) \quad , \tag{12.13}$$

where

$$P_i = \frac{8}{\pi^2} \sum_{n=1,3,5...}^{\infty} \frac{1}{n^2} \exp\left(-n^2 \pi^2 \frac{D_e t}{R L_i^2}\right) \quad . \tag{12.14}$$

for $i = 1, 2, 3$, representing the three principle directions. P is described as the "part remaining" by Glover (1974) for the groundwater drainage problem, and represents the fractional part of the matrix storage capacity remaining at time t for the diffusion problem presented here. P is a function of the dimensionless time variable $D_e t / RL^2$. The quantity M_{ft} is the mass that remains as DNAPL in the fracture at time t. M_{ft} equals the initial mass in the fracture minus the amount of chemical mass that has diffused into the fracture so that

$$M_{ft} = \phi_f \rho L_1 L_2 L_3 - S_w R \phi_m L_1 L_2 L_3 (1 - P_1 P_2 P_3) \tag{12.15}$$

or

$$\frac{M_{ft}}{\phi_f \rho L_1 L_2 L_3} = 1 - \frac{S_w R \phi_m}{\phi_f \rho}(1 - P_1 P_2 P_3) \tag{12.16}$$

Eq.(12.16) expresses the mass remaining in the fracture at a particular time as a fraction of the original amount in the fractures at $t = 0$, and can be used for any idealized rectangular parallelepiped matrix block size.

The results of calculations based on the above equations are presented for two specific cases in Figure 12.10: 1) equally-spaced parallel fractures in 1-D (Figure 12.10.a) so that $L_2 = L_3 = \infty$, and therefore $P_2 = P_3 = 1$; and 2) 3-D matrix block cubes where

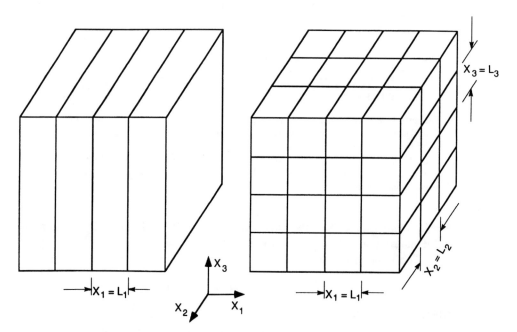

Figure 12.10   Block diagram illustrating idealized fractures networks. a. Parallel fractures in one principal direction (1-D finite distance case). b. Orthogonal sets of parallel fractures in all three principal directions (3-D matrix cube case).

the fracture sets are orthogonal and the distances between parallel fractures in each dimension are equal (Figure 12.10.b) so that $L_1 = L_2 = L_3$ and therefore $P_1 = P_2 = P_3$. The ratio of chemical mass remaining in the fracture at any time relative to the *initial* mass in the fractures equals $M_{ft}/\phi_f \rho L_1 L_2 L_3$, and is a function of the mass storage capacity ratio and the dimensionless time variable $(D_e t/RL^2)$, both of which depend on the properties of the porous medium and the chemical of interest. As noted above in Section 12.2.2, for complete DNAPL disappearance in the fractures to occur, we require that $M_m \geq M_f$. Figures 12.11.a and 12.11.b show that the fraction of DNAPL remaining in the fractures decreases logarithmically toward zero as the dimensionless time increases for the 1-D and 3-D cube cases, respectively.

It is evident from Figures 12.11.a and 12.11.b that the dimensionless disappearance time $(D_e t_D/RL^2)$ decreases as the mass storage capacity ratio increases. When $M_m/M_f = 1$, the curve becomes asymptotic to the x-axis, and the dimensionless disappearance time approaches infinity. Comparing the results for the 1-D finite distance case to the 3-D cube case, for equal values of M_m/M_f, the rate of mass removal from the fractures for the 3-D cube case is greater due to its larger surface area for diffusion than for the 1-D finite distance case. This results in shorter DNAPL phase disappearance times for the 3-D case for specific chemical and porous media conditions. For example, for $M_m/M_f = 4$, the dimensionless disappearance time for the 1-D case is ~ 0.01 compared to ~ 0.001 for the 3-D case.

Disappearance times can be calculated using the dimensionless variables by substituting actual parameter values for the chemical and geologic properties. For TCE and PCE in a fractured clay and in a sedimentary rock, the chemical and porous media parameters may be taken to be the same as in Tables 12.1 and 12.2. For a fracture porosity of 10^{-4}, disappearance times for the two solvents in a 1-D parallel fracture system and in a 3-D orthogonal fracture network are presented for the two porous media types in Table 12.4. Since $M_m/M_f > 1$ in all four combinations, the time periods for DNAPL disappearance from the fractures are finite in every case. For any specified fracture porosity, numerous combinations of fracture aperture and fracture spacing are possible. Three examples are used for each of the four cases to show the effect of fracture aperture on rates of DNAPL phase disappearance. Smaller, more closely-spaced fractures result in larger surface to volume ratios for the DNAPL, enhancing the dissolution rate. This effect is also observable in disappearance times for the 1-D and 3-D cube cases where for constant fracture porosity and fracture spacings, the fracture apertures differ between the two systems. For a 1-D parallel fracture network, the disappearance times are rapid for TCE and PCE in a clay matrix with a fracture porosity of 10^{-4}. For TCE and PCE, these disappearance times range from a few minutes to several weeks, increasing to five years for widely spaced, larger aperture fractures. Disappearance times in fractured sedimentary rocks are longer, and range up to several years to decades.

12.2.5 Limitations

The results presented thus far are based on a number of simplifying assumptions, including single-component DNAPLs, and single idealized fractures or simple fracture

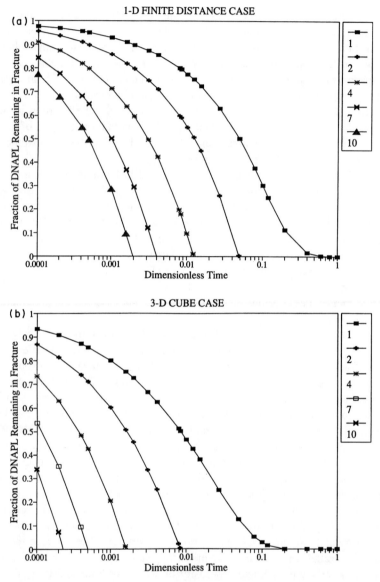

Figure 12.11 Fraction of DNAPL mass remaining in the fractures *vs.* dimensionless time as a function of various chemical mass storage capacity ratios (matrix/fracture). a. 1-D finite distance case. b. 3-D matrix cube case.

networks. The effects of changing various chemical and porous media properties on the disappearance times are easily interpreted for such cases. The values of the chemical properties used in the calculations pertain to 20–25°C. This is warmer than the subsurface temperatures at most North American sites. Although the magnitude and direction

TABLE 12.4 DNAPL Phase Disappearance Times for 1-D and 3-D Finite Dimension Matrix Block Cases. (Porous media and chemical parameter values are provided in Tables 12.1 and 12.2. Both porous media have fracture porosities of 10^{-4}.)

	Type-Clay				Type-Sedimentary Rock			
Chemical	Mass Storage Ratio Matrix/Fracture	Matrix Block Dimension L (cm)	t_D 1-D Finite Distance (days)	t_D 3-D Cubes (days)	Mass Storage Ratio Matrix/Fracture	Matrix Block Dimension L (cm)	t_D 1-D Finite Distance (days)	t_D 3-D Cubes (days)
TCE	17.7	1	0.01	0.002	5.3	1	0.44	0.06
		10	1.1	0.15		10	44	5.6
		100	113	15		100	4,400	560
PCE	9.5	1	0.15	0.02	2.8	1	5.8	0.8
		10	15.0	1.8		10	580	85
		100	1500	180		100	58,000	8,500

Note: For a constant fracture porosity, varying the matrix block dimensions results in changes to the fracture aperture for both cases. For fracture spacings of 1, 10 and 100 cm, the fracture apertures are 1, 10 and 100 μm respectively for the 1-D finite distance block case, and 0.33, 3.3, and 33 μm respectively for the 3-D cube case.

of the necessary temperature corrections depend on the chemical and the system parameters, they are small in comparison to the order of magnitude approximations utilized here for the pertinent geologic parameters (*e.g.*, fracture spacing, fracture aperture, matrix tortuosity, and matrix sorption). Also, assumptions have been made by representing the fractures as smooth parallel-plates. In addition, we have ignored situations in which advection of dissolved contaminant occurs in the water in the fractures, and situations in which the DNAPL in the fractures is replenished from above by downward flow. When relaxed, some of these assumptions have opposite effects on calculated disappearance times.

Thus far, only single-component DNAPLs have been considered. At actual field sites, however, DNAPLs composed of two or more chemicals are common, *e.g.*, mixtures of TCE, PCE, and other solvents. Evaluating matrix diffusion from such multi-component liquids requires consideration of changes in the chemical mole fractions in the DNAPL phase with time as individual components leave by diffusion at different rates due to different aqueous solubilities (thus different concentration gradients), and different diffusion coefficients. The effective solubilities for each component at the fracture surface thus change continuously as the composition of the DNAPL changes with time. Also, physical properties of the DNAPL (*e.g.*, DNAPL density) change due to the changes in composition.

12.3 IMPLICATIONS FOR DNAPL DISAPPEARANCE FROM FRACTURES

12.3.1 Interpretation of Monitoring Well Data

Issues concerning real fractured porous media contaminated with DNAPLs include matters ranging from the interpretation of site conditions to the selection and design of remediation systems. The actual presence of a DNAPL phase in monitoring wells or in boreholes in fractured porous media occurs only seldomly, and when it does occur, it often does so only once (Feenstra and Cherry, 1988; Mercer and Cohen, 1990; U.S.EPA, 1992). This is often taken as evidence of the difficulty in characterizing the fractured media sufficiently well to identify the discrete DNAPL transport pathways. At many sites, an alternative explanation is that much of the DNAPL that may have once filled the fractures has been lost by diffusion into the matrix. Indeed, the calculations presented in this chapter indicate that in many fractured media, a DNAPL solvent phase may persist in the fractures only for a short time relative to the typical age of a DNAPL site.

For the common chlorinated solvents, the concentrations in groundwater obtained from monitoring or extraction wells located within or close to DNAPL source zones are seldom at or approaching the aqueous solubility limit(s). This is commonly attributed to dilution caused when wells are purged and sampled; it is often assumed that some fractures contain groundwater that are at or near the solubility limit, and other fractures that are less connected to the DNAPL source have much lower concentrations. Thus upon sampling, a mixed or diluted value is obtained. However, based on the conceptual model of DNAPL disappearance discussed above, we can envision situations where DNAPL at one time occupied many or all of the fractures in the zone of a monitoring well, but has disappeared due to diffusive mass loss to the matrix, with the aqueous phase concentrations then declining below the solubility limit. In such a situation, concentrations in a monitoring well will be below the solubility limit regardless of where the well intake is situated. Moreover, if the monitoring well is sampled after the point in time when the DNAPL originally entered the monitoring zone, the concentrations in the well could decline progressively with time. This could give the erroneous impression that the overall system is in the process of being "cleaned up" due to flushing by the groundwater flow.

12.3.2 Flow, Immobilization, and Invasion Distances

The flow of NAPLs in rough-walled fractures has been evaluated using 2-D numerical models (Pruess and Tsang, 1990; Kueper and McWhorter, 1991; and Murphy and Thomson, 1993), and using laboratory models (Schwille, 1988). The model simulations indicate that the DNAPL travels in single, rough-walled fractures at rates ranging from minutes to several hours per one meter length of fracture. Kueper and McWhorter (1991) (see also Chapter 11) have examined the influence of various parameters on DNAPL entry into and flow rates through water-saturated fractures. The parameters include fracture aperture and aperture distribution, groundwater gradient, fracture dip from horizontal, DNAPL pool height above the fracture, and DNAPL fluid properties. Given the numerous site specific influences on DNAPL migration through real fractures and the current infeasibility of validating these above referenced models in relation to real fractures, a comparison of DNAPL disappearance times with simulated DNAPL travel times is not yet possible.

Although diffusive mass loss to matrix materials was not considered in the studies discussed in the preceding paragraph, diffusive mass loss into the porous matrix causes the region available for mass distribution to be significantly larger than the fracture porosity. For matrix diffusion to have an effect on DNAPL flow rates and distribution does not require complete DNAPL phase disappearance from fractures, but rather only sufficient mass loss to have a measureable affect on the DNAPL driving forces and permeability in the fracture by changing fluid pressures and resultant fluid saturations.

At the fracture-network scale, the rate of advance of a DNAPL front will be slowed by DNAPL mass loss to the matrix. Assuming a continuous DNAPL phase, the maximum capillary pressure of a DNAPL at its advancing front in the fracture network is a function of the total depth of penetration. Thus, if DNAPL mass in the fractures is continually lost into the matrix, the ability of the DNAPL to invade smaller and smaller fractures with depth will be reduced. The driving forces for penetration of DNAPL in the fracture network will be reduced further if DNAPL mass loss from the fractures results in a disconnection of the DNAPL phase in the fractures (Figure 12.3.b). For a multi-component DNAPL, the driving forces are also affected by changes in the DNAPL composition over time (Parker *et al.*, 1994). Depending on the initial chemical composition, the DNAPL may become heavier or lighter as dissolution proceeds.

For many old industrial waste disposal sites on fractured media, there is concern that free-phase DNAPL continues to flow, causing expansion of the DNAPL zone to locations increasingly distant from the site. There is also a concern of re-mobilizing free DNAPL during drilling or groundwater pumping within source zones. It is often not possible to determine conclusively from site monitoring or mathematical modeling whether DNAPL flow has ceased. However, the probability that DNAPL flow has ceased is highest at sites where the potential for diffusion into the matrix is greatest; likelihood that DNAPL can be remobilized within source zones is also reduced by such conditions.

Ultimately, matrix diffusion affects the distribution of DNAPL in the subsurface by reducing the portion of the fracture network invaded before immobilization of the DNAPL. Thus, the "source zone" is smaller than it would otherwise be, and a portion or all of the contaminant mass then exists in the dissolved and sorbed states within the matrix blocks between the fractures that once contained the DNAPL.

12.3.3 Source Zone Definition and Delineation

Chapter 2 indicated that sites where DNAPL contamination of groundwater is present are generally characterized by two regions of contamination, the source zone and the plume. In the simplest context, the source zone is the domain where DNAPL exists as residual or as pools, and the plume is the domain where contamination exists only in the dissolved and sorbed phases. The plume is caused by dissolution and transport of dissolved contaminant mass away from the immiscible liquid in the source zone. This simple conceptualization of the source zone and its plume is applicable to sites where DNAPL persists with minimal mass loss in porous media as is typical of DNAPLs in sand or gravel, or in fractured non-porous rock such as granite. At sites where DNAPL has entered fractured clay or fractured sandstone, the above discussion has illustrated that the zone initially occupied by the DNAPL can be diminished in size due to diffusion to the matrix.

We now know that in some cases, the DNAPL originally present in fractures can disappear completely due to dissolution and transfer to the matrix. In such a case, the zone that was initially the DNAPL source zone will still contain the contaminant mass, but the contaminant is now all in the dissolved and sorbed phases. While these are the same two phase types that contain the portion of the contaminant that is in the plume, they still act as a source zone inasmuch as chemical mass will be released continuously from the matrix due to the reversed concentration gradients that develop once lower concentrations occur in the fractures of the source zone. We also note that the dissolved concentrations that will ultimately occur in the fractures in this zone after disappearance of the immiscible phase may be small, making it very difficult to determine that this zone was formerly a zone of DNAPL occurrence.

An increasingly-common approach for the remediation of DNAPL sites is the placement of vertical cut-off wall enclosures around the source zones so that the plumes are prevented from causing continued contamination. Once a cut-off wall is in place, the plume outside the enclosure can be controlled and ultimately removed by pump-and-treat. However, at fractured-porous-media sites where appreciable disappearance of the DNAPL has occurred, and also where it is difficult to determine where DNAPL still exists, the potential success of attempts at source-zone isolation can be difficult to determine.

12.3.4 Data Needs for Site Characterization

The selection of an appropriate conceptual model for interpreting site data is essential for the effective design of remedial actions. The effective evaluation of the likelihood of DNAPL persistence in fractured porous media requires a discrete-fracture approach and certain types of field and laboratory data that are rarely obtained. Nevertheless, a basis for evaluating the relative importance of matrix diffusion can be obtained from calculations for DNAPL disappearance times of the type presented in Sections 12.2.3 and 12.2.4 using representative data for the geologic formation, the contaminant(s) present, and an estimate of the elapsed time since the initial contamination by DNAPL. Unfortunately, reliable information on fracture porosity and aperture is exceptionally difficult to obtain, making it difficult to accurately predict disappearance times. However, methods for estimating fracture apertures and fracture porosities exist using various combinations of site data. For example, fracture patterns and frequency with depth can be estimated from core logs, borehole geophysics, and outcrop mapping. Hydraulic data obtained from aquifer tests and well tests can be combined with information regarding fracture frequency to calculate equivalent hydraulic fracture apertures or fracture porosities. At some sites, additional site-specific data should be obtained, including the collection of site-specific samples to determine matrix pore-water concentrations, sorption characteristics, and effective diffusion coefficients. Accounting for the mass that has diffused into the matrix will, in many fractured porous media cases, change the interpretation of the contaminant mass distribution, the processes controlling mass removal, and cleanup times.

12.3.5 Remediation

The restoration of fractured porous media contaminated by DNAPL compounds is a task which is exceptionally difficult, and in many cases, even futile. The difficulty in remediating such sites derives from three main factors: 1) complex fracture networks cause the initial distribution of DNAPL mass to be difficult to predict or locate; 2) dead-end fractures or fractures not well-connected to active groundwater flushing impede cleanup by pump-and-treat systems; and 3) the existence of much or nearly all the contaminant mass in the relatively immobile pore water of the matrix as a result of matrix diffusion greatly increases the time scales required for cleanup. New technologies have been put forth for flushing DNAPLs out of fracture networks such as flushing with surfactants or alcohols with the goal of greatly enhancing the DNAPL solubility and hence increasing the mass removal rates. To be effective, these technologies depend on the presence of and access to DNAPL in the fracture network. They are therefore unsuitable for sites at which the DNAPL has dissolved and diffused into the matrix. Technologies having the best prospects for restoration of fractured porous media are those that rapidly extract dissolved and sorbed contaminant mass from the matrix, or that destroy the contaminant mass by reactions that occur within the matrix.

12.4 DISSOLVED-PHASE TRANSPORT IN FRACTURED POROUS MEDIA

As with the flow of DNAPLs in fractures, groundwater flow in fractured porous media occurs predominantly in the fractures. If the fracture apertures are large, then the groundwater velocity and down-gradient transport of contaminants can be rapid. Dissolved contaminants are subject to diffusion into and out of the matrix.

Plumes of dissolved contaminants can result from groundwater infiltrating through zones of dissolved or DNAPL-phase contamination above the water table, from the dissolution of DNAPLs in source zones below the water table, or from dissolved chemical mass residing in the matrix blocks between the fractures. As with the dissolution and diffusion of DNAPL material in fractures, the influence of matrix diffusion on the overall solute transport in fractures depends upon the combined chemical and geologic characteristics of the system of interest.

For illustrative purposes, two hypothetical scenarios of solute transport in fractured media have been created using a 2-D numerical model developed by Sudicky and McLaren (1992). This model simulates steady-state groundwater flow and transient contaminant transport in discrete parallel-plate fractures within a porous medium. In the first example (Harrison *et al.* 1992), the numerical model was used in a cross-section analysis to assess the importance of vertical planar fractures on solute transport downward through a 15-m thick aquitard overlying a sand aquifer. The second scenario is a plan-view analysis to evaluate two cases of plume development in porous and relatively non-porous fractured rock.

12.4.1 Example 1: Solute Transport Through a Vertically Fractured Clay Aquitard

Figure 12.12 shows the conceptual setting adopted by Harrison *et al.* (1992). The fractured clayey aquitard with a shallow water table overlies a sand aquifer where flow is horizontal. Flow is downward through the aquitard. Contaminants emanate from a near-surface waste zone in the aquitard. The waste zone is generic in the sense that it could represent buried waste, a lagoon, industrial leakage, or some other type of source for which *dissolved* contaminants enter the groundwater flow system from a localized source zone near the water table. The aquitard provides the aquifer with a degree of protection from contamination. This is a common scenario in many regions. The simulation of the contaminant migration though the aquitard into the underlying aquifer provides insight into how a small number of narrow vertical fractures in an aquitard can allow significant leakage of dissolved contaminants through the aquitard.

The simulations for this case were performed for the hydrogeologic cross section shown in Figure 12.13.a. The water table is at the top of the aquitard. The waste zone is 5 m deep and 50 m long. The top of the waste zone is 1.5 m below ground surface. The aquitard has a network of fractures, where nearly all fractures are vertical, with decreasing frequency at depth. Few fractures penetrate the entire thickness of the aquitard. Three vertical fractures extend from the bottom of the waste zone all the way through the aquitard to the aquifer. The fracture frequency and the properties of the clay matrix

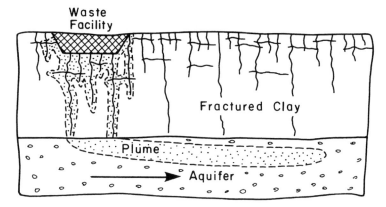

Figure 12.12 Schematic diagram of vertically fractured clay aquitard with contaminant source. Solute transport through the fractures creates a contaminant plume in the underlying aquifer. (Adapted from Harrison *et al.* (1992).)

are assumed to be similar to what has been found by Ruland *et al.* (1991), McKay (1991), McKay *et al.* (1993a and 1993c). The waste zone and the overlying cap material are assumed to be devoid of fractures. The simulations were performed using chemical properties typical of the chlorinated solvents, particularly TCE. Table 12.5 provides the hydraulic conditions and porous media properties used as input parameters.

TABLE 12.5 Numerical Model Input Parameters for Fractured Clay Aquitard Example: 2-D Vertical Flow and Solute Transport (after Harrison *et al.*, 1992).

Parameter	Aquitard	Aquifer	Waste Zone	Cap
Matrix porosity (ϕ_m)	0.50	0.35	0.40	0.50
Hydraulic conductivity (K), cm/s	1.0×10^{-8}	1.0×10^{-2}	1.0×10^{-6}	1.0×10^{-8}
Longitudinal dispersivity (a_1), m	0.0	1.0	1.0	0.0
Transverse dispersivity (a_t), m	0.0	0.02	0.02	0.0
Tortuosity (τ)	0.2	0.7	0.7	0.2
Effective diffusion coefficient (D_e), cm^2/s	1.49×10^{-6}	5.22×10^{-6}	5.22×10^{-6}	1.49×10^{-6}
Distribution coefficient[1] (K_d), mL/g	1.26	0.025	1.26	1.26
Retardation factor[2] (R)	4.2	1.12	5.5	4.2
Fraction of organic carbon (f_{oc})	0.01	0.0002	0.01	0.01

[1]$K_d = f_{oc} K_{oc}$; $K_{oc} = 126$ mL/g
[2]$R = 1 + \rho_b K_d / \phi_m$

The boundary conditions for flow in the calculations consist of specified hydraulic head values along the surface which decline linearly from 26.5 m on the upper left corner to 25.0 m in the upper right corner. This results in a horizontal gradient of 1.67×10^{-3} in the aquifer. These heads were also fixed to provide an average downward hydraulic gradient of 0.95 through the aquitard. Initially, the contaminant mass is assumed to exist entirely in the waste zone at a relative aqueous phase concentration of $C_w/C_o = 1$. In

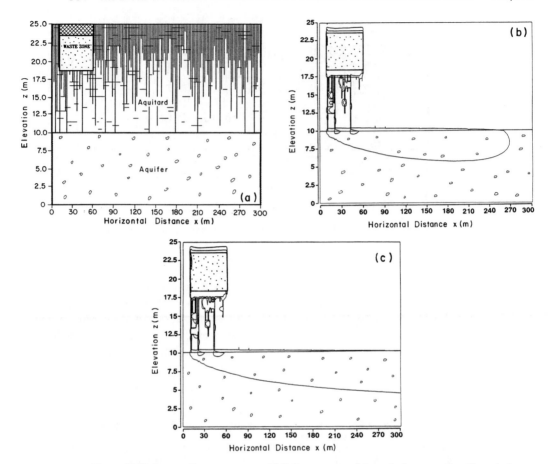

Figure 12.13a,b,c   a. Computer generated 2-D fracture network in vertical cross-section. Numerical simulations for five scenarios: b. 25 μm fractures/25 years solute transport. c. 25 μm fractures after 50 years.

the following results, the outer isoconcentration line represents a relative concentration of $C_w/C_o = 0.01$ and the inner concentration contour represents $C_w/C_o = 0.10$. For the case where the contaminant is TCE and the source concentration equals the aqueous solubility (1,400 mg/L), the outer contour represents 14 mg/L of TCE, which is four orders of magnitude above the maximum TCE contaminant level allowed by the U.S. EPA in public drinking water supplies.

Figures 12.13.b-f show patterns of contaminant migration for five simulations. Groundwater flow causes downward transport of dissolved contaminants from the waste zone into the aquifer. Diffusion to the matrix causes the downward rate of movement of the contaminant front to be greatly retarded relative to groundwater velocity in the fractures. Greater retardation occurs in the smaller aperture fractures. When the fractures are assigned aperture values ranging from very small (5 μm) to slightly larger (25 μm)

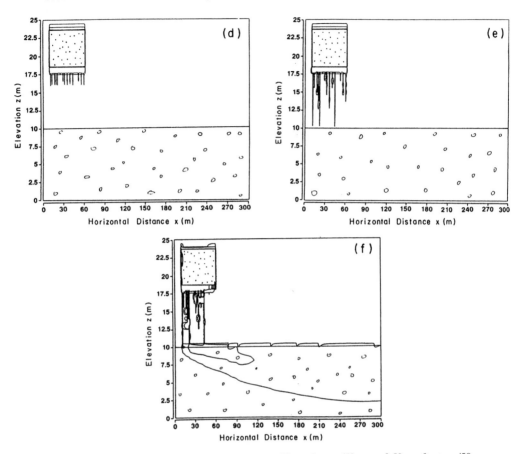

Figure 12.13d,e,f   d. 5 μm fractures/50 years. e. 10 μm fracture/50 years. f. 50 μm fractures/50 years. (Adapted from Harrison *et al.* (1992).)

in size, there is a large difference in the rate of contaminant migration. Over a 50 year period, 5 or 10 μm fractures cause no significant impact on the aquifer (Figures 12.13.d and 12.13.e), whereas fractures of 25 μm or larger cause a large impact on the aquifer in less than 25 years (Figure 12.13.b). In cases where the fractures have apertures less than 10 μm, the contamination front moves downward very slowly not only because the groundwater average velocity in the fracture is reduced by the square of the fracture aperture, but also because the mass of contamination in each fracture is small relative to the surface area of the fracture across which mass transfer by molecular diffusion occurs. Although the 25 μm fractures that fully penetrate the aquitard cause severe contamination of the aquifer, these fractures are nevertheless very small in the context of the hydraulic conductivity that they impart to the aquitard. For example, the bulk vertical hydraulic conductivity of the aquitard when the fractures have 25 μm apertures is on the order of 10^{-9} m/s.

12.4.2 Example 2: Solute Transport in Fractured Porous Rock

This example is taken from Sudicky *et al.* (1993) and Moncur (1992). It uses the same conceptual model as the previous case, and involves 2-D numerical simulations of a plume of dissolved contaminants for two contrasting types of fractured rock, a moderately-porous fractured sandstone and a relatively non-porous fractured granite. Groundwater flow occurs in a square horizontal flow domain, 200 m by 200 m by 10 m thick. The flow domain has fractures generated randomly with the constraint of a minimum fracture spacing of 3 m, and minimum and maximum fracture lengths of 20 to 50 m, respectively (Figure 12.14). Matrix porosity values of 0.20 and 0.02 and hydraulic conductivities of 10^{-6} and 10^{-9} m/sec were used for the sandstone and granite simulations, respectively. The hydraulic characteristics were selected so as to be generally representative of these two different media types. All other hydraulic parameters and system dimensions were the same for all simulations for both media types, with a constant fracture aperture of $100 \, \mu$m, a fracture dispersivity of 0.5 m, a longitudinal dispersivity of 0.10 m, a transverse dispersivity of 0.01 m, an effective diffusion coefficient of 10^{-6} cm^2/sec, and no decay. The resulting fracture porosity calculated for this system is $10^{-4.8}$. These model input values are summarized in Table 12.6.

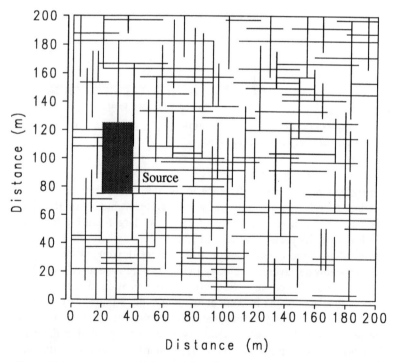

Figure 12.14   Computer-generated horizontal fracture network in two dimensions with contaminant source area. (After Sudicky *et al.* (1993) and Moncur (1992).)

TABLE 12.6 Numerical Model Input
Parameters for Fractured Rock Example: 2-D
Horizontal Flow and Solute Transport (after
Sudicky *et al.* 1993, and Moncur, 1992).

Fracture System (both cases)	
Hydraulic Gradient	0.01
Fracture Aperture $2b$	100 μm
Fracture Porosity ϕ_f	$10^{-4.8}$
Thickness	10 m

No Retardation ($R = 1$)	
Sandstone Case	
Matrix Porosity ϕ_m	0.20
Matrix Hydraulic Conductivity	10^{-6} cm/s
Diffusion Coefficient D_e	10^{-6} cm^2/s
Granite Case:	
Matrix Porosity ϕ_m	0.02
Matrix Hydraulic Conductivity	10^{-9} cm/s
Diffusion Coefficient D_e	10^{-6} cm^2/s

Groundwater flow from left to right in Figure 12.14 is driven by a hydraulic gradient of 0.01. The contaminant source is a 20 m by 50 m zone near the left (upgradient) side of the system, and has an isotropic hydraulic conductivity of 10^{-2} cm/sec. The source is considered to be a "slug source" with initial solute concentration $C_w/C_o = 1$, allowing the source to be depleted with time. The simulations presented in Figure 12.15 show the effects of matrix diffusion for 20 and 100 year periods. The sandstone has an order of magnitude greater matrix porosity than does the granite. This increases the effective diffusion coefficient, and hence the rate of solute mass transfer from the fracture to the matrix. Thus, the downgradient travel distances of the plume in the fractured granite cases far exceed the distances of migration for the sandstone cases.

12.5 CONCLUSIONS

Matrix diffusion from DNAPLs in fractures can cause a significant portion of chemical mass to be transferred to matrix materials with low hydraulic permeabilities. The most important parameters governing the rate of disappearance of a given DNAPL compound are its water solubility, the matrix porosity, and the matrix sorption capacity. This becomes evident when comparing disappearance times from single fractures for equivalent DNAPL film thicknesses for various chemicals, and for clay materials *vs.* sedimentary

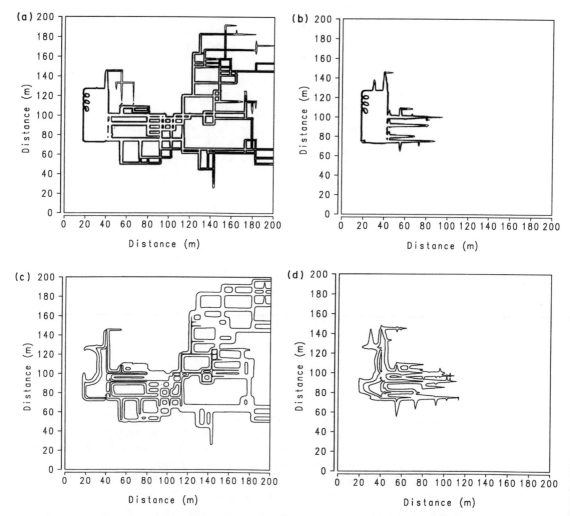

Figure 12.15 Computer simulations of contaminant plumes after 20 and 100 years of transport in 100 μm fractures for: a. granite aquifer after 20 years. b. sandstone aquifer after 20 years. c. granite aquifer after 100 years. d. sandstone aquifer after 100 years. (After Sudicky *et al.* (1993) and Moncur (1992).) The outside contour represents $C_w/C_o = 0.01$ for the 20-year simulations and $C_w/C_o = 0.1$ for the 100-year simulations.

rocks. The pertinent parameters for the chlorinated solvents and fractured media of interest vary over several orders of magnitude. Therefore, the values selected for specific calculations have a strong influence on the calculated DNAPL disappearance times from fractures. For typical fractures in unlithified, clay-rich deposits, matrix diffusion can cause the common chlorinated solvents to completely dissolve and disappear as DNAPLs in time periods that vary from a few months to years. This is also the case for small to medium size fractures in sedimentary rocks. Hence, matrix diffusion is an important process in the conceptual model used to describe DNAPL flow and distribution in fractured porous media. Indeed, calculations show that there is considerable potential for chlorinated solvent DNAPLs to completely disappear from fractures, that is to undergo a complete phase change from DNAPL in the fractures to the dissolved and sorbed phases in the matrix. This suggests that at many industrial sites where chlorinated solvents and other modestly soluble DNAPLs have entered fractured porous media in past decades, it is likely that little or no DNAPL remains in the fractures.

The concepts discussed above apply to single as well as multi-component DNAPLs, and also to NAPLs that are lighter than water (*i.e.*, to "LNAPLs"). For larger fracture porosities where the matrix/fracture mass storage capacity ratio is less than one, complete disappearance will not occur by diffusion into the matrix alone. However, advection of solutes away from the DNAPL zone(s) in the fracture network will enhance the potential for such disappearance. Examples of geological conditions where rapid disappearance is not expected are fractured rocks with very large fractures (*e.g.*, dissolution channels in karst formations), and rocks with matrix porosities of less than 1% (*e.g.*, granite and most other crystalline rocks). In rocks with low matrix porosities, DNAPL disappearance from fractures of typical aperture could take centuries to millennia. Also, complete disappearance is not expected to occur in situations where flow of the DNAPL (or LNAPL) replenishes the liquid lost by diffusion to such a degree that the storage capacity in the matrix is exceeded.

In low-permeability deposits that are not fractured, or have fractures of very small apertures, matrix diffusion plays a dominant role in determining the migration distances of dissolved organic solutes. The result is long time frames for contaminant migration, even over short distances. In cases where contaminants are released to aquitards overlying aquifers, a high degree of protection is provided to the underlying aquifers.

The presence of small-aperture fractures in otherwise low-permeability deposits has been found to increase the bulk hydraulic conductivities by one to three orders of magnitude. Also, given that the average linear groundwater velocity in such fractures can be large, the travel times for water to underlying aquifers are very short. However, due to diffusive mass loss of the contaminant from the fracture into the matrix, chlorinated solvents moving in the fractures will advance only slowly relative to the average linear groundwater velocity in the fracture network. Chemicals that sorb to the fracture surfaces and matrix solids advance more slowly than non-sorbing solutes due to increased rate of mass loss to the matrix. We can conclude that if realistic transport rates of contaminants to groundwater receptors are to be estimated, then it will be important to determine the nature and frequency of any fractures present in the media of interest as well as the properties of the matrix (porosity, sorption capacity, and diffusion characteristics).

DNAPL loss from fractures and contaminant distribution in the matrix has important implications with respect to the interpretation of data from monitoring wells, assessment of ultimate risk to receptors, and selection and design of remedial measures. We note though that two inherent difficulties exist with interpreting the transport and fate of NAPLs and dissolved contaminants in fractured porous media: 1) the contaminant mass in the fractures can be difficult to quantify due to the difficulty in characterizing the fractures; and 2) the contaminant mass in the matrix is rarely measured in site investigations. Even though detailed determinations of this type are not generally feasible, it should be possible to make significant advances in transport and fate assessments by acquiring information of this nature in site investigations.

ACKNOWLEDGEMENTS

Funding support for this research was provided in part by the University Consortium Solvents-in-Groundwater Research Program. Sponsors of the Program between 1988 and 1994 have included: The Boeing Company, Ciba-Geigy Corporation, Dow Chemical Canada/USA, Eastman Kodak Co., General Electric Co., Laidlaw Environmental Systems Ltd., Mitre Corporation, The Natural Sciences and Engineering Research Council of Canada, and the Ontario University Research Incentive Fund.

12.6 REFERENCES

Anderson, M. R. and J. F. Pankow (1986) "A case study of a chemical spill: polychlorinated biphenyls (PCBs). 3. PCB sorption and retardation in soil underlying the site", *Water Resources Research*, **22**, 1051-1057.

Barone, F. S., R. K. Rowe, and R. M. Quigley (1990) "Laboratory determination of chloride diffusion coefficient in an intact shale", *Canadian Geotech. J.*, **27**, 177-184.

Bonoli, L. and P. A. Witherspoon (1968) "Diffusion of aromatic and cycloparaffin hydrocarbons in water from 2 to 60°", *J. Phys. Chem.*, **72**, 2532-2534.

Broholm, K., J. A. Cherry, and S. Feenstra (1992) "Dissolution of heterogeneously distributed solvents residuals". In: *Proceedings: Subsurface Restoration Conference,* 3rd International Conference on Ground Water Quality Research, June 21-24, 1992, Dallas, Texas.

Carslaw, H. S. and J. C. Jaeger (1959) *Conduction of Heat in Solids*, Oxford University Press, New York.

Crank, J. (1975) *The Mathematics of Diffusion, Second Edition*, Clarendon Press, Oxford.

Day, M. J. (1977) *Analysis of Movement and Hydrochemistry of Groundwater in the Fractured Clay and Till Deposits of the Winnipeg Area, Manitoba*, M.Sc. Thesis, Dept. of Earth Sciences, University of Waterloo, Waterloo, Ontario Canada.

Dullien, F. A. L. (1992) *Porous Media: Fluid Transport and Pore Structure, 2nd Ed.* Academic Press, Inc., San Diego, California.

Feenstra, S., J. A. Cherry, E. A. Sudicky, and Z. Haq (1984) "Matrix diffusion effects on contaminant migration from an injection well in fractured sandstone", *Ground Water*, **22**, 307-316.

Feenstra, S. and J. A. Cherry (1988) "Subsurface contamination by dense non-aqueous phase liquid (DNAPL) chemicals". Presented at the International Groundwater Symposium, International Association of Hydrogeologists, Halifax, Nova Scotia, May 1-4, 1988.

Feenstra, S. (1993) *Waterloo Centre for Groundwater Research Short Course Lecture Notes: Dissolved Organic Contaminants in Groundwater*, Feb. 15-18 in Chicago, Illinois.

Fetter, C. W. (1993) *Contaminant Hydrogeology*, Macmillan Publishing Company, New York.

Foster, S. S. D. (1975) "The chalk groundwater tritium anomaly-a possible explanation", *J. Hydrology*, **25**, 159-165.

Francis, R. and J. Gale (1988) "Permeability distribution in a fractured sedimentary aquifer system". Presented at the International Groundwater Symposium of the International Association of Hydrogeologists, Canadian National Chapter, Atlantic Region, Halifax, Nova Scotia, May 1-5, 1988.

Germain, D. and E. O. Frind (1989) "Modelling of contaminant migration in fracture networks: Effects of matrix diffusion". In: *Proceedings: International Symposium on Contaminant Transport in Groundwater*, Stuttgart, Germany, April.

Glover, R. E. (1974). *Transient Ground Water Hydraulics*. Unpublished report, Dept. of Civil Engineering, Colorado State University, Fort Collins, Colo.

Goodall, D. C. and R. M. Quigley (1977) "Pollutant migration from two sanitary landfill sites near Sarnia, Ontario", *Canadian Geotech. J.*, **14**, 223-236.

Grisak, G. E. and J. F. Pickens (1980) "Solute transport through fractured media. 1. The effects of matrix diffusion", *Water Resources Research*, **16**, 719-730.

Grisak, G. E., J. F. Pickens, and J. A. Cherry (1980) "Solute transport through fractured media: 2. Column study of fractured till", *Water Resources Research*, **16**, 731-739.

Grisak, G. E. and J. F. Pickens (1981) "An analytical solution for solute transport through fractured media with matrix diffusion", *J. Hydrology*, **52**, 47-57.

Harrison, B., E. A. Sudicky, and J. A. Cherry (1992) "Numerical analysis of solute migration through fractured clayey deposits into underlying aquifers", *Water Resources Research*, **28**, 515-526.

Hoek, E. and J. W. Bray (1977) *Rock Slope Engineering, 2nd Ed.*, Institution of Mining and Metallurgy, London.

Johnson, R. L., J. A. Cherry and J. F. Pankow (1989) "Diffusive contaminant transport in natural clay: A field example and implications for clay-lined waste disposal sites", *Environ. Sci. Technol.*, **23**, 340-349.

Kueper, B. H. and D. B. McWhorter (1991) "The behavior of dense, nonaqueous phase liquids in fractured clay and rock", *Ground Water*, **29**, 716-728.

Lerman, A. (1979) *Geochemical Processes: Water and Sediment Environments*, John Wiley & Sons, Inc. New York.

McKay, L. D. (1991) *Groundwater Flow and Contaminant Transport in Fractured Clay Till*, Ph.D. Thesis, Dept. of Earth Sciences, University of Waterloo, Waterloo, Ontario.

McKay, L. D., J. A. Cherry, and R. W. Gillham (1993a) "Field experiments in a fractured clay till: 1. Hydraulic conductivity and fracture aperture", *Water Resources Research*, **29**, 1149-1162.

McKay, L. D., J. A. Cherry, R. C. Bales, M. T. Yahya, and C. P. Gerba (1993b) "A field example of bacteriophage as tracers of fracture flow", *Environ. Sci. Technol.*, **27**, 1075-1079.

McKay, L. D., R. W. Gillham, and J. A. Cherry (1993c) "Field experiments in a fractured clay till: 2. Solute and colloid transport", *Water Resources Research*, **29**, 3879-3890.

Mercer, J. W. and R. M. Cohen (1990) "A review of immiscible fluids in the subsurface: Properties, models, characterization and remediation", *J. Contaminant Hydrology*, **6**, 107-163.

Millington, R. J. and J. P. Quirk (1961) "Permeability of porous solids", *Trans. Faraday Soc.*, **57**, 1200-1207.

Moncur, M. C. (1992) *Simulation of Contaminant Movement and Pump and Treat Remediation in Fractured Porous Media*, M.Sc. Project, Dept. Earth Sciences, University of Waterloo, Waterloo, Ontario.

Murphy, J. R. and N. R. Thomson (1993) "Two-phase flow in a variable aperture fracture", *Water Resources Research*, **29**, 3453-3476.

Myrand, D., R. W. Gillham, E. A. Sudicky, S. F. O'Hannesin, and R. L. Johnson (1992) "Diffusion of volatile organic compounds in natural clay deposits: Laboratory tests. *J. Contaminant Hydrology*, **10**, 159-177.

Novakowski, K. S. and J. A. Cherry (1988) "Evaluating groundwater velocity in a low-permeability fractured shale". In: *Proceedings: Technology Transfer Conference*, Ontario Environment, Canada, Nov. 28-29, 1988, pp. 273-282.

Parker, B. L. and D. B. McWhorter (1994) "Diffusive disappearance of immiscible phase organic liquids in fractured media: Finite matrix blocks and implications for remediation". Presented at the International symposium on "Transport and Reactive Processes in Aquifers," ETH Zurich, Switzerland, April 11-15.

Parker, B. L., R. W. Gillham, and J. A. Cherry (1994) "Diffusive dissappearance of dense, immiscible phase organic liquids in fractured geologic media", *Ground Water*, **32**, 805-820.

Pruess, K. and Y. W. Tsang (1990) "On two-phase relative permeability and capillary pressure of rough-walled rock fractures", *Water Resources Research*, **26**, 1915-1926.

Reichart, Todd M. (1992) *Influence of Vertical Fractures in Horizontally-Stratified Rocks*. M.Sc. Thesis, Dept. of Earth Sciences, University of Waterloo, Waterloo, Ontario.

Rowe, R. K. and F. S. Barone (1991) *Diffusion tests for chloride and dichloromethane in Halton Till, Halton Waste Management Site,* Unpublished report to Gartner Lee, Ltd., Markham, Ontario. December, 1991.

Ruland, W. W., J. A. Cherry, and S. Feenstra (1991) "The depth of fractures and active groundwater flow in a clayey till plain in southwestern Ontario", *Ground Water*, **29**, 405-417.

Russell, B. M. (1993) *Nitrate Persistence in Slightly Permeable Sediments in Southern Ontario,* M.Sc. Thesis, Dept. of Earth Sciences, University of Waterloo, Waterloo, Ontario.

Schwarzenbach, R. P., P. M. Gschwend, and D. M. Imboden (1993) *Environmental Organic Chemistry*, John Wiley and Sons, New York.

Schwille, F. (1988) *Dense Chlorinated Solvents*, translated by James F. Pankow, Lewis Publishers, Boca Raton, Florida.

Skagius, K. and I. Neretnieks (1986) "Porosities and diffusivities of some nonsorbing species in crystalline rocks", *Water Resources Research*, **22**, 389-398.

Starr, R. C., R. W. Gillham, and E. A. Sudicky (1985) "Experimental investigation of solute transport in stratified porous media: 2. The reactive case", *Water Resources Research*, **21**, 1043-1050.

Sudicky, E. A. and E.O. Frind (1982) "Contaminant transport in fractured porous media: Analytical solutions for a system of parallel fractures", *Water Resources Research*, **18**, 1634-1642.

Sudicky, E. A., R. W. Gillham, and E. O. Frind (1985) "Experimental investigation of solute transport in stratified porous media: 1. The nonreactive case", *Water Resources Research*, **21**, 1035-1041.

Sudicky, E. A. and R. G. McLaren (1992) "The Laplace Transform Galerkin technique for large-scale simulation of mass transport in discretely fractured porous formations", *Water Resources Research*, **28**, 499-514.

Sudicky, E. A., R. G. McLaren, and J. VanderKwaak (1993) *Characterization of contaminant migration processes in fractured geologic media and numerical analysis of pump-and-treat re-*

mediation, Progress Report on Project No. 596G, Ontario Ministry of the Environment, March 8, 1993.

Tang, D. H., E. O. Frind, and E. A. Sudicky (1981) "Contaminant transport in fractured porous media: Analytical solution for a single fracture", *Water Resources Research*, **17**, 555-564.

U.S.EPA (1992). *Dense Nonaqueous Phase Liquids–A Workshop Summary*, EPA/600/R-92/030, Dallas, Texas, April 16-18, 1991.

Wilke, C. R. and P. Chang (1955) "Correlation of diffusion coefficients in dilute solutions", *Am. Inst. Chem. Eng. J.*, **1**, 264-270.

13

Diagnosis and Assessment of DNAPL Sites

Stan Feenstra[1] and John A. Cherry[2]

[1]Applied Groundwater Research Ltd.
2550 Argentia Road
Mississauga, Ontario
Canada, L5N 5R1

[2]Waterloo Centre for Groundwater Research
University of Waterloo
Waterloo, Ontario
Canada, N2L 3G1

ABSTRACT

At many sites that are contaminated with chlorinated solvent compounds, there is no direct visual evidence of solvent in the form of dense non-aqueous phase liquid (DNAPL) either in soil cores or in monitoring wells. A lack of direct evidence does not, however, necessarily mean that DNAPL material is not in the subsurface. Indeed, spatial variability in the subsurface distribution of DNAPLs as well as the nature of the field investigation methods typically used to investigate DNAPL sites can prevent subsurface DNAPL from being found, even when there are large amounts present. The likelihood that DNAPL will be identified if encountered in borings can be improved through the use of: 1) careful visual examinations during drilling; 2) enhanced visual inspections using dyes and/or UV light; 3) vapor analyses; 4) chemical analyses of soils and rock samples; and 5) borehole geophysics. The identification of DNAPL in wells will also be enhanced by use of appropriate drilling, well construction, and well sampling procedures. The presence and distribution of DNAPL can be assessed indirectly by evaluating the character of dissolved plumes, and in some circumstances, through the use of soil gas surveys. Overall, a number of lines of evidence can be pursued at any given site to evaluate the possible presence of subsurface DNAPL. In any given circumstance, however, usually just a few of those lines of evidence yield valuable information. The challenge at a given site is to render an opinion, based on the available evidence, regarding the likely presence or absence of subsurface DNAPL.

13.1 INTRODUCTION

In order to develop rational and cost-effective plans for remediation at sites having groundwater contaminated by chlorinated solvents, it is essential to determine if any **dense non-aqueous phase liquid (DNAPL)** is present in the subsurface, and if so, to also determine the nature of that DNAPL contamination. The purpose of this chapter is to describe the use of various types of site information for the diagnosis and assessment of the presence and distribution of DNAPLs in the subsurface.

The term "DNAPL site" will be used here to designate any site at which appreciable DNAPL (either residual or free (*i.e.*, mobile) phase) exists below the water table. At many sites there is no direct visual evidence from soil cores or from samples from monitoring wells that DNAPL exists in significant quantities in the groundwater zone. However, because of the potential variability in the spatial distribution of DNAPLs and of the investigative methods commonly used, this need not mean that DNAPL is not present.

Many problems can arise when a DNAPL site is mis-diagnosed as a non-DNAPL site. For example, a failure to diagnose the presence of DNAPL can result in the failure of groundwater pump-and-treat measures intended to provide aquifer restoration. Failure to identify the presence of DNAPL during drilling through source zones or during the design of remedial measures in source zones can result in remobilization of the DNAPL and further spreading of the DNAPL, and worsening of the groundwater contamination problem.

The diagnosis of DNAPL sites can occur in different ways. Until recently, many diagnosis exercises involved consideration of various types of existing data obtained during normal hydrogeological site investigations. In some of these cases, DNAPL diagnosis has been part of a retrospective exercise after remedial actions such as groundwater pump-and-treat have already begun. Frequently, the diagnosis exercise is conducted during a post-mortem to determine the "cause of death" of the remedial action. In other cases, supplemental field investigations are conducted which focus specifically on the issue of the presence of DNAPL. Ideally, the consideration of the potential presence of DNAPL and the collection of the appropriate field information to allow DNAPL diagnosis should be a fundamental part of the initial site investigation.

The primary goal in the diagnosis and assessment of DNAPL sites is to establish the likelihood that significant quantities of DNAPL are present in the subsurface. Of the techniques that can be considered at the present time, only the visual observation of DNAPL or measurement of dissolved contaminants at saturation levels provides unequivocal evidence of DNAPL presence. Until recently, this was the only type of information which would have lead site investigators and regulators to recognize the presence of DNAPL.

Many lines of evidence can contribute to the diagnosis of DNAPL sites, but normally, only a few contribute strongly to the diagnosis of any particular site. At most sites, sufficient data are not available or conditions are not appropriate to allow all possible techniques to be used. The site information that may be most convincing at one site may be less convincing at another site. The challenge at any given site is to assess the various lines of evidence to in order to render a judgment based on the preponderance of all of the available evidence. Because the diagnosis of DNAPL sites considers much evidence that requires careful interpretation, the conclusions depend frequently on the experience of the site diagnostician. It is our observation that less experienced site assessors are less likely to conclude that DNAPL is present, whereas site assessors with greater experience at DNAPL sites are more likely to conclude that DNAPL is present.

This chapter is intended to provide a comprehensive description of the investigative and interpretive techniques for the diagnosis of the presence of DNAPL. These techniques include: assessment of the site with regard to the chemicals used, nature of handling and disposal, and subsurface conditions; observations made during drilling and in wells, and results from analyses of soil, rock, and groundwater samples. While it might be preferred by regulators that a more formal procedure for the determination of DNAPL presence be developed, many of the possible lines of evidence are subjective in nature and it is unlikely that a quantitative assessment of the probability of DNAPL occurrence is possible.

The simple recognition that DNAPL is present somewhere in the groundwater zone will not be sufficient for a detailed analysis of past or future DNAPL migration, or the detailed design of remedial measures which involve containment or *in situ* treatment of the source zone. These types of activities require definition of the spatial distribution of the DNAPL zone vertically and laterally, including the location and size of lenses, pools, and residual zones. We note in this context that many of the field investigation techniques used to assess DNAPL presence can also be utilized to assess the spatial distribution of DNAPLs. For a detailed assessment of DNAPL migration, information on the chemical composition, density, viscosity and interfacial tension for the DNAPL will be required, and efforts will often be undertaken specifically to collect DNAPL samples for laboratory testing. Such samples might also be required to allow bench-scale testing of remediation technologies such as surfactant or alcohol flooding.

13.2 GENERAL SITE ASSESSMENT

A general assessment of an industrial or waste disposal site can be made to determine the potential presence of a DNAPL in the groundwater zone. This general assessment can usually made early in a site investigation program using existing information about the site. The site assessor must consider if the chemicals found at the site, or expected at the site, could comprise DNAPLs, and if the activities at the site could have resulted in the release of significant quantities of DNAPL into the subsurface.

13.2.1 Types of Chemicals That Are DNAPLs

The first step in the assessment of a potential DNAPL site is a consideration of the types of chemicals which are found, or might be present at the site. For example, information that large quantities of chlorinated solvents were used or disposed of at a site is an obvious warning of the possible presence of a DNAPL phase in the subsurface.

A wide variety of chemical products and wastes may comprise a DNAPL. For a chemical to be regarded here as a potential DNAPL in a given circumstance, it must have a fluid density greater than 1.01 g/cm^3, a solubility in water of less than 2% (or about 20,000 mg/L), and a vapor pressure of less than 300 torr. For a potential DNAPL to be an actual DNAPL at a given site, then the amount of the chemical that was released to the subsurface will need to have been in excess of the total amount that could have dissolved into the water and sorb to the soil materials in the source zone. Compounds which are either more soluble than 2% or more volatile than 300 torr would not generally be expected to persist as DNAPL phases in the subsurface.

Chlorinated solvents are regarded as the most important class of DNAPL chemicals. Other classes of DNAPL chemicals include some halogenated aromatics, phthalates, coal tar, creosote, PCB Aroclors, and some pesticides (see Table 1.1). Some of these other compound classes have chemical and physical properties that are comparable to those of the chlorinated solvents, but they have been produced in smaller quantities and have been used in fewer industries.

As is discussed in detail in Chapter 1, the **chlorinated solvents** have been produced, transported and used in very large quantities by a wide variety of industries for almost fifty years. The U.S. production of the four principal chlorinated solvents of perchloroethylene (PCE), trichloroethylene (TCE), 1,1,1-trichloroethane (1,1,1-TCA), and dichloromethane (DCM) have ranged from 250 million kg to 350 million kg per year. As a result of occupational health considerations, TCE use has declined in favor of 1,1,1-TCA for many degreasing and cleaning operations. 1,1,1-TCA use will, in turn, begin to decline as a result of reductions in the production of ozone-depleting chemicals.

Most chlorinated solvents have densities that range from 1.1 g/cm^3 (as for chlorobenzene) to 1.63 g/cm^3 (as for PCE). Viscosities are less than or similar to that of water. These high densities and low viscosities make this class of DNAPLs the most mobile as a separate non-aqueous phase, and therefore the one possessing the greatest potential for migration in the subsurface. Also, while the chlorinated solvents have solubilities that are as much as a hundred thousand times higher than their respective drinking water standards, these solubilities are low in absolute terms, thus favoring the persistence of a separate DNAPL phase following a spill.

Coal tar is a waste product of coal or oil gasification, and iron and steel production. Coal and oil gasification was used to produce gas for heating and lighting in most North American cities from the mid-1800's until about 1950 when natural gas became widely available. From the beginning of gasification operations until about 1900, coal tar was generally disposed of on-site at the gasification plants. Coal tar is currently produced almost exclusively as a by-product from blast furnace coking in iron and steel production. **Creosote** is typically distilled from coal tar. Creosote, in its pure form or mixed with petroleum hydrocarbons (such as fuel oil), has been used as a wood preserving chemical in North America for more than one hundred years. Coal tar and creosote have physical and chemical properties which are very different from those of the chlorinated solvents.

Their densities are only slightly greater than water (1.01 g/cm^3 to 1.05 g/cm^3), and their viscosities are greater than water (10 to 100 cP). These properties make coal tar and creosote the least mobile of the common DNAPLs. However, coal tar and creosote sites are generally characterized by the presence of very large volumes of DNAPL. The components of coal tar and creosote such as the polycyclic aromatic hydrocarbons (PAHs) have very low solubilities, and sorb strongly to geologic media. As a result, coal tar/creosote DNAPL sites seldom create large dissolved contaminant plumes in groundwater.

Polychlorinated biphenyls (PCBs) have been used as dielectric fluids in electrical transformers and capacitors, and have had a variety of other industrial uses from about 1930 until the mid-1970s when the manufacture of these chemicals was discontinued in the U.S. In the late 1960s, PCB production reached almost 35 million kg per year with about 50% of the production used in transformers and capacitors. A significant portion of the PCB inventory produced is still in service in transformers and capacitor installations. Aroclors 1221, 1232, 1242, and 1248 are fluid PCB oils with densities ranging from 1.18 g/cm^3 to 1.42 g/cm^3. Some commercial formulations for dielectric fluids were comprised of mixtures of one or more Aroclors with trichlorobenzenes. For example, the product Askarel Inerteen 70-30 was formulated as 70% Aroclor 1254 and 30% trichlorobenzenes, and is a liquid with a density of 1.49 g/cm^3. The viscosities of the Aroclors range from about 5 cP for Aroclor 1221 to 65 cP for Aroclor 1248. The Aroclors and PCB/trichlorobenzene mixtures have densities comparable to the chlorinated solvents, but their viscosities are higher. Consequently, the Aroclors would be expected to be somewhat less mobile as a DNAPL phase than the chlorinated solvents, but more mobile than coal tar or creosote. The PCB compounds present in the Aroclor mixtures have very low solubilities and are strongly sorbed on geologic media. As a result, PCB DNAPL sites are usually not characterized by large dissolved contaminant plumes in groundwater. A general comparison of the mobility of chlorinated solvents, coal tar/creosote, and the Aroclors as DNAPL phases is given in Figure 13.1.

A significant number of **pesticide products** are dense liquids. These products exhibit very wide ranges of physical and chemical properties as compared to other compound classes discussed above, and it is not possible to generalize regarding their mobilities as DNAPL phases. Their densities can range from close to 1.0 g/cm^3 to more than 2.0 g/cm^3. The mobilities of pesticides dissolved in groundwater can also range considerably because of varying solubility, potential for sorption on geologic media, and degradability.

The DNAPLs released to the subsurface at many **manufacturing sites** may be relatively pure. The chemical composition of the DNAPL found in a leaking disposal lagoon at an aerospace manufacturing facility is given in Table 13.1.a. In this case, the DNAPL was predominantly TCE. The small proportions of 1,1,1-TCA and DCM may reflect impurities in the original TCE product, or the use of smaller amounts of these solvents at the site. The trans-1,2-dichloroethylene may have been an impurity in the original TCE, or may have formed by chemical transformation of the TCE during use, or in the lagoon.

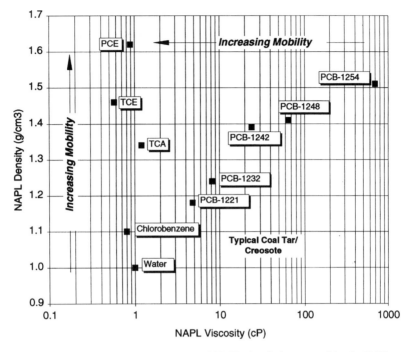

Figure 13.1   Relative mobility of selected DNAPL chemicals presented by the NAPL density and viscosity.

TABLE 13.1.a   Chemical Composition of a DNAPL Recovered From a Disposal Lagoon at an Aerospace Manufacturing Facility. DNAPL Density = 1.45 g/cm^3.

Compound	Weight %
Trichloroethylene	94.1
1,1,1-Trichloroethane	3.3
Trans-1,2-dichloroethylene	1.45
Dichloromethane	1.15

At **waste disposal sites**, the DNAPLs encountered in the subsurface are frequently complex mixtures of many organic chemicals, reflecting the disposal of various used chemical products. Some of the constituent chemicals of these mixed DNAPLs can be DNAPLs themselves in their pure forms. Other constituents of the DNAPLs may be light non-aqueous phase liquids (LNAPLs) in their pure forms (*e.g.*, benzene). Yet other constituents of the DNAPLs might be miscible in water (*e.g.*, acetone). The chemical and physical properties of such mixed DNAPLs will depend on their exact chemical composition. Except for coal tar and creosote, mixed DNAPLs are more dense than water generally because of the presence of substantial concentrations of halogenated organics such as the chlorinated solvents. Mixed DNAPLs at waste disposal sites commonly have densities ranging between 1.05 g/cm^3 to 1.3 g/cm^3, which is lower than for pure chlorinated solvents. The lower densities are usually due to the presence of petroleum hydrocarbons and other non-halogenated organics. The viscosities of mixed DNAPLs are generally in the 10 to 100 cP range, which is significantly greater than that of either water or pure chlorinated solvents. Tables 13.1.b gives the complex chemical composition of a DNAPL recovered from a landfill used for the disposal of wastes from a chemical manufacturing facility. The majority of the identified components can themselves be DNAPLs, and as a result the density of the mixture is relatively high. This DNAPL mixture was also found to contain a very large proportion of components that could not be characterized using conventional analytical methods such as gas chromatography/mass spectrometry (GC/MS). This is typical for the DNAPLs found at landfills and waste disposal sites. Table 13.1.c gives the chemical composition of the DNAPL recovered from beneath an illegal chemical and septic waste lagoon. In this case, the mixture is a DNAPL because of the high concentration of 1,2,3-trichloropropane. All the other identified components are less dense than water. The density of the mixture is 1.12 g/cm^3 compared to the pure-phase density of 1.39 g/cm^3 for 1,2,3-trichloropropane. As for the DNAPL considered in Table 13.1.b, a large proportion of this DNAPL could not characterized by GC/MS.

Table 13.1.d gives the chemical composition of the DNAPL recovered from beneath a PCB storage facility. The mixture is a DNAPL because of the large proportion of Aroclors and trichlorobenzenes. The physical movement and behavior of this DNAPL is controlled by properties imparted by the major components. However, despite the fact that TCE comprises less than 2% of this DNAPL, it is the dominant groundwater contaminant because it is much more soluble than the PCB compounds, and because it sorbs so weakly to aquifer materials.

TABLE 13.1.b Example of Chemical Composition of DNAPL Recovered from a Landfill at a Chemical Manufacturing Facility. DNAPL Density = 1.5 g/cm^3.

Compound	Weight %
Chlorobenzene	4.6
Tetrachloroethylene	4.5
Toluene	3.9
Trichlorofluorotoluenes	3.0
1,2-Dimethyl benzene	2.5
1,3-Dimethyl benzene	2.4
1,1,2,2-Tetrachloroethane	0.92
Trichloroethylene	0.75
Dichlorotoluene	5.1
1,1'-Thiobisdodecane	1.7
Pentachloroethane	0.87
Methyl ester (p-chlorophenyl) phenyl acetic acid	0.62
Unresolved by GC/MS Analysis	61.1

TABLE 13.1.c Example of Chemical Composition of DNAPL Recovered from an Illegal Chemical and Septic Waste Dump. DNAPL Density = 1.12 g/cm^3.

Compound	Weight %
1,2,3-Trichloropropane	23
Xylenes	17
Ethyl benzene	3.8
Toluene	4.2
Unresolved by GC/MS Analysis	52

TABLE 13.1.d. Example of Chemical Composition of DNAPL Recovered from a PCB Storage Facility. DNAPL Density = 1.2 g/cm^3

Compound	Weight %
PCB Aroclors 1242, 1248, 1254	47
1,2,4-Trichlorobenzene	9.2
1,2,3-Trichlorobenzene	2.9
Trichloroethylene	1.8
Mineral Oils	40

The presence of substantial concentrations of chlorinated solvents or other halogenated organics in groundwater or soil is commonly the first indication that DNAPL may be present at a site. The evaluation of what chemical concentrations in groundwater and soil might reflect the presence of DNAPL in the subsurface will be discussed in following sections.

13.2.2 Uses for Chemicals That Are DNAPLs

Site assessors must understand not only the types of chemicals which may comprise DNAPLs, but also how these chemicals have been, or are currently being used. In many cases, site assessors must consider industrial or waste disposal sites where releases of DNAPL may have occurred many years ago. In such cases, there may be no specific records of the chemicals used or wastes received, and there be no past employees with useful recollections of past activities.

When site assessors (often hydrogeologists) consider the past or present use of DNAPL chemicals at industrial and commercial facilities, it must be recognized that many chemical products are known by a wide variety of **chemical synonyms and product names**. As has been described in Table 1.2, even the four most common chlorinated solvents are known by a large number of names, many of which would not suggest their common chemical name. For example, in the examination of historical records of chemical purchases at an industrial site to look for evidence of the use of DNAPL chemicals, references to products like Nema (PCE), Westrosol (TCE), and Chlorothene (1,1,1-TCA) should not go unnoticed. Information on chemical synonyms and product names for chemicals of relevance to groundwater contamination can be found in handbook sources such as Howard (1989) and Montgomery and Welkom (1990). General information on synonyms and product names for chemicals can be found in the *Merck Index* as compiled by Merck & Co. (1989).

At old waste disposal facilities, many of the industries that contributed the wastes may now be defunct. In these cases there may only be information on the general type of business conducted by these industries, and the nature of their wastes must be estimated. The principal uses for the wide range of organic chemicals which can be DNAPLs are found in Tables 1.4-1.10. There are separate tables for: the most common chlorinated solvents, other common chlorinated organics, halogenated organics, substituted aromatics and phthalates, PCBs, and pesticides. Of particular note are the uses of: 1) chlorinated solvents for metal cleaning and degreasing; 2) PCE for dry cleaning of fabrics and clothing; 3) 1,2-dichloroethane in the manufacture of PVC; 4) chlorobenzene as a chemical intermediate for the manufacture of other chemical products; 5) PCB Aroclors in hydraulic fluids.

With an appreciation for the varied uses of DNAPL chemicals, a site assessor can identify general industrial and commercial activities that should be associated with DNAPL use. A summary of some of the key industrial and commercial activities which use DNAPL chemicals is found in Table 1.11. These activities are separated into four categories: 1) production and distribution; 2) manufacturing uses; 3) service uses; and 4) waste disposal. Obvious potential sources of DNAPL contamination are activities associated with the production and distribution of DNAPL chemicals themselves or the use of DNAPL chemicals in the production of other products. The key manufacturing activities which used DNAPL chemicals involved the use of chlorinated solvents for metal cleaning and degreasing. Wood preserving activities used very large quantities of creosote. The manufacture of electrical transformers and capacitors is a well known use for PCB Aroclors. A lesser known use for PCB Aroclors is in fire-resistant hydraulic fluids used in foundries, metal casting, iron and steel production, and in natural gas pipeline compressors. The key service uses of DNAPL chemicals is probably commercial and retail dry cleaning using PCE and 1,1,1-TCA presently, and TCE and carbon tetrachloride in earlier times. Most pesticide products which are DNAPLs are not applied and used as DNAPLs, but releases of DNAPL pesticides can occur during distribution, mixing, and preparation for application. Activities such as the past operation of coal and oil gasification facilities and past and present blast furnace coking operations produce very large quantities of DNAPLs as waste products.

13.2.3 Assessment of Site Operations

For an industrial site, the assessor needs to determine the type(s) of manufacturing operations as well as the types and quantities of chemicals that have been used at the site. Specific information should be sought on the locations and manner of chemical storage, distribution, use areas, wash-down processes, waste stream handling, and the means of ultimate disposal. Possible information sources include: 1) interviews with present or former employees; 2) records of chemical purchases, off-site waste disposal, or waste received; 3) historical site engineering drawings; and 4) archival aerial photographs.

Records of the volumes of DNAPLs that were produced, used, or disposed of at a site are an important line of evidence. However, such records are often not available. Estimates of usage can sometimes be made from anecdotal evidence from past employees. The level of chemical usage at different sites may vary widely. For example, a small metal fabrication plant with a single TCE degreaser may have used only a few drums (about 200 L) of solvent per month. In contrast, a large electronics plant involved in the manufacture of semiconductors may have used several hundred thousand liters per month. Estimates of the quantities of DNAPL chemicals which might have actually been released to the subsurface are much more difficult to obtain. Claims by site owners or operators that a site has had no known or suspected major spills of DNAPL are generally not reliable.

A common cause of DNAPL releases to the subsurface are small repeated spills or disposals that occur routinely as "*de minimus*" losses. At industrial sites, common locations for such releases are chemical off-loading areas, floor drains, sumps and catch basins, septic tanks and leach fields, process lines and sewers, and storage tanks. In many hydrogeologic situations, a DNAPL can easily penetrate below the water table if released as drips or very small periodic discharges at the same location. Prior to the mid-1980s, the standard operating practices of numerous solvent-using industries was such that routine or *de minimus* DNAPL losses were common. Poulsen and Kueper (1992) illustrated the significance of such small leaks or spills by means of field experiments in a stratified sandy aquifer. They found that a release of 6 L of PCE at the ground surface could penetrate the vadose zones to depths of 2.0 to 3.2 m. For soil conditions comparable to the experimental site and a release of one barrel ($\sim$200 L) of PCE, Poulsen and Kueper (1992) estimated a penetration depth of 70 to 110 m.

For disposal facilities such as landfills and lagoons, the locations and nature of the liquid waste must be determined. In a landfill or disposal pit, liquids may have been introduced as bulk liquids, or in drums or other containers. DNAPLs dumped as bulk liquids generally have a greater potential for migration out of the disposal site and into the subsurface. Bulk liquids wastes were received at many older landfills, and were frequently discharged into specific pits or bermed areas within the landfill. Similarly, in the past, many industrial facilities had on-site pits and lagoons for waste disposal operations, but the locations were not recorded. Examination of historical aerial photographs can be particularly useful in locating such areas. At old waste disposal facilities there are seldom records of the types and quantities of waste received. The possible types of wastes and the potential for the disposal of DNAPLs may need to be estimated based on information about the industries which used the facility.

13.2.4 Assessment of DNAPL Penetration

13.2.4.1 Influencing factors

An estimation of the potential **depth of DNAPL penetration** through the vadose zone and into the groundwater zone is an important component of site assessment. Estimates of the potential depth of DNAPL penetration are commonly attempted during initial site studies based on general information about the site operations and the subsurface conditions. The depth of DNAPL penetration will depend on the properties of the DNAPL, the nature (*e.g.*, the rate, areal distribution, etc.) of the DNAPL release, and the properties and geological structure within the vadose and groundwater zones. Unfortunately, it will never be possible to predict precisely the extent or rate of DNAPL migration. Indeed, even if complete and reliable information about the DNAPL properties and release are available, the spatial scales of the geological properties which will control DNAPL migration are much smaller than can be characterized by site investigations. Nevertheless, it is important to recognize, in general terms, the factors which will influence the depth of DNAPL penetration through the vadose and groundwater zones. These factors and the circumstances in which they might be important are summarized in Tables 13.2 and 13.3.

13.2.4.2 DNAPL penetration in the vadose zone

It has been common practice in the assessment of petroleum hydrocarbons spills (de Pastrovich *et al.*, 1979) to estimate the depth D of penetration of a DNAPL or LNAPL spill through the vadose zone on the basis of the volume V released, the area A of the release, and the **retention capacity** R_s of the soil according to

$$D = \frac{V}{A R_s} \tag{13.1}$$

TABLE 13.2   Factors Which Facilitate DNAPL Penetration Through the Vadose and Groundwater Zones.

Factors facilitating DNAPL penetration	Typical circumstances
High DNAPL density	Chlorinated solvents. PCB Aroclors.
Low interfacial tension	Surfactants or miscible co-solvents such as methanol, methyl ethyl ketone or acetone in the DNAPL. Surfactants and co-solvents in aqueous wastes or groundwater. Complex DNAPL mixtures.
Low viscosity	Chlorinated solvents
Large DNAPL volume release	Disposal of bulk liquid wastes in landfills, lagoons. Catastrophic spills and on-going leakages.
Long duration DNAPL release	Disposal of bulk liquid wastes in landfills, lagoons. On-going leakages.
High permeability	Sand, sand & gravel, fractured rock.
Vertical and sub-vertical geological structure	Angled beddings in sandy aquifers. Fractures, fissures, erosional windows in fine-grained aquitards. Fractured rock.

TABLE 13.3 Factors Which Inhibit DNAPL Penetration Through the Vadose and Groundwater Zones.

Factors inhibiting DNAPL penetration	Typical circumstances
Low DNAPL density	Coal tar / creosote. Chlorinated organics at low concentrations in petroleum hydrocarbons.
High interfacial tension	Relatively pure chemical products.
High viscosity	Coal tar / creosote. PCB Aroclors. DNAPL mixtures with high concentrations of high molecular weight hydrocarbons.
Small DNAPL volume release	Small spills and leaks.
Short duration DNAPL release	Small one-time spills and leaks.
Low permeability	Unfractured silt and clay aquitards. Unfractured rock.
Horizontal geological structure	Horizontal bedding in sandy aquifers. Horizontal silt and clay aquitards. Horizontal bedding plane partings in sedimentary rock.

Eq.(13.1) assumes that the NAPL penetrates directly downward from the release area with negligible lateral spreading, and forms a regular prismatic or cylindrical residual NAPL zone. The residual saturations of NAPLs measured in the laboratory for sandy aquifer materials range from about 5 to 25% of the pore space (Mercer and Cohen, 1990). For a total porosity of 30%, this range of residual saturations yields retention capacities of 15 to 75 L/m^3, or 1.5 to 7.5% of the bulk volume of the soil. This range of values is typically used for estimating NAPL penetration through the vadose zone. Thus, for a release of 6 L of DNAPL over an area of 0.1 m^2, the depth of penetration would be estimated to range from 0.8 to 4.0 m. The higher the retention capacity, the smaller the depth of DNAPL penetration. Obviously, such calculations assume that the residual saturations measured in the laboratory are applicable to undisturbed soils, and that the residual zone in the soil is homogeneous.

The reliability of the above type of calculation can be examined by comparison with the results of two controlled experimental releases of PCE into a stratified sandy aquifer (Poulsen and Kueper, 1992). In one experiment, referred to as the instantaneous (or "ponded") release, 6 L of PCE was spilled at the ground surface over an area of 0.1 m^2 over a period of 90 s. In the other experiment, referred to as the "drip" release, 6 L of PCE was released over an area of about 1 cm^2 over a period of 100 min. For both spills, the PCE was dyed red and the distribution of PCE residual was mapped after excavation both visually and by analysis of soil samples. In both spills, the migration of PCE was strongly influenced by the angled bedding structure of the sands. PCE migrated preferentially along those layers with the highest permeability, and exhibited a highly variable distribution on a scale of millimeters. In both cases, the migration of PCE along small-scale angled bedding (laminations) caused a substantial lateral displacement of the

resulting residual zone away from the release location. The instantaneous release penetrated to a depth of 2.0 m and the drip release penetrated all the way to the water table
at a depth of 3.2 m. Had the bedding been more horizontal, greater lateral spreading and
less vertical penetration would have been expected.

In the Poulsen and Kueper (1992) spills, the PCE residual saturations were measured in small, ~1 cm^3 soil samples at numerous locations within the residual zones.
The average residual saturation at various depths are shown for the two experiments
in Figure 13.2. The highest residual saturations are comparable to previously-reported
laboratory values (*i.e.*, 1.5 to 7.5%), but many values are considerably lower. When the
volume of the release is divided by the volume of the DNAPL residual zone, the average
retention capacity of the soil is calculated to be 1.3% and 0.5% for the instantaneous
and the drip releases, respectively. These experiments clearly illustrate the difficulties in
estimating the potential depths of DNAPL penetration through the vadose zone. Indeed,
the bulk retention capacities of soils may be significantly lower than laboratory values

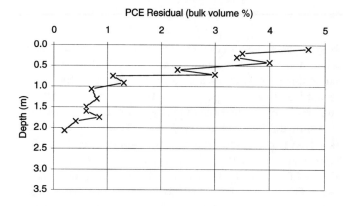

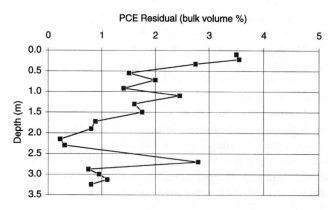

Figure 13.2 Vertical profiles of DNAPL
residual content resulting from experimental
releases of PCE in the vadose zone. Data
from Poulsen and Kueper (1992).

for residual saturation so that the use of laboratory values in penetration calculations can lead to underestimates of the depth of DNAPL penetration. At the same time, however, this effect can be partly compensated for by geological structures which can cause a substantial degree of lateral spreading which can expand the volume of the DNAPL zone and restrict the depth of penetration.

13.2.4.3 Effects of DNAPL vaporization

The depth of DNAPL penetration through the vadose zone can be influenced by the **vaporization** of the DNAPL components. If the vadose zone is thick and the vapor pressure of the DNAPL high, vaporization may deplete the DNAPL mass sufficiently to prevent the DNAPL from reaching the groundwater zone. Vaporization will create a halo of lower level contamination in the soil gas, soil water, and soil around the DNAPL zone. Numerical modeling by Mendoza and Frind (1990) of NAPL sources in the vadose zone can be used to gain some insight into the persistence of DNAPLs having relatively high vapor pressures. The numerical modeling considered a cylindrical NAPL source zone situated within a sandy vadose zone. The source zone was assumed to have a radius of 1.05 m, a height of 0.9 m, and to contain 125 kg of NAPL. A generic organic chemical with a vapor pressure of 182 torr was considered. For comparison, the vapor pressures of DCM, TCE, 1,1,1-TCA, and PER are 353, 58, 96, and 8 torr at 20 °C, respectively. In the simulation, 83% of the source was depleted after 8 days, and 94% of the source was depleted after 16 days. Higher vapor pressures and smaller NAPL source zones would require shorter periods of time to vaporize, and *vice versa*.

13.2.4.4 DNAPL penetration in the groundwater zone

The factors which influence penetration of DNAPL into the groundwater zone are generally comparable to those which influence penetration in the vadose zone. The effects of layered geological structures on DNAPL migration were clearly illustrated in a laboratory experiment by Kueper (1989) and Kueper *et al.* (1989), and are shown in Figure 13.3. In this experiment, even relatively small differences in hydraulic conductivity were found to inhibit downward migration and cause lateral spreading of PCE.

   Stratification and variability in geological structure in the groundwater zone will cause highly variable DNAPL distributions. This was illustrated clearly in a field experimental release of 231 L of PCE below the water table in a stratified sandy aquifer by Kueper *et al.* (1993). The experiment was conducted within a steel-sheet-pile test cell measuring 3 m by 3 m, and anchored into an underlying clay aquitard to a depth of 3.5 m. The PCE was dyed red. Following the release, the upper 1 m of the cell was excavated for visual examination and analysis of soil samples. Three continuous cores were collected from the lower 2.5 m of the cell for the analysis of soil samples. The cores were divided into 5 cm segments and a small sample ($\sim$1 cm^3) was removed from each for determination of the degree of PCE saturation. The results from one of these cores is shown in Figure 13.4. The highest PCE saturations occur in the upper portion, the middle portion and the lower portion of the core. Each of these zones is interpreted to represent layers (or pools) of PCE which accumulated on horizontal zones of lower

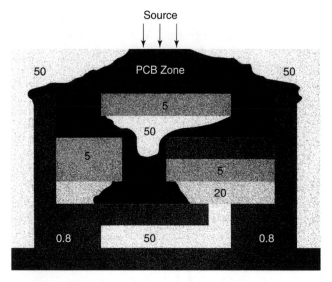

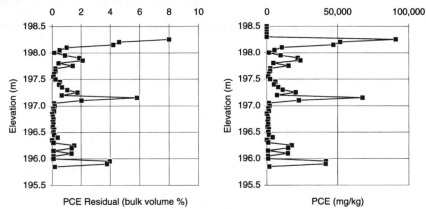

Figure 13.3 An illustration of the effect of geologic variability on the migration of DNAPL in the saturated zone. Results from a laboratory experiment performed by Kueper *et al.* (1989). Hydraulic conductivity of each sand layer is indicated in cm/s times 10^{-2}. Adapted from Kueper (1989).

Figure 13.4 Vertical profiles of DNAPL residual content resulting from an experimental release of PCE in the groundwater zone. Data from Kueper *et al.* (1993).

permeability. The deepest pool was found on the clay aquitard. Between the layers, the PCE saturations were lower and highly variable. Measurable PCE could not be found in some zones. A smaller experiment yielded similar results (see Figure 13.5). The variability exhibited in these experiments illustrates that estimating the depth of penetration of DNAPL into the groundwater zone will be as difficult as in the vadose zone.

13.2.4.5 DNAPL penetration in fractured media

Layers of fine-grained media such as silt or clay can be effective barriers to vertical DNAPL migration, and substantial amounts of potentially mobile DNAPL can accumulate on such barriers. The same applies to intact low-permeability rock. However, these strata

(a)

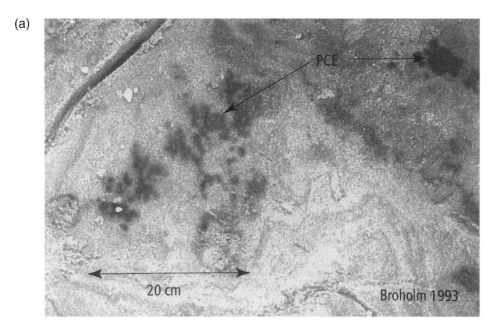

(b)

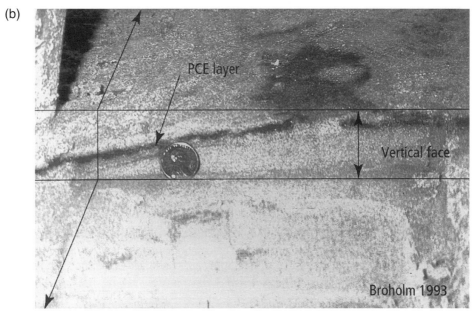

Figure 13.5 Example of scale and spatial variability in DNAPL distribution resulting from an experimental release of PCE in the groundwater zone. PCE is dyed red using Sudan IV dye. (Photographs by Kim Broholm.) a) Horizontal view of top of layer; b) vertical section through PCE layer.

will not act as barriers if they contain **fractures** or other **discontinuities**. Silt and clay
strata may contain fractures as a result of desiccation and weathering, stress relief, and
tectonic stresses; almost all sedimentary and crystalline rocks contain fractures.

Calculations and modeling conducted by Kueper and McWhorter (1991) indicate
that DNAPLs can penetrate fractures having apertures as small as 10 to 20 μm under the
types of DNAPL heads that are likely to occur at chemical spill and waste disposal sites.
Detailed studies of clay strata by Rudolph *et al.* (1991) and McKay *et al.* (1993) have
found that vertical fractures of this aperture are commonly present in strata normally considered to be competent aquitards. Although it might be anticipated that vertical fractures
should be closed at some small distance below the water table as a result of confining
stress imparted by the overlying geologic material, field studies have shown that open
fractures can exist in many types of clayey deposits to considerable depths, many tens of
meters in some cases. Such vertical fractures can provide important pathways for DNAPL
migration downward through silt and clay strata. Similarly, vertical fracture orientations,
fracture zones, and fault zones in rock strata can provide pathways for the downward
migration of DNAPLs. The variability of fracture characteristics, the difficulty of field
measurements of fracture characteristics, and the complexity of fracture networks prevent
all but the simplest of assessments of the depth of DNAPL penetration in fractured media. Such assessments will in most cases be limited to simple determinations of whether
downward migration is "*likely*" or "*unlikely*".

As an example, consider a situation where a shale layer separates two carbonate
rock aquifers. Liquid PCE has been found pooled at the base of the upper aquifer and,
dissolved PCE has been found in the lower aquifer. The question to be addressed is
whether liquid PCE has penetrated into the lower aquifer, or whether the PCE in the
lower aquifer is due solely to the leakage of dissolved PCE from the upper aquifer.
Hydraulically, the shale unit behaves like an aquitard with a consistent and significant
difference in head between the aquifers. A pumping test of the lower aquifer and monitoring of the upper aquifer suggest a bulk hydraulic conductivity of 2×10^{-7} cm/s for
the shale. Exposure of the shale in a nearby outcrop exhibits continuous vertical fractures spaced at about 2 to 5 m apart. A simplified relationship between bulk hydraulic
conductivity and fracture frequency for smooth planar fractures (see Figure 12.2.a) can
be used to estimate a range of fracture apertures, and the result is 20 to 30 μm. Using
an available relationship between fracture aperture and DNAPL head (see Figure 11.2),
a head of only 0.1 to 0.7 m would be necessary, depending on the interfacial tension, to
allow liquid PCE to penetrate into these fractures. Thus, given that pooled liquid PCE is
present on top of the shale unit, these calculations suggest that it is likely that liquid PCE
has penetrated into the lower aquifer, and could be the source of the dissolved PCE there.

13.2.4.6 Reliability of estimates

The variable distributions of DNAPLs expected within the vadose zone and the groundwater zone make simple estimates of DNAPL penetration depths unreliable. However,
provided that these uncertainties are recognized, such calculations can be useful in assessing the range of possibilities at a DNAPL site. More rigorous calculations of DNAPL

migration are possible using two-phase and three-phase flow numerical modeling techniques for homogeneous geological media and for simple heterogeneous systems. We note though that the scale of the geological variability that can influence DNAPL migration is far smaller than that which can currently either be characterized in the field, or accounted for in numerical models.

13.3 DETERMINING THE PRESENCE OF DNAPL BASED ON FIELD OBSERVATIONS

13.3.1 Observations During Drilling

13.3.1.1 Visual evidence

Valuable direct and indirect evidence of the presence and distribution of DNAPLs can be obtained by careful observation and field testing during drilling and recovery of soil and rock samples. There are some circumstances where the presence of a DNAPL is obvious. Abundant dark-colored DNAPL at high residual saturation, or in layers and pools is usually readily visible in soil cores. This is frequently the case for coal tar and creosote which are very dark and have sometimes been released to the subsurface in very large quantities (see Sections 13.2.1 and 13.2.2). It is less common to find clear visual evidence of liquid chlorinated solvents since the source quantities are usually smaller and the source zones are more variable; in most cases, careful centimeter-by-centimeter examination of soil cores is essential for any visual identification of DNAPL presence.

In the shallow vadose zone, there may commonly be dark staining of soil, but no visual evidence of DNAPL. In the case where the original DNAPL was a mixture of volatile and less volatile compounds, such staining may be due to the presence of the less volatile residues following vaporization of the volatiles. Such observations would suggest that DNAPL had been present in the past and had migrated at least to the depth of the observed staining. Visual evidence of DNAPL or staining in soil samples can provide clear information on the vertical distribution of DNAPL because the depth of the observations can be defined.

13.3.1.2 Field testing

Enhanced Visual Identification. Visual identification of DNAPL in soil samples can be enhanced using methods such as ultraviolet (UV) fluorescence and various types of soil-water shake tests. These methods have not yet been used widely, but have been evaluated in controlled laboratory studies by Cohen *et al.* (1992). The UV fluorescence method involves the examination of soil samples under a portable UV light. Since many aromatic and polycyclic aromatic hydrocarbons fluoresce, UV fluorescence has been used for decades in the petroleum industry to identify crude oil in cores, drill cuttings, and drilling mud. Many unsaturated aliphatic hydrocarbons such as TCE and PCE also fluoresce. Examination by UV fluorescence can be accomplished in transparent plastic bags so that the samples can be manipulated without excessive loss of volatiles. Samples of soil known to be uncontaminated should also be examined as controls because some minerals and shell fragments also fluoresce.

The soil-water shake test involves the transfer of a soil sample to a clear centrifuge tube with an equal volume of water. The tube is stoppered and the mixture shaken by hand. The DNAPL is identified by examination of the tube walls and bottom. This test can be enhanced by centrifugation of the mixture to facilitate the accumulation of the DNAPL at the bottom of the tube. It can also be enhanced by the addition of a small amount of hydrophobic dye such as red Sudan IV or Oil Red O to the mixture. (These dyes are insoluble in water, but are soluble in many organic liquids.) Any DNAPLs present in the sample thereby become red in color. These methods can be performed readily in the field during drilling and soil sampling activities.

Cohen *et al.* (1992) compared the performance of unaided-visual identification of NAPLs in soil samples with UV fluorescence and four types of soil/water shake tests. The methods were compared using prepared soil samples. Using three different soil types, 78 samples were mixed with varying quantities of kerosene, chlorobenzene, and PCE. The residual NAPL saturations ranged from 1 to 23% of the soil pore space; 22 of the 78 soil samples were blanks. Each sample was assessed using each test method by examiners unaware of their contents. The results of these tests are summarized in Figure 13.6. Unaided-visual examination correctly identified the presence of NAPL only 30% of the time, whereas the enhancements permitted correct identification 55 to 90% of the time. UV fluorescence and the addition of dye to the soil/water shake test provided correct identification of NAPL 80% of the time. These laboratory tests suggest that simple and effective means of enhancing direct visual identification of some DNAPLs in soil samples are available.

Vapor Analyses. The determination of organic vapor concentrations is commonly performed during drilling and sampling to determine compliance with health and safety conditions in the working environment, and for screening of soil samples for contami-

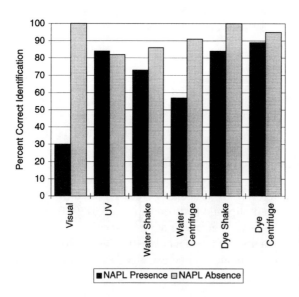

Figure 13.6 Comparison of the effectiveness of various field testing methods for the identification of NAPLs in soil samples. Results are from laboratory testing of spiked samples performed by Cohen *et al.* (1992).

nation by volatile organics. Such analyses are often performed using a portable organic vapor analyzer (OVA), and may be useful in the assessment of the presence of DNAPLs.

Many DNAPL chemicals have high vapor pressures and correspondingly high saturated vapor concentrations (see Table 13.4). The saturated vapor concentration of each individual component of a multi-component DNAPL will be lower than its pure phase saturated vapor concentration. The individual saturated vapor concentrations from a mixture can be estimated using Raoult's Law

$$S_{g,i} = X_i S^o_{g,i} \quad , \tag{13.2}$$

where $S_{g,i}$ is the saturated vapor concentration of component i in equilibrium with the multi-component DNAPL, X_i is the mole fraction of i in the mixture, and $S^o_{g,i}$ is the pure-phase saturated vapor concentration of component i. As an example, at 20 °C, TCE has a saturated vapor concentration of 76,000 ppmV. Thus, for a mixture containing a 5% molar concentration of TCE in a mineral oil ($X_{TCE} = 0.05$), the saturated vapor concentration of TCE would be ~3,800 ppmV.

Data on the vapor pressure of pure compounds are commonly reported for temperatures of 20 or 25 °C. However, the vapor pressure of any given compound will decrease strongly as the temperature decreases. At 0 °C, the vapor pressures for the common chlorinated solvents are lower by a factor of 1/3 to 1/4 of what they are at 20 or 25 °C. This effect must be taken into consideration when interpreting vapor concentration data.

Because of their nature and use, and because of the complex chemical composition of vapors expected at most sites, OVA instruments usually provide only a semiquantitative measure of organic vapor concentrations at most field sites. OVA instruments can utilize flame ionization detectors (FIDs) or photo-ionization detectors (PIDs) for the determination of organic vapor concentrations. FID and PID instruments have different sensitivities for a given organic compound. PID instruments have different sensitivities depending on the ionization energy of the lamp utilized in the detector. OVA instruments are commonly capable of indicating vapor concentrations from about 1 ppmV to a full-scale reading of 1,000 or 2,000 ppmV. In addition, OVA instruments are normally calibrated to a gas standard containing a single compound which may

TABLE 13.4 Saturated Vapor Concentrations at 20 °C for Selected DNAPL Compounds.

Compound	Vapor pressure (torr)	Vapor conc. in air (mg/L)	Vapor conc. in air (ppmV)
Tetrachloroethylene	14	127	19,300
Trichloroethylene	58	417	76,700
1,1,1-Trichloroethane	100	730	132,000
Dichloromethane	349	1,620	459,000
Carbon Tetrachloride	90	758	118,000
Chloroform	151	987	199,000
Chlorobenzene	12	74	15,700
1,2-Dichlorobenzene	2.3	19	3,100
1,2-Dichloroethane	61	331	80,400

or may not be a compound of interest. Consequently, for a complex mixture of organic vapors, the total concentration indicated by an OVA measurement may be substantially different than the actual total concentration. In most circumstances, an OVA measurement must be considered to be an "order-of-magnitude" estimate of the actual total concentration. However, despite these limitations, OVA measurements can still provide useful information on the presence of a DNAPL because OVA measurements can be performed readily in the field, and because OVA instruments can measure relatively low vapor concentrations compared to the vapor concentrations emitted from many DNAPLs.

The field screening of vapor concentrations emitted from soil samples can be performed in several ways. One way is to remove a soil core from the sampler and pass the inlet tip of the OVA slowly along the length of the core while observing the indicated vapor concentrations. We note that the observed concentrations may be lowered by dilution in the air, and by slow emission of vapors from the samples. Dilution effects can be reduced by transferring the sample into a bag or jar equipped with access for the OVA inlet tip. The emission of vapors is slow from samples at low temperatures and/or with high water contents. The transfer and temporary storage of samples in a bag or jar may minimize these effects by permitting the sample to warm and vapors to accumulate in the container.

Cohen *et al.* (1992) have shown in laboratory studies that the vapor concentrations emitted from a soil sample containing a pure, volatile DNAPL may be substantially lower than the corresponding saturated vapor concentration. A total of 56 soil samples were prepared consisting of three different soil types. The porosity saturations of PCE and chlorobenzene ranged from 1% to 23%. The saturated vapor concentrations for PCE and chlorobenzene at 20 °C are 19,300 ppmV and 15,700 ppmV respectively. Of the 56 samples, 11 were blanks and 7 contained only chemicals dissolved in the pore water. Each of these samples was prepared in a sealed polyethylene bag and tested by inserting the inlet tip of the OVA with an FID into the bag. The results of the tests are shown in Figure 13.7. The OVA readings for the blanks ranged from 1 ppmV to 20 ppmV. Readings for the samples containing only dissolved chemicals ranged from 1.5 ppmV to 30 ppmV. For the samples containing PCE and chlorobenzene in the form of DNAPL, OVA measurements were much higher, but variable, ranging from 80 ppmV to the full-scale reading of 1,000 ppmV. These tests illustrate the difficulty in relating OVA readings to the presence of DNAPL in a quantitative manner. However, as a "rule of thumb", full-scale OVA readings of 1,000 to 2,000 ppmV are probably a reasonable indication of the presence of DNAPL when the DNAPL is comprised of one or more chlorinated solvent.

Sampling Drilling Water. The sampling, examination, and analysis of drilling water can be useful in the identification of a DNAPL phase during drilling. As will be described below, this type of inspection may be needed in order to avoid drilling through DNAPL zones and causing contamination of deeper zones by "short circuiting". The presence of a DNAPL phase can be inferred from observations of oily films and sheens on the drilling water returned to the ground surface. The determination of appropriate indicator chemicals in the drilling water, or using methods such as field gas chromatography can provide real time information during drilling.

Unfortunately, not all drilling methods are compatible with sampling and analysis during drilling. Methods that employ mud or that add water to the formation during

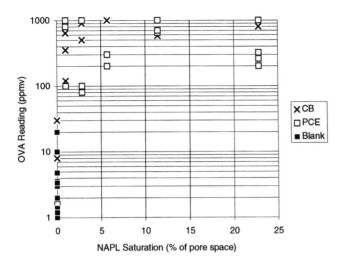

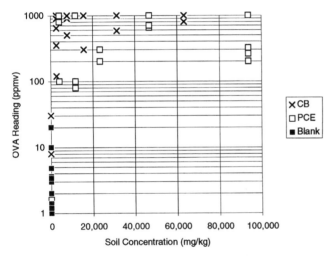

Figure 13.7 Effectiveness of organic vapor analyzer (OVA) measurements for identification of NAPLs in soil samples. Results are from laboratory testing of spiked samples performed by Cohen *et al.* (1992).

drilling are unlikely to yield water samples that reflect the composition of the groundwater. Similarly, methods that employ air flush are not compatible with the determination of VOCs in the return water because of losses to the air stream. Sampling and analysis of the return air using an OVA or GC is possible, but the degree of dilution resulting from the high air flow makes the detection of VOCs difficult.

An alternative to sampling of drilling water during drilling is to stop drilling at frequent intervals, purge the water from the drill string, and collect a sample for analysis or inspection. This is possible when using drilling methods which advance a hollow drill string or casing. Taylor and Serafini (1988) describe the use of a specially-designed hollow-stem auger for the delineation of dissolved contaminant plumes. The first auger flight was constructed with a slotted screen to allow collection of groundwater for analysis in the field.

13.3.2 Observations in Wells

At some sites, DNAPL can be found in one or more monitoring or pump-and-treat wells. Although this finding confirms that the site is a DNAPL site, it is generally impossible to relate the thickness of DNAPL in such wells to the volume of DNAPL in the subsurface. In addition, it is generally not possible relate the finding of DNAPL in wells to the vertical distribution of DNAPL in the subsurface. The only circumstance in which it might be possible to relate DNAPL thickness in wells to the thickness of DNAPL pools in the subsurface is when DNAPL occurs in large discrete pools in granular media. This has been found at some creosote and coal tar sites where very large volumes of product have been released to the subsurface, but it is rare for chlorinated solvent DNAPL sites. Even when large pools of solvent are found, wells must be installed precisely to intersect the entire vertical thickness of the pool. If the wells do not extend to the full thickness of the pool, the observed DNAPL thickness will be erroneously small. If the wells extend deeper than the base of the pool, the observed DNAPL thickness will be erroneously large. And, even when wells are installed appropriately within the pool, the DNAPL thickness in the well can only be related to the pool thickness through the use of information on the capillary properties of the formation and of the well material, together with the properties of the DNAPL. This type of information is seldom available.

Of course, if DNAPL free product has not been detected in wells, it cannot be concluded that DNAPL is not present in the aquifer. At many sites, the zones of free-product DNAPL may be very small in areal extent relative to the spacings of borings. Consequently, the DNAPL zones may be intersected only infrequently by borings. Even when DNAPL zones are intersected, there are numerous circumstances in which the DNAPL may not be found in the well. For example, a DNAPL zone may be thin in vertical extent, and may not contact the open interval of a monitoring well which passes through it. Also, most of the DNAPL in the subsurface may be present only at residual saturation, and such DNAPL will not be able to enter the boring or monitoring well.

Figure 13.8 illustrates several circumstances that will inhibit identification of the presence and distribution of a DNAPL using monitoring well observations. In most circumstances, the sand pack or filter pack material used in well construction is more permeable than the geologic media and should allow unrestricted entry of DNAPL into the well bore. However, DNAPL will always migrate along the most permeable pathways, and will commonly accumulate in relatively permeable zones that are bounded by lower permeability zones. If DNAPL occurs in thin layers or pools, there may not be sufficient fluid potential in the DNAPL to overcome the capillary resistance of the sand pack and allow entry into the boring (see Figure 13.8.a). To minimize this possibility, sand pack material can be sized to promote DNAPL entry.

DNAPL layers and pools are generally thin compared to the open interval of a boring, and may not be identified during drilling operations. If DNAPL enters a boring, it will sink to the bottom (see Figure 13.8.b). If the DNAPL accumulation is sufficiently large, it will enter the well screen and may be found by well sounding or sampling. However, it will not be possible to relate the elevation of the DNAPL in the monitoring well to the elevation of DNAPL zones in the formation because DNAPL could have entered anywhere along the open interval of the boring.

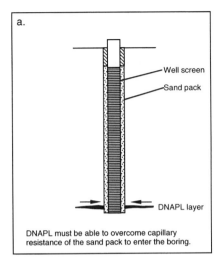
DNAPL must be able to overcome capillary resistance of the sand pack to enter the boring.

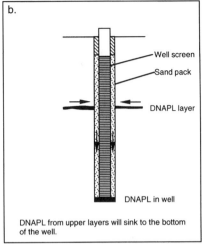
DNAPL from upper layers will sink to the bottom of the well.

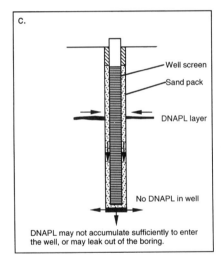
DNAPL may not accumulate sufficiently to enter the well, or may leak out of the boring.

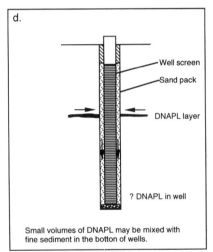
Small volumes of DNAPL may be mixed with fine sediment in the botton of wells.

Figure 13.8 Various conditions required for the accumulation and identification of DNAPL in a monitoring well.

DNAPL that enters the boring and sinks to the bottom will not enter the well screen unless the DNAPL accumulates as high as the bottom of the well screen. Monitoring wells are commonly constructed so that the well screen is some distance above the bottom of the sand pack. If the volume of DNAPL that enters a boring is small, it may not be sufficient to rise up to the well screen. If the formation surrounding the bottom of the boring is relatively permeable, it is also possible that the DNAPL may exit the boring before it can accumulate sufficiently to enter the well screen (see Figure 13.8.c). In this case, not only will the DNAPL go unidentified in the monitoring well, but the boring will become a conduit for DNAPL migration deeper into the subsurface. Niemeyer *et al.*

(1992) proposed that these situations could be avoided by the use of a **cement basket and sump** attached to the bottom of the well screen (see Figure 13.9). The cement basket is a funnel-like device used to set grout seals for well construction. Any DNAPL that migrates down the sand pack is deflected by the cement basket through the well screen and accumulates in the sump. Although this type of construction may avoid making the borings a pathway for downward DNAPL migration, it will not prevent downward migration that might occur during drilling and well installation.

The accumulation of DNAPL in the bottom of a monitoring well can be determined most effectively by use of interface probes, or by sampling at the bottom of the well. **Interface probes** are down-hole sensors on a graduated cable or tape. They commonly use an optical sensor for detecting the air-water interface, and a conductivity sensor for detecting a water/DNAPL interface. (In wells that also contain an LNAPL, the optical sensor would detect the air/LNAPL interface, and the conductivity sensor would detect the LNAPL/water interface.) Under ideal conditions, a DNAPL thickness of about 0.5 cm or greater can be detected. However, a DNAPL can be difficult to detect by these means when it is mixed with fine sediment at the bottom of the well, when it is conductive, or when it preferentially wets the probe materials.

Sampling of the bottom of a well can provide direct visual evidence of the presence of a DNAPL. It can also provide samples for measurement of the chemical composition and fluid properties of the DNAPL. Samples can be collected using pumps, bottom-loading bailers, and discrete-depth canister samplers. In general, evacuated discrete-depth samplers provide the most reliable method with the least degree of sample disturbance. Common DNAPL chemicals can degrade many pump materials. For relatively high density DNAPLs, the depth from which suction pumps, inertial-lift pumps, or positive-displacement pumps can be operated may be limited. When using a bottom-

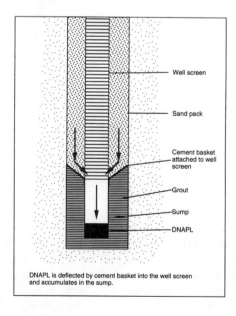

Figure 13.9 Schematic of a funnel collector device to enhance the accumulation and identification of DNAPL in a monitoring well. Concept from Niemeyer *et al.* (1992).

loading bailer to sample DNAPLs with densities greater than about 1.3 g/cm^3, PVC and Teflon will not provide adequate valve seating and the DNAPL may leak out as the bailer is retrieved. (PVC has a density of about 1.4 g/cm^3, and Teflon has a density of about 2.2 g/cm^3.) Thus, for sampling of a high density DNAPL, a steel ball valve should be used to ensure adequate valve seating.

Although significant quantities of DNAPL may accumulate in some wells, frequently the DNAPL is present only as thin layers or globules at the bottoms of the wells. In cases where a large quantity of fine-grained sediment is also recovered from the bottom of a well, some type of phase separation or chemical analysis may be required to identify the presence of the DNAPL. Separation may be as simple as mixing the sediment with clean water and "panning" for DNAPL. The soil-water shake methods and the addition of hydrophobic dyes described in Section 13.3.1.2 for soils (Cohen *et al.*, 1992) can also be used.

At sites where DNAPL has been found in one or more monitoring wells, it is common that many of the monitoring wells were installed before a single well exhibited any DNAPL. Then, in some cases, many more wells needed to be installed before a second encounter occurred. At most sites, once many monitoring wells are installed without a single DNAPL encounter, it is not reasonable to continue installing wells so as to determine definitively that the site is a DNAPL site. The collection and use of other lines of evidence may be a more effective approach.

13.3.3 Short Circuiting of DNAPL During Drilling and Sampling

13.3.3.1 Short circuiting pathways

When a boring or monitoring well installation intersects and also extends deeper than a DNAPL layer or pool, there is a potential for further downward migration of the DNAPL and expansion of the zone of contamination. This situation is sometimes referred to as **"short circuiting"**, and is obviously to be avoided. The potential for short circuiting is also of concern in the interpretation of sampling results from most wells.

DNAPL may move downward within a boring along the open borehole during drilling and sampling before well installation, along the sand pack of a completed well installation, and along an unsealed boring. The potential for short circuiting is greatest when borings intersect DNAPL accumulated in thick lenses or pools, especially when the DNAPL has a low viscosity and/or a high density. An example of short circuiting along the sand pack of a completed well is illustrated in Figure 13.8.c. The experimental release and subsequent excavation of a PCE spill in a stratified sandy aquifer (Broholm *et al.*, 1994) has provided clear visual evidence of DNAPL short circuiting. Figure 13.10 provides an illustration of downward leakage of PCE along a unsealed boring, and along the outside of a core tube that intersected a thin (1 cm to 2 cm) DNAPL pool. We can conclude that short circuiting of DNAPLs can occur along the contact between the formation and: 1) the drill casing; and/or 2) the augers or core tubes during drilling and sampling operations.

Given the nature of DNAPL behavior, it is likely that many of the borings and wells installed in the past at DNAPL sites have caused short circuiting of DNAPL, thereby

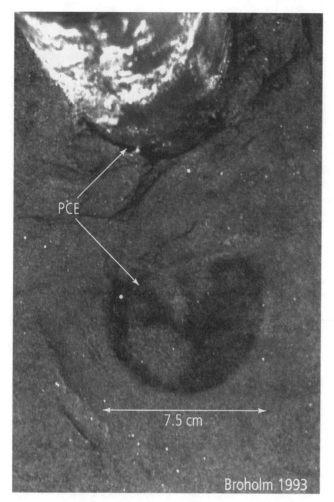

Figure 13.10 Example of short circuiting of DNAPL downward along an unsealed boring (circular area) and along the outside of a core tube. Both the boring and core tube intersected the thin PCE layer shown in Figure 13.5 and allowed PCE to migrate to deeper levels. PCE is dyed red using Sudan IV dye. (Photograph by Kim Broholm.)

leading to misleading conclusions regarding the *original* morpology of the DNAPL in the subsurface. In some cases, short circuiting down borings may have contributed significantly to expanded zones of contamination.

13.3.3.2 Investigation using the "outside-in" approach

Obviously, the potential for remobilization of DNAPL along borings can be reduced most easily by not drilling in areas that are known or suspected to be DNAPL source zones. However, site investigations often focus first on the source zone(s), and only then expand to include the dissolved plume(s). In the context of a site investigation strategy, emphasis should often rather be placed on defining the extent of the dissolved plume(s) first, *then* working back toward the source zone(s). This is referred to as the **"outside-in"** approach. This approach is also attractive because the migration of dissolved plumes almost always represents the most important pathway leading to exposure to chemicals from the subsurface, and should thus be focus for site investigations and risk assessments in any event.

In many circumstances, even the evaluation and design of DNAPL remedial measures do not require work that involves drilling directly through the source zone(s). As will be described in subsequent sections, information on the general spatial distribution of DNAPL zone(s) can often be inferred from soil gas surveys and from monitoring of the dissolved groundwater plume(s) outside the source zone(s). This level of source zone characterization is then generally sufficient for the design of remedial measures such as the hydraulic containment of the source zone(s) by groundwater pump-and-treat.

When undertaking remedies involving the *in situ* treatment of a DNAPL source zone, it may be necessary to drill directly into the source zone in order to obtain information on the physical and chemical characteristics of the DNAPL, as well as detailed information on the nature and shape of the source. Because of the potential for short circuiting, such drilling should be conducted using suitable precautions, and only when absolutely necessary.

13.3.3.3 Precautions during drilling and sampling

Various precautions can be taken to minimize the potential for short circuiting when drilling through DNAPL zones. In most geological settings, although it is possible to minimize it, one can probably never eliminate any chance of short circuiting. It is especially difficult to prevent short circuiting in fractured rock formations having complex fracture networks. However, in all cases where drilling through known or suspected DNAPL zones takes place, efforts should be made to reduce the length of the boring interval that remains open as well as the time that borings remain open during drilling, sampling, and well installation. In some cases, the precautions taken to minimize DNAPL short circuiting may limit the usefulness of the borings for the collection of other types of hydrogeological information.

The entry of DNAPL into a boring can be inhibited by high drilling water levels within the boring, or by the use of high-density drilling muds. In relatively permeable strata, the former will result in substantial loss of drilling water into the formation. Large volumes of drilling water in the formation around the well may then interfere with the interpretation of dissolved phase data for groundwater samples collected soon after well installation. The use of high density drilling muds may form a filter cake on the boring walls that is difficult to remove during well development. This remaining filter cake may interfere with the interpretation of inorganic and metals data for the groundwater, and with the measurement of the hydraulic conductivity using single-well response tests. The filter cake might also inhibit DNAPL migration into the completed monitoring wells.

One strategy for minimizing DNAPL short circuiting during drilling is to terminate boring at the first evidence of a DNAPL. However, this method requires the ability to obtain accurate evidence of a DNAPL by visual inspection, vapor monitoring, or field-testing of borings during drilling. However, such techniques may not be sufficiently accurate to eliminate the potential for drilling through DNAPL zones. Another drilling strategy that may be used to minimize DNAPL short circuiting is to terminate borings at the top of geological barriers such as at the top of a major aquitard stratum. In this way, any short circuiting of DNAPL that did occur would be halted at the barrier stratum. However, the application of this strategy is limited to those sites where previous drilling has determined the presence and location of the major local geological barriers; this information does not exist at many sites.

A common drilling strategy employed to minimize DNAPL short circuiting is the use of telescoped casing to isolate a specific depth interval from the zone above. This strategy involves the setting of casing and the advancing of progressively smaller diameter casing to the required depth of the monitoring interval (see Figure 13.11). This strategy will be effective in a multi-layer system of aquifers and aquitards where the end of each casing segment can be sealed in an aquitard stratum. In this manner, any mobile DNAPL that exists in upper aquifers cannot move down through the open boring or along the sand pack into deeper aquifers. (In situations when aquitard strata cannot be defined, the depths of the casing intervals must be selected arbitrarily.) This drilling strategy is slow and more costly than conventional drilling. There is also a practical limit to the number of casing segments that can be telescoped within a single boring, and that limit will depend on the drilling rig employed and the required diameter of the mon-

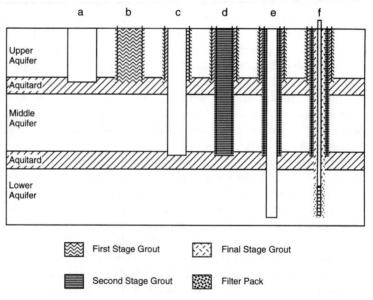

Figure 13.11 Illustration of the use of multiple casings for drilling to prevent short circuiting of DNAPL in areas of suspected DNAPL source zones. This method is most suited to sites were aquitard units can be accurately defined. a. Extend large diameter boring into top of aquitard unit. b. Set and grout large diameter casing into top of aquitard. c. Extend smaller diameter boring through grouted casing and through the formation into the next aquitard unit. d. Set and grout casing into top of aquitard. e. Extend smaller diameter boring through grouted casing and through the formation into the aquifer unit. f. Complete monitoring well.

itoring interval. Such installation seldom employ more than three or four casing segments.

The drilling strategy described above can be modified in fractured rock with the use of pressure grouting of the boring at sequential intervals until the required depth of the monitoring interval is reached (see Figure 13.12). In this manner, mobile DNAPL that exists in fractures in the upper portions of the rock cannot enter the boring and migrate downward along the open boring.

13.3.4 Alternatives to Drilling and Wells

13.3.4.1 Test pits

Test pits in overburden materials can provide valuable information that cannot be readily obtained by means of borings. Test pits can excavated using a backhoe or a power shovel, and can be dug to depths of about 5 to 8 m. The depth of test pits will be limited by the equipment used, sidewall stability, and worker safety regulations. Test pits afford

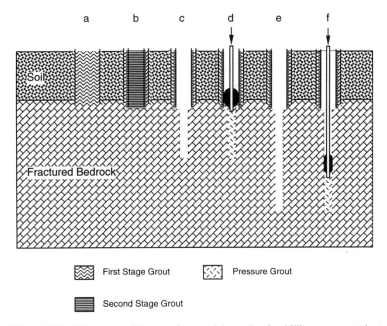

Figure 13.12   Illustration of the use of sequential grouting for drilling to prevent short circuiting of DNAPL in areas of suspected DNAPL source zones in fractured rock. a. Set and grout large diameter casing to top of rock. b. Where upper part of bedrock is highly weathered and fractured, set and grout second casing through to intact rock. c. Extend smaller diameter boring through grouted casing and through the formation to the target depth. d. Pressure grout the open interval in the rock to seal the fractures in the formation around the boring. e. Ream out the grouted interval and extend the boring to the next target depth. f. Pressure grout the lower interval to seal the fractures is this interval. Steps e and f are repeated to the final depth.

the opportunity for direct visual examination of stratigraphy and geological structure. In particular, vertical fractures in clayey strata, and the lateral continuity of fine-grained layers can be identified in test pits. Such features are difficult to identify in borings. Test pits also allow the visual examination of DNAPL distribution and the relationship between the geological structure and the DNAPL distribution. Because DNAPL distribution and geological structure may be visible in the test pits in at least two dimensions, soil samples selected for chemical analysis have the potential to be much more representative than those collected from borings.

13.3.4.2 Drive-point investigations

Monitoring wells and sampling points can be constructed using **drive-point devices**. Drive-point wells consist of an intake fitted with a conical point at the end. A tubing or pipe extends from the intake to the ground surface. The drive-point assembly is pushed into the ground on drill rods to the desired depth using a hydraulic ram or vibratory hammer. Drive-point installations are suitable for use in most sand, silt and clay strata to depths of about 30 to 40 m under ideal conditions. The depth of penetration will be limited by the soil density and the presence of gravel, cobbles, or boulders. Most drive-point devices have relatively short intakes (< 0.5 m) and the likelihood of intersecting and recovering DNAPL directly is probably low unless DNAPL pools are thick. Drive-point installations are used most commonly as permanent installations in the vadose zone for soil-gas sampling, and in the groundwater zone for groundwater sampling. Although drive-point installations avoid short-circuiting of DNAPL along an open borehole, DNAPL short circuiting may still occur along the sides of the drill rods or casing.

Several types of **removable drive-point devices** for obtaining soil-gas or groundwater samples are commercially available (Edge and Cordry, 1989). These devices are pushed into the subsurface, and soil gas or groundwater samples are collected at a specific depth. Devices such as the HydroPunch® are removed after collection of a sample from a single depth. Other devices such as the BAT® sampler allow the collection of sequential samples at increasing depth within the same hole; following completion of the sampling, the device is removed and the hole may be grouted. Comparable sampling devices can be used in combination with a **cone penetrometer** (Litherland et al., 1985; Smolley and Kappmeyer, 1991; Chiang et al., 1992). Cone penetrometers have been used for many years in geotechnical investigations to interpret continuous vertical profiles of soil type, stratigraphy, and geotechnical properties. A cone penetrometer consists of a conical point of standardized size and shape that is pushed into the ground at a steady rate using a hydraulic ram. The cone has electronic sensors to measure the resistance to penetration at the tip and along the sides of the cone. The magnitude of the tip resistance and side friction resistance and the ratio of the resistances are used to assess the soil type. For example, sands will exhibit high tip resistance and low side friction, whereas clays will exhibit low tip resistance and high side friction. A combination cone penetrometer/sampler can provide a range of information. As for permanent drive-point installations, the likelihood of direct intersection and recovery of DNAPL is low. The information from a cone penetrometer is very valuable to interpreting the geologic structure that may control DNAPL migration.

Drive-point devices have an advantage over conventional monitoring wells in that they are less costly and do not generate contaminated drill cuttings or drillwater that require special handling and disposal. In addition, drive-point devices can be installed manually, or with light-weight equipment to allow access in restricted spaces (*e.g.*, inside buildings). However, the use of drive-point devices does not eliminate the potential for short circuiting of DNAPL when working directly within DNAPL zones. When permanent drive-point devices are used, there remains the potential for downward migration along the contact between the casing and the formation as shown in Figure 13.10. In the case of removable drive-point devices, there is the additional potential for DNAPL short circuiting down the open hole after the device is withdrawn, even if the hole is subsequently grouted.

The use of drive-point devices is probably more useful in the detailed delineation of dissolved contaminant plumes emitted from DNAPL source zones than it is in the investigation of DNAPL source zones directly. Drive-point devices that allow the collection of sequential samples with increasing depth can be used to compile detailed vertical profiles of dissolved contaminant concentrations. Information on the vertical distribution of dissolved concentrations can provide insight regarding the location and nature of DNAPL zones below the water table. Examples of the use of vertical profiles of dissolved concentrations in the interpretation of DNAPL zones are described in Section 13.6. The results of such one-time vertical concentration profiles can then be used to determine optimum sampling intervals if permanent monitoring wells are required.

13.3.4.3 Geophysics

Electromagnetic (EM) resistivity logs can be run in conjunction with natural gamma logs to aid interpretation of the stratigraphy and target zones in which DNAPL accumulation were mostly likely to occur. However, although surface and borehole geophysical methods such as seismic refraction and reflection, EM resistivity, and ground penetrating radar (GPR) can provide valuable information on subsurface geological structure, the ability of geophysics to detect DNAPLs in the subsurface is still unclear.

Field experiments involving the release of PCE into a 3 m thick sand aquifer showed that borehole electrical methods, borehole dielectric permittivity, and surface GPR methods were able to detect the migration and final distribution of the DNAPL (Schneider and Greenhouse, 1992; Brewster *et al.*, 1992). These electrical methods were successful because most DNAPLs have an electrical conductivity much lower than geologic media. However, these experiments were conducted under ideal conditions at shallow depth in a relatively homogenous sand, and with background measurements having been taken at the exact same locations before the release. Schneider and Greenhouse (1992) and Brewster *et al.* (1992) concluded that while these methods were effective in assessing *changes* in the DNAPL distribution, they may not have been able to detect the presence and corresponding distribution of the DNAPL without the benefit of the exact background measurements. This is especially the case because the DNAPL distribution was greatly affected by horizontal layers which are only a few centimeters thick, with lateral continuities of as little as a meter as less. Research on the use of these methods is continuing.

For attempts at monitoring DNAPL occurrence or potential DNAPL migration, borehole EM resistivity logging tools (*e.g.*, the Geonics EM39) are commercially available and may be applicable. These tools focus EM energy outside the radius of a typical borehole (>10 to 150 cm) to measure the formation conductivity outside the borehole. Measurements can be taken within an open boring immediately following drilling, within a PVC monitoring well, or within a sealed PVC casing. Measurements can be taken within installations as small as 5 cm in diameter. A possible application of this method might involve the identification of DNAPL layers with high pore saturations that have accumulated above fine-grained beds in aquifers. Surveys could be performed in existing monitoring wells, yielding data from the entire vertical depth, not just the screened intervals of the wells. Zones of DNAPL accumulation would exhibit electrical conductivities that are higher than in the underlying aquifer materials. The minimum vertical resolution of such logs is probably about 0.5 m. As caveats, we note that: 1) DNAPL accumulations thinner than 0.5 m will probably not be detectable; 2) when the change in the electrical conductivity response of a zone of DNAPL accumulation is small relative to the natural variabilities in electrical conductivity, DNAPL accumulations will be difficult to identify; 3) zones of *residual* DNAPL will not likely exhibit electrical conductivities sufficiently different from that of the host medium to be detected.

Experimental work is underway to examine the combination of cone penetrometer testing with *in situ* resistivity measurements for the detection of DNAPLs (Westinghouse Savannah River Company, 1992). The objective of this method is to obtain a profile of the geologic conditions together with a resistivity profile. As with borehole EM logging, DNAPL accumulations should exhibit low conductivities. Field testing of this technique at a site expected to have large quantities of DNAPL in the subsurface has not demonstrated that DNAPL accumulations can be identified in this way. However, it is not certain whether the technique is not effective, or just that no significant DNAPL accumulations were present at the tested locations. Further experimental work is underway at this site to assess the use of a cone penetrometer probe with a fiber-optic Raman spectroscopy probe for direct *in situ* analysis of the presence of DNAPL.

In the field of soil science, neutron logging is employed to measure *in situ* moisture contents in soils, and in the petroleum exploration field to determine the water-filled porosity in reservoirs. A neutron logging tool is comprised of a fast neutron source (typically americium-beryllium) with a neutron and/or gamma detector. Fast neutrons emitted from the source enter the formation and are slowed (moderated) by the hydrogen in the water. The slowed or thermal neutrons are then susceptible to capture by other atomic nuclei in the formation with the consequent emission of gamma rays. The detector measures either the neutrons or the gamma rays. The measured thermal neutron counts increase with increasing water content of the formation. Since chlorine has a high neutron capture cross section, it reduces the neutron counts; it also causes gamma emissions. Therefore, in petroleum reservoir logging, corrections must be made to neutron logs to account for the chloride in reservoir brines. Because many DNAPLs are chlorinated compounds, many DNAPLs are effective in capturing thermal neutrons. Thus, a zone in which a DNAPL occupies a substantial proportion of the pore space will exhibit a neutron count that is lower than the surrounding formation where the pore space is filled with water or air. Although a zone of low neutron count can also be due lower porosity or lower moisture content, the presence of a DNAPL can lower neutron counts beyond the range of likely variations in porosity or moisture content. The PCE release field experiments examined by Schneider and Greenhouse (1992) and Brewster *et al.* (1992) have illustrated that borehole neutron logging can be an effective method for the direct detection of DNAPLs comprised of chlorinated compounds.

13.4 SOIL GAS SURVEYS

13.4.1 Description

Soil gas surveys to delineate source zone areas and dissolved-phase plumes in the groundwater zone are now a common component of site investigations. The general principles of soil gas surveys and several case studies are described by Marrin and Thompson (1987), and by Marrin and Kerfoot (1988). Discussions of some of the limitations of this method are given by Marrin (1988). Soil gas surveys involve the collection of soil gas samples from the shallow subsurface at locations distributed across a site. Grab sampling of soil gas may be accomplished from permanent or removable probes installed below ground surface. Surveys typically employ probes installed at a consistent depth of from 0.3 to 3 m below ground surface, but in some cases also employ clusters of probes installed at various depths through the vadose zone. Soil gas samples are captured in suitable containers, or passed through sorbent cartridges. Samples can be analyzed using on-site equipment, or in off-site analytical facilities. Soil gas surveys that employ both laterally-distributed and vertically-distributed sampling locations are those most likely to provide useful information for the identification of DNAPL in the vadose zone. However, recent investigations of the soil gas from controlled field experiments conducted by Rivett (1995) indicate that soil gas surveys are unlikely to be capable of identifying the location of dissolved plumes that exist more than a meter or two below the water table.

Soil gas surveys are expected to reflect only the effects of the migration of vapor away from source zones and the effect upward vapor migration from very shallow dissolved-phase plumes at the vadose zone/groundwater zone interface. If residual zones or accumulations of volatile DNAPL are present in the vadose zone, they will emit vapors at saturated vapor concentrations. The finding of vapor concentrations that approach expected saturated vapor concentrations (as based on the compounds present, the composition of the DNAPL, and the temperature) would yield convincing evidence that DNAPL is present in the vadose zone. Evidence of DNAPL deep in the vadose zone would be valuable in the further assessment of the potential for DNAPL to have penetrated into the groundwater zone. However, there are many processes that will act to reduce vapor concentrations in the vadose zone so that, in most circumstances, vapor concentrations close to saturation should only be expected directly within or very close to DNAPL source zones. Given the spacing of sample locations in most soil gas surveys and the potential spatial variabilities in DNAPL distributions, a lack of saturated-level vapor concentrations in soil gas cannot be interpreted to mean that DNAPL is not present.

13.4.2 Factors Influencing Vapor Concentrations

The pattern of vapor concentrations emanating from a DNAPL source zone will depend on many factors related to the nature of the DNAPL source zone and the vadose zone. In most circumstances, diffusion will be the dominant migration process and will cause vapors to migrate outward in all directions and create a halo of lower vapor concentrations around the DNAPL zone. Many chlorinated solvents have vapor pressures sufficiently high to cause the contaminated air to have a density much greater than the surrounding uncontaminated air. This high relative vapor density may induce downward advection of vapors that is much more rapid than downward migration by diffusion. Advective sinking of vapors can be important in media having hydraulic conductivities greater than about 10^{-2} cm/s. In media with lower hydraulic conductivities, diffusion will be the dominant migration process.

The present understanding of the size of the vapor halo that may form around a DNAPL source zone and the persistence of a DNAPL source in the vadose zone under different circumstances is based on what is currently a limited number of experimental and computer modeling studies. Under favorable conditions, vapor migration through the vadose zone may be rapid, and the size of the vapor halo around a DNAPL source zone may be relatively large. Controlled field experiments were conducted with source zones of residual TCE in the vadose zone of a sand aquifer (Hughes, 1991; Hughes *et al.*, 1992; Mendoza *et al.*, 1992). Lateral profiles of TCE vapor concentrations *vs.* distance from the source zone are shown in Figures 13.13 and 13.14. Vapor concentrations that approach the saturated vapor concentration (88,000 ppmV at the ambient temperature) are found only close to the source zone. The concentrations decline exponentially with distance, suggesting a transient diffusion profile. Detectable (>10 ppmV) concentrations were found at a distance of about 7 m from the source zone after only 18 days, though it should be recognized that the rate of lateral diffusion outward from a DNAPL source zone will decline with time because the concentration gradient around the source zone will decline with time. We also note that the above example reflects the most favorable conditions for rapid vapor migration: the total porosity was relatively high (0.4), the moisture content was relatively low (25% saturation), and the sorption coefficient for TCE on the aquifer material was low. Higher moisture contents will substantially lower the effective diffusion coefficient for organic vapors (see Figure 13.15), and will reduce the rate and extent of vapor migration.

The effects of variability of the spatial distribution of the DNAPL source zone, spatial variability in the properties of the vadose zone, and scenarios for vapor migration through low permeability/high moisture content media have not yet been assessed, either experimentally or by computer modelling. Although there have been attempts to relate measured soil gas concentrations to measured soil concentrations at actual field sites (*i.e.*, Siebenmann, 1993; Sohn *et al.*, 1993; Einberger *et al.*, 1993), there is considerable scatter in most of the data sets and quantitative correlations are poor. However,

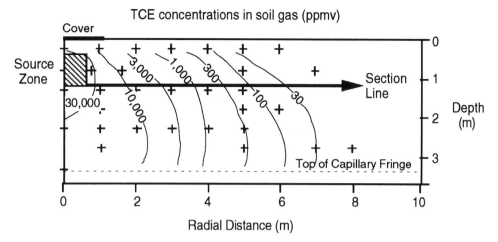

Figure 13.13 Example of lateral transport of TCE vapor in a sandy aquifer resulting from a experimental placement of a DNAPL source in the vadose zone. This vapor distribution developed 18 days after placement of a source zone that contained 42 L of TCE. Adapted with permission from Hughes *et al.* (1991); described further in Hughes *et al.* (1992).

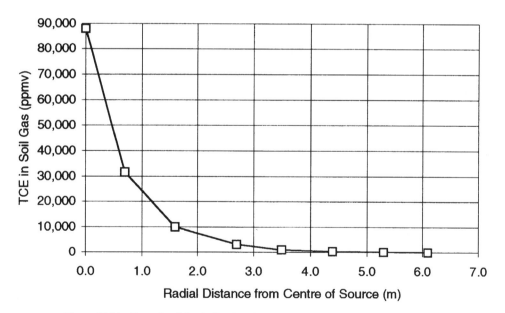

Figure 13.14 Example of the decline in TCE vapor concentrations with distance from the DNAPL source in the vadose zone. This profile corresponds to the section line shown in Figure 13.13. Data from Hughes *et al.* (1992).

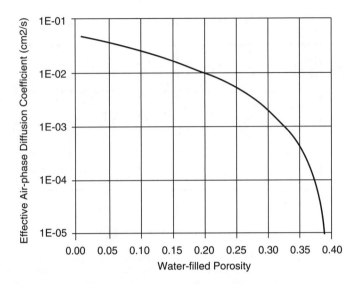

Figure 13.15   Relationship between effective air-phase diffusion coefficient (D_e) and the percent water saturation in soil. The effective air-phase diffusion coefficient is calculated according to $D_e = D_o \tau$, where the tortuosity $\tau = \theta_a^{2.33}/\theta_t^2$ is as defined by Karimi *et al.* (1987); θ_a is the air-filled porosity, and θ_t is the total porosity.

with regard to the delineation of DNAPL sources in the vadose zone, we can conclude that: 1) the finding of vapor concentrations that approach saturated vapor concentration for the compound of interest is evidence that DNAPL is likely to be present near the sampling point; and 2) because DNAPL source zones may be small in relation to the lateral and vertical spacing of sampling points and because of the rapid decline in vapor concentrations that can result from vapor transport by diffusion, the absence of saturated vapor concentrations is not necessarily evidence that DNAPL is absent. Comparable conclusions with regard to groundwater concentrations are discussed in later sections.

13.5 CHEMICAL ANALYSIS OF SOIL AND ROCK

13.5.1 Soil Samples

13.5.1.1 Sample collection

Chemical analyses of soil samples can be useful in determining the presence and distribution of DNAPL in both the vadose and groundwater zones. However, such analyses may be ineffective unless the soil sampling and analysis methods used are suitable for the specific task at hand. The critical issues related to soil sample collection are: 1) the lateral and vertical spacings of the samples; 2) cross-contamination during sample collection; and 3) the selection of subsample portions for analysis. The critical factor related to the chemical analysis of soil samples is the loss of volatiles during sample collection, handling, and storage.

As has been discussed above, the migration pathways and distribution of DNAPLs in the subsurface are strongly influenced by variations in geologic structure at both small and large scales. Consequently, in most circumstances, the spatial distribution of a DNAPL will be highly irregular. In stratified unconsolidated deposits, much of the DNAPL mass may be present as thin horizontal accumulations on less permeable strata. Depending on the geologic variability, these accumulations may be as thin as a few centimeters (see Figures 13.4 and 13.5). Reliable identification of such accumulations can be made only through the collection of **vertically-continuous soil samples**. Therefore, the common practice of recovering of a single 2 ft. long split-spoon sample for every 5 ft. of drilling will not likely be effective in understanding the distribution of DNAPLs in the subsurface.

Vertically-continuous soil samples can be collected in a number of ways. Conventional 2 ft. long split-spoon samples or Shelby-tube samples can be collected on a continuous basis, though such sampling can be laborious and costly. Alternatively, there are a variety of soil sampling devices available that will allow recovery of continuous cores that are 5 ft. in length or longer. Some of these devices allow sample collection while advancing a boring with hollow-stem augers (Central Mine Equipment Co.; George E. Failing Co.). Other devices are thin-tube piston-type samplers that are advanced separately, or ahead of drill casing or augers (Zapico *et al.*, 1987; Starr and Ingleton, 1992). The recovery of samples of cohesionless sand from below the water table is generally unreliable with devices that rely on mechanical traps or catchers to hold the soil in the sampling barrel. This can be overcome with the use of piston-type samplers.

Special problems may arise in sampling soils containing mobile DNAPL. During sample recovery, it may be possible for mobile DNAPL from a specific layer or accumulation to **cross-contaminate** other portions of the sample. An example of this form of cross-contamination is shown in Figure 13.16. In this case, a thin-walled aluminum core tube was used to recover soil samples from an experimental spill of PCE. Because the PCE was dyed red, it is clear that DNAPL migrated along the interface between the sample and the core barrel. The potential for this type of cross-contamination is particularly high for cases where the DNAPL has a high density and low viscosity, as is generally the case for chlorinated solvents. The effect of such cross-contamination on the results of soil analyses can be reduced by subsampling the interior of a soil core. The elimination of cross-contamination and the effective recovery of DNAPL pore fluids can also be achieved using cryogenic core samplers that freeze the sample in place in the core tube. Durnford *et al.* (1991) demonstrated the effectiveness of such a sampler for the recovery of an LNAPL product at the water table, and it would likely be similarly effective for DNAPLs residing in potentially mobile accumulations or pools.

The volume of soil needed for a chemical analysis is generally much smaller than the volume of soil recovered during sampling. Typical soil analysis methods require only 5 to 20 g of soil, though some methods can accommodate up to 250 g of soil. A 24 in. long split-spoon sampler contains 2,100 to 2,500 g of soil, and typical sampling programs would only yield one soil sample per split-spoon. Because the spatial distribution of a DNAPL can vary at the centimeter scale, even within a single split-spoon sample, DNAPL may be present in some portions but not in others. Consequently, the results of

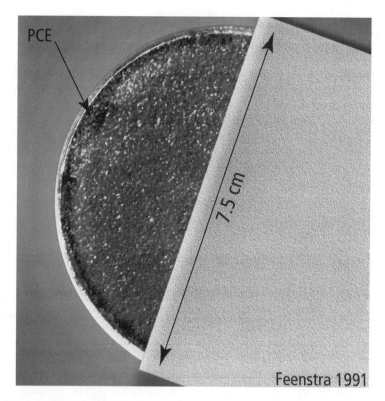

Figure 13.16 Example of cross-contamination of soil core resulting from migration of DNAPL PCE along the inside of a core tube. PCE is dyed red using Sudan IV dye. (Photograph by Stan Feenstra.)

the chemical analysis will depend strongly on where the subsample(s) are collected, and it becomes difficult to decide where the subsample(s) should be taken to best reflect the chemical concentrations in the overall section of core.

If one of the goals is to determine the presence/absence of DNAPL, subsampling should be directed at the most contaminated zones, and subsamples of the soil cores need not be large. If the goal is to attempt to estimate the chemical mass in the subsurface, the subsampling approach needs to be more complex. If DNAPL is present in localized zones in the cores, subsampling of only the DNAPL zones will result in serious overestimation of the chemical mass. At the same time, if the DNAPL zones are missed by the subsampling, the chemical mass in the core will be seriously underestimated. Because of the potential centimeter scale of variability in DNAPL distributions, subsampling from multiple locations within a core followed by compositing may be then be advantageous. However, composite subsampling requires more sample handling and therefore risks volatilization losses. Another approach might be to collect and analyze relatively large subsamples of the core in order to "average" the effects of small-scale variabilities. These issues are discussed further in the next section.

13.5.1.2 Sample analysis

The results of chemical analyses of soil samples for VOCs such as chlorinated solvents can be greatly affected by the methods used for sample handling, preservation, and analysis. Conventional methods suitable for the determination of inorganic chemicals and semi-volatile organic compounds are not suitable for VOCs because of the potential for **volatilization losses** from the sample before the analysis can be completed.

Methods for the sampling and determination of VOCs in soil have involved the following steps: 1) collection of soil cores using split-spoon or comparable core tubes; 2) examination of the samples in the field; 3) transfer of a small subsample to a 40 mL vial or larger jar; 4) storage at 4 °C during shipment and storage before analysis; 5) opening of the jar in the laboratory to remove a small portion for analysis; and lastly 6) extraction of the VOCs with methanol for high-concentration samples, or with water followed by purge-and-trap for low-concentration samples. Direct analysis of the headspace (air) in contact with the sample may be possible in either the original sample vial, or following transfer of the sample to a suitable container in the laboratory.

Voice and Kolb (1993) compared purge-and-trap, direct headspace, and methanol extraction in the laboratory under controlled conditions. Samples of three different natural soils were spiked with known amounts of various VOCs and analyzed by the three methods. The results for the chlorinated VOCs are given in Table 13.5. All the methods were found to underestimate the actual soil concentrations, *i.e.* the recoveries were less than 100%. The direct headspace analyses were more effective than the purge-and-trap analyses. The methanol extraction method was not consistent, being as effective as direct headspace for some compounds, but less effective for other compounds.

Although there are differences among the results obtained using different soil analysis methods, these differences are relatively small compared to the differences that can result from sample handling. Siegrist and Jenssen (1990) studied the effect of different sample handling methods under controlled laboratory conditions. A spiked soil column was sampled simultaneously using various handling methods. Of particular interest is their comparison of the effect of using a scoop or a tube to obtain a subsample from the soil and transfer it to the sample container, and whether the sample was then immersed in methanol. In all cases, the samples were contained in 40 mL vials. For scoop

TABLE 13.5   Laboratory Comparison of Percent Recoveries by Purge-and-Trap, Direct Headspace, and Methanol Extraction Methods for the Determination of VOCs in Soil. (Data are from Voice and Kolb (1993). Percent recoveries are averages of 8 to 10 replicate spikes each on 1 to 3 different soil types.)

Compound	Purge and trap	Direct headspace	Methanol extraction
Dichloromethane	35%	71%	44%
1,1,1-Trichloroethane	25%	72%	57%
Trichloroethylene	35%	73%	61%
Tetrachloroethylene	33%	76%	72%

sampling, the soil was collected from the soil column with a stainless steel scoop and transferred to the vial; for the tube sampling, a small stainless steel tube was used to remove soil from the column and the subsample was extruded directly into the vial. The vials were later re-opened for removal of a portion for analysis by isopropanol-pentane extraction. For the methanol immersion, tube sampling was used to extrude the subsample directly into methanol in the vial. The results for the chlorinated VOCs using these methods are given in Table 13.6. The highest, and presumably most accurate, concentrations were obtained when the methanol immersion method was used. Use of scoop sampling generally yielded the lowest concentrations. The concentrations obtained using methanol immersion range from 1.2 to 6.7 times higher than those obtained using scoop sampling.

TABLE 13.6 Laboratory Comparison of Soil Concentrations in mg/kg after Sample Handling by Scoop Sampling, Tube Sampling, and Methanol Immersion. (Data are from Seigrist and Jenssen (1990). Results are averages of duplicate samples.)

Compound	Scoop sampling	Tube sampling	Methanol immersion
Dichloromethane	6.1	4.9	7.2
1,1,1-Trichloroethane	0.28	0.36	1.9
Trichloroethylene	0.42	0.55	2.3
Chlorobenzene	0.58	0.69	0.76

Urban *et al.* (1989) provided a field comparison of different soil sample handling methods. Portions of the same split-spoon sample were analyzed by field methanol immersion/extraction, and by scoop sampling followed by analysis using either laboratory methanol extraction or purge-and-trap depending on the concentration level. The results of these analyses are given in Table 13.7. The TCE concentrations obtained using the field methanol immersion/extraction method were found to be consistently the highest, ranging from 2.5 to 45 times higher than those obtained using the other methods. Unlike the controlled laboratory studies described above, true duplicate samples could not be collected in the field. Consequently, some of the differences between the sampling methods may have been due to true differences among the samples.

At the present time, there is no recognized standard method for the handling and analysis of soil samples for VOCs (Lewis *et al.*, 1991). The most reliable methods are those that minimize the loss of volatiles during handling. Field methanol immersion/extraction has been shown to be effective in this regard. The field methanol method will be particularly useful in the collection and analysis of large samples (> 100 g), or composite samples comprised of multiple subsamples from the same core. Immersion in methanol provides a mechanism for the homogenization of such samples that is more effective than mechanical mixing, and also reduces volatilization losses.

Field methanol immersion/extraction has the disadvantage of having a relatively high detection limit (~0.1 mg/kg) compared to: 1) direct headspace or purge-and-trap

TABLE 13.7 Field Comparison of Methanol Field Immersion/Extraction Methods with Methanol Laboratory Extraction and Purge-and-Trap for the Determination of TCE in Soil. (All values are in mg/kg. Data are from Urban *et al.* (1989). "J" suffix designates samples in which the TCE that was detected below the limit of quantification.)

Sample code	Field methanol immersion/ extraction	Laboratory methanol extraction	Purge and trap
A. 2.0 feet to 4.0 feet	124	2.7	—
6.0 feet to 7.8 feet	79.9	5.5	—
B. 1.95 feet to 4.0 feet	212	47.2	—
D. 1.0 feet to 3.0 feet	5.31	0.27	—
E. 3.0 feet to 5.0 feet	0.81	0.32	—
I. 1.5 feet to 3.5 feet	0.66	—	0.015 J
3.5 feet to 5.5 feet	0.28	—	0.035
5.5 feet to 7.0 feet	0.096 J	—	0.065 J
M. 2.0 feet to 4.0 feet	0.34	—	0.015 J
H. 2.0 feet to 3.5 feet	0.11 J	—	< 0.025

($\sim$0.01 mg/kg); and 2) the soil clean-up targets defined for numerous sites. This limitation is not significant when diagnosing the presence of DNAPLs, since much higher concentrations are then of interest. However, large soil sampling programs or the collection of large volume samples can require substantial quantities of methanol. Use of the field methanol method will consequently require special precautions by field personnel to protect against toxicity and fire hazard both before and after extraction; it can also create a disposal problem for the contaminated methanol.

An alternative to the field methanol method would be any technique that does not require any handling or exposure of the sample to the atmosphere after it has been collected. For example, direct headspace analyses can be performed on soil samples collected in 40 mL vials with septum caps. (In this case, the only avenue for loss of volatiles is diffusion through the Teflon/silicone septa during storage.) Similarly, modified caps can be used on 40 mL vials so that purge-and-trap analysis can be performed without having to open the vial in the laboratory. The possible loss of VOCs from soil samples must be considered when interpreting historic soil analysis data.

13.5.2 Partitioning Calculations

13.5.2.1 General

Sampling of soil from the vadose and groundwater zones for quantitative chemical determinations has been a common procedure during site investigations for many years. The analysis of soil samples provides a measure of the total chemical mass in the soil. The results of soil analyses can be used in a quantitative manner to assess the possible presence of residual DNAPL contamination when there is no visual evidence of the presence of a DNAPL. Feenstra *et al.* (1991) describe a method for assessing the possible presence of DNAPL in soil samples based on the results of chemical and physical analyses, and the fundamental principles of chemical partitioning in soil.

13.5.2.2 Method description

This method is a simple semi-quantitative tool to allow the investigators of chemical spill and waste disposal sites to assess whether soil chemical analyses indicate the presence of residual DNAPL in the subsurface. Information that is needed for this method includes: 1) total chemical concentrations; 2) moisture content; 3) porosity; 4) sorption parameters for the chemicals of interest; and 5) physical and chemical properties of the chemicals of interest.

The chemical analysis of a soil sample for organic compounds can proceed by extraction of the sample using water leaching, solvent leaching, or heating. The analysis generally provides a measure of the total amount of the chemical of interest in the sample, expressed typically as the mass of chemical per unit dry weight of soil. The result includes the chemical that is: 1) dissolved in the pore water of the sample; 2) sorbed on the soil solids; 3) in the soil gas; and 4) in any DNAPL phase. The analysis *cannot* indicate directly how the chemical is distributed among these phases, nor whether any DNAPL phase is present. The method *can* be used to calculate whether a DNAPL phase is likely present in the sample.

The **hypothetical pore-water concentration** of the constituent of interest is calculated from the measured total soil concentration by assuming equilibrium chemical partitioning between the solid phase, the pore water, and the soil gas, and assuming that no DNAPL phase is present. This pore-water concentration C_w (mg/L, or equivalently $\mu g/cm^3$) can be expressed in terms of the total soil concentration C_t ($\mu g/g$ dry weight) as

$$C_w = \frac{C_t \rho_b}{K_d \rho_b + \theta_w + H_c \theta_a} \tag{13.3}$$

where: ρ_b = dry bulk density of the soil sample (g/cm^3); θ_w = water-filled porosity (volume fraction); θ_a = air-filled porosity (volume fraction); K_d = partition coefficient between pore water and soil solids for the compound and temperature of interest (cm^3/g); and H_c = dimensionless Henry's Gas Law constant for the compound and temperature of interest.

If no DNAPL is present, there is a maximum amount of chemical which can be contained in a sample of soil that contains soil solids, pore water, and soil gas. This maximum total soil concentration is determined by: 1) the solubility concentration S_w of the chemical in water; 2) the concentration in the soil gas that would be in equilibrium with S_w; and 3) the concentration sorbed to the solids that would be in equilibrium with S_w. The only way that the chemical in the form of a DNAPL phase can be present in a sample would be for the value of C_w as *calculated* by Eq.(13.3) to be greater than S_w. In that case, we know that at equilibrium, some DNAPL phase is present, and for the true aqueous concentration we have that $C_w = S_w$.

The parameters ρ_b, θ_w, and θ_a can be determined from the standard measurements of soil density and water content that are often performed. Even when these parameters must be estimated rather than measured, the possible value ranges are relatively narrow, and the uncertainty imparted to a value of C_w calculated by Eq.(13.3) will be correspondingly small. If possible, measured values of K_d should be obtained from batch or column experiments. However, in many situations, it will be necessary to estimate K_d values using K_{oc} and f_{oc} values (see Chapter 8). Although factors such as differences in the nature of the soil organic material, sorption on mineral surfaces, intergranular diffusion, very high dissolved chemical concentrations, and the presence of dissolved organic matter or cosolvents in the ground water may cause K_d values so obtained to be in error, the K_{oc} approach still provides the only general means of estimating K_d values without direct measurement. For most compounds of interest here, H_c values can be obtained from published data (*e.g.*, Montgomery and Welkom, 1990; Howard, 1989; Howard, 1990; and Appendix I in this book). In general, the largest uncertainty in the C_w values calculated using Eq.(13.3) will be due to uncertainty in K_d. Figure 13.17 presents some example calculations for the proportion of TCE (as a single component) in the gas, dissolved, sorbed, and DNAPL phases for a typical sandy soil. At soil concentrations greater than several thousand mg/kg, these results show that the majority of the TCE is found in the DNAPL phase.

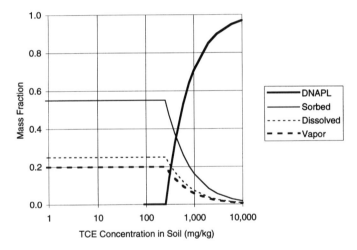

Figure 13.17   Relative proportion of TCE in soil gas, water, and soil solid phases for a typical sandy soil. Calculated based on the partitioning relationships described in Feenstra *et al.* (1991) assuming a total porosity θ_t of 0.4, a water-filled porosity θ_w of 0.1, a dimensionless Henry's Gas Law constant of 0.27, and a K_d of 0.12.

For a *multicomponent* DNAPL, the value of C_w calculated according to Eq.(13.3) for one of the components of interest must be compared not to the pure phase solubility S_w of that component, but rather to the estimated effective solubility of that component *from the mixture*. If the calculated C_w value exceeds that estimated solubility, then it can be concluded that the multicomponent DNAPL phase could be present. If a sample of the multicomponent DNAPL is available, then the water solubility of the component of interest can be measured directly. Alternatively, in a manner that is totally analogous to Eq.(13.2), the effective solubility of one component of a DNAPL requires information on the chemical composition of the DNAPL and the use of Raoult's Law (see Chapter 7). The chemical composition of the DNAPL can be determined by analysis of samples of DNAPL recovered from the subsurface; in some cases, there may be suitable information on the chemical composition of the product released at the site. Unfortunately, we note that at many waste disposal and chemical spill sites: 1) the DNAPL contains a substantial proportion of organic compounds which cannot be readily identified and quantified by standard analytical methods; or 2) samples of the DNAPL are simply not available for analysis. In these situations, assumptions must be made regarding the composition of the DNAPL. Or, it may be possible to use chemical analysis results for soil samples which exhibit visual evidence of DNAPL, or are clearly very highly contaminated (thousands of mg/kg or more): at very high soil concentrations, almost all of the chemical mass will be in the DNAPL phase.

In some circumstances, it will be useful to have an estimate of the DNAPL-filled porosity θ_{DNAPL} to assess the potential mobility of the DNAPL. Such an estimate can be made using the equation

$$\theta_{DNAPL} = \frac{C_t \rho_b - S_e(K_d \rho_b + \theta_w + H_c \theta_a)}{C_{DNAPL}} \qquad (13.4)$$

where S_e is the effective solubility of the compound of interest from the DNAPL phase ($= S_w$ in the case of a single-component DNAPL), and C_{DNAPL} ($\mu g/cm^3$) is the concentration of the component of interest in the DNAPL phase.

13.5.2.3 Example calculation: contamination with TCE

Soil samples were collected from borings around an industrial facility in order to assess the source of TCE contamination in the groundwater beneath the site. Several of these results are given in Table 13.8. The TCE concentrations in these samples ranged from 210 to 3,100 mg/kg. There was no visual evidence of DNAPL in any of the samples. The samples were all collected from near or below the water table. The value of ρ_b was estimated to be ~1.86 g/cm³, the total porosity was estimated to be 0.3, and θ_a was taken to be zero. The value of K_{oc} for TCE at ~20 °C is 126, and f_{oc} was taken to be 0.001. Using these parameter values and the measured values of C_t, the calculated C_w values were found to range from 730 to 11,000 mg/L.

TABLE 13.8   Results of Trichloroethylene Analyses of Soil and Calculation of Hypothetical Pore-Water Concentrations. (Parameters used for calculations: $\theta_w = 0.3$; $\theta_a = 0$; $\rho_b = 1.86$ g/cm³; $K_{oc} = 126$; $f_{oc} = 0.001$.)

Sample depth (m)	Measured TCE levels in soil (mg/kg)	Calculated pore water conc. ($\mu g/L$)	NAPL saturation (% bulk vol.)
2.13	3,100	11,000	0.3
6.10	420	1,500	—
9.14	210	730	—

TCE was used as a degreasing solvent at this site; no other chemicals were detected in the soil samples at significant concentrations. It is not known whether the TCE released to the subsurface was pure solvent, or used solvent which may have contained substantial proportions of oil and grease compounds. The effective solubility of TCE in a used solvent mixture at 20 °C would be somewhat less than the 1,400 mg/L solubility of pure-phase TCE at 20 °C.

The calculated pore-water concentration for the sample from 2.13 m depth is much greater than the pure-phase solubility of TCE of 1,400 mg/L. We can there-fore conclude that liquid TCE was present in this sample. The calculated pore-water concentrations in the samples from 6.10 m and 9.14 m depths are slightly greater and slightly lower respectively, than the pure-phase solubility of TCE. Given that the effective solubility of TCE in used solvent would be lower than that of pure-phase TCE, these results suggest that small quantities of liquid TCE may have also been present in both of these samples. To summarize, for these samples, any soil concen-tration greater than $\sim$300 mg/kg would be consistent with the presence of residual liquid TCE.

A generic graph relating C_t values in soil to the calculated C_w values is given in Figure 13.18. This graph is based on a typical water-saturated soil with $\theta_w = 0.3$, and $\rho_b = 1.86$ g/cm^3. Four lines are shown representing four chemicals with relatively low K_d values of 0.0, 0.1, 1.0 and 10, the range expected for the chlorinated solvents in most soils. For the preceding TCE example, K_d was $\sim$0.1. Thus, the results in Table 13.8 can be obtained from this graph by locating the intersection of a measured C_t value with the appropriate K_d curve to obtain the calculated C_w value.

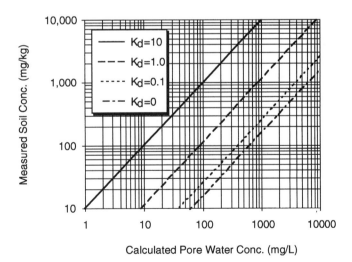

Figure 13.18   Generic graph for the relationship between the pore water and soil con-centrations for weakly sorbed contaminants in a typical sandy aquifer. Calculated based on the partitioning relationships described in Feenstra *et al.* (1991) assuming a total porosity θ_t of 0.3 and a water-filled porosity θ_w of 0.3.

13.5.2.4 Example calculation: contamination with PCBs in hydrocarbons

Soil samples were collected from borings around disposal pits in which PCB-contaminated hydrocarbon liquids had been released. Results from some of the soil analyses are given in Table 13.9. The total PCB concentrations in these samples ranged from 71 to 590 mg/kg, and the PCB compound pattern resembled that of the mixture Aroclor 1248. The samples were all collected from near or below the water table. The value of ρ_b was assumed to be $\sim$1.86 g/cm^3, the total porosity was taken to be 0.3, and θ_a was taken to be zero. The *average* value of K_{oc} for Aroclor 1248 reported by Chou and Griffin (1986) is 54,626, and f_{oc} was taken to be 0.003. Using these parameter values, the calculated C_w values were found to range from 430 to 3,600 μg/L.

TABLE 13.9 Results of PCB Analyses of Soil and Calculation of Hypothetical Pore-Water Concentrations. (Parameters used for calculations: $\theta_w = 0.3$; $\theta_a = 0$; $\rho_b = 1.86$ g/cm^3; $K_{oc} = 54{,}626$; $f_{oc} = 0.003$.)

Sample depth (m)	Measured PCB levels in soil (mg/kg)	Calculated pore water conc. (μg/L)	NAPL saturation (% bulk vol.)
0.63	590	3,600	2.0
0.91	310	1,900	1.0
1.04	170	1,000	0.6
1.77	71	430	0.2

PCBs were contaminants in the hydrocarbon liquids released to the subsurface at this site, and were believed to be present at concentrations up to 5% by weight. The overall chemical composition of the hydrocarbon mixture is not known, so we have assumed that the PCB mole fraction in the hydrocarbon mixture was also approximately 5%. The estimated effective solubility of PCB in hydrocarbon mixture would be 5% of the total pure-phase solubility of 54 μg/L for Aroclor 1248 (Chou and Griffin, 1986), or 2.7 μg/L. All of the calculated C_w values greatly exceed both the pure-phase and estimated effective solubility of Aroclor 1248, indicating the presence of liquid PCB-containing waste in all of the samples analyzed.

A generic graph relating measured total concentrations in soil to the calculated C_w values is given in Figure 13.19 for chemicals which sorb much more strongly to soil than those considered in Figure 13.18. This graph is based on a typical water-saturated soil having a θ_w of 0.3 and a ρ_b of 1.86 g/cm^3. Three lines are shown, representing compounds having K_d values of 100, 1,000, and 10,000, the range which would be expected for typical soils for compounds such as those in the common PCB mixtures, and for many polycyclic aromatic hydrocarbons (PAHs).

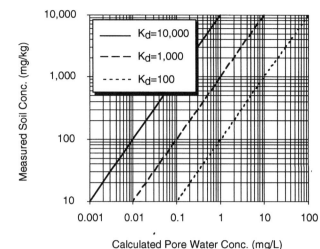

Figure 13.19 Generic graph for the relationship between pore water and soil concentrations for strongly sorbed contaminants in a typical sandy aquifer. Calculated based on the partitioning relationships described in Feenstra *et al.* (1991) assuming a total porosity θ_t of 0.3 and a water-filled porosity θ_w of 0.3.

13.5.2.5 Reliability

The method represented by Eq.(13.3) is intended to be a simple semi-quantitative tool to allow the investigators of chemical spill and waste disposal sites to assess whether soil chemical analyses indicate the presence of residual DNAPL. At the present time, such calculations are the only way to assess the presence of residual DNAPL in soil samples using simple, conventional soil analysis methods. Moreover, the direct laboratory confirmation of the presence of low levels of DNAPL by any method is currently difficult.

Conclusions regarding the presence of DNAPL in soil samples are most reliable for cases when: 1) the values of C_t are either very high or very low; 2) the soil/pore water K_d values can be measured for the compounds and soil(s) of interest; 3) the composition and solubility of the DNAPL phase is well understood. Conclusions regarding the presence of a DNAPL phase are less reliable when parameters such as K_d and the effective solubility must be estimated.

13.5.3 Direct Determination of DNAPLs

As has been described in Section 13.3.1.2 on testing in the field, for qualitative visual identification, methods such as UV fluorescence, soil/water shake tests, and shake tests with the addition of a hydrophobic dye can be used (Cohen *et al.*, 1992). These analyses provide only a determination of the presence or absence of a NAPL. Although a presence/absence determination for a NAPL may be sufficient in many situations, there will also be situations in which a quantitative measure of the degree of NAPL saturation is desired. Cary *et al.* (1991) proposed a method for determining the NAPL content in a soil by shaking a suspension of soil and water with a strip of **porous polyethylene** treated with a light hydrocarbon oil. NAPL that is released from the soil into the suspension is absorbed onto the polyethylene. The polyethylene strip is weighed before and after the test to determine the NAPL content. Although this method has not been used with samples from actual field sites, laboratory tests with sands, loamy sand, and silt loam soils have indicated recoveries of 82 to 99% for two LNAPLs, a mineral oil and a light petroleum distillate. This method may therefore also be useful in the quantification of DNAPL content in soil samples.

13.5.4 Sampling and Analysis of Fractured Media

Determining the presence of DNAPL in fractured rock or clay is considerably more complex than in soils. In DNAPL cases involving fractured media, the DNAPL will only penetrate into the porous matrix of the rock between the fractures if the rock matrix is itself highly permeable, or the pressures driving the DNAPL migration are very high; the DNAPL will accumulate in the fractures in zones where capillary forces resist further migration.

As is discussed in detail in Chapter 12, DNAPL in fractures will slowly dissolve into the surrounding groundwater, including that in the matrix. Modeling studies discussed in Chapter 12 show that much or all of the original DNAPL mass can dissolve and diffuse into the matrix in a relatively short period of time when the: 1) DNAPL component(s) is (are) relatively soluble; 2) DNAPL mass in the fractures is sufficiently small; and/or 3) the porosity of the rock matrix is sufficiently large. These studies have shown that in many fractured sedimentary rock and fractured clay systems, DNAPLs comprised of the common chlorinated solvents can disappear from most or all of the fractures with a few years; the DNAPL phase can persist longer if comprised of low solubility components such as PCBs and PAHs.

13.5.4.1 DNAPL in fractures

In a situation when DNAPL persists in the fractures, the challenge is to obtain samples of rock or soil core without the loss of the DNAPL. In fractured clays, dark-colored, viscous DNAPL may be visible within fractures or on fracture surfaces in conventional soil cores (see Figure 13.20). In rock cores on the other hand, although dark-colored and viscous DNAPL, staining, or oily sheens may be visible on the fracture surfaces, in most circumstances, the water, air or mud drilling fluids will wash out any evidence of DNAPL that was present within the fractures. In circumstances where major components of the DNAPL are relatively non-volatile (as with the PCBs and PAHs), a **"swab test"** of a fracture surface may be useful in assessing whether DNAPL had been present in the fracture.

Swab tests on the surfaces of building interiors and equipment are commonly used in the occupational health and industrial hygiene fields. For a fracture swab test, both sides of the fracture are wiped with a surgical cotton gauze pad that has been soaked in a solvent such as decane. Any small, but invisible, quantity of DNAPL that remains on the fracture surface is thereby dissolved by the solvent in the swab. The swab is then placed in a jar and shipped to the laboratory for analysis where it is extracted with solvent and analyzed. The analysis is reported in terms of the mass of the compound(s) of interest per swab. The concentration per unit area of fracture can then be determined. Although the

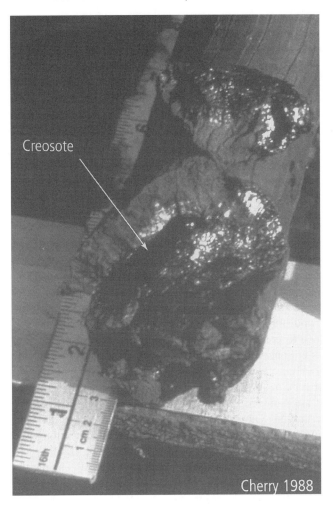

Figure 13.20 Example of DNAPL creosote observed along a fracture in a core sample from below the water table at a depth of about 10 m in a lacustrine clay formation. (Photograph by John A. Cherry.)

results of swab tests are qualitative, they can provide information on DNAPL presence that may not be obtainable by other means.

The results of swab analyses from an investigation of PCB contamination in fractured shale are shown in Table 13.10. PCB concentrations were found to range from less than 0.05 to 1,300 μg/100 cm^2. The difficulty in the interpretation of swab tests is determining what concentration might reflect the presence of a DNAPL phase prior to drilling. As a means of comparison, even under natural conditions, the DNAPL residual content within a fracture will likely be rather low. For example, laboratory studies of chlorinated solvents in simulated fractures conducted by Schwille (1988) suggested a residual content of 0.05 L/m^2 ($=$ 0.5 mL/100 cm^2). In the above example, the DNAPL spilled was believed to be comprised of about 10% PCBs. If all the residual DNAPL was retained on the fracture surface during drilling and was then extracted by the swab, the PCB concentration would have been 45,000 μg/100 cm^2. However, most of any

TABLE 13.10   Results of PCB Analyses
of Swab Test in a Fractured Shale
Formation.

Sample depth (m)	PCB swab test (μg/100 cm^2)
2.5	1,300
4.2	160
5.0	170
6.0	90
9.5	< 0.05

residual DNAPL would likely have been washed out of the fracture during drilling. Because of this, concentrations in the range of several hundred to several thousand μg/100 cm^2 would likely reflect the former presence of this DNAPL. At this site, then, this DNAPL phase likely existed in the fractures to a depth of 5.0 m, but not beyond 9.5 m.

Sponge coring is a technology from the petroleum reservoir engineering industry that may be applicable to the investigation of DNAPLs in fractured rock. Sponge coring provides for the collection of undisturbed rock core and core fluids. The drill bit and core barrel are specially designed to prevent the intrusion of drilling fluids into the core barrel. The core barrel contains an inner sleeve of "oleophyllic" absorbent polyurethane sponge which surrounds the rock core as it enters the core barrel. Any organic NAPL present in the rock fractures or rock matrix is attracted to the sponge liner and trapped. On recovery, the sponge liners are removed, split length-wise, and examined under UV light. Any areas of the sponge that have absorbed a fluorescing NAPL will be evident. This method is used in the study of petroleum reservoirs to estimate oil saturation since many PAHs fluoresce strongly. In the study of a contaminated LNAPL site, Hardisty and Johnson (1993) used sponge coring to investigate the distribution of LNAPL below the water table in a fractured sandstone. Evidence of LNAPL was found in some fractures but not in others. The zones of LNAPL presence as based on the sponge coring correlated well with observations of LNAPL in monitoring wells. Research is required on sponge coring to assess its potential for use in DNAPL investigations.

13.5.4.2 DNAPL components in the matrix

In situations where the DNAPL has dissolved and has diffused significantly into a rock or clay matrix, it may be possible to determine the former presence of DNAPL by **analysis of the matrix material**. This may be also be important in cases where other evidence of DNAPL presence in the fractures is not available. The sampling and chemical analysis for VOCs such as chlorinated solvents in rock or clay cores are prone to the same pitfalls as for soil samples: handling and analysis methods must reduce the potential for losses prior to analysis. We also note that sample handling and transfer to sample containers is more difficult for consolidated rock or cohesive clay samples than with soil samples. The field methanol immersion/extraction method is probably the method most suitable for the analysis of segments of rock core. Breaking of rock into small pieces to fit into a 40 mL vial for analysis by headspace or purge-and-trap would likely lead to significant losses of VOCs.

If the purpose of the analysis of rock core is to determine whether a DNAPL is present, core samples should be collected immediately adjacent to the fractures since that is where the highest concentrations in the matrix will occur. Depending on the nature of the matrix material and the length of time that the DNAPL might have resided in the fracture, diffusion may have caused contamination of the matrix out to distances up to a meter or more over a period of years. However, concentrations may decline very rapidly with distance from the fracture.

The analysis of rock or clay core will yield the total concentration in the matrix. This total will be the sum of the chemical mass dissolved in the pore water and sorbed on the geologic solids. (In most circumstances, there will be no significant air or DNAPL phase in the matrix.) The same partitioning calculations described in the preceding sections for soil can be used to estimate the pore-water concentration in the matrix based on the total matrix concentration. In this case, if the calculated pore-water concentration is a substantial fraction of the effective solubility for the component of interest, then it is likely that DNAPL was present in the adjacent fracture prior to diffusion into the matrix.

Lawrence *et al.* (1990) used the analysis of matrix samples to assess the presence and distribution of a DNAPL in the fractured Chalk aquifer in eastern England. The Chalk is a soft microporous limestone formation that is a major water supply aquifer. The matrix of the Chalk has a porosity of 25% to 45% and a low hydraulic conductivity. Primary and secondary fracture networks provide the avenues for groundwater flow in the aquifer. The primary fractures comprise a regular set of orthogonal fractures spaced at 0.05 m to 0.2 m apart. The secondary fractures are spaced at intervals of 5 m to 10 m and represent primary fractures that have been enlarged by dissolution and weathering processes.

Lawrence *et al.* (1990) collected cores from a 55 m deep boring in the Chalk aquifer in an area where the groundwater had been found to be seriously contaminated by PCE. A total of 21 cores, each 0.5 m in length, were collected from the boring. (The Chalk is sufficiently soft to allow coring using a thin-walled tube sampler.) In a field laboratory, each core was extruded and 6 subsamples were collected along its length. Each subsample consisted of about 2 g of material, and was transferred to a pre-weighed 8 mL vial containing 6 mL of water and 0.5 mL of pentane. The vials were shaken in a vortex mixer to disaggregate the material and then centrifuged to separate the sediment from the pentane. The pentane was then analyzed using a gas chromatograph with a photoionization detector (GC/PID). The PCE concentration in the chalk pore water was calculated based on the measured PCE mass, and the weight and moisture content of the sample.

The profile of the PCE concentrations in the Chalk matrix pore water are shown in Figure 13.21. For each sample interval, the range in pore-water concentrations in the six subsamples is shown by the solid bar. In the interval between 10 and 20 m in depth, PCE concentrations in the matrix were as high as 40 mg/L ($\sim$20% of saturation). Pore-water concentrations as high as 5 mg/L ($\sim$2% of saturation) were found to a depth of 50 m.

As will be described in the following section, dissolved concentrations of this magnitude generally indicate proximity to a zone of DNAPL. On the basis of these concentrations, Lawrence *et al.* (1990) concluded that the DNAPL had penetrated to a depth of ~50 m. The higher concentrations found between 10 and 20 m coincide with a transition from a weathered chalk stratum to a less weathered, less permeable stratum. In this zone, DNAPL may have accumulated, occupying more of the fractures and permitting greater diffusion into the matrix. At greater depths, DNAPL may have penetrated fewer fractures, or the important fractures were more widely spaced. Consequently, pore-water concentrations in the matrix at these depths were found to be lower.

In addition to the cores, samples of groundwater were obtained as the Chalk boring was advanced. The PCE concentrations in these samples are given in Figure 13.21. The boring water concentrations ranged from 10 to 25 mg/L (5 to 10% of saturation), *i.e.*, sufficiently high to lead to the conclusion that DNAPL was present in the proximity of the boring. However, although the highest concentrations in the boring water coincided with the highest matrix pore-water concentrations at a depth of 10 to 20 m, the boring water concentrations at greater depth were much higher than the pore-water concentrations. This is likely the result of the migration of boring water from the upper portions of the boring into the lower portions of the boring during drilling. If unrecognized, this cross-contamination would lead to the interpretation that abundant DNAPL had penetrated to the full depth of 50 m, whereas the matrix pore-water concentration profile suggests that the greatest accumulation of DNAPL may be in the 10 to 20 m depth interval. These findings illustrate the potential effectiveness in using the analysis of matrix pore water in assessing DNAPL distributions.

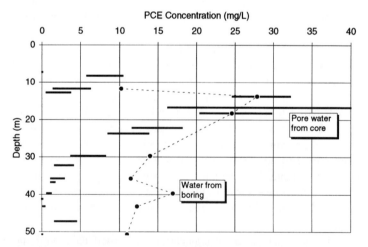

Figure 13.21.   Vertical profile of pore water PCE concentrations in core samples from the Chalk aquifer in eastern England. The bars show the ranges in concentration from six sub-samples collected from each 0.5 m section of core. The dashed curves shows the PCE concentrations in groundwater collected from the boring during core sampling. Data from Lawrence *et al.* (1990).

13.6 CHARACTER OF DISSOLVED PLUMES

13.6.1 General

The **spatial distribution of dissolved contaminant plumes** in the groundwater zone can yield valuable information when assessing the presence and spatial distribution of DNAPLs in the subsurface. The spatial distribution of dissolved plumes within an aquifer, the magnitude of the dissolved concentrations, the temporal variability in the dissolved concentrations, and the response of dissolved concentrations to groundwater pump-and-treat operations can each be influenced by the nature of the DNAPL source zone(s) in the subsurface. This section considers the theoretical and experimental evidence regarding the character of dissolved plumes from DNAPL sources and then describes a case study that exemplifies many of these findings.

13.6.2 Spatial Distribution of Dissolved Plumes

The spatial distribution of the dissolved plume that develops at a DNAPL site in the subsurface may be unique in several ways. Many DNAPL chemicals, including the chlorinated solvents, have high vapor pressures. The release of a significant quantity of DNAPL can create a large plume or halo of contamination in the vadose zone as a result of vapor diffusion. Groundwater contamination will then develop at the water table as a result of infiltration of water through the vapor halo and the DNAPL zones in the vadose zone. In most circumstances, the vapor halo will be much larger than the DNAPL zone, and will result in a dissolved plume much larger than the DNAPL zone itself. Field experiments and computer modeling have shown that the groundwater contamination that results from this type of release remains as a thin plume close to the water table.

In contrast to the above case, when DNAPL residual and/or pools are present in the groundwater zone, the dissolved plume(s) will reflect the size(s) and depth(s) of the source zone(s). The dissolved plumes may occur far below the water table, but will not be significantly wider than the DNAPL source zones from which they are derived because of weak transverse dispersion processes. As discussed in Section 13.3.3, attempts to determine the lateral extent and depth to which DNAPL has penetrated below the water table by drilling within the DNAPL zone is unreliable and generally undesirable because of the potential for short circuiting along borings. In most circumstances, lateral and vertical delineation of dissolved plumes downgradient of DNAPL source zones is the most effective and safest way of assessing the vertical distribution of DNAPL sources.

The contrast between dissolved plumes derived from DNAPL sources in the vadose zone and those derived from DNAPL sources groundwater zone is illustrated by controlled field experiments that have been conducted at the Borden test site. The vadose zone experiments are described by Conant *et al.* (1995), and the groundwater zone experiment is described by Rivett *et al.* (1995). Detailed monitoring utilizing hundreds of sampling points spaced vertically at intervals of 0.2 to 0.3 m have permitted a detailed understanding of the groundwater plumes created at the site. In the vadose zone experiments, cylindrical source zones were created in the unsaturated zone by mixing 42 L of

TCE with sand. A source zone measured 1.2 m in diameter and 0.8 m in height. TCE concentrations in soil gas measured 18 days after placement of the first source are given in Figure 13.13; TCE concentrations above 30 ppmV (about 170 μg/L) extended as far as 7 m from the source zone. This source remained in place for 1 month, and was then removed. The area of the vapor halo was then treated by soil vapor extraction. A similar experiment was conducted at the same location 20 months later. In this case, the TCE source zone remained in place for 3 months before it was removed and the area treated by soil vapor extraction. Despite the fact that the DNAPL source zones remained in the vadose zone for only short periods of time, a very substantial dissolved TCE plume was created at the interface between the vadose and groundwater zones. This interface zone plume is shown in plan view in Figure 13.22, and in section view in Figure 13.23. The interface plume in these figures is as much as 40 m wide, but only 1 to 2 m thick. The width of the dissolved plume reflects the size of the vapor halo, not the size of the DNAPL zone. Dissolved concentrations in the core of the plume were as high as 6 mg/L, reflecting the peak of Experiment #2, but extended over only very short vertical intervals (<0.5 m).

The dissolved plume created by the groundwater zone source at Borden was substantially different from that generated by the vadose zone sources. In this experiment, a rectangular source zone measuring 1.5 m long, 1 m high, and 0.5 m thick was created 1 m below the seasonal low water table. The source zone contained 14.8 L of a solvent mixture comprised of 6% chloroform (trichloromethane, or TCM), 39% TCE, and 55% PCE. After 11 months, the TCM and TCE plumes had migrated about 40 m downgradient. Due to retardation processes, the PCE plume had migrated only about 30 m downgradient. The TCE plume from the groundwater zone experiment is shown in plan view in Figure 13.22 and in section view in Figure 13.23. The maximum width of the groundwater zone plume at 11 months was about 5 m, reflecting a small degree of lateral dispersion. This occurred despite the fact the groundwater flow direction varied seasonally over an arc of as much as 30 °. Without the seasonal fluctuation in flow direction, the width of the plume would have been even smaller. The maximum vertical thickness of the plume was about 3 m. Downward spreading likely resulted from density-induced sinking of the plume in response to dissolved concentrations of up to 1 g/L in the core of the plume close to the source zone, and from variations in hydraulic conductivity. The maximum TCE concentrations in the plume close to the source ranged as high as 600 mg/L, which was the effective solubility of TCE in the source-zone mixture; dissolved concentrations downgradient of the source zone were considerably lower as a result of dispersion.

Although the Borden experiments represent idealized cases, they do reflect the general features of dissolved plumes that would be anticipated at a site where volatile DNAPL was released to the subsurface and entered the groundwater zone. Compared to the original DNAPL zone in the vadose zone, the interface plume created by a vapor halo in the vadose zone would be expected to be broad in width but vertically thin. Within this type of thin interface plume, dissolved concentrations will generally be much lower than saturation concentrations. In contrast, a plume created by DNAPL in the groundwater zone would be expected to reflect the size and vertical location of the DNAPL zone. If the DNAPL zone is narrow, the resultant dissolved plume will be narrow. If the DNAPL

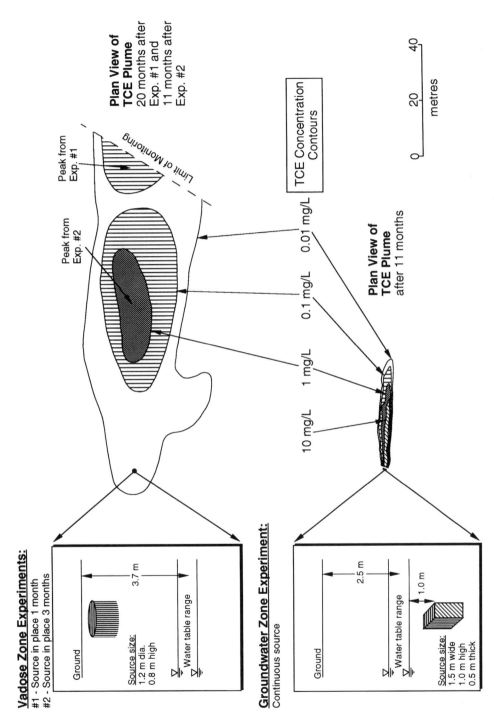

Vadose Zone Experiments:
#1 - Source in place 1 month
#2 - Source in place 3 months

Peak from Exp. #1

Peak from Exp. #2

Limit of Monitoring

Plan View of TCE Plume
20 months after Exp. #1 and 11 months after Exp. #2

Ground

3.7 m

Source size:
1.2 m dia.
0.8 m high

Water table range

Groundwater Zone Experiment:
Continuous source

TCE Concentration Contours

10 mg/L   1 mg/L   0.1 mg/L   0.01 mg/L

Plan View of TCE Plume
after 11 months

Ground

2.5 m

Water table range

1.0 m

Source size:
1.5 m wide
1.0 m high
0.5 m thick

0   20   40

metres

Figure 13.22 Plan views of dissolved plumes derived from vadose-zone and groundwater-zone experimental sources in the Borden aquifer. The vadose zone experiment was performed by Conant *et al.* (1995), and the groundwater-zone experiment was performed by Rivett *et al.* (1995).

451

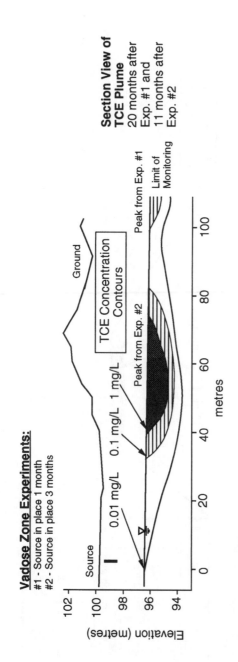

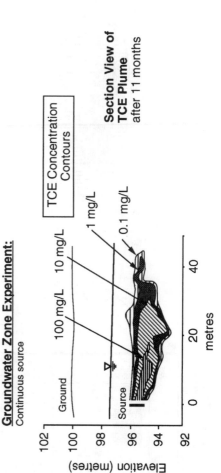

Figure 13.23 Section views of dissolved plumes derived from vadose-zone and groundwater-zone experimental sources in the Borden aquifer. The vadose-zone experiment was performed by Conant *et al.* (1994), and the groundwater-zone experiment was performed by Rivett *et al.* (1994).

zone extends to a substantial depth in the aquifer, the dissolved plume will extend to a similar depth.

Because of the thin vertical extent of interface plumes, groundwater samples obtained from such a plume using conventional wells will generally exhibit low dissolved concentrations due to dilution with uncontaminated water from below the plume: well intakes are usually long relative to the thickness of an interface plume. Monitoring using conventional wells will fail to identify the plume if the well intake does not straddle the water table. For plumes derived from DNAPL sources in the groundwater zone, because of the limited vertical and lateral extents of such plumes, groundwater monitoring in this case can: 1) also yield low dissolved concentrations as a result of dilution with uncontaminated water from above or below the plume when well intakes are long; or 2) fail to identify the plume if the well intake does not intersect the plume. The manner in which an interface zone plume and deeper plumes derived from DNAPL in the groundwater zone can affect the results of groundwater monitoring at an actual field site is discussed in Section 13.6.5 based on groundwater monitoring at three different depths within the aquifer.

Good depth resolution and therefore information regarding the vertical distribution of DNAPL below the water table can be obtained using drive-point devices to obtain a vertical profile of the dissolved plume downgradient of a DNAPL source zone. Clausen *et al.* (1993) used a drive-point device to collect groundwater samples from discrete depths to assess the presence of liquid TCE within a confined sand and gravel aquifer. The aquifer was about 9 m thick, and the top of the aquifer occurred at a depth of about 13 to 20 m below ground surface. Four groundwater samples were collected at approximately 2 m intervals through the aquifer. TCE concentrations were 4.1 mg/L at the top, ~8.2 mg/L in the middle and 16 mg/L at the bottom of the aquifer. The increase in TCE with depth and the relatively high concentrations led Clausen *et al.* (1993) to conclude that liquid TCE had likely penetrated to the base of the aquifer, to a total depth of about 30 m.

Pitkin *et al.* (1994) used detailed vertical profiling to delineate the dissolved plume in a sand aquifer created by a release of PCE from a retail dry cleaner. A drive-point device was used to collect groundwater samples at vertical intervals of 0.1 to 0.25 m, to depths as great as 15 m. A total of 23 vertical profiles were collected from 3 transects across the dissolved plume. An example of two of the vertical profiles is shown in Figure 13.24. Profiles B1 and B2 were located about 20 and 50 m downgradient, respectively, of the suspected source zone. The profiles indicate that the dissolved plume occurs below the water table in the zone between 7 and 10 m deep. Dissolved concentrations in the center of the plume are as high as 40 mg/L. The highest PCE concentrations were found in a zone of silty fine sand within the sand aquifer, which may represent the stratum in which the DNAPL source resides. It is not clear why PCE concentrations were found to be very low above the silt and peat layer. It is possible that the lateral direction of groundwater flow in this upper zone differs from the zone below, and the dissolved plume in this zone has not yet been found. Below the core of the dissolved plume in profile B2, concentrations were found to decline rapidly to 0.01 mg/L or less within a vertical distance of only 1 to 2 m. In profile B1, concentrations beneath the

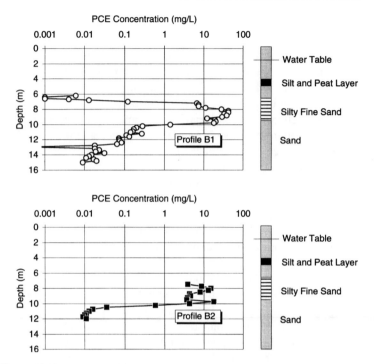

Figure 13.24   Vertical profiles of a PCE plume obtained using a drive-point device. Data from Pitkin *et al.* (1994).

core of the plume were found to decline less rapidly. PCE concentrations in the range of 0.1 down to 0.01 mg/L were found for a distance of about 4 m below the plume. Because of its location nearest the suspected source zone, it is not known whether this dissolved profile reflects the presence of minor amounts of DNAPL at greater depth, or the effect of cross-contamination of the deeper samples by groundwater from the core of the plume. If conventional monitoring wells with 3 to 10 m long intake intervals had been used in this case, much lower dissolved concentrations would have been found and the localized nature of the source zone would not have been evident. Such a result may have led to a mistaken interpretation that DNAPL was not present at this site.

13.6.3 Magnitude of Dissolved Concentrations

One of the simplest tasks that can be performed to assess the likelihood that a DNAPL phase is present in the subsurface at a given site involves the **comparison of dissolved concentrations in groundwater with pure-phase solubilities or estimated effective solubilities**. Chapter 7 describes the present understanding of the mechanisms of DNAPL dissolution as based on theoretical, experimental, and computer-modeling studies. This understanding indicates that when groundwater moves at less than ~1 m/day through at least a few centimeters of a DNAPL source zone that is at a typical residual saturation, then that groundwater will exit that zone saturated (at the effective solubility) with the compound(s) in the DNAPL phase. Consequently, if groundwater samples are collected in close proximity to the DNAPL zone and the intake length of the monitoring wells is comparable to the size of DNAPL residual zone, near-saturated dissolved concentrations can be expected. On the other hand, if the DNAPL residual zone is small relative to the spacing of the monitoring wells or relative to the intake length of the wells, then less-than-saturated concentrations are to be expected: dilution by less contaminated and uncontaminated groundwater will occur.

Studies of the dissolution of DNAPL pools indicate that saturated concentrations in groundwater will be found only: 1) immediately above a pool: and 2) in a thin layer at the elevation of the pool in the near-downgradient area. This is a result of the facts that: 1) a horizontal pool presents little cross-sectional area to on-coming, horizontal groundwater flow; and 2) the high DNAPL-saturation levels within a pool inhibit groundwater flow directly through the pool itself. These effects are illustrated in Figure 13.25 for which the dissolved concentrations above a hypothetical DNAPL pool in a typical sandy aquifer have been calculated using an analytical solution from Johnson and Pankow (1992). The 10 m by 10 m pool was located at the base of a 15 m thick aquifer. The linear groundwater velocity was set at 0.5 m/d, and the vertical dispersivity was set at 0.001 m. At the downgradient edge of the pool, contamination is limited to elevations of less than 1.0 m above the pool. *Each* of the five hypothetical monitoring wells now considered is located *at the downgradient edge of the pool*. For a well that is screened over the lower 3 m of the aquifer, the dissolved concentration is only 4.6% of the saturation concentration, regardless of the compound. For a longer well intake length, the concentration exhibited in the well would be even lower; for an intake length equal to the full thickness of the aquifer, the dissolved concentration would be less than 1% of saturation. If the intake is terminated 0.3 m above the pool, the dissolved concentration in the well would be only 0.1% of saturation; if the intake is terminated 0.5 m above the pool, the dissolved concentration in the well would be 0.001% of saturation, or barely above normal detection limits for most chlorinated solvents.

Based on computer modeling studies of DNAPL migration in heterogeneous media, and based on controlled field experiments in horizontally-stratified deposits, it is likely that much of the DNAPL mass present in the subsurface at a site will be distributed in horizontal layers or pools that have accumulated on zones of lower permeability. The zones in which the DNAPL is present in residual form would be the vertical columns or "fingers" that connect the horizontal layers. Anderson *et al.* (1992) used a 3-D analytical model to simulate the dissolved plumes that would develop in a 15 m thick sandy aquifer from a complex DNAPL source zone comprised of multiple horizontal pools and vertical residual zones. Figure 13.26 is a section view of the simulated source zone, looking upgradient. Figure 13.27 gives the dissolved concentrations that would be exhibited in monitoring wells downgradient of the source zone. The hypothetical wells each had 2 m long intake intervals located in the upper, middle and lower portions of the aquifer. The highest dissolved concentration exhibited in a well was 12% of saturation, and that occurred at the bottom of the aquifer close to the source zone. Despite the fact that the wells were located relatively close to, and directly downgradient of a relatively large source zone, most of the concentrations were only a few percent

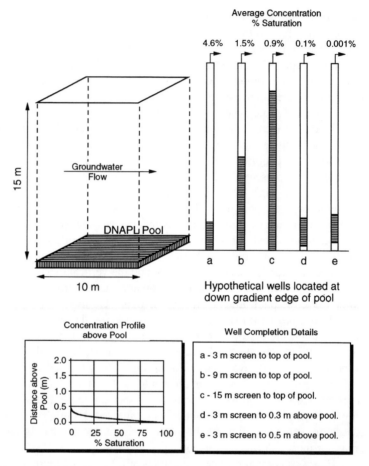

Figure 13.25   Dissolved concentrations observed in five hypothetical monitoring wells at the downgradient edge of a DNAPL pool. Each well is located at the same place, but is screened over a different interval. Dissolved concentrations were calculated using the analytical solution from Johnson and Pankow (1992).

of saturation. The dissolved plumes are described in longitudinal and transverse cross-sections in Figure 13.28. The contamination that extends furthest downgradient is that derived from the pools. However, the contamination from a given pool is relatively thin; even monitoring wells with relatively short well intakes situated directly across such plumes would exhibit dissolved concentrations of only a few percent of saturation, at most.

We can conclude that conventional monitoring wells are not likely to allow detection of peak dissolved concentrations at DNAPL sites because: 1) the intakes are generally too long; and/or 2) an insufficient number of wells is used in each well cluster or nest. Drive-point devices used to collect detailed vertical profiles of dissolved concentration provide the highest probability for detecting peak concentrations. These devices

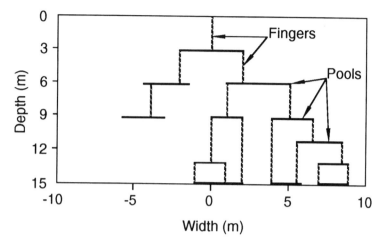

Figure 13.26 Configuration of a complex DNAPL source zone for dissolved plume modeling. Adapted with permission from Anderson (1988); described further in Anderson *et al.* (1992).

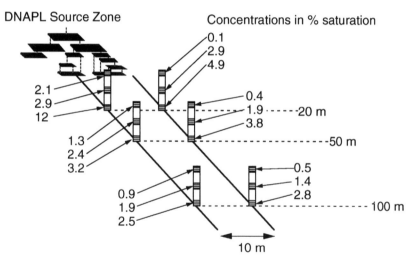

Figure 13.27 Dissolved concentrations in hypothetical monitoring wells downgradient of the complex DNAPL source zone. Well screens are 2 m in length, situated in the upper, middle and lower portion of the aquifer. Concentrations are shown as percent of saturation. Adapted from Anderson *et al.* (1992).

make it possible to sample groundwater at vertical intervals of 0.5 m or less (Pitkin *et al.*, 1994), and the resulting data is of great assistance in the assessment of the location and morphology of the DNAPL source zone(s).

In fractured rock, the distribution of the DNAPL and its dissolution into groundwater is very poorly understood. However, on a conceptual basis, we can expect that

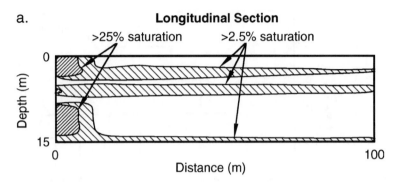

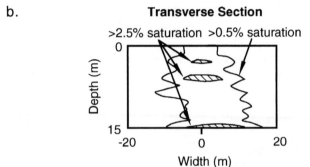

Figure 13.28 Longitudinal and transverse sections downgradient of the complex DNAPL source zone. The longitudinal section (a) extends from the center of the source zone. The transverse section (b) is situated 100 m downgradient of the source zone. Adapted from Anderson *et al.* (1992).

DNAPL will be present in some fractures and absent from others. The groundwater captured in a monitoring well in fractured rock may therefore comprise some water that has contacted DNAPL, and other water that has not. It is not possible to predict the resultant dissolved concentrations, but they will in general be much lower than saturation. As an example, Table 13.11 gives the dissolved concentrations in a monitoring well and a pumping well in a fractured sandstone aquifer (EPA, 1992). DNAPL was recovered from each of these wells. The principal component of the DNAPL was 1,2,3-

TABLE 13.11   Dissolved 1,2,3-Trichloropropane Concentrations Found in Wells From Which DNAPL Was Recovered in a Fractured Sandstone Formation.

	Monitoring well W-81	Pumping well EW-4
Intake Interval	35 m to 41 m	9 m to 55 m
Effective Solubility (mg/L)	1,400	1,400
Initial Concentration (mg/L)	150	240
Concentration While Pumping (mg/L)	—	50

trichloropropane having an effective solubility of approximately 1,400 mg/L. Both of these wells are situated directly within a large bedrock zone known to contain DNAPL to considerable depth. The dissolved concentration in well W-8I was about 11% of saturation. The dissolved concentration in well EW-4 was 17% of saturation at the start of pumping, but declined during pumping to about 3.5% of saturation. Although this well was installed directly within a large DNAPL zone, this reduction was likely due to dilution by less contaminated groundwater. Thus, wells installed downgradient of a DNAPL source zone in a fractured aquifer can exhibit concentrations that are much lower than saturation.

These findings have critical implications for the interpretation of groundwater monitoring data. Before it was recognized how DNAPLs can behave in the subsurface, the presence of a DNAPL phase in the subsurface was not considered unless DNAPL was actually recovered directly, or groundwater concentrations in monitoring wells approached saturation levels. It is now clear that less-than-saturated concentrations will occur in monitoring wells in many, or even most cases of DNAPL contamination. During the mid-1980s, the finding of dissolved concentrations of **10% of saturation** was suggested as a **"rule-of-thumb"** for inferring the presence of a DNAPL phase (Feenstra and Cherry, 1988). Recently, it has been suggested that this rule-of-thumb concentration be reduced to **1% of saturation** (Newell and Ross, 1991). We believe that this is reasonable. This value, however, should not be viewed as strict criterion since, based on the above discussion, we know that the magnitude of the dissolved concentrations observed in a monitoring well will depend on factors other than the presence or absence of DNAPL phase source zones (*e.g.*, well location and well intake length, and size and nature of the source zone). The use of a 1% rule-of-thumb in any assessment of the spatial distribution of DNAPL zones must be performed cautiously, particularly in the downgradient direction. For example, the dissolved plume emitted from a very large DNAPL zone may exhibit dissolved concentrations above 1% of saturation for a substantial distance downgradient of the source zone. A conclusion that the size of the DNAPL zone corresponds to the size of the dissolved plume exceeding 1% of saturation, in such a case, could be an extreme overestimate.

13.6.4 Persistence and Temporal Variability of Dissolved Concentrations

The DNAPL phase in the vadose and groundwater zones at many sites probably represents sufficient chemical mass to cause dissolved plumes to **persist for centuries** or longer (see also Chapter 7). Many dissolved plumes at DNAPL sites have now been monitored for more than a decade and show no indication of diminishing concentration or plume size. During the early stage (perhaps the first few decades) of dissolution of a DNAPL zone, the dissolved concentrations found in the groundwater may remain relatively constant, with the highest concentrations found close to the source zone. In contrast, plumes derived from the leaching of sorbed-phase contamination on soil will likely exhibit ever-declining dissolved concentrations. Similarly, dissolved plumes derived from past releases of aqueous-phase contaminants will likely exhibit areal maximum concentrations, or peaks, someplace downgradient of the release area. Thus, the persistence of elevated groundwater concentrations over monitoring periods of 5 to 10 years, particularly close to suspected source areas, is generally indicative of a DNAPL source zone.

In the case of fractured clay or sedimentary rock, significant dissolved concentrations may persist in the groundwater even long after the DNAPL has disappeared. As described in Chapter 12, the dissolution of DNAPL in fractures in a fractured porous medium will be enhanced by diffusion of dissolved contaminants into the matrix. When the DNAPL disappears and less-contaminated groundwater flushes through the fractures, dissolved contaminants will diffuse back out of the matrix and into the water flowing through the fractures. As shown in Figure 13.21 for the Chalk aquifer in eastern England, the pore water in the matrix between fractures can contain high dissolved concentrations that represent a significant continuing source of contaminants to the groundwater.

Extreme temporal variations in dissolved concentrations observed in monitoring wells may be another indication of a DNAPL source zone. Because the dissolved plume derived from a DNAPL source in the groundwater zone will reflect the size of the DNAPL zone, such plumes may be of limited lateral extent with very steep concentration gradients between the margins and the core of the plume (see Figures 13.22 and 13.23). If a monitoring well is situated close to the margin of a plume, fluctuations in groundwater flow direction may cause the plume to move into or out of the zone of capture of the well, thereby resulting in large variations in the dissolved concentrations observed in the well; dissolved plumes derived from larger and less localized source zones would be less likely to cause this type of effect.

13.6.5 Response of Dissolved Concentrations During Aquifer Pump-and-Treat

The **time-dependent behavior of dissolved concentrations** in groundwater pumping wells can provide evidence regarding the presence/absence of DNAPL in the groundwater zone. During the 1980s, aquifer pump-and-treat systems were installed at many sites of groundwater contamination. The apparent failure of many of these systems to achieve complete aquifer restoration is the result of DNAPL zones remaining in the subsurface (EPA, 1992). A typical pattern in dissolved concentrations in a pumping well that is influenced by the presence of a DNAPL source zone is a **rapid decline** in concentration as a result of dilution effects followed by a **plateau** at a significant concentration level. Effects such as slow desorption from aquifer solids and diffusion out of finer-grained layers can inhibit restoration by pump-and-treat, but these effects are more likely to cause long tails of slowly declining concentration rather than a long plateau at an elevated concentration.

An example from Rivett (1993) is shown in Figure 13.29 for a pump-and-treat system applied to the experimental plume in Figures 13.22 and 13.23. In this case, three pumping wells were installed along the axis of the plume; PW-2 is nearest the source zone, PW-4 is located at the leading edge of the plume, and PW-3 is located between the other two. The wells were each pumped at a rate of 5 L/min. Based on data from the monitoring network, it was found that the TCE plume between the wells was substantially

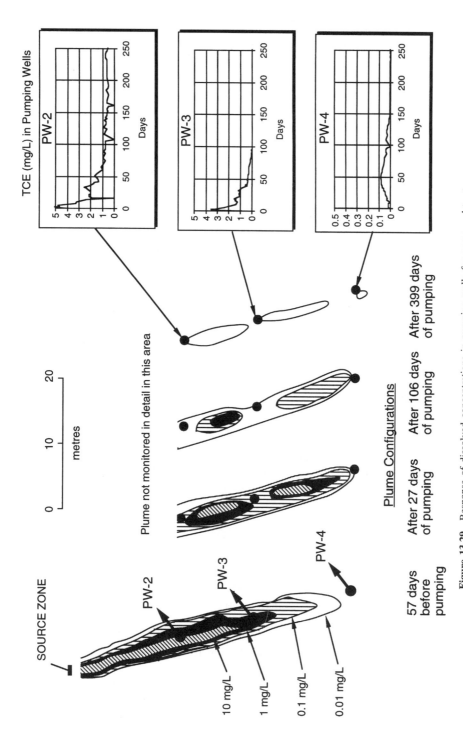

Figure 13.29 Response of dissolved concentrations in pumping wells for pump-and-treat remediation of the plume from the groundwater zone experimental source in the Borden aquifer. Data from Rivett (1993).

removed, with concentrations reduced from initial levels of 1 to 10 mg/L down to 0.01 to 0.1 mg/L. The highest concentrations remained in the zones of hydraulic stagnation between the wells, and in the finer-grained beds of the aquifer. At the leading edge well (PW-4), the concentration rose initially as the plume was drawn toward the well, then the concentration declined to less than 0.01 mg/L. In the middle well (PW-3), initial concentrations were about 3 mg/L, then declined to below 0.01 mg/L after about 100 days. The lateral zone of capture of each of the pumping wells was several times larger than the width of the plume. Therefore, much of the initial rapid decline in concentrations in the pumping wells was due to dilution from water outside the plume. The concentration response in PW-2 was considerably different. Concentrations were initially about 5 mg/L, and then declined rapidly for about 100 days, after which concentrations leveled off at between 0.5 mg/L and 1 mg/L; these elevated, plateaued concentrations reflect the on-going contribution to PW-2 from dissolution of the source zone.

13.6.6 Case History-Chlorinated Solvent Plume, Dayton, New Jersey

13.6.6.1 Background

Several of the important factors related to the diagnosis of DNAPL in the subsurface can be illustrated by examining the groundwater contamination and remedial measures taken at an industrial plant site near Dayton, New Jersey (EPA, 1989). The plant site was used for the manufacture of inked printer ribbons and punch cards for computers. The aquifer consists of about 15 m of coarse sand and gravel overlying a discontinuous layer of interbedded sand and clay about 1 to 3 m thick. The water table occurs at a depth of about 6 to 7 m below ground surface, and the average hydraulic conductivity is about 8×10^{-2} cm/s. In December 1977, PCE and 1,1,1-TCA were discovered at concentrations of about 0.2 and 0.6 μg/L, respectively, in a municipal water supply well located about 500 m east of the plant. The municipal well was shut down and investigations of the plant site began in early 1978. The actual contribution of this site to the contamination of the municipal well cannot be determined precisely because other groundwater contamination sites are present in the neighborhood.

13.6.6.2 Extent of groundwater contamination

A plume of PCE and 1,1,1-TCA moving eastward towards the municipal well was found on the plant site. The groundwater concentrations ranged as high as 6.1 mg/L for PCE and 9.5 mg/L for 1,1,1-TCA (see Figure 13.30). These maximum concentrations represent 2.5% of saturation for pure-phase PCE and 0.8% of saturation for pure-phase 1,1,1-TCA. However, when these studies were conducted in 1978, no understanding of DNAPL behavior in the subsurface existed in the groundwater profession. Therefore, the magnitude of these concentrations did not lead to the conclusion that DNAPL was present in the aquifer.

Chlorinated solvents had been used at the plant and it was believed that the groundwater contamination originated from releases of solvent product from the chemical off-loading and storage areas. Records from the plant indicated that only PCE had been pur-

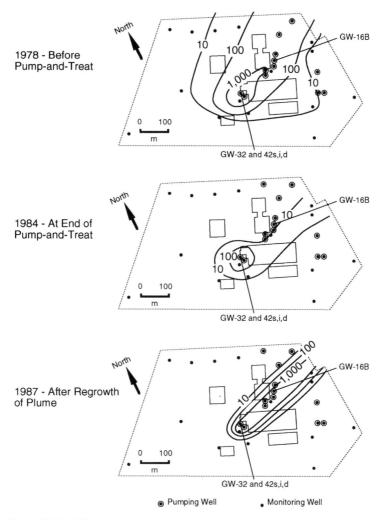

Figure 13.30 PCE plume configuration for the Dayton site in 1978 before the implementation of the pump-and-treat remedy, in 1984 at the end of the initial pump-and-treat effort, and in 1987 after regrowth of the plume.

chased. For a time it was thought the 1,1,1-TCA may have originated from another site. Subsequently, an analysis of the solvent used at the plant revealed that the PCE contained about 15% 1,1,1-TCA. This illustrates the difficulties that can be encountered in assessing the chemical composition of DNAPL releases. The composition suggests that the effective solubilities of PCE and 1,1,1-TCA for the site are about 200 and 190 mg/L, respectively. As a result, the maximum observed groundwater concentrations noted above represent ∼3% of saturation for PCE and ∼5% saturation for 1,1,1-TCA. In the light of our current understanding, finding dissolved concentrations of this magnitude would lead us to consider the presence of DNAPL below the water table. Indeed, the maximum groundwater concentrations were observed in wells screened across the full thickness of the aquifer. With the dilution expected from these long-screened wells, dissolved concentrations of this magnitude are very strong evidence of the presence of DNAPL in the aquifer.

No soil sampling/analysis for volatiles was conducted until 1985-1986. At that time, the highest level of soil contamination was found at a depth of about 7 m, close to the water table. The total VOC concentration of 13 mg/kg is considerably lower than levels that would suggest the presence of DNAPL based on partitioning calculations (*i.e.*, Eq.(13.3)). However, in the assessment of these historical data, we must remember that this older soil concentration data probably suffered from volatilization losses due to the sample handling and analysis methods used at that time.

The plume was found to be wide compared to the size of the suspected release area. There are several possible explanations for this observation: 1) time-dependent variations in off-site pumping in the municipal well to the east and other private wells to the north may have acted to draw the plume back and forth; 2) a broad plume of relatively low concentration (10 to 100 μg/L) in the groundwater could have resulted from the initial transport of vapors through the vadose radially outward from the release area; and/or 3) the broad dissolved plume was a composite plume caused by several different sources on the site. As regards the second possibility, we note that vapors in the vadose zone would have resulted in a thin, relatively high concentration groundwater plume immediately at the water table, any thin plume at the water table would have been diluted significantly during sampling from the fully-screened wells.

13.6.6.3 Remedial measures

Remedial measures at the site commenced at the Dayton site in mid-1978 with the removal of the chemical storage tanks, excavation of several tens of cubic meters of soil from around the tanks, and the installation of a network of groundwater pumping wells on the plant site. Since it was believed at the time that the dissolved plumes were due to leaching of contaminants from the shallow soil zone, removal of the tanks and shallow soil together with removal of the dissolved plume by groundwater pump-and-treat were expected to provide full and permanent restoration of the aquifer within a few years. However, it was not recognized that DNAPL phase solvent had penetrated below the water table where it would comprise an on-going source of contamination for many years.

The remedial measures for the overall plume involved on-site pumping wells, off-site pumping wells, and a resumption of pumping of the municipal water supply well. We now consider only the performance of the on-site pumping because this area includes the source zone, and because on-site monitoring was much more detailed than off-site monitoring. For simplicity, only the PCE plumes will be considered. The on-site pumping system consisted of up to 13 wells. Seven of the wells operated almost continuously from mid-1978 until late-1984 when on-site pumping ceased. The other wells operated for shorter intervals during this period. Three of the pumping wells yielded from 250 to 390 L/min, and the remaining 10 wells yielded from 20 to 40 L/min. A typical pumping rate for the overall system was about 1,100 L/min. The discharge from the pumping system was treated by air stripping and recharged to the aquifer by spray irrigation along the western side of the plant site.

By late 1984, dissolved concentrations in the aquifer had been reduced significantly from levels as high as several thousand μg/L down to 10 μg/L or less (see Figure 13.30). During this period, a total of 3.4 billion liters of groundwater and an equivalent of 7,500 L of solvents had been removed by the on-site pumping system. Reductions down to low μg/L concentrations occurred in monitoring wells and pumping wells throughout the plume zone except in the area close to the suspected release. In that source zone, the solvent concentrations in two pumping wells were reduced significantly, but declined only to concentrations of 300 to 500 μg/L. The differences in response between the plume zone and the source zone during pumping from 1978 to 1984 are shown in Figure 13.31 for pumping wells GW-32 and GW-16B respectively. Although not recognized at the time, the elevated, plateaued concentrations in the pumping wells near the suspected source zone indicated an on-going source of contamination, probably DNAPL below the water table. The reduction in concentrations in the pumping wells in that zone that were observed were likely due to dilution by water drawn from outside the source zone.

Although chlorinated solvents are only weakly sorbed to geologic media and can therefore produce large contaminant plumes, their recovery by groundwater pump-and-treat is facilitated by their weak sorption. At the Dayton site, groundwater pump-and-treat resulted in a very substantial reduction in the size of the dissolved plume by removing ~7 plume volumes of groundwater in 6.5 years. The groundwater pump-and-treat also provided containment of the source zone by preventing further release of dissolved solvents to the plume.

13.6.6.4 Regeneration of the plume

Although it was not recognized at the time, groundwater pump-and-treat did not provide restoration of the source zone. In late 1984, the state environmental regulatory agency determined that the remedial measures had reached the appropriate clean-up target for the majority of the plume area, and had reached the point of diminishing return for the release area. With this conclusion, groundwater pump-and-treat was stopped. Within about 6 to 9 months, monitoring indicated that the concentrations had begun to rise in the wells close to the source zone (*e.g.*, GW-32). Eventually, concentrations in several of the monitoring wells rose to levels higher than were observed in 1978 (see Figure 13.32). By mid-1987, about 2.5 years after pumping had ceased, the dissolved solvent plume had grown as far as the eastern plant boundary (Figure 13.30). The regrowth of the plume was, in itself, irrefutable evidence of a DNAPL source zone below the water table.

Further evidence of the nature of the source zone is the aquifer was derived from multi-level monitoring wells. The majority of the monitoring at the site was conducted in wells screened over the entire saturated thickness of the aquifer. In 1985, three multilevel wells (42s, 42i, and 42d) were installed in the upper, middle and lower portions of the aquifer at about 20 m from the suspected source zone. These samplers were monitored regularly during the period after the groundwater pump-and-treat operations ceased; the results are shown in Figure 13.33. At the beginning of 1985, dissolved contamination

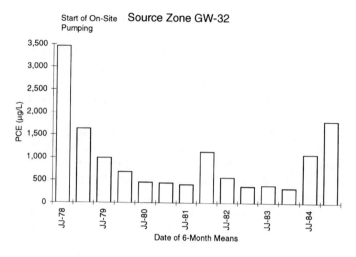

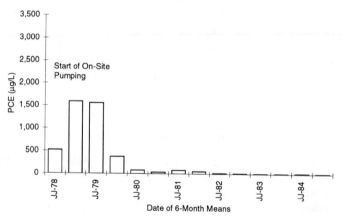

Figure 13.31 Response of dissolved concentrations in pumping wells during pump-and-treat remediation at the Dayton site. GW-32 is situated within 20 to 40 m of the suspected source zone. GW-16B is situated about 200 m downgradient of the source zone.

was found only at the bottom of the aquifer. However, with regrowth of the plume, moderate concentrations developed during 1985 and 1986 in the top part of the aquifer, very low concentrations were found in the middle part of the aquifer, and the highest concentrations developed at the bottom of the aquifer. These findings suggest that a significant accumulation or pool of DNAPL solvent exists at the bottom of the aquifer. The source zone in the aquifer likely consists of multiple accumulations or layers of DNAPL at various depths within the aquifer as well as a pool at the bottom of the aquifer. These layers and pools were connected, at some point in time, by vertical pathways ("fingers") which likely drained to residual saturation. However, after as many as ten to

Source Zone GW-32

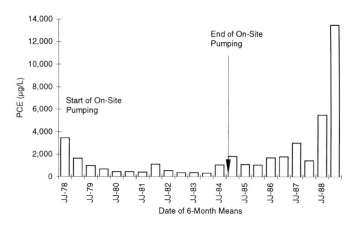

Plume Zone GW-16B

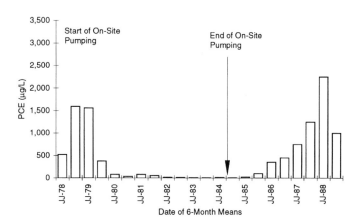

Figure 13.32   Regrowth of the dissolved plume following cessation of pump-and-treat at the Dayton site as reflected by the increase in concentrations in well GW-32 close to the source, and GW-16B downgradient of the source.

twenty years of dissolution by groundwater, it is cannot be known whether significant zones of residual DNAPL in fingers still exist in the aquifer.

In 1990, the groundwater pump-and-treat system was reactivated with a network of four pumping wells: one near the source, one close to the middle of the plume (near GW-16B), and two at the eastern boundary of the plant site. The goals of this system are containment of the plume to prevent further migration off-site, and restoration of the aquifer in the current plume zone. It is hoped that in several years the dissolved plume will be again eliminated, and containment of the source zone can be provided by a single pumping well.

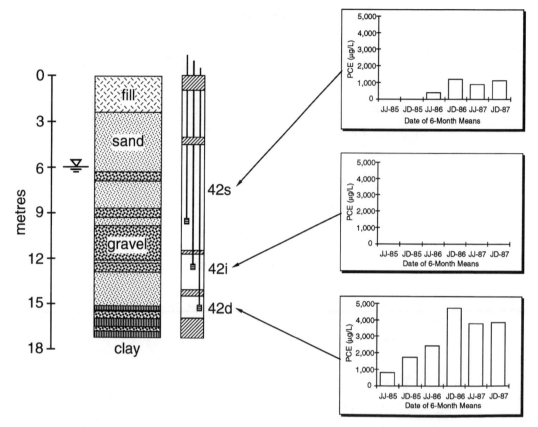

Figure 13.33 Vertical distribution of dissolved concentrations in the aquifer at the Dayton site following the cessation of pump-and-treat.

13.7 CONCLUSIONS

In order to develop rational and cost-effective plans for the remediation of soil and groundwater contamination at many industrial and waste-disposal sites, a first goal in diagnosis and assessment is the determination of whether DNAPL is present in the subsurface, particularly if it exists below the water table. Preliminary lines of evidence that should be examined at any possible DNAPL site include the types and volumes of the chemicals that may have been released to the subsurface. At an industrial facility, this would include examination of how and where the chemicals were used, stored, and disposed of at the site.

There are many types of site information that can contribute to the diagnosis and assessment of the presence and distribution of DNAPLs in the subsurface. At many sites, there is no direct visual evidence from soil cores or from samples from monitoring wells that DNAPL exists in significant quantities in the groundwater zone. However, because of the potential variability in the spatial distribution of DNAPLs and the investigative methods commonly used, this does not necessarily mean that DNAPL is not present.

The investigative methods that can be used to improve the likelihood that DNAPL will be identified if encountered in borings and monitoring wells include careful observations during drilling by means of visual inspection, enhanced visual inspection using dyes or UV light, vapor analyses, the chemical analysis of soil and rock samples, the use of borehole geophysics. The identification of DNAPL in wells can be made more reliable by using appropriate well construction and well sampling procedures. Special care during drilling and well construction in DNAPL zones is also necessary to prevent "short-circuiting" of DNAPL deeper levels into the subsurface. In many circumstances, drilling directly into suspected DNAPL zones should be avoided in favor of indirect means which do not risk remobilization of the DNAPL. At many sites, uncertainties in the location of any DNAPL source zone(s) are sufficiently great that inadvertent drilling through DNAPL zones is very possible. There is therefore a need for improved methods for drilling, sampling, and *in situ* analyses that will enable the detection of DNAPL while drilling is in progress.

There are many investigative methods that can be used to indirectly assess the presence and distribution of DNAPLs in the subsurface. These methods include soil gas surveys and the evaluation of the character of the dissolved plumes emitted from the source area. In support of these methods, we now have a sufficiently good understanding of DNAPL migration patterns, dissolution processes, dissolved contaminant migration processes, as well as adequate monitoring methods to allow a meaningful evaluation of the possible presence of DNAPL at many field sites.

A conclusion that DNAPL is present in the groundwater zone will influence the selection of remedial measures. For example, the mere existence of a DNAPL source zone will usually eliminate any likelihood of complete aquifer restoration in the foreseeable future, and force reliance on remedial measures which provide containment of the source zone. A recognition that DNAPL is present somewhere in the groundwater zone will not be sufficient to permit a detailed analysis of past or future DNAPL migration. Such analyses require information on the amounts and types of DNAPL released to the subsurface, and the spatial distribution of DNAPL in the subsurface in the case of predictions of future migration. The selection and design of remedial measures which involve containment and/or *in situ* treatment of DNAPL source zones will also require this level of information. Unfortunately, at most sites, such information is difficult or impossible to acquire.

We conclude that many lines of evidence can potentially contribute to the diagnosis of DNAPL sites, but normally, only a few contribute strongly at a particular site. The challenge is to assess the various lines of evidence and then render a judgment based on the preponderance of all of the available evidence.

ACKNOWLEDGEMENTS

Funding support for this research was provided in part by the University Consortium Solvents-in-Groundwater Research Program. Sponsors of the Program between 1988 and

1994 have included: The Boeing Company, Ciba-Geigy Corporation, Dow Chemical Canada/USA, Eastman Kodak Co., General Electric Co., Laidlaw Environmental Systems Ltd., Mitre Corporation, The Natural Sciences and Engineering Research Council of Canada, and the Ontario University Research Incentive Fund.

13.8 REFERENCES

Anderson, M. R., R. L. Johnson, and J. F. Pankow (1992) "Dissolution of dense chlorinated solvents into groundwater. 3. Modeling of contaminant plumes from fingers and pools of solvent", *Environ. Sci. Technol.*, **26**, 901-908.

Brewster, M. L., A. P. Annan, J. P. Greenhouse, G. W. Schneider, and J. D. Redman (1992) "Geophysical detection of DNAPLs: Field experiments". In: *Proceedings: International Association of Hydrogeologists Conference*, Hamilton, Ontario, May 1992, pp. 176-194.

Broholm, K., S. Feenstra, and J. A. Cherry (1994) "Solvent release into a sandy aquifer. 1. Overview of source behavior and distribution", in preparation.

Cary, J. W., J. F. McBride, and C. S. Simmons (1991) "Assay of organic liquid contents in predominantly water-wet unconsolidated porous media", *J. Contaminant Hydrology*, **8**, 135-142.

Chiang, C. Y., K. R. Loos, and R. A. Klopp (1992) "Field determination of geological/chemical properties of an aquifer by cone penetrometry and headspace analysis", *Ground Water*, **30**, 428-436.

Chou, S. F. J. and R. A. Griffin (1986) "Solubility and soil mobility of polychlorinated biphenyls", In: *PCBs and the Environment*, J. S. Waid (Ed.), CRC Press, Boca Raton, Florida.

Clausen, J. L., J. Zutman, and N. Farrow (1993) *Characterization of the Northwest Plume Utilizing a Driven Discrete-Depth Sampling System.* Report by Martin Marietta Energy Systems Inc. to the U.S. Dept. of Energy, Document No. KY/ER-22.

Cohen, R. M., A. P. Bryda, S. T. Shaw, and C. P. Spalding (1992) "Evaluation of visual methods to detect NAPL in soil and water", *Ground Water Monitoring Review*, **12**, No. 4, 132-141.

Conant, B. H., M. M. Broholm, J. A. Cherry, and R. W. Gillham (1995) "Shallow groundwater contamination in "the interface zone" associated with chlorinated solvent vapor transport", in preparation.

de Pastrovich, T. L., Y. Baradat, R. Barthel, A. Chiarelli, and D. R. Fussell (1979) *Protection of Groundwater from Oil Pollution*, CONCAWE, Water Pollution Special Task Force No. 11, NTIS PB82-174608.

Durnford, D., J. Brookman, J. Billica, and J. Milligan (1991) "LNAPL distribution in a cohesionless soil: A field investigation and cryogenic sampler", *Ground Water Monitoring Review*, **11**, No. 2, 115-122.

Edge, R. W. and K. Cordry (1989) "The HydroPunch™: An *in situ* sampling tool for collecting ground water from unconsolidated sediments", *Ground Water Monitoring Review*, **9**, 177-183.

Einberger, C. M., G. C. Patrick, A. S. Burgess, and K. M. Angelos (1993) "Correlating soil and soil vapor concentrations at suspect DNAPL sites: A case study", *Ground Water*, **31**, No. 5, 837 (abstract).

EPA (1989) *Evaluation of Ground-Water Extraction Remedies: Volume 2. Case Studies 1-19*, EPA 540/2-89/054b, Washington, D.C.

EPA (1992) *Evaluation of Ground-Water Extraction Remedies: Phase II*, PB92-963346.

Feenstra, S. and J. A. Cherry (1988) "Subsurface contamination by dense non-aqueous phase liquid (DNAPL) chemicals". In: *Proceedings: International Groundwater Symposium*, International Association of Hydrogeologists, May 1-4, 1988, Halifax, Nova Scotia, pp. 62-69.

Feenstra, S., D. M. Mackay, and J. A. Cherry (1991) "Presence of residual NAPL based on organic chemical concentrations in soil samples", *Ground Water Monitoring Review*, **11**, No. 2, 128-136.

Halogenated Solvents Industry Alliance (1987) personal communication.

Hardisty, P. E. and P. M. Johnson (1993) "Characterization of occurrence and distribution of LNAPL in fractured rocks". In: *Proceedings: Conference on Petroleum Hydrocarbons and Organic Chemicals in Ground Water: Prevention, Detection and Restoration*, Houston, Texas, November 10-12, 1993, pp. 113-129.

Howard, P. H. (1989) *Handbook of Environmental Fate and Exposure Data for Organic Chemicals Volume I. Large Production and Priority Pollutants*, Lewis Publishers, Chelsea, Michigan.

Howard, P. H. (1990) *Handbook of Environmental Fate and Exposure Data for Organic Chemicals Volume II. Solvents*, Lewis Publishers, Chelsea, Michigan.

Hughes, B. M. (1991) *Vapor Transport of Trichloroethylene in the Unsaturated Zone: A Field Experiment*, M. Sc. Thesis, Dept. of Earth Sciences, University of Waterloo, Waterloo, Ontario.

Hughes, B. M., R. W. Gillham and C.A. Mendoza (1992) "Transport of trichloroethylene vapours in the unsaturated zone: a field experiment". In: *Proceedings: International Association of Hydrogeologists Conference on Subsurface Contamination by Immiscible Liquids*, Calgary, Alberta, A. A. Balkema, Rotterdam, pp. 81-88.

Johnson. R. L. and J. F. Pankow (1992) "Dissolution of dense chlorinated solvents into groundwater. 2. Source functions for pools of solvent", *Environ. Sci. Technol.*, **26**, 896-901.

Karimi, A. A., W. J. Farmer, and M. M. Cliath (1987) "Vapor-phase diffusion of benzene in soil", *J. Environ. Qual.*, **16**, 38-43.

Kueper, B. H. (1989) *The Behavior of Dense Non-Aqueous Phase Liquid Contaminants in Heterogeneous Porous Media*, Ph.D. Thesis, Dept. of Earth Sciences, University of Waterloo, Waterloo, Ontario.

Kueper, B. H., W. Abbott, and G. Farquhar (1989) "Experimental observations of multiphase flow in heterogeneous porous media", *J. Contaminant Hydrology*, **5**, 83-96.

Kueper, B. H. and D. W. McWhorter (1991) "The behavior of dense, non-aqueous phase liquids in fractured clay and rock", *Ground Water*, **29**, 716-728.

Kueper, B. H., Redman, D., Starr, R. C., Reitsma, S., and Mah, M. (1993) "A field experiment to study the behavior of tetrachloroethylene below the water table: Spatial distribution of residual and pooled DNAPL", *Ground Water*, **31**, 756-766.

Lawrence, A. R., P. J. Chilton, R. J. Barron, and W. M. Thomas (1990) "A method for determining volatile organic solvents in chalk pore waters (southern and eastern England) and its relevance to the evaluation of groundwater contamination", *J. Comtaminant Hydrology*, **6**, 377-386.

Lewis, T. E., A. B. Crockett, R. L. Seigrist, and K. Zarrabi (1991) *Soil Sampling and Analysis for Volatile Organic Compounds*, Ground-Water Issue Paper, U.S. Environmental Protection Agency, EPA/540/4-91/001, Washington, D.C.

Litherland, S. T., T. W. Hoskins, and R. L. Boggess (1985) "A new ground water survey tool: The combined cone penetrometer/vadose zone vapor probe". In: *Proceedings: Conference on Petroleum Hydrocarbons and Organic Chemicals in Ground Water* Houston, Texas, National Water Well Association, Nov. 13-15, 1985, pp. 322-330.

Marrin, D. L. and G. M. Thompson (1987) "Gaseous behaviour of TCE overlying a contaminated aquifer", *Ground Water*, **25**, 21-27.

Marrin, D. L. (1988) "Soil-gas sampling and misinterpretation", *Ground Water Monitoring Review*, **8**, 51-54.

Marrin, D. L. and H. B. Kerfoot (1988) "Soil-gas surveying techniques", *Environ. Sci. Technol.*, **22**, 740-745.

Mendoza, C. A., B. M. Hughes, E. O. Frind (1992) "Trichloroethylene vapours in the unsaturated zone: Numerical analysis of a field experiment". In: *Proceedings: International Association of Hydrogeologists Conference on Subsurface Contamination by Immiscible Liquids*, Calgary, Alberta, A. A. Balkema, Rotterdam, 221-227.

Mercer, J. W. and R. M. Cohen (1990) "A review of immiscible fluids in the subsurface: Properties, models, characterization and remediation", *J. Contaminant Hydrology*, **6**, 107-163.

Merck & Co., Inc. (1989) *The Merck Index: An Encyclopedia of Chemicals, Drugs and Biologicals*, Eleventh Edition, Merck & Co. Inc., Rahway, New Jersey.

Montgomery, J. H. and L. M. Welkom (1990) *Groundwater Chemicals Desk Reference*, Lewis Publishers, Boca Raton, Florida.

Montgomery, J. H. (1991) *Groundwater Chemicals Desk Reference: Volume 2*, Boca Raton, Florida.

Newell, C. and R. R. Ross (1991) *Estimating Potential for Occurrence of DNAPL at Superfund Sites*, Quick Reference Guide Sheet, U.S. Environmental Protection Agency, publication number 9355.4-07FS, Washington, D.C.

Niemeyer, R. A., M. A. Palmer and D. R. Hargis (1992) "An innovative well design for DNAPL recovery from the saturated zone", *Ground Water*, **30**, 793 (abstract).

Pitkin, S., R. A. Ingleton, and J. A. Cherry (1994) "Use of a drive-point sampling device for detailed characterization of a PCE plume in a sand aquifer at a dry cleaning facility". In: *Proceedings: Outdoor Action Conference*, National Ground Water Association, Minneapolis, Minn., May 23-25.

Poulsen, M. and Kueper, B. H. (1992) "A field experiment to study the behavior of tetrachloroethylene in unsaturated porous media", *Environ. Sci. Technol.*, **26**, 889-895.

Rivett, M. O. (1993) "A field evaluation of pump-and-treat remediation". In: *Proceedings: National Conference on Environmental Engineering*, joint conference of the Canadian Society of Civil Engineering and the American Society of Civil Engineering, Montreal, Quebec, July 12-14, 1993, pp. 1171-1178.

Rivett, M. O. (1995) "Soil-gas signatures from volatile chlorinated solvents: Borden field experiments". *Ground Water*, 33, 84–98.

Rivett, M. O., S. Feenstra and J. A. Cherry (1995) "A natural gradient experiment on solute transport from a residual solvent source. 1. Overview", in preparation.

Rudolph, D. L., J. A. Cherry and R. N. Farvolden (1991) "Groundwater flow and solute transport in fractured lacustrine clay near Mexico City", *Water Resources Research*, **27**, 2187-2201.

Schneider, G. W. and J. P. Greenhouse (1992) "Geophysical detection of perchloroethylene in a sandy aquifer using resistivity and nuclear logging techniques". In: *Proceedings: Symposium on the Application of Geophysics to Engineering and Environmental Problems*, Society of Engineering and Mineral Exploration Geophysics, April 26-29, 1992, pp. 619-628.

Schwille, F. (1988) *Dense Chlorinated Solvents in Porous and Fractured Media - Model Experiments*, translated by J. F. Pankow, Lewis Publishers, Chelsea, Michigan.

Siebenmann, K. (1993) "Problems with the use of near-surface soil gas results for source identification". *Ground Water*, **31**, 850 (abstract).

Seigrist, R. L. and P. D. Jenssen (1990) "Evaluation of sampling method effects on volatile organic compound measurements in contaminated soil", *Environ. Sci. Technol.*, **24**, 1387-1392.

Smolley, M. and J. C. Kappmeyer (1991) "Cone penetrometer tests and HydroPunch sampling: A screening technique for plume definition", *Ground Water Monitoring Review*, **11**, No. 2, 101-106.

Sohn, M. D., S. R. Custance, J. Ryer-Powder, and M. J. Sullivan (1993) "Comparison of measured and predicted trichloroethylene concentrations in soil gas resulting from ground water", *Ground Water*, **31**, 850 (abstract).

Starr, R. C. and R. A. Ingleton (1992) "A new method for collecting core samples without a drilling rig", *Ground Water Monitoring Review*, **12**, No. 1, 91-95.

Taylor, T. W. and M. C. Serafini (1988) "Screened auger sampling: The technique and two case studies", *Ground Water Monitoring Review*, **8**, No. 3, 145-152.

U.S. International Trade Commission (1991) *Synthetic Organic Chemicals: United States Production and Sales*, USITC Publication 2470, Washington, D.C.

Urban, M. J., J. S. Smith, and R. K. Dickinson (1989) "Volatile organic analysis for a sample for a soil, sediment or waste sample", In: *Proceedings: Fifth Annual Waste Testing and Quality Assurance Symposium*, U.S. EPA, Washington, DC, pp. II87-II101.

Voice, T. C. and B. Kolb (1993) "Static and dynamic headspace analysis of volatile organic compounds in soils", *Environ. Sci. Technol.*, **27**, 709-713.

Westinghouse Savannah River Company (1992) *Assessing DNAPL Contamination, A/M Area, Savannah River Site: Phase I Results*, Report to the U.S. Department of Energy, Report No. WSRC-RP-92-1302.

Zapico, M., S. Vales, and J. A. Cherry (1987) "A wireline piston core barrel for sampling cohesionless sand and gravel below the water table", *Ground Water Monitoring Review*, **7**, No. 3, 74-82.

14

Concepts for the Remediation of Sites Contaminated with Dense Non-Aqueous Phase Liquids (DNAPLs)

John A. Cherry[1], Stan Feenstra[1,2], and Douglas M. Mackay[1]

[1]Waterloo Centre for Groundwater Research
University of Waterloo
Waterloo, Ontario
Canada N2L 3G1

[2]Applied Groundwater Research, Ltd.
The Pentagon Building, Suite 207
2550 Argentia Road
Mississagua, Ontario
Canada L5N 5R1

ABSTRACT

At each site where a dense non-aqueous phase liquid (DNAPL) has contaminated the local groundwater, there are two principal components to the problem: a subsurface source zone and a groundwater plume. Usually, most of the contaminant mass is in the source zone, but at solvent sites, the plume usually occupies a much larger portion of the aquifer. Therefore, for most sites, unless essentially all of the contaminant mass (>99.9%) is removed from the source zone, permanent aquifer restoration to drinking water standards will not be achievable in the near term. Pump-and-treat methodologies remove contaminant mass too slowly, and excavation is generally not practical because of the depths to which the DNAPL has moved.

New technologies being developed for source-zone restoration are of two types, those that bring contaminant mass to the surface for treatment or disposal (*e.g.*, the flush technologies that use steam, air, surfactants, or co-solvents), and those that destroy DNAPLs *in situ* (*e.g.*, chemical oxidation, chemical reductive dehalogenation, and enzyme-catalyzed reductive dehalogenation.) The efficacies of the *in-situ* technologies have not yet been assessed in the field. Heterogeneities in the geology and in the DNAPL distribution will likely often severely limit the performance of remediation technologies, especially the flush technologies.

Pump-and-treat and cutoff-wall enclosures used alone or in combination with other remediation steps are proven technologies for source-zone containment. However, while pump-and-treat can be used for containing or removing plumes, its long-term costs are often large due to the stringent water treatment standards that are frequently applied. Moreover, in cases where diffusion from many low-permeability zones severely restricts the rate of mass removal, plume removal by aggressive pump-and-treat can take many decades or longer.

In-situ treatment in conjunction with cutoff walls and funnel-and-gate systems comprise new systems to control dissolved contamination. The contaminant flux in most plumes is sufficiently small for these *in-situ* treatment systems to offer good potential for the containment of plumes in cases involving contamination in shallow porous-media aquifers. In contrast, for most fractured rock sites and for porous-media sites with deep DNAPL, no permanent restoration technologies exist and pump-and-treat remains as the only proven containment option.

14.1 INTRODUCTION

The realization that **dense non-aqueous phase liquids (DNAPLs)** are common at industrial and military sites and that they pose exceptional problems at these sites came gradually, and evolved from a recognition by a few groundwater scientists in the early 1980s to broad recognition by the groundwater profession in the early 1990s (see the related discussion in Chapter 1). Subsurface contamination at DNAPL sites poses much greater technical problems and financial burdens than exists at sites contaminated with other materials. Most sites in North America that have received or will soon receive major remediation work are afflicted with DNAPLs, the most common being chlorinated solvents and mixed organic liquid industrial wastes that are quite similar to chlorinated solvents. Meeting the clean-up criteria specified by regulatory agencies has been and will continue to be elusive at most DNAPL sites. Progress towards the cost-effective management of this immense groundwater problem has been slow. A major impediment to progress has been the difficulty of moving beyond conventional concepts and strategies for subsurface remediation to new approaches best suited for the particular characteristics of DNAPL problems. Approaches that have long served for remediation of sites contaminated with **light non-aqueous phase liquids (LNAPLs)** and for the remediation of non-NAPL sites are generally ineffective for DNAPL sites. Advances in technology for the remediation of DNAPL sites are urgently needed.

The immense need for effective subsurface remediation strategies for either containment or restoration at DNAPL sites has resulted in the accelerated application of new and emerging technologies without the attention to independent and rigorous performance assessment that technology developments normally require. We do not attempt in this chapter to describe technologies in detail or to evaluate technologies. Rather, our goal is to describe conceptually the nature of subsurface remediation problems at DNAPL sites as well as the remediation approaches and technologies that are now available or that are being developed. For more detailed descriptions of many of the technologies, the reader is referred to the report of Grubb and Sitar (1994).

For our discussions of DNAPL site remediation, it is important to establish the following definitions for technology development:

- **Proven Technology:** A technology for which: 1) a considerable base of site experience and success currently exists; 2) commercial organizations offer the technology in the marketplace; and 3) the performance of the technology is reasonably predictable.

- **Emerging Technology:** A technology for which considerable laboratory research and development have been conducted, and the technology has been used with encouraging results at one or more field sites. The technology is available in the commercial marketplace, but actual site performance and costs for specified performance have considerable uncertainty. More research and development and detailed assessments of field trials are needed.

- **Experimental Technology:** A technology which is new and offers promise, but which is still being investigated primarily in the laboratory and has had few, if any, successful prototype or pilot-scale field trials.

Figure 14.1 describes the stages according to which remediation technologies can evolve from the initial experimental stage, through the emerging stage, to the proven technology stage. For a technology to become proven, it must evolve from the bottom of the Figure 14.1 triangle, where numerous technologies can exist as concepts or in the initial experimental stage, to the top of the triangle, where few arrive because of technical failure or excessive cost. To enhance commercial prospects, technology vendors commonly claim that their technologies rank higher in the progression of categories on the triangle than the actual performance data warrant. Moreover, there is a paucity of

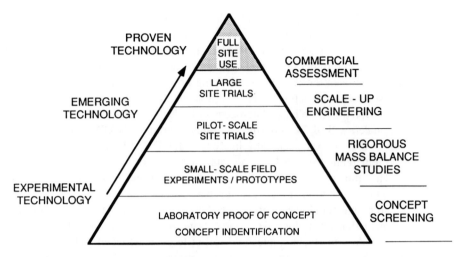

Figure 14.1   Stages in the evolution of a new technology for site remediation; many technologies exist in the concept stage, but few survive to the proven stage.

published, peer-reviewed literature on new and emerging technologies for which successful application to DNAPL sites has been proven.

14.2 CHARACTERISTICS OF DNAPL SITES

The major differences between groundwater contamination at non-NAPL, LNAPL, and DNAPL sites are shown in Figure 14.2. DNAPL sites usually differ from non-NAPL and LNAPL sites by the **vertical position** within the hydrogeologic system of the principal source of the contamination. In particular, at most DNAPL sites, much or all of the contaminant source mass causing the plume is DNAPL situated below the water table. Commonly, much of the mass is far below the water table where it causes deep groundwater contamination. In contrast, at non-NAPL sites, waste material or contaminated soil that cause groundwater contamination are usually situated entirely above the water table. At most LNAPL sites, the source material is hydrocarbon liquid which can be found in the soil zone, in the capillary fringe, and in the upper part of the groundwater zone.

Many industrial sites are characterized by a combination of two or three of the conceptual models shown in Figure 14.2. For example, at some non-NAPL sites, a portion of the waste may be below the water table. Horizontal groundwater flow through the waste then contributes contaminant mass to the plume in much the same way as does flow through DNAPL below the water table. At some sites, both LNAPL and DNAPL are present, though we note that the DNAPL is usually the cause of the most severe or extensive groundwater contamination.

Permanent subsurface restoration of a typical non-NAPL site is relatively simple, although not necessarily inexpensive. Remediation possibilities include: 1) remove the contaminated soil or waste by excavation; or 2) remove the soil/waste contaminant mass by *in-situ* methods so that the "source" is removed, then extract the plume by **pump-**

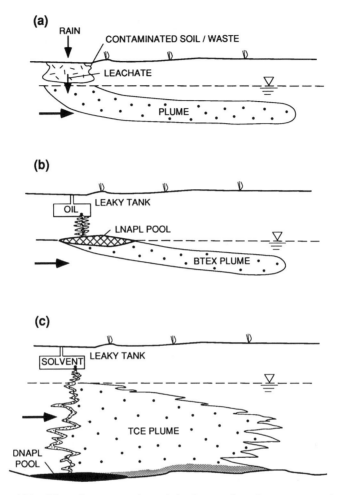

Figure 14.2   Schematic representations of simple cases for point-source groundwater contamination: a) non-NAPL case; b) LNAPL case; and c) DNAPL case.

and-treat, or let it dissipate by natural groundwater flushing. Alternatively, if there are no volatile contaminants, and if the contaminants are located only in the vadose zone, the ability of the source to generate a plume can be eliminated by placing an impervious cover over the source area. The benefits to the groundwater environment provided by impervious covers on non-NAPL sites of the type shown in Figure 14.2.a are clear. However, the benefits to groundwater from impervious covers at DNAPL sites are generally much less evident. At many DNAPL sites, such covers will provide no measurable reduction in groundwater contamination.

At LNAPL sites, significant contaminant source mass commonly extends all the way down to the water table, thereby causing excavation to be difficult or excessively expensive, and impervious soil covers to be less effective for source control. Fortunately, most LNAPLs are comprised of petroleum hydrocarbons for which natural microbiological processes cause gradual but effective destruction of the plume and ultimately of the **source zone**†. As a result of biodegradation, an unremediated plume from an LNAPL source rarely extends more than a few hundred meters from the source zone. Provision of oxygen to an LNAPL source zone and/or to its plume will often enhance the rate of subsurface restoration.

At most DNAPL sites, the source zone has **multiple DNAPL entry points or entry areas** where the DNAPL was spilled onto soil or leaked into the soil (Figure 14.3). Source zones may have buried drums, sludge, or other waste material located primarily

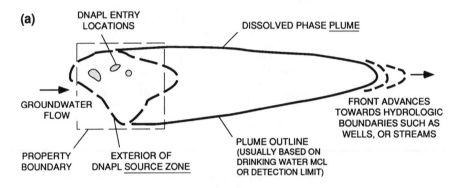

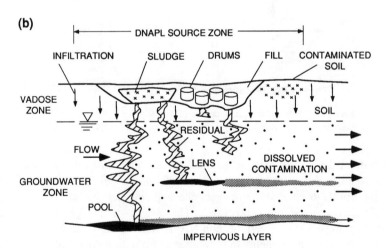

Figure 14.3 Anatomy of a DNAPL site on unconsolidated deposits: a) plan view; and b) cross-sectional view.

---

†In this chapter, we use the term *source zone* to refer collectively to the entire subsurface zone where DNAPL contamination exists, including both the vadose and groundwater zones.

or exclusively in the vadose zone, as well as DNAPL below the water table. If DNAPL is below the water table, that portion of the source has typically contributed most of the mass to the plume and presents the greatest obstacles to remediation. Contaminant contributions to groundwater from DNAPL in the vadose zone cause shallow plumes at some sites. These shallow plumes are likely to terminate at local natural hydrologic barriers such as streams, while contamination from DNAPL below the water table is more likely to feed plumes that follow **regional groundwater flowpaths** extending to major rivers, lakes, or wells beyond the local hydrologic barriers. Therefore, the remediation of deep DNAPL source zones can be particularly important but difficult.

At DNAPL sites on **porous media** such as sand or gravel, the source zone includes the entire volume wherein DNAPL is found. However, the regulatory and legal communities have more generally perceived the "significant source" on an industrial property to be buried drums or contaminated soil or sludge which are close to the ground surface, and typically all above the water table. Since regulatory and legal viewpoints have governed most remedial actions, at many DNAPL sites, large remedial efforts have commonly been directed at the drum or sludge portion of the source, with little effort directed at the DNAPL below the water table. At many DNAPL sites, this confusion in the concept of source has resulted in remediation efforts that, while very expensive, have provided minimal risk reduction or groundwater protection.

Defining the source zone at solvent DNAPL sites on **fractured porous media** (*e.g.*, fractured clayey deposits or fractured porous sandstone or shale) is complicated because the DNAPL mass initially in the fractures may have been depleted fairly quickly by diffusive transfer to the dissolved and sorbed phases in the matrix (see Chapters 2 and 12, as well as Parker *et al.*, 1994). Therefore, in a fractured porous medium, the size of the subsurface zone in which DNAPL exists can diminish with time. In some cases, the DNAPL can disappear altogether. However, even with total DNAPL disappearance, the initial zone will contain essentially all of the contaminant mass, and will thus represent a long-term source zone as contaminants are slowly released by diffusion from the matrix to groundwater flowing through the fracture network. As noted above, at DNAPL sites on porous media such as sand or gravel, the "source zone" includes the entire volume wherein DNAPL is found. In contrast, at DNAPL sites on fractured porous media, we use the term "source zone" to refer to the zone containing the relatively large and immobile or nearly immobile contaminant mass, regardless of whether DNAPL still exists in the fractures.

Groundwater plumes have two components of contaminant mass, the dissolved and sorbed components. Estimates of the dissolved contaminant mass in large plumes in sand and gravel aquifers at solvent DNAPL sites are in the range of 0.5 to 70 drums (55 US gallons) of equivalent DNAPL (see Chapter 2). Annual plume fluxes are usually one-tenth or less of the total dissolved mass. The amount of the sorbed mass in these plumes is generally unknown; for moderately hydrophobic DNAPLs such as trichloroethylene (TCE), tetrachloroethylene (PCE), and 1,1,1-trichloroethane (1,1,1-TCA), it is expected to be of about the same order of magnitude as the dissolved mass. To permanently clean up a plume, sufficient dissolved and sorbed mass must be removed so that aquifer-restoration criteria can be met even if some remaining mass desorbs to the groundwater.

14.3 REMEDIATION GOALS

14.3.1 Plume Containment

Risks from groundwater contamination can be reduced or eliminated by controlling the migration of the aqueous- and vapor-phase plumes to achieve **plume containment**. By definition, when complete or full containment of a plume is achieved, the affected volume of the aquifer ceases to grow. In some cases, the condition of complete containment is imposed naturally by hydrologic boundaries. An example would be a plume that discharges into a nearby stream (Figure 14.4.a). Although such a plume may cause the contamination of surface water, the zone of aquifer contamination does not expand. At many DNAPL sites, complete containment cannot be achieved unless engineered controls (*e.g.*, pump-and-treat) are applied for as long as the DNAPL source persists (Figure 14.4.b). At many sites, this is expected to be many decades or longer.

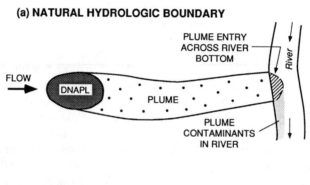

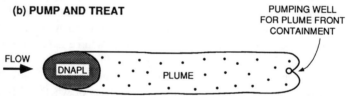

Figure 14.4   Plume containment: a) a river as a natural hydrologic boundary; and b) pump-and-treat captures the front of a plume.

14.3.2 Aquifer Restoration

Aquifer restoration is much different from plume containment. Complete aquifer restoration requires subsurface source removal as well as plume removal to a degree sufficient to allow the original beneficial use of the aquifer, which is usually as a source of drinking water. A completely restored aquifer is one that requires no on-going remedial activity. To accomplish complete aquifer restoration at a DNAPL site, the plume must be removed, either by groundwater extraction, by *in-situ* treatment, or by natural flushing.

Sufficient contaminant mass must also be removed from the source-zone so that ground-water flowing through the source zone no longer creates a plume downgradient of the source zone at concentration levels above regulatory limits. Of the thousands of sites that are contaminated with DNAPLs in North America, while successful measures for source zone or plume containment are on-going, none has been fully restored to drinking water standards. Generally, claims of complete aquifer restoration have either not been confirmed by adequate testing, or the cleanup requirements have been relaxed to values above drinking water standards (National Research Council, 1994).

14.3.3 Source-Zone Containment/Plume Removal

Although complete aquifer restoration is an elusive goal, better prospects exist for restoring parts of aquifers by removing all or part of the plume while at the same time isolating the source zone in place. For a portion of the aquifer to remain restored, contamination from the source zone must not be allowed to enter that portion: therefore, **source-zone containment** using proven technologies is needed. The source zone can be isolated from groundwater flow by a low-permeability barrier, or by hydraulic capture using groundwater extraction wells (Figure 14.5.a,b). Once source-zone containment is effected,

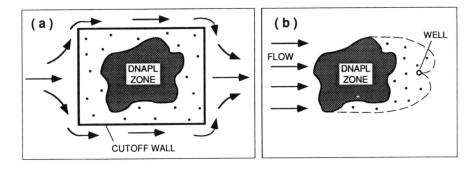

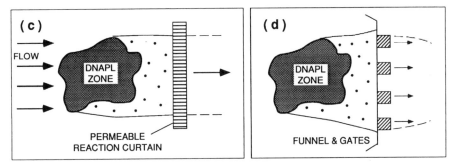

Figure 14.5   DNAPL source zone isolation provided by: a) a low permeability enclosure; b) hydraulic containment by pump-and-treat; c) a permeable reaction curtain; and d) a funnel-and-gate.

plume removal can be accomplished naturally, as the plume will eventually disappear as it is flushed by groundwater through the aquifer to a natural hydrologic barrier or into water supply wells. After the source zone is isolated, pump-and-treat can play one of two roles: 1) plume-front capture, until natural flushing removes the contamination extending from the source zone to the plume front; or 2) aggressive removal of the plume using more pumping wells placed throughout the plume (Figure 14.6). In the second case, removal of the plume is accomplished sooner, but by a greater effort. In addition, the aggressive pumping causes much uncontaminated water to be removed from the aquifer and mixed with plume water. This can represent a substantial waste of the water resource if the treated water is discharged to sewers or surface water rather than being used or reinjected into the aquifer.

(a)

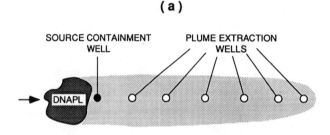

(b)   **(c)**

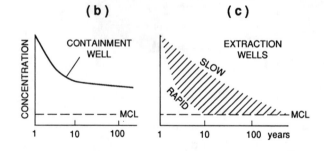

Figure 14.6   Remediation of a source-zone and its plume by pump-and-treat: a) containment well at the source zone and multiple wells in the plume for aggressive plume removal; b) response of containment well; and c) response envelope for plume-extraction wells.

14.4 LOW PERMEABILITY ENCLOSURES

A low permeability enclosure placed around a DNAPL source zone will divert much of the groundwater flow around the enclosure. The lower the permeability of the enclosure walls, the smaller will be the flow through the DNAPL zone inside the enclosure (Figure 14.7). If desired, enclosure walls of very low permeability can be constructed. Many types of engineered barrier technologies are available for creating **low-permeability enclosures** around DNAPL source zones (Table 14.1). Mutch and Ash (1993) describe several of these technologies. Most types of barriers are **proven technologies** in that, when constructed with stringent quality-control procedures, they can be depended upon to provide very low permeability enclosures for a long time. Two main design options

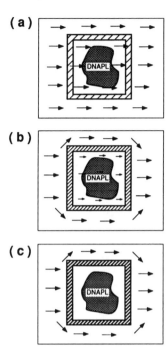

Figure 14.7 Decreasing groundwater flow through a source-zone enclosure with decreasing hydraulic conductivity of the enclosure walls.

exist for enclosures around source zones: the **keyed enclosure**, and the **hanging enclosure** (Figure 14.8). The keyed enclosure has the wall set into a low-permeability layer (aquitard) at the bottom of the aquifer, whereas the bottom of the hanging enclosure does not terminate in a low permeability zone. The hanging enclosure has the wall set at some level above the bottom of the aquifer. To provide a high degree of source-zone containment, the enclosure need only extend somewhat deeper than the bottom of the DNAPL source zone, particularly in cases where pumping inside the enclosure is used to cause upward flow at the bottom of the enclosure. However, higher rates of groundwater pumping will be required inside a hanging enclosure to provide effective containment at the bottom of the enclosure. At some sites, the DNAPL zone does not reach the bottom of the aquifer and therefore the cost of the enclosure can be minimized because the enclosure need not penetrate to the bottom of the aquifer.

Enclosures are not a practical option at many sites. In cases where the bottom of the DNAPL zone is very deep, enclosure construction to depths below the DNAPL zone is not feasible. At other sites, difficulties in determining conclusively the maximum depth of DNAPL causes unacceptable uncertainty for specification of the enclosure depth. Of the technologies listed in Table 14.1, only borehole grouting is capable of creating enclosures in hard bedrock. Where DNAPL occurs in fractured bedrock, the high cost of creating enclosures by borehole grouting usually renders enclosures impractical, in which case the only option available for source zone containment is groundwater pump-and-treat.

In situations where there is no pumping in or near a low permeability enclosure, inward groundwater flow occurs across the upgradient enclosure wall face; outward flow

TABLE 14.1   Major types of low-permeability cutoff walls for source-zone enclosures and funnel-and-gate systems in unconsolidated deposits and soft bedrock.

General type	Materials options	Construction	Comments
1. Slurry Trench	• soil/bentonite • soil/cement • soil/attapulgite	• backhoe • backhoe and clamshell	thick wall (0.5 to 1 m), large volume of earth removed for disposal
2. Vibrated Beam Wall	• bentonite • bentonite/cement • asphaltic mixtures	driven beam with injection down annulus of beam	thin wall (0.1 m), no soil removed for surface disposal
3. Plastic Sheets in Slurry Trenches	• high density polyethylene (HDPE) or PVC sheets	sheets inserted into slurry trenches; sealed joints between sheets	thin plastic sheets in trench (0.3 to 1 m), large volume earth removed for disposal, exceptionally low permeability
4. Jet Grout Walls	bentonite/cement mixture	high-pressure injection of slurry down drill rods; drill holes spaced 0.3 to 0.1 m apart	minimal soil removed in return to surface of excess slurry from boreholes
5. Auger Mix Wall	• soil/bentonite • bentonite/cement	injection of sealant into auger mix zone	thick wall, minimal soil removed
6. Steel Sheet Piling: Conventional	steel sheets; thickness options from 4 to 15 mm	driven directly into ground using electric hammer vibration or diesel hammers	no earth material removed from ground; cannot be driven through large boulders, hard soil or rock
7. Steel Sheet Piling: Sealable Joints	same as in type 6, except that joints have larger annulus that is grouted with bentonite, cement, epoxy or other sealants	same as in type 6	same as in type 6; the annulus in joints can be inspected before grouting; exceptionally low permeability

carries contamination across the downgradient wall face (Figure 14.7). Side faces can have areas of inwards and outwards flow. The outflow parts of the enclosure cause formation of a **plume downgradient of the enclosure** (Figure 14.9).

The normal design goal for enclosures is the achievement of extremely low permeability so that contaminant advection across the barrier will be insignificant. However, **molecular diffusion** is another mechanism for contaminant migration across enclosure walls. Chlorinated solvents can diffuse through slurry walls and even through high density polyethylene walls (HDPE). Devlin and Parker (1995) have shown that molecular diffusion can cause outwards diffusion across low-permeability walls even when the

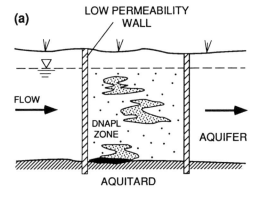

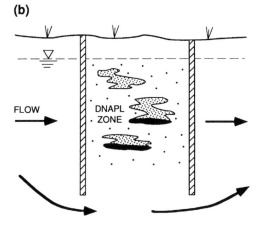

Figure 14.8   Cutoff wall enclosure: a) keyed enclosure—groundwater is diverted laterally around the enclosure; and b) hanging enclosure—groundwater is diverted laterally and vertically (downward) around the enclosure.

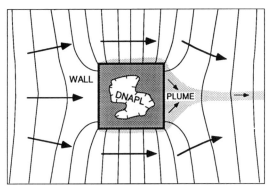

Figure 14.9   A plume of dissolved contamination downgradient of a source-zone enclosure. Dissolved contaminants diffuse through the walls to cause the plume. (Adapted from Devlin and Parker, 1994).

hydraulic gradient is directed inwards due to pumping inside the enclosure. Indeed, very low hydraulic conductivity increases the importance of outward diffusion by reducing inward advection. For any set of conditions, there is an **optimum hydraulic conductivity** for the enclosure wall for which both higher and lower values result in greater contaminant flux through the wall. Steel sheet pile walls with grouted joints can prevent both advective and diffusive flux through the enclosure walls.

Enclosures around source zones need not provide zero outward contaminant flux in order to effectively isolate the source. The enclosure must only limit the outward flux sufficiently to result in concentrations that meet regulatory standards at a specified location outside of the enclosure, *e.g.*, at the downgradient site boundary. Figure 14.9 illustrates the formation of a plume from an enclosure in a uniform flow field in a moderately permeable sandy aquifer. Contamination diffuses outwards through the enclosure walls where it is transported downgradient, forming a narrow, almost linear plume following the groundwater flowpath. Whether or not this plume exceeds water-quality criteria depends on many site specific factors such as source concentration(s), aquifer dispersivity, the regulatory standard(s) for the contaminant(s), and the spatial scale of the groundwater sampling.

Under conditions of natural groundwater flushing, many DNAPL source zones will probably require **centuries** or longer for natural restoration (see Chapters 2 and 7). When surrounded by an enclosure, the DNAPL will persist much longer. Therefore, questions arise regarding the **longevity of enclosures**. Predictions are uncertain, but expectations for most wall materials are a century or longer if the walls are designed initially to be chemically compatible with their subsurface environment. It is reasonable to expect that slow deterioration over hundreds of years will eventually make replacement of the enclosure necessary, unless new technologies to destroy or remove the DNAPL become available at or before that future time.

At many sites, the DNAPL source zone has no readily-definable boundary, particularly when the DNAPL is a chlorinated solvent because mobile or even residual DNAPL is seldom encountered directly in boreholes or wells. The **presence and approximate spatial distribution of DNAPL** must usually be inferred based on **indirect evidence** (see Chapter 13). Obviously, for a low-permeability enclosure to be most effective, the enclosure must surround all of the DNAPL. To accomplish this, the DNAPL residuals or accumulations need not be located precisely. It is sufficient to drill at or beyond the outermost boundary of the suspected DNAPL zone to establish a circumference which DNAPL has not crossed. However, the enclosure designed on this basis would be larger than would be needed if the exact morphology of the DNAPL zone were known. There will be a point at which the cumulative cost of determining the precise extent of the DNAPL zone exceeds the incremental cost of a larger enclosure.

Pump-and-treat and low-permeability enclosures are both proven technologies for source-zone containment. Pump-and-treat can be used in any hydrogeologic environment whereas enclosures are most practical for sites where the DNAPL zone is not deep and is not in bedrock. At sites where enclosures around DNAPL source zones are technically feasible, cost is usually the reason for selecting an enclosure rather than pump-and-treat as the primary technology for source zone containment. Enclosures have larger initial (capital) costs, but lower long-term costs for operations and maintenance (O&M) than pump-and-treat. Depending on the capital costs, O&M costs, and interest rates, the predicted cumulative cost (present worth) of the enclosure may be lower in some cases than the predicted cumulative cost of pump-and-treat for operation times exceeding some critical duration (*T*-critical in Figure 14.10). A low-permeability enclosure may also be selected

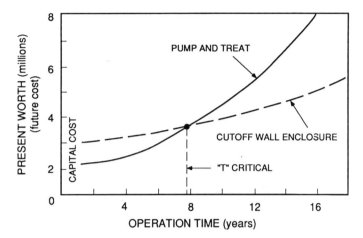

Figure 14.10 Comparison of hypothetical future cost relations for pump-and-treat system *vs.* a low-permeability enclosure for DNAPL source zone isolation.

because it may facilitate the use of DNAPL removal or destruction technologies inside the enclosure, or because it would be perceived by the public as more secure containment.

14.5 PUMP-AND-TREAT

There have been numerous attempts across North America to restore DNAPL source zones by pump-and-treat. Figure 14.6 shows the typical concentration response of a pumping well near a source zone compared to the response of wells in the plume after the source zone has been contained by pump-and-treat. At early time, wells at the DNAPL source zone show a decline in concentration due primarily to **dilution** caused by capture of clean water with source-zone water. There is little or no subsequent reduction of concentration except over very long time. Concentrations in the pumping wells in a source zone can be higher than those observed in nearby monitoring wells because pumping draws flowlines from the source zone.

Pumping wells in or near solvent DNAPL source zones commonly exhibit concentrations in the range of 1 ppm (mg/L) to 100 ppm of total dissolved solvents. Wells with this concentration range pumping at a relatively high rates of say 1000 L/min (250 gpm), would extract between 2 and 200 drums of equivalent DNAPL mass per year. Clearly, whether or not this annual mass extraction rate permits significant progress towards source-zone restoration depends on the total mass of solvent in the source zone. Unfortunately, that **source-zone mass is rarely known**, even within an order of magnitude. The fact that pump-and-treat systems have been operating for more than a decade at many DNAPL sites without appreciable concentration decline is evidence that a large ratio of source-zone mass to annual mass removed is typical at DNAPL sites. The rate of mass removal at some sites can be increased by adding more pumping wells in or near the source zone. However, the increase in mass removal will not be proportional to the increase in the groundwater pumping rate because of limitations on the DNAPL dissolution kinetics, and because of further dilution with clean water drawn from outside the source zone (Figure 14.11.c).

As noted above, the main capability that pump-and-treat offers at DNAPL sites is plume containment or source zone containment. Therefore, the tactic should be to pump at the lowest rate needed to achieve the desired capture of the contaminant flux from the source zone. At most sites this pumping needs to yield a dissolved contaminant flux of less than a few drums of equivalent DNAPL per year to achieve complete plume capture or complete source zone containment. The rate of contaminant mass removal is then equal to or only slightly greater than the mass flux emanating from the source zone under natural conditions (Figure 14.11.b).

The segment of aquifer occupied by the plume at some sites is sufficiently large and the groundwater resource sufficiently valuable to warrant removal of the plume by **"aggressive pump-and-treat"** (Figure 14.6). For this purpose, wells are distributed throughout the plume to remove multiple pore-volumes (*i.e.*, plume volumes) of contaminated water much more rapidly than occurs by natural flushing. Clean water from outside the plume is drawn into the plume zone as the plume is removed. If prior isolation of the source zone has occurred, the pump-and-treat system need operate only until sufficient

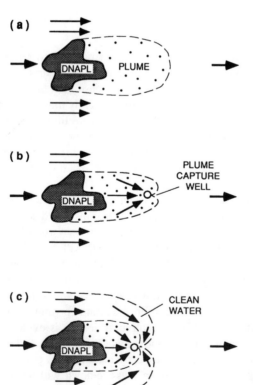

Figure 14.11   Source-zone capture with wells illustrating: a) an uncontrolled plume; b) a well providing capture at the minimum pumping rate; and c) excessive pumping causing capture of clean water along with clean groundwater.

water has flushed the plume zone to cause contaminant concentrations to decline and then remain below the regulatory value. The wells can then be shut off. The aquifer beyond the source zone then remains restored for as long as the source zone containment is maintained.

Plume restoration by aggressive pump-and-treat after source-zone isolation is simple in concept, but in practice there are several factors that commonly extend the time period needed to attain regulatory limits throughout the plume, particularly if the limits specified are the ppb (μg/L) levels of drinking water standards discussed in Chapter 2. These factors include **non-optimal location** of extraction wells, **slow desorption** of contaminants from soil particles, and **slow release** of contaminants by diffusion from low permeability strata or lenses, or from the low-permeability matrix in a fractured porous medium. In a situation where much of the contaminant mass is stored in the lower permeability portions of an aquifer, slow diffusion out of these zones causes the decline in plume concentrations to approach the required restoration level only very slowly (Figure 14.6.c). In some heterogeneous granular aquifers and in many fractured porous aquifers, the prospects for attaining restoration levels by aggressive pump-and-treat within several decades are uncertain, even if the source zone has been successfully isolated.

14.6 IN-SITU TREATMENT FOR MIGRATION CONTROL

Figure 14.5 illustrates four approaches for the containment of DNAPL source zones. Two of the four are the proven approaches discussed above (Figures 14.5.a,b). The other two (Figures 14.5.c,d) are emerging technologies, known as the **in-situ treatment curtain** and the **funnel-and-gate** system. In the latter two systems, the plume moves due to the natural hydraulic gradient through an emplaced permeable zone (curtain or gate). The zone can be designed to: 1) destroy or immobilize contaminants using reactive media; 2) volatize contaminants (Pankow *et al.* 1993); or 3) add amendments to the water to support biodegradation downgradient (see also below).

The permeability of the curtain or gate should be equal to or greater than the natural permeability of the surrounding aquifer material. In concept, the contaminated water that passes through the curtain or gate forms a different plume in the downgradient part of the aquifer, one in which the chemical quality of the water at some point meets regulatory standards even though the water chemistry may differ from the ambient water in the aquifer. In practice, use of treatment curtains will be limited to shallow plumes due to cost and installation difficulties.

At some sites where plumes are wide and/or deeper, funnel-and-gate systems offer cost advantages. The funnel is a low-permeability wall placed across the plume with one or more gaps (*i.e.*, gates) through which plume water flows while receiving treatment. The barriers available to form the low-permeability portion of a funnel are those listed in Table 14.1. Treatment curtains and funnel-and-gate systems are emerging technologies in the sense that the treatment materials and gate designs are still the subject of intensive research and, as of 1995, only a few have been installed at field sites.

Research on treatment curtains and funnel-and-gate systems for organic contaminants began in the late 1980s with the first publications appearing a few years later (Burris and Cherry, 1992; Pankow *et al.*, 1993; Starr and Cherry, 1994). Treatment curtains or gates may in principle penetrate the entire aquifer, or they can be partially penetrating or "hanging" to a depth sufficient to treat the entire plume (Figure 14.12). A funnel-and-gate system causes a **rise in the upgradient water table** which then induces some **downward flow** at the gate. The bottom of the funnel-and-gate must therefore penetrate to an impermeable layer, or to an appropriate depth below the plume so that no part of the plume passes beneath the gate.

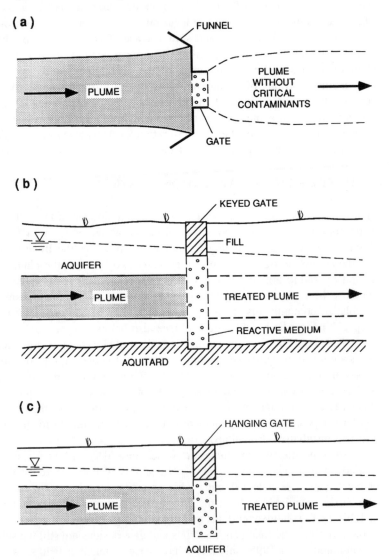

Figure 14.12 Schematic illustration of a funnel-and-gate system: a) plan view; b) cross-sectional view, keyed case; and c) cross-sectional view, hanging case.

Treatment curtains and funnel-and-gate systems have the same goal: to treat the plume *in situ* in a manner that requires little or no water extraction, energy use, or maintenance. The most **passive** *in-situ* treatment system involves no external energy or chemical input, no extraction or forced fluid circulation, and no maintenance or replacement of reactive materials. Many different types of reactive materials can be placed in a curtain/gate, depending on the chemical composition of the plume. Research and development is most advanced for chlorinated solvent compounds. Gillham and O'Hannesin (1993, 1994) describe laboratory and field prototype trials of a solid-phase treatment material (**zero-valent, elemental iron filings**) for the *in-situ* destruction of chlorinated solvents. Iron offers good prospects to achieve passive treatment of solvent plumes over long periods of time.

Approaches for *in-situ* plume control that are less passive than elemental iron are emerging, particularly for use in gates. For example, an alternative to the use of solid particles in a gate is the slow release and mixing of dissolved chemicals in a gate. These chemicals react with the plume constituents causing **destruction of contaminants** during passage through the gate, or in a reaction zone that develops in the aquifer downgradient of the gate. Thus, the gate or curtain can function as both the **source of the treatment chemicals** *and* the **treatment zone**, or simply as the chemical source that induces treatment in an aquifer zone downgradient of the gate.

Microbiological systems are being investigated for use with curtains (Devlin and Barker, 1994) and gates (Wilson and Mackay, 1995). The research is investigating two paths: 1) the release of nutrients to the aquifer to enhance **natural biodegradation** of chlorinated solvents by aquifer bacteria; or 2) the emplacement of **cultured or genetically-engineered bacteria** in the gate. All *in-situ* microbial approaches require the provision of nutrients (and in some cases other chemicals) over long periods (either continuously or pulsed) to sustain the necessary biodegradation processes. The technical challenge for *in-situ* microbial approaches is to develop release systems for nutrients and other microbial life support chemicals that can function in a relatively passive mode for long-times with minimal maintenance and monitoring.

In a funnel-and-gate system in which iron particles are used for dehalogenation of chlorinated solvents, the particles can be mixed with sand and/or other media and deposited in a gate. If the need arises to replace the reactive medium, it can be excavated by auger equipment. Other designs for gates have been developed wherein the treatment medium is contained in a slotted or screened metal enclosure (**treatment cassette**) that is inserted into the gate. The cassette can be hoisted from the gate when replacement is necessary. Removable cassettes offer convenience for cultured or genetically-engineered microbial treatment systems for which periodic microbe regeneration will likely be necessary.

The concepts presented here pertain specifically to DNAPL sites, however, they also are relevant to many non-NAPL and LNAPL sites. They provide a spectrum of approaches for plume containment ranging from an active option like pump-and-treat, to the most passive, which include the reaction curtain and the funnel-and-gate (Figure 14.13). *In-situ* treatment curtains and funnel-and-gate systems are advancing rapidly from pilot scale trials to full-scale systems. The contaminant mass flux that these technologies

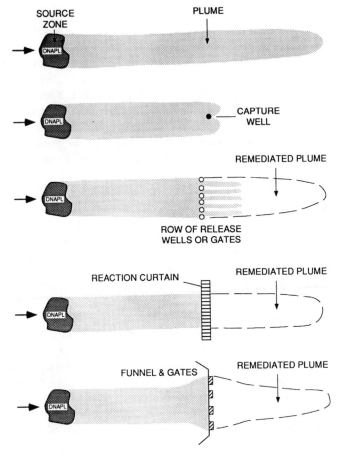

Figure 14.13   A spectrum of options for containment of plumes, from no action in the top case to a funnel with multiple gates in the lower case.

must remove from plumes is not large, and therefore the remaining technical challenges are likely surmountable. However, even when these new technologies are fully developed, the hydrogeologic conditions at many sites, particularly those with deep plumes or in fractured rock, will render them unsuitable, leaving only pump-and-treat as the technically- and economically-viable option for source zone or plume control.

14.7 SOURCE ZONE RESTORATION

14.7.1 Source Zone Restoration in the Vadose Zone

At many DNAPL sites, remediation efforts for the purpose of reducing or preventing groundwater contamination have been directed at the vadose zone. As has been discussed in Section 14.2, vadose-zone remediation in the source zone commonly receives priority over deeper remediation in the groundwater zone, even though vadose-zone contamination usually causes much less degradation of groundwater quality than does the deeper DNAPL[†].

The common selection of the vadose zone as the remediation priority at DNAPL sites derives, at least initially, from the common belief that a restored vadose zone will appreciably diminish groundwater contamination, and, of course, from the belief that successful restoration of the vadose zone is feasible. Although vadose zone restoration will ultimately be required to achieve complete aquifer restoration, by itself the benefit will generally be minimal or undetectable for as long as significant DNAPL mass persists below the water table. Furthermore, where the primary contaminants are volatile organic chemicals such as chlorinated solvents, transfer of these contaminants from the groundwater zone upwards to the restored vadose zone offers the potential at many sites to cause parts of the vadose zone to become re-contaminated (Feenstra and Conant, 1994). Thus, if the groundwater zone remains contaminated, much of the benefit from vadose-zone restoration may be temporary.

In 1986, the U.S.EPA issued regulations that imposed **severe restrictions** on the excavation of contaminated soil if the soil was to be deposited off-site. These restrictions, and the high cost of available on-site treatment of excavated soil, prompted rapid development of new *in-situ* technologies for the vadose zone. At solvent DNAPL sites, the emerging technology of choice during the late 1980s and early 1990s was **soil vacuum extraction (SVE)**. Unfortunately, there have been few examples of restoration to normal cleanup standards. SVE involves the application of a vacuum to slotted pipes in the vadose zone to draw air through the contaminated earth material. The air flow volatilizes contaminants from the DNAPL, soil, and/or aqueous phases. Air injection wells can be used in combination with air extraction wells to enhance the air flow. At some sites, the depth at which SVE can be applied can be increased by lowering the water table with groundwater pumping wells.

The ultimate goal of most SVE operations at solvent DNAPL sites is to remove contaminant mass to the point where water infiltrating through the vadose zone will no longer generate contaminant concentrations above drinking water standards. SVE has best potential to achieve these stringent standards in relatively homogeneous sand or gravel where rapid air flow can circulate throughout the contaminant zone. However, even in such an ideal vadose zone, SVE is not effective in the capillary fringe. Fine-grained layers or lenses in heterogeneous deposits also limit the effectiveness of SVE because both high water contents and low intrinsic soil permeabilities will limit air flow. Slow diffusion of contaminants out of these zones will limit the restoration rate and can cause the time required to achieve full restoration of the vadose zone to stretch to decades or longer.

[†]Near-surface contamination in the vadose zone *can* cause unacceptable risk to land users due to the escape of vapor at the surface, diffusion into buildings, soil erosion, or by direct contact. At such sites, the surficial soil (uppermost 1-3 m) is often removed and replaced by clean soil, or an impervious cover is placed on the surface to reduce risk. Such efforts are unrelated to groundwater remediation, and are not considered in this chapter.

SVE commonly removes considerable contaminant mass rapidly in the early stage of operations. This is followed by rapidly diminishing mass-removal rates that approach asymptotic or nearly **asymptotic mass-removal rates**. When the asymptotic condition is reached, much contaminant mass usually remains in the vadose zone, and the continued use of SVE provides minimal benefit. At DNAPL sites, the history of SVE for vadose-zone restoration is similar to that of groundwater pump-and-treat for the restoration of source zones. Indeed, optimism was high for both of these approaches in the 1980s, but by the 1990s, applications usually revealed that performance was much below initial expectations.

Heat and steam are now being investigated as means to achieve **enhancements of SVE**. Other adaptations are also being tried for low permeability deposits. These include borehole injection technologies that create artificial fractures for the enhancement of air flow. Although such enhancements offer potential for improvement in mass-removal efficiency, the restrictions caused by heterogeneities of geology and DNAPL distribution will continue to impose severe limitations at most sites.

14.7.2 Source Zone Restoration in the Groundwater Zone

14.7.2.1 General

As noted above, at the time of this writing, aggressive pump-and-treat has been underway at many DNAPL sites for ten years and at a few sites for nearly twenty years. Unfortunately, it has proven to be largely **ineffective source-zone restoration**. An examination of concentration *vs.* time records for wells at long-duration pump-and-treat DNAPL sites indicates that progress towards aquifer restoration is slow and that the prospects for achieving drinking water quality within decades (or even much longer) are minimal. The only other approach that has been used at many DNAPL sites is excavation, but it rarely extends deep enough to remove all of the known or suspected DNAPL.

14.7.2.2 Pumping of pools

Large pools of DNAPL have been located at a few chlorinated solvent DNAPL sites. Some pools are large enough to allow **pumping of free-product DNAPL from wells** screened at the bottom of the pool. Many thousands of gallons of DNAPL have been pumped from some exceptionally large pools situated at the bottom of granular aquifers. Free-product pumping can be enhanced by means of dual pumping wells, one in the DNAPL pool, and one in the groundwater above the pool. The flow of water across the pool enhances DNAPL flow towards the DNAPL pumping wells. Under the most favorable circumstances, free-product pumping removes a maximum of one-half or two-thirds of the DNAPL, leaving abundant DNAPL to serve as a long-term source.

Removal of free-product from a pool causes part of the pool to desaturate with respect to DNAPL, leaving residual DNAPL where the former pool existed. This causes an increase in the water permeability of this zone, and consequently larger groundwater flux through the zone. This carries the potential to worsen water quality in the plume (Figure 14.14). Ultimately, this enhanced contaminant flux from the former pool zone will decline and the DNAPL in this zone will disappear sooner than would be the case

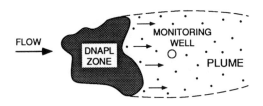

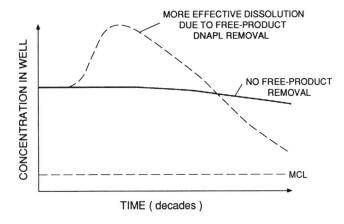

MCL = maximum concentration level for drinking water use.

Figure 14.14 Schematic illustration of the effect of free-phase DNAPL removal on the downgradient plume concentration. After free-phase DNAPL is removed from pools, dissolution of the remaining DNAPL (residual) produces a temporarily greater contaminant flux.

if it had not been pumped. Thus, in this case, to achieve better groundwater quality in the future, it is necessary to have more severe contamination for an initial period; the length of that period is difficult to predict.

The decision to pump DNAPL from a large pool discovered during the normal course of a site investigation is easily made since such pumping will minimize the potential for re-occurrence of DNAPL flow. Indeed, DNAPL movement might otherwise be initiated by changing groundwater conditions around the pool as could be caused by pump-and-treat or other influences on the groundwater flow system. The decision to search aggressively for smaller pools so that they can be pumped is much more difficult because: 1) search costs can be large; 2) the prospects are minimal for significant mass removal from small, poorly delineated pools; and 3) there is considerable risk of remobilizing DNAPL by drilling.

14.7.2.3 *In-situ* mass removal

The failure of pump-and-treat and the impracticality of excavation for the restoration of DNAPL source zones provides motivation for developing new *in-situ* technologies for this task. We will consider these experimental technologies in two categories: 1) **mass removal**; and 2) **mass destruction** (Figure 14.15). Mass-removal technologies include circulating steam or water containing chemical additives through the DNAPL zone. Flow is from injection wells to withdrawal wells where fluid is pumped into water treatment facilities at the surface (Figure 14.16). These technologies are a type of **enhanced pump-and-treat**. **Surfactants** and **co-solvents** such as alcohols are currently receiving most of the research attention. They are used to greatly increase the effective solubility of the DNAPL components so that circulation of the water/chemical mixture through the DNAPL zone will remove contaminant mass much more rapidly than conventional pump-and-treat. To avoid prohibitive cost, the chemical additive (surfactant or co-solvent) must usually be recycled. The contaminants must therefore be removed from the effluent at the surface. The efficient removal of contaminants from the effluent can be difficult. And, once removed, the contaminants must be disposed of, or destroyed.

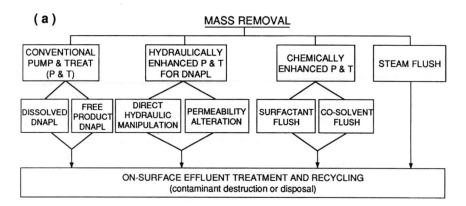

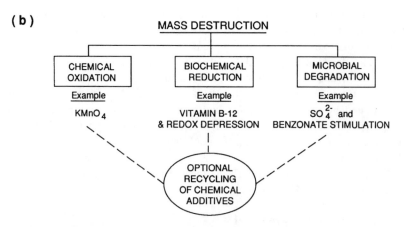

Figure 14.15   Categories of experimental technologies for the restoration of a DNAPL source zones with examples: a) mass-removal technologies; and b) *in-situ* mass destruction technologies.

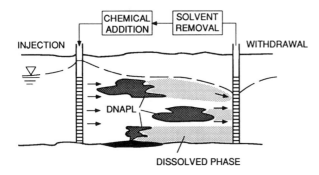

Figure 14.16 Schematic illustration of a surfactant or alcohol flush system for the removal of DNAPL: a) plan view; and (b) cross-sectional view.

Steam injection combined with vacuum extraction is another way to remove DNAPL from the vadose and groundwater zones. When saturated steam is injected into an aquifer, chlorinated solvents with boiling points lower than that of water are vaporized efficiently. Vacuum extraction wells are used to remove the vapor. As steam sweeps through the aquifer, condensate at the steam front mobilizes and pushes free-phase DNAPL towards the extraction wells (Stewart and Udell, 1992). However, the mobilized zone of DNAPL at the steam front may cause DNAPL to escape downwards into deeper zones where it will not be captured by the extraction wells. Other approaches described by Grubb and Sitar (1994) exist that use heat, low-quality steam, or hot water for the removal of DNAPL. Whether these other approaches offer distinct advantages over steam flushing with vacuum extraction remains to be determined.

The use of surfactants, co-solvents, and steam for the restoration of DNAPL source zones is associated with **three types of technical difficulties**. As with other methods, the *first* is caused by heterogeneities in the permeability and DNAPL distributions. For the DNAPL zone to be restored to the point where groundwater flushed through the zone meets or approaches drinking water standards, nearly all of the DNAPL mass must be removed. Delineation of all or even most of the DNAPL in the source zone is generally not feasible at solvent sites. Therefore, the surfactant solution, the alcohol solution, or the steam must be flushed through the *entire* zone where DNAPL is expected. After some initial flushing, detailed monitoring can provide more specific delineation of the DNAPL distribution so that flushing can be focused on these locations. For the flushing of surfactants, co-solvents, or steam to remove DNAPL efficiently, the flushing fluid must come into direct contact with the DNAPL to cause mobilization and then to carry the contaminant mass to the extraction wells. A main impediment to the full restoration of a DNAPL zone is therefore inadequate contact of the flushing fluid with **DNAPL in low permeability zones**.

DNAPL accumulations lying in depressions at the bottom of an aquifer or in depressions on low-permeability lenses within an aquifer are particularly difficult to remove. Fractured media and fractured porous media present even more severe limitations for flush technologies because while the flushing fluid will flow primarily through the larger connected fractures, considerable DNAPL mass can exist in small and dead-end fractures. In fractured porous media (*e.g.*, fractured clay or sandstone), much of the DNAPL mass present initially in the fractures is, by the time remediation is started, likely to exist in dissolved or sorbed form in the low-permeability matrix where flushing is ineffective. In such cases, a chemical flush removes the contaminant mass from the zones of active flushing, causing chemical concentration gradients from the stagnant zones. Diffusion from these zones to the flush zones results in continual but slow mass removal.

The *second* type of technical difficulty with the use of surfactants or co-solvents is the potential for adverse impacts on groundwater quality from the **enhanced mobility** of the DNAPL phase. For example, surfactants and co-solvents generally cause a decrease in the interfacial tensions of solvent DNAPLs, and this may mobilize DNAPL in residual or accumulation zones. Mobilization may cause the DNAPL to move deeper into formerly uncontaminated zones, thereby exacerbating the problem. Whether DNAPL mobilization could occur to an unacceptable degree will be site specific. Research on surfactant and co-solvent flushing for DNAPL site restoration is still at an early stage; reliable predictions of the effects of DNAPL mobilization are not yet possible.

The *third* difficulty with use of surfactants or co-solvents derives from the necessity to capture the groundwater that has been contaminated with the injected chemicals. The injection wells will cause distortion of the groundwater flow pattern, and it is necessary that the extraction wells provide **complete capture of the resulting, new zone of contamination**. To minimize the potential risk of DNAPL mobilization, the developing technologies of surfactant or co-solvent flushing should be used first at sites where deeper penetration of DNAPL would be acceptable, such as at sites where the deeper groundwater is too saline for drinking, or where deeper aquifers simply do not exist.

Air sparging is another method for restoring solvent DNAPL sources. In this method, air is injected into the aquifer below or within the DNAPL zone. As the air travels through the DNAPL zone, contaminant mass moves from the DNAPL phase into the surrounding water, then volatilizes into the air. The air then travels upwards through the groundwater zone to the vadose zone where it is generally collected in vacuum extraction wells. In the mid- to late-1980s, when air sparging was first applied in aquifers, it was thought that the air travelled as bubbles dispersed through the contaminated zone and that the bubbles cause efficient mass transfer from the DNAPL phase to the air. However, recent laboratory and mathematical-modeling investigations show that the air travels in air stream tubes or filaments (Ahlfeld *et al.*, 1993; Goodman *et al.*, 1993; Unger *et al.*, 1995; see also Figure 1.b of Pankow *et al.*, 1993). No well-documented case of a successful restoration of a DNAPL source zone by this technology has been reported in the literature. Studies are in progress to determine the effectiveness of air sparging in heterogeneous porous media. Current indications are that air sparging shows more promise for the remediation of petroleum product LNAPL source zones. In this case, the provision of air to the subsurface brings oxygen that permits aerobic biodegradation of petroleum hydrocarbons. Unfortunately, oxygenation of solvent DNAPL zones is not likely to stimulate significant aerobic biodegradation unless other organic compounds (*e.g.*, BTEX, phenol) are provided to support co-metabolic degradation.

14.7.2.4 Mass-destruction technologies

For *in-situ* **mass destruction**, chemicals are mixed with water that is injected into the DNAPL zone. The hydraulic aspects of these technologies are similar in general terms to the chemical flush technologies described in the prior section. The chemical/water mixture is flushed through the DNAPL zone towards extraction wells that capture the treatment solution. In most circumstances, the destruction is usually not complete on the first pass through the DNAPL zone. We also note that the effluent from the extraction wells will contain altered chemical additive concentrations. A surface facility is therefore generally needed to adjust the chemistry of the flush solution prior to reinjection/recirculation.

Several mass-destruction technologies are currently in the experimental stage. We have selected two promising methods from a broad range of new possibilities for discussion here. The first involves chemical oxidation; the second involves chemical reduction. The use of **permanganate** (MnO_4^-) to scavenge and oxidize organic contaminants has a long history in water and wastewater treatment. Adapting this history to DNAPL remediation, Gonullu *et al.* (1994) and Truax *et al.* (1995) have shown $KMnO_4$ solutions to be effective in destroying two solvent DNAPLs, trichloroethylene (TCE) and tetrachloroethylene (PCE). This oxidant cleaves the double bond in these compounds, forming CO_2, Cl_2, Cl^-, and $MnO_{2(s)}$, none of which pose a problem in groundwater at the levels typically involved. These investigators conducted laboratory batch and column tests, as well as two small field experiments. In the latter, water containing dissolved $KMnO_4$ near the solubility limit of 30 g/L was flushed through TCE and PCE DNAPL zones 1.0 and 8.0 L in volume, located in a moderately heterogeneous sand aquifer (the Borden aquifer). After flushing six pore volumes through the DNAPL zones, the effluents from the extraction wells were close to or below the drinking water limit for TCE and PCE (5 μg/L). The $KMnO_4$ remaining in the aquifer was removed by passing clean water though the flush zone after the destruction of DNAPL was complete. Pilot-scale tests at actual PCE/TCE DNAPL sites have been designed and are expected to proceed in 1995. $KMnO_4$ has good potential for use in the *in-situ* destruction of other chlorinated alkenes, but not for chlorinated alkanes like 1,1,1-trichloroethane (1,1,1-TCA). Prospects for other chemical oxidants to destroy alkanes and other DNAPLs are being assessed.

Lesage and Brown (1993) used laboratory batch and column experiments to demonstrate the effectiveness of **enzymes** in destroying chlorinated alkane and alkene solvents by reductive dechlorination. The dechlorination process is catalyzed by vitamin B12, but the process needs strongly reducing conditions to be effective. As in the other chemical technologies described above, it is envisioned that DNAPL destruction might be accomplished by flushing a source zone with water that contains dissolved vitamin B12 plus chemicals for the control of the redox chemistry and the pH. This reductive dehalogenation technology offers more versatility than $KMnO_4$ oxidation in the restoration of solvent DNAPL sites because it has potential for the destruction of a larger variety of DNAPL chemicals. However, its field implementation is complicated by the need to control the subsurface redox and pH conditions. The cost of chemicals per unit mass DNAPL destroyed will also probably be higher than with $KMnO_4$ oxidation. Research on the vitamin B12 process has progressed to the field prototype trial stage.

Of the various approaches being explored for the restoration of aquifers contaminated by chlorinated solvents, *in-situ* **microbiological** processes have been investigated the most. One category of microbiological approach involves flushing chemical additives through a DNAPL zone to stimulate reductive (Beeman *et al.*, 1993) or oxidative degradative processes carried out by bacteria inherent in the aquifer (intrinsic bacteria). In a second category, cultured or genetically-engineered bacteria are injected into a DNAPL zone along with bacterial life-support chemicals. However, the high aqueous contaminant concentrations in and near a DNAPL zone are toxic to bacteria, and this severely reduces the likelihood that *in-situ* microbiological methods will become effective for the restoration of DNAPL source zones. Microbiological methods offer better possibilities for assisting in source-zone restoration when applied at a later stage, after other methods have lowered the concentrations below microbial toxicity limits.

14.7.2.5 Prospects for source zone restoration

As has been discussed above, the task of removing or destroying sufficient contaminant mass to achieve the restoration of a DNAPL source zone is often a formidable one. The petroleum industry has spent billions of dollars on research and field trials to enhance the recovery of petroleum LNAPLs from oil fields. The petroleum industry considers that it has achieved exceptional success in favorable geologic situations when the efficiency of oil recovery increases from the 5 to 15% common to conventional oil extraction to the 30 to 40% range that can sometimes be achieved using enhanced oil recovery technologies. (The petroleum industry has tried many technologies in these pioneering efforts to extract LNAPLs from porous and fractured media, including the use of polymers, surfactants, and steam.) In contrast, when remediating a DNAPL source zone, we must normally aim for **>99.9% contaminant removal** if we are to approach the restoration levels needed to allow the use of an aquifer as a drinking-water supply.

The limitations on DNAPL mass removal and *in-situ* destruction imposed by the combined effects of heterogeneities in the geology, heterogeneities in the DNAPL distribution, and occasionally complex DNAPL mixtures mean that only **very limited prospects** exist for the complete restoration of DNAPL source zones. This judgement remains reasonable even if we assume that research and development efforts in this field will intensify in this decade. Conceptually, technologies that destroy DNAPL *in-situ* should be preferred to those that remove DNAPL for above-ground treatment and disposal. *In-situ* technologies in which DNAPL destroying-chemical additives are capable of seeking out DNAPL without having to be advected to the DNAPL have inherent advantages. Oxidation of TCE and PCE by $KMnO_4$ is an example. $KMnO_4$ in solution oxidizes TCE and PCE in solution. Thus, when the $KMnO_4$ solution arrives in the vicinity of DNAPL TCE or PCE, this increases the concentration gradient of the $KMnO_4$ towards the DNAPL and increases the concentration gradient of dissolved solvents towards the KMnO$_4$ solution. Therefore, chemicals causing *in-situ* destruction of DNAPL may need only periodic or occasional flushing to replenish the supply of the reactive chemicals. These technologies offer good possibilities for being relatively passive if the time period allowed to achieve restoration is many years. In contrast, mass-removal methods using surfactant or alcohol flushing depend on advective flushing for mass removal, and require continual or near-continual flushing and surface treatment of effluent for long-term restoration.

14.8 CONCLUSIONS

A DNAPL site has two principle components, a subsurface source zone and a groundwater plume. Most of the contaminant mass at a DNAPL site is expected to be in the source zone, but the plume usually occupies a much larger portion of the aquifer. To achieve complete restoration of an aquifer to drinking water standards, essentially all of the contaminant mass must be removed from both the source zone and the plume. If the plume is restored but the source is not, the plume will reestablish itself unless contaminant flux from the source zone is halted. Pump-and-treat and low-permeability enclosures are proven technologies for the containment of source zones. Pump-and-treat can also be used to capture or remove plumes. Emerging technologies, known as *in-situ* treatment curtains and funnel-and-gates, are becoming available for source-zone containment and plume control. Since annual contaminant mass flux in plumes is generally small, the technical challenge for these *in-situ* containment technologies is probably not insurmountable, except at sites where DNAPL is very deep or where the DNAPL is in fractured rock.

No proven technologies exist for the restoration of DNAPL source zones. The difficulty of this technical challenge is unprecedented in the field of groundwater engineering. We illustrate this challenge by means of conceptual diagrams. Figure 14.17 describes progress paths towards DNAPL source-zone restoration expressed as cumulative contaminant mass removed *vs.* time. For the experimental mass-removal technologies described earlier in this chapter, this **mass-removal relation** typically exhibits an exponential decrease in removal when the level of removal effort per unit time remains constant. Eventually, in the ideal case (Figure 14.17.a), the mass-removal line intersects the complete restoration line at which time source-zone restoration is achieved. Actual situations differ greatly from the ideal. Firstly, technology performance is less than ideal because of heterogeneity effects. Secondly, the position of the complete restoration line is uncertain. Therefore, as the restoration effort proceeds, the rate of approach to the desired end point is unknown. The benefit in risk reduction derived from continuing the remediation effort for a specified time interval cannot, consequently, be predicted or later determined quantitatively.

As noted above, the technologies available for the removal of DNAPL from the groundwater zone at appreciable rates are still experimental, and no DNAPL source zone of significant size has been fully restored using any of them. Thus, controversies exist regarding the reasons or circumstances that would justify use of these experimental technologies. A technical argument for using an experimental technology derives from the

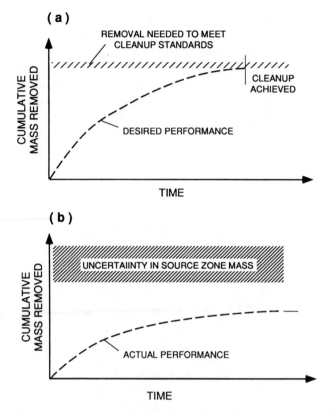

Figure 14.17 Graphical concepts for progress paths towards DNAPL source zone restoration: a) the ideal case—contaminant mass in the source zone is known and mass removal or destruction is fully effective; and b) the typical field case—the contaminant mass is not known and mass removal technology performance is not 100% effective.

necessity for site trials as a means of advancing the knowledge and effectiveness of new technologies. However, the scale and monitoring of such site trials must be commensurate with the goal of performance assessment and process elucidation. The degree of complexity at most DNAPL sites usually necessitates intense monitoring to enable rigorous performance assessment. Insufficient monitoring and data analyses render trials wasteful, and often confusing. When the trial is funded solely by the organization responsible for the particular site cleanup, such high monitoring costs for performance assessment are often deemed unwarranted because adequate performance is not guaranteed or, in some cases, not expected. In many cases, the main benefits from intense monitoring accrue to industry and government at large rather than the organization responsible for cleanup of a particular site.

A philosophical argument for the application of experimental mass-removal or mass-destruction technologies at actual sites derives from the premise that any amount of mass removed is beneficial because it moves the site closer to restoration, and therefore provides some inherent future benefit. A public-perception argument for the application of experimental technologies for mass removal is founded on the premise that public support for groundwater remediation or protection may wane unless observable and well-intentioned remedial actions involving mass reduction are pursued, regardless of the poor prospects for measurable or predictable benefit to groundwater quality in the next few years or decades. For any particular DNAPL site, there is normally opposition to such open-ended mass-removal actions from the financially responsible parties who base their arguments on generic economic principles and/or site-specific cost-benefit analyses.

The dilemma for decision makers regarding mass removal from DNAPL source zones centers on the relevance and value attributed to possible future benefits, such as increased availability of potable water or environmental risk reduction. In many cases, the benefits are not expected to be significant or even measurable until many decades have passed, and estimates of these future benefits are unreliable. The degree to which today's society should allocate financial resources to mass-removal efforts to achieve undefinable benefits for future society is the essence of a debate that is tied to both financial and ethical issues. Decisions regarding containment of source zones or plumes, whether they involve hydraulic capture, cutoff-wall enclosures, *in-situ* reaction curtains or funnel-and-gates are much less problematic because fewer technical difficulties exist and because risk reduction or economic benefits can be achieved rapidly.

ACKNOWLEDGEMENT

Funding support for this research was provided in part by the University Consortium Solvents-in-Groundwater Research Program. Sponsors of the Program between 1988 and 1994 have included: The Boeing Company, Ciba-Geigy Corporation, Dow Chemical Canada/USA, Eastman Kodak Co., General Electric Co., Laidlaw Environmental Systems Ltd., Mitre Corporation, The Natural Sciences and Engineering Research Council of Canada, and the Ontario University Research Incentive Fund.

14.9 REFERENCES

Ahlfeld, D., A. Dahami, E. Hill, J. Lin, and J. Wei (1993) "Laboratory study of air sparging: Air flow visualization", *Ground Water Monitoring and Remediation*, **4**, 115-126.

Beeman, R. E., J. E. Howell, S. H. Shoemaker, E. A. Solazar, and J. R. Buttram (1993) "A field evaluation of in situ microbial reductive dehalogenation by biotransformation of chlorinated solvents". In: *Proceedings of the In Situ and On Site Bioremediation Conference*, Battelle, San Diego, April 1993, 19 pp.

Burris, D. and J. A. Cherry (1992) "Emerging plume management technologies: In situ treatment zones". In: *Proceedings of the Air and Waste Management Association*, Annual Meeting, Kansas City, Missouri, June 21-26, 1992.

Devlin, J. F. and J. F. Barker (1994) "A semi-passive nutrient injection scheme for enhanced in-situ bioremediation", *Ground Water*, **32**, 374-380.

Devlin, J. F. and B. L. Parker (1995) "Optimum hydraulic conductivity to limit contaminant flux through cutoff walls" (unpublished work, University of Waterloo).

Feenstra, S. and B. H Conant (1994) "Vapor transport: A practical source of soil contamination following completion of remedial measures". Conference on Toxic Substances and the Hydrologic Sources, Austin, Texas, April 10-13, 1994.

Gillham, R. W. and S. F. O'Hannesin (1993) "Metal enhanced abiotic degradation of halogenated aliphatics: Laboratory tests and field trials". In: *Proceedings of the HazMat Central Conference*, Chicago, Illinois, March 9-11.

Gillham, R. W. and S. F. O'Hannesin (1994) "Enhanced degradation of halogenated aliphatics by zero-valent iron", *Ground Water*, **32**, 958-967.

Gonullu, F., G. J. Farquhar, C. Truax, M. J. Schnarr, and B. Stickney (1995) "Studies on the use of permanganate to oxidize chlorinated solvents in soil" (unpublished work, University of Waterloo).

Grubb, D. G. and N. Sitar (1994) "Evaluation of technologies for in-situ cleanup of DNAPL contaminated sites", U.S. Environmental Protection Agency, EPA/600/R-94/120, 173 pp.

Goodman, I., R. E. Hinchee, R. L. Johnson, P. C. Johnson, and D. B. McWhorter (1993) "An overview of in situ air sparging", *Ground Water Monitoring and Remediation*, **4**, 127-135.

Lesage, S. and S. Brown (1993) "In-situ biochemical degradation of perchloroethylene present as residual DNAPL". In: *Proceedings of the I&EC Special Symposium on Emerging Technologies for Hazardous Waste Management*, ACS, Atlanta, Georgia, September 27-29.

Mutch, R. D. and R. E. Ash (1993) "Subsurface cutoff walls still valuable in site remediation role", *HazMat World*, February, 37-44.

National Research Council (NRC) (1994) *Alternatives for Ground Water Cleanup*, Committee on Ground Water Cleanup Alternatives, Commission on Geosciences, Environment and Resources, National Academy Press, Washington, D.C., 315 pp.

Pankow, J. F., R. L. Johnson, and J. A. Cherry (1993) "Air sparging in gate wells in cutoff walls and trenches for control of plumes of volatile organic compounds", *Ground Water*, **31**, 654-663.

Parker, B. L., R. W. Gillham, and J. A. Cherry (1994) "Diffusive dissappearance of dense, immiscible phase organic liquids in fractured geologic media", *Ground Water*, **32**, 805-820.

Starr, R. C. and J. A. Cherry (1994) "In situ remediation of contaminated ground water: The funnel-and-gate-system", *Ground Water*, **32**, 465-476.

Stewart, L. D. and K. S. Udell (1992) "Combined steam injection and vacuum extraction for aquifer cleanup". In: *Proceedings of the IAH Conference on Subsurface Contamination by Immiscible Fluids*, K. U. Weyer (Ed.), Calgary, Alberta, April 18-20, 1990, A. A. Balkema, Rotterdam, The Netherlands.

Truax, C., C. J. Farquhar, M. J. Schnarr, and B. Stickney (1995) "Field experiments using permanganate to oxidize trichloroethylene and perchloroethylene spilled into soil", (unpublished work, University of Waterloo).

Unger, A. J. A., E. A. Sudicky, and P. A. Forsyth (1995) "Mechanisms controlling vacuum extraction coupled with air sparging for remediation of heterogeneous formations contaminated by dense non-aqueous phase liquids", *Water Resources Research*, **31** (in press).

Wilson, R. D. and D. M. Mackay (1995) "A method for passive release of solutes from an unpumped well", *Ground Water*, **33** (in press).

Appendix
Physical and Chemical Properties of Dense Non-Aqueous Phase Liquid (DNAPL) Compounds

James F. Pankow and Richard L. Johnson

Department of Environmental Science and Engineering
Oregon Graduate Institute
P.O. Box 91000
Portland, Oregon 97291-1000

TABLE A1 Summary of Physical and Chemical Properties of DNAPL Compounds at 25°C[†].

Compound	MW[†]	Vapor Pressure ($p°$, torr)	Calculated Solubility (S, mg/L)	Literature Solubility (S, mg/L)	Henry's constant (H, atm-m³/mol)	Relative Vapor Density	Boiling Point (°C)	K_{oc} (mL/g)	Density (g/cm³)	Absolute Viscosity (cP)	Kinematic Viscosity (cS)
dichloromethane	84.9	415	21867	20000	0.00212	2.05	41	8.8	1.33	0.44	0.32
chloroform	119.4	194	8513.5	8000	0.00358	1.80	62	44	1.49	0.56	0.38
bromodichloromethane	163.8	64.2	6716.9	4500	0.00206	1.39	90	61	1.97	1.71	0.87
dibromochloromethane	208.3	17	4051.6	4000	0.00115	1.14	119	84	2.38		
bromoform	282.8	6.21	4360.0	3000	0.000530	1.07	149	116	2.89	2.07	0.72
trichlorofluoromethane	137.4	796	1620.6	1100	0.0888	4.91	23.8	159	1.49		
carbon tetrachloride	153.8	109	740.21	825	0.0298	1.62	76.7	439	1.59	0.97	0.61
1,1-dichloroethane	99	221	5301.7	5100	0.00543	1.70	57.3	30	1.17	0.5	0.43
1,2-dichloroethane	99	82.1	7129.7	8500	0.0015	1.26	83.5	14	1.25	0.84	0.67
1,1,1-trichloroethane	133.4	124.6	1309.6	1300	0.0167	1.59		152	1.35	0.84	0.62
1,1,2-trichloroethane	133.4	24.4	3965.6	4400	0.00108	1.12	113.7	56	1.44	1.19	0.83
1,1,2,2-tetrachloroethane	167.9	6.36	3061.1	2900	0.000459	1.04	146.4	118	1.6	1.76	1.12
1,1-dichloroethylene	97	603	3018.1	3350	0.0255	2.86	31.9	65	1.22	0.36	0.3
1,2-dibromoethane (EDB)	187.9	13.8	5017.5	4200	0.000680	1.10	131.6	92	2.18	1.72	0.79
cis-1,2-dichloroethylene	97	205	6995.8	3500	0.00374	1.63	60	86	1.28	0.48	0.38
trans-1,2-dichloroethylene	97	315	4389.1	6300	0.00916	1.97	48	59	1.26	0.4	0.32
trichloroethylene (TCE)	131.5	75	1384.9	1100	0.00937	1.35	86.7	126	1.46	0.57	0.39
tetrachloroethylene (PCE)	165.8	18.9	236.96	200	0.0174	1.12	121.4	364	1.63	0.9	0.54
1,2-dichloropropane	113	52.3	2968.0	2800	0.00262	1.20	96.8	51	1.16	0.87	0.75
trans-1,3-dichloropropylene	110	34	2994.9	2800	0.0013	1.10	112	48	1.22		
bis(chloro)methylether	115	30	16572.0	22000	0.00021	1.09	104	1.2	1.32		
bis(2-chloroethyl)ether	143	1.11	1139.1	10200	0.00013	1.004	178	14	1.22	2.41	1.98
bis(2-chloroisopropyl)ether	171	0.73	1049.3	1700	0.00011	1.003	189	61	1.11		
2-chloroethylvinylether	106.6	34.3	15148.0	15000	0.00025	1.010	108	6.6	1.05		
chlorobenzene	112.6	11.7	444.52	500	0.00390	1.04	132	330	1.11	0.8	0.72
o-dichlorobenzene	147	1.39	135.84	140	0.00198	1.01	179	1700	1.31	1.41	1.28
m-dichlorobenzene	147	2.25	133.91	119	0.00325	1.01	172	1700	1.29	1.08	0.84

†Footnotes:

Solubility (S, mg/L = ppm). There are many papers in the literature that discuss measurements of the solubilities of halogenated solvent compounds. Unfortunately, not all of them agree. An effort was therefore made to select the best values for inclusion in column five of this table. The primary source used in this effort was Horvath (1982). Mabey et al. (1982) was used to obtain S values for the chlorinated ether compounds.

For a given compound, of the three parameters $p°$ (vapor pressure, torr = mm Hg), Henry's Gas Law constant H (atm-m^3/mol), and S, knowledge of any two allows calculation of the third. Therefore, in order to provide a set of $p°$, H, and S values that are consistent with one another, in addition to giving the literature values for solubilities, S values were calculated from $p°$ and H according to the equation

$$S(mg/L) = p° MW/(760H)$$

where MW (g/mol) is the molecular weight. These calculated solubilities are given to five significant figures for those who wish to employ the $p°$, H, and S values in computer modelling efforts.

Vapor Pressure ($p°$, torr). The primary source for the vapor pressure data was Weast and Astle (1979). The $p°$ values given therein were interpolated and extrapolated as necessary to the desired temperature 25°C. The interpolations and extrapolations were carried out in a log $p°$ vs. $1/T$ format, where T is temperature in degrees Kelvin. Mabey et al. (1982) was used to obtain $p°$ values for the chlorinated ether compounds.

Henry's Gas Law Constants (H). A number of different references were used to obtain H values as a function of temperature. Gossett (1987) was used for 10 compounds, namely: dichloromethane, chloroform, carbon tetrachloride, 1,1-dichloroethane, 1,1,1-trichloroethane, 1,1-dichloroethylene, cis-dichloroethylene, trans-dichloroethylene, trichloroethylene, and tetrachloroethylene. Howe et al. (1987) was used for 8 compounds, namely: 1,2-dichloroethane, 1,1,2-trichloroethane, 1,1,2,2-tetrachlorethane, 1,2-dibromoethane (EDB), 1,2-dichloropropane, chlorobenzene, o-dichlorobenzene, and m-dichlorobenzene. Nicholson et al. (1984) was used for bromodichloromethane. The H values for dibromochloromethane were obtained by averaging values from Howe et al. (1987) and Nicholson et al. (1984). Munz and Roberts (1987) was used for bromoform. Hunter-Smith et al. (1983) was used for trichlorofluoromethane. Mabey et al. (1982) was used for 5 compounds, namely: trans-1,2-dichloropropylene, bis(chloromethyl)ether, bis(2-chloroethyl)ether, bis(2-chloroisopropyl)ether, and 2-chloroethyl vinyl ether.

Water/Organic Carbon Partition Coefficients (K_{oc}). The primary source for K_{oc} values was Mabey et al. (1982).

Relative Vapor Density (RVD) Values. As discussed by Pankow (1988), RVD values were calculated here as the ratio of the density of dry air that is saturated (at 25°C and 1 atm total pressure) with the compound of interest, to the density of dry air. The equation used was

$$RVD = \frac{\frac{p°}{760}MW + \frac{(760-p°)29.0}{760}}{29}$$

where $p°$ is the saturated vapor pressure, MW (g/mol) is the molecular weight of the compound of interest, and 29.0 is the mean molecular weight of dry air. This method of calculating the RVD is more meaningful than the more common approach of taking the RVD to be the relative vapor density at the *boiling point*. That RVD equals the ratio of the MW of the compound to 29.0, the mean molecular weight of dry air.

509

TABLE A2 Vapor Pressure ($p°$, torr), Henry's Gas Law Constants (H, atm-m^3/mol), and Solubilities (S, mg/L) as a Function of Temperature[†]. S Values are Given as Calculated Based on $p°$ and H Values.

Compound	MW		5°C	10°C	15°C	20°C	25°C	30°C
dichloromethane	84.9	$p°$	173	218	272	337	415	507
		H	0.000844	0.00108	0.00136	0.0017	0.00212	0.00262
		S	22898.	22549.	22342.	22145.	21868.	21617.
chloroform	119.4	$p°$	76.3	98.0	124	156	194	240
		H	0.00117	0.00157	0.00209	0.00274	0.00358	0.00462
		S	10245.	9806.6	9321.1	8944.7	8513.5	8161.3
bromodichloromethane	163.8	$p°$	23.8	30.9	39.8	50.8	64.2	80.7
		H	0.000586	0.000817	0.00112	0.00153	0.00206	0.00275
		S	8753.5	8151.5	7658.9	7156.0	6716.9	6324.7
dibromochloromethane	208.3	$p°$	5.72	7.62	10.0	13.1	17.0	21.8
		H	0.000284	0.00041	0.000585	0.000824	0.00115	0.00159
		S	5520.2	5093.9	4685.1	4357.3	4051.6	3757.8
bromoform	282.8	$p°$	1.93	2.63	3.53	4.71	6.21	8.12
		H	0.000171	0.00023	0.000307	0.000405	0.000530	0.000687
		S	4199.8	4254.9	4278.6	4327.4	4359.9	4398.1
trichlorofluoromethane	137.4	$p°$	371	454	551	664	796	948
		H	0.0467	0.0553	0.0651	0.0762	0.0888	0.103
		S	1436.3	1484.2	1530.2	1575.4	1620.6	1663.9
carbon tetrachloride	153.8	$p°$	41.5	53.6	68.6	87.0	109	136
		H	0.0103	0.0136	0.0178	0.0232	0.0298	0.0381
		S	815.37	797.57	779.91	758.88	740.21	722.36
1,1-dichloroethane	99	$p°$	89.6	115	143	179	221	272
		H	0.00201	0.00261	0.00336	0.00429	0.00543	0.00683
		S	5806.8	5739.6	5543.9	5435.2	5301.7	5187.6
1,2-dichloroethane	99	$p°$	30.4	40.0	51.3	65.1	82.1	103
		H	0.000797	0.000941	0.00111	0.00129	0.0015	0.00173
		S	4968.6	5537.2	6020.3	6573.7	7129.7	7755.6
1,1,1-trichloroethane	133.4	$p°$	47.8	61.7	78.9	100	124.6	154
		H	0.00616	0.00801	0.0103	0.0132	0.0167	0.021
		S	1362.0	1352.1	1344.6	1329.7	1309.6	1287.2
1,1,2-trichloroethane	133.4	$p°$	8.1	11.0	14.5	18.9	24.4	31.2
		H	0.000657	0.000749	0.000849	0.000959	0.00108	0.00121
		S	2164.0	2577.8	2997.8	3459.3	3965.6	4526.0
1,1,2,2-tetrachloroethane	167.9	$p°$	1.83	2.54	3.49	4.74	6.36	8.46
		H	0.000225	0.000271	0.000325	0.000387	0.000459	0.000540
		S	1796.8	2070.6	2372.4	2705.9	3061.1	3461.1
1,1-dichloroethylene	97	$p°$	262	326	403	495	603	730
		H	0.0104	0.0131	0.0165	0.0206	0.0255	0.0314
		S	3215.3	3176.2	3117.3	3066.9	3018.1	2967.2
1,2-dibromoethane (EDB)	187.9	$p°$	5.45	6.85	8.56	10.8	13.8	17.7
		H	0.000266	0.000340	0.000432	0.000544	0.000680	0.000843
		S	5065.6	4981.1	4898.9	4908.4	5017.5	5191.1
cis-1,2-dichloroethylene	97	$p°$	79.8	102	130	164	205	255
		H	0.00136	0.00178	0.00230	0.00294	0.00374	0.00472
		S	7489.0	7313.7	7213.9	7119.6	6995.8	6895.4
trans-1,2-dichloroethylene	97	$p°$	129	163	205	255	315	387
		H	0.00334	0.00436	0.00563	0.00721	0.00916	0.0116
		S	4929.5	4771.5	4647.3	4514.0	4389.1	4258.1
trichloroethylene (TCE)	131.5	$p°$	27.6	36.2	46.7	59.4	75.0	94.0
		H	0.00296	0.00400	0.00537	0.00713	0.00937	0.0122
		S	1613.3	1565.9	1504.7	1441.5	1384.9	1333.2
tetrachloroethylene (PCE,PER)	165.8	$p°$	5.86	7.97	10.7	14.3	18.9	24.7
		H	0.0053	0.00724	0.00979	0.0131	0.0174	0.0228
		S	241.21	240.15	238.44	238.14	236.96	236.34

TABLE A2 Cont.

Compound	MW		5°C	10°C	15°C	20°C	25°C	30°C
1,2-dichloropropane	113	$p°$	18.9	24.7	32.0	41.2	52.3	66.0
		H	0.000841	0.00113	0.00151	0.00200	0.00262	0.00340
		S	3341.4	3250.0	3150.9	3062.9	2968.0	2886.2
trans-1,3-dichloropropylene	110	$p°$				26.9		
		H				0.0013		
		S				2994.9		
bis(chloro)methylether	115	$p°$				23		
		H				0.00021		
		S				16572.		
bis(2-chloroethyl)ether	143	$p°$				0.787		
		H				0.00013		
		S				1139.1		
bis(2-chloroisopropyl)ether	171	$p°$				0.513		
		H				0.00011		
		S				1049.3		
2-chloroethylvinylether	106.6	$p°$				27		
		H				0.00025		
		S				15148.		
chlorobenzene	112.6	$p°$	3.49	4.8	6.54	8.8	11.7	15.2
		H	0.00209	0.00242	0.00285	0.00334	0.00390	0.00452
		S	247.40	293.87	339.98	390.36	444.47	498.23
o-dichlorobenzene	147	$p°$	0.348	0.501	0.712	1.00	1.39	1.91
		H	0.00109	0.00127	0.00148	0.00172	0.00198	0.00227
		S	61.752	76.302	93.051	112.40	135.78	162.75
m-dichlorobenzene	147	$p°$	0.619	0.87	1.21	1.66	2.25	3.03
		H	0.00183	0.00213	0.00246	0.00284	0.00325	0.00372
		S	65.429	79.003	95.138	113.06	133.91	157.54

†Footnotes:

Vapor Pressure ($p°$, torr). The primary source for the vapor pressure data was Weast and Astle (1979). The $p°$ values given therein were interpolated and extrapolated as necessary to the desired temperatures of 5, 10, 15, 20, 25, and 30°C. The interpolations and extrapolations were carried out in a log $p°$ vs. $1/T$ format, where T is temperature in degrees Kelvin. Mabey *et al.* (1982) was used to obtain $p°$ values for the chlorinated ether compounds.

Henry's Gas Law Constants (H, atm-m³/mol). A number of different references were used to obtain H values as a function of temperature. Gossett (1987) was used for 10 compounds, namely: dichloromethane, chloroform, carbon tetrachloride, 1,1,-dichloroethane, 1,1,1-trichloroethane, 1,1-dichloroethylene, *cis*-dichloroethylene, *trans*-dichloroethylene, trichlorethylene, and tetrachloroethylene. Howe *et al.* (1987) was used for 8 compounds, namely: 1,2-dichloroethane, 1,1,2-trichloroethane, 1,1,2,2-tetrachlorethane, 1,2-dibromoethane (EDB), 1,2-dichloropropane, chlorobenzene, *o*-dichlorobenzene, and *m*-dichlorobenzene. Nicholson *et al.* (1984) was used for bromodichloromethane. The H values for dibromochloromethane were obtained by averaging values from Howe *et al.* (1987) and Nicholson *et al.* (1984). Munz and Roberts (1987) was used for bromoform. Hunter-Smith *et al.* (1983) was used for trichlorofluoromethane. Mabey *et al.* (1982) was used for 5 compounds, namely: *trans*-1,2-dichloropropylene, bis(chloromethyl)ether, bis(2-chloroethyl)ether, bis(2-chloroisopropyl)ether, and 2-chloroethyl vinyl ether.

Solubility (S, mg/L = ppm). For a given compound, of the three parameters $p°$ (vapor pressure, torr = mm Hg), Henry's Gas Law constant H (atm-m³/mol), and S, knowledge of any two allows calculation of the third. S values were calculated from $p°$ and H according to the equation S (mg/L) $= p°MW/(760H)$ where MW (g/mol) is the molecular weight. These calculated solubilities are given to five significant figures for those who wish to employ the $p°$, H, and S values in computer modelling efforts.

REFERENCES

Gossett, J. M. (1987) "The measurement of Henry's Law constants for C_1 and C_2 chlorinated compounds", *Environ. Sci. Technol.*, **21**, 202-208.

Hovarth, A. L. (1982) *Halogenated Hydrocarbons. Solubility-Miscibility with Water*, Marcel Dekker, New York, 889 p.

Howe, G. B., M. E. Mullins, and T. N. Rogers (1987) "Evaluation and prediction of Henry's Law constants and aqueous solubilities for solvents and hydrocarbon fuel components. Vol. 1: Technical discussion". Report prepared by: Research Triangle Institute, P.O. Box 12194, Research Triangle Park, NC, 27709. Report prepared for: Engineering & Services Laboratory (ESL), Air Force Engineering & Services Center, Tyndall Air Force Base, Florida, 32403. ESL report number: ESL-TR-86-66/Vol. 1.

Hunter-Smith, R. J., P. W. Balls, and P. S. Liss (1983) "Henry's Law constants and the air-sea exchange of various low molecular weight halocarbon gases", *Tellus*, **35B**, 170-176.

Mabey, W. R., J. H. Smith, R. T. Podoll, H. L. Johnson, T. Mill, T.-W. Chou, J. Gates, and D. Vandenberg (1982) *Aquatic Fate Processes Data for Organic Priority Pollutants*, EPA 440/4-81-014, Washington, D.C., December 1982.

Munz, A. and P. V. Roberts (1987) "Air-water phase equilibria of volatile organic solutes", *J. Am. Water Works Assoc.*, May, 62-70.

Nicholson, B. C., B. P. Maguire, and D. B. Bursill (1984) "Henry's Law constants for the trihalomethanes: Effects of water composition and temperature", *Environ. Sci. Technol.*, **18**, 518-523.

Pankow, J. F. (1988) "Translator's Appendix: Physical and Chemical Properties of Dense Solvent Compounds". In: *Dense Chlorinated Solvents in Porous and Fractured Media: Model Experiments*, Lewis Publishers, Boca Raton, FL, 146 p.

Weast, R. C. and M. J. Astle (1979) *CRC Handbook of Chemistry and Physics*, section entitled "Vapor Pressure; Organic Compounds (Pressures Less than One Atmosphere)", pp. D-203 to D-217, CRC Press, Boca Raton, Florida.

Index